COLLEGE ALGEBRA AND TRIGONOMETRY

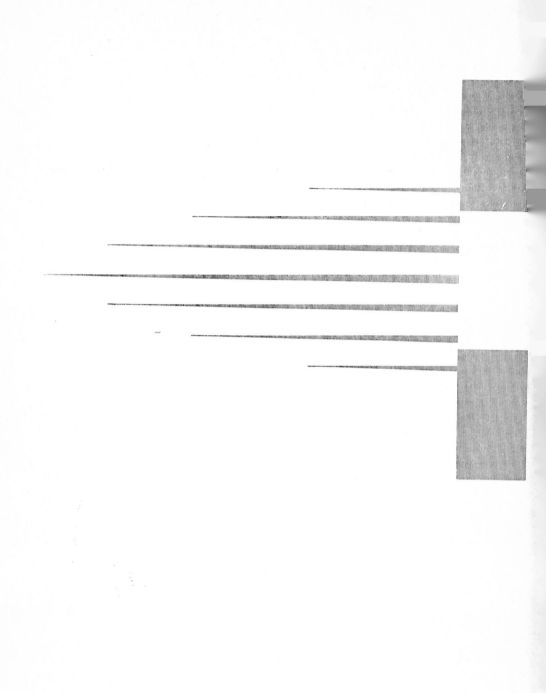

College Algebra and Trigonometry

WILLIAM L. HART

Professor of Mathematics, University of Minnesota

D. C. Heath and Company Boston

Library of Congress Catalog Card Number: 59–6735

Printed March 1967

Preface

GENERAL PLAN AND OBJECTIVES

This book presents all the content in college algebra and trigonometry which is desirable as preparation for a first course in analytic geometry and calculus. The text is thorough in its treatment of fundamentals and endeavors to be sensibly modern in the selection of topics, the methods employed, and the general tone of all discussion. The aim is to present the content so that the student will not have something to unlearn in more advanced mathematics, and also will save time there by having had a well-coordinated approach in this text. Attention is called particularly to the presentation of the following subject matter, all of which is discussed at a maturity level within the range of the typical student.

The substantial modern presentation of the function concept.

The basic content from analytic geometry, with emphasis on affine features, well beyond the limited stage which is customary in college algebras.

The collegiate development of trigonometry, employing results from analytic geometry and closely coordinated with the future role of trigonometry in calculus.

The generous treatment of combinations and permutations.

The elementary introduction to sets.

The development of probability from a postulational viewpoint for a finite sample space, with a simple introduction to random variables.

The solution of systems of linear equations by a nondeterminantal method involving operations on matrices, as well as by use of determinants.

The text was planned for students who need either a complete treatment of trigonometry or at least a more sophisticated appreciation of analytic trigonometry, as well as additional algebraic content. Various details were designed as aids in adjusting the text to one-semester courses, or two-quarter courses meeting three, four, or five hours per week. The length of the course and the initial preparation of the students will determine possible omissions in Chapters 1, 2, 4, 5, and 6, where associated review exercises are included to facilitate mere review rather than complete discussion. It is believed that complete study of Chapter 3 will appear essential in all cases.

THE TREATMENT OF TRIGONOMETRY

The content occurs mainly in separate but not wholly consecutive chapters, and is coordinated with appropriate topics in algebra and analytic geometry. Various aspects of the presentation should give this material freshness even for a student who has studied the subject previously.

Simple general proofs of key formulas are obtained by use of the distance formula of analytic geometry.

Numerical trigonometry is segregated and is arranged so that, when appropriate in a course, the material may be treated lightly or may be essentially omitted without inconvenience.

Accuracy of approximate computation receives careful consideration.

The analytic trigonometric functions of numbers are emphasized as a natural and essential development. These functions are introduced by a simple change of viewpoint with respect to the domain of the geometric trigonometric functions of angles, originally defined by the classical method.

The inverse trigonometric functions (single-valued), as employed in calculus, are introduced in the effective manner resulting from appreciation of the general notion of an inverse function.

The use of radian measure and its role in the introduction of the standard trigonometric functions of numbers are given deserved emphasis.

Features involving degree measure receive appropriate attention because of their importance in applied mathematics. However, the major emphasis is placed on radian measure and the corresponding viewpoint about the trigonometric functions of numbers.

THE CONSIDERATION OF THE FUNCTION CONCEPT

The terminology of **domain, range,** and a **correspondence** between their elements, and the distinction between a **function and its values** receive both initial emphasis and continued employment.

Ordered pairs of elements from two sets (where the word *set* is introduced intuitively at this stage) are adopted as the basic feature of the definition of a function, but all other current forms of acceptable terminology for the definition receive attention.

Notational agreements are introduced in a fashion consistent with modern practice.

THE CONTENT FROM ANALYTIC GEOMETRY

The extensive introduction to coordinate systems and graphs is presented as if this material formed the initial stage of a course in analytic geometry and calculus, instead of merely a part of college algebra.

Affine features, where the units on the coordinate axes need not be equal, are given the primary emphasis.

The analytic geometry of straight lines, based on the concept of slope (*not inclination*), is developed in fairly complete form.

Point-wise graphing of polynomials and of the conic sections in the simplest standard positions is presented.

Graphs of inequalities are introduced.

Supplementary content in the Appendix introduces transformation by translation of axes, corresponding forms for the equations of conics, and their definitions as loci involving focal radii.

MATRICES AND DETERMINANTS

The chapter on general systems of linear equations is written with the viewpoint that, apart from other objectives, an opportunity is at hand for introducing the student to the manipulation of *matrices.*

Elementary transformation of matrices is employed in solving a system by reducing it to a *triangular form*, without determinants.

Determinants of general order and **Cramer's rule** are considered.

COMBINATIONS, PERMUTATIONS, SETS, AND PROBABILITY

A first purpose is to train the student in solving combinatorial problems. The main objective is to present a substantial introduction to *probability for a finite sample space.* The intrinsic nature of probability as a function whose domain consists of sets of outcomes, in a sample space, provides an environment in which the student will appreciate being led from his former intuitive use of the word *set* to a more technical appreciation of set terminology.

Permutations and combinations are presented thoroughly.

The binomial theorem is proved in connection with combinations.

The brief chapter on sets introduces the fundamental operations on them and Venn diagrams.

Probability, associated with a finite sample space, is defined on a strictly modern basis,* where one discards the inadequate classical definition involving just "equally likely events." The ensuing discussion arrives logically at the discarded definition as a theorem.

---

* For an earlier elementary treatment in this vein, see the chapter on probability in *College Algebra, Fourth Edition* (1951), by William L. Hart; D. C. Heath and Company.

Mathematical probability models are presented, with agreements for their use in concrete examples, sufficient for solving the major applications of probability which have been customary in college algebras. **The concepts of a random variable and its expected value** are introduced, and are applied to a moderate extent.

THE LOGICAL LEVEL

The book couches the discussion at a reasonably high logical level, within limits imposed by the assumed prerequisites. As illustrations:

The transition to the signed numbers of algebra from the system of numbers of arithmetic is made in a logical fashion.

The discussion of equivalent equations, or inequalities.

The formalities in definitions, theorems, and proofs.

The demonstrations of identities, and of absolute inequalities.

The postulational foundation for probability.

THE CLASSICAL CONTENT OF ALGEBRA

The standard topics of college algebra are treated without abbreviation.

Elementary topics, considered partly or wholly as a review, are treated systematically.

Advanced topics in quadratic equations and the solution of systems involving quadratics are presented without abbreviation.

Logarithms receive substantial treatment.

A systematic treatment of **inequalities and their graphs** is presented.

A substantial chapter is devoted to the **theory of equations.**

The chapter on **complex numbers** is complete, and includes De Moivre's theorem and roots of complex numbers.

PEDAGOGICAL AIDS

The book employs devices common to all of the author's texts to assist both the teacher and the student.

Illustrative examples are used profusely.

The problem material for the student is extensive.

Review or miscellaneous exercises occur frequently.

The problems in exercises are arranged in order of difficulty.

Answers are given in the text for almost all of the odd-numbered problems; answers to the even-numbered problems are furnished free to the student in a separate pamphlet when requested by the instructor.

WILLIAM L. HART

Contents

COLLEGE ALGEBRA AND TRIGONOMETRY

Basic Algebraic Topics

1. The real number system

Any number system consists of arbitrarily invented elements called *numbers*, for which operations are defined as the basis of a mathematical game played with the numbers. In arithmetic, the number system consists of the endless set of *integers* 1, 2, 3, $\cdots$, also called *whole numbers*, or *natural numbers; zero*, 0, also called an integer; *fractions* p/q where p and q are integers and $q \neq 0$; and *other numbers*, which are endless nonrepeating decimals, such as $\sqrt{2} = 1.41421\cdots$. We notice that, by division, any fraction p/q also can be expressed as a decimal. Then, we may describe the numbers of arithmetic as the set of *all numbers which can be written by use of the decimal notation*, where we visualize an endless sequence of decimal places in each number.

Note 1. A **terminating decimal** is one with an endless sequence of zeros at the right of a certain decimal place; these zeros usually are omitted in writing the number. An **infinite decimal** is one which does not terminate. The notion of the value of an infinite decimal will be analyzed on page 132.

Illustration 1. 35.675, or $35.675000\cdots$, is a terminating decimal.

$\frac{3}{4} = .75$, a terminating decimal.

$\frac{1}{3} = .333\cdots$, an infinite repeating decimal.

$\pi = 3.14159\cdots$, an infinite nonrepeating decimal.

To form a number system for algebra, we first take into our system all numbers of arithmetic, attaching a plus sign, +, at the left of each of them when desired. Hereafter, each of these numbers, except for zero, is to be called a **positive number**. Next, we invent a new number, -1, read **"minus 1."** Then, corresponding to each positive number P, we introduce a new number $-P$, read *"minus P,"* to represent the product $(-1) \times P$, read *"minus 1 times P."* That is, $-P = (-1) \times P$, and we call $-P$ a **negative number**. We specify that $(-1) \times 0 = 0$, or $-0 = 0$. Thus, 0 may be written 0, -0, or $+0$, as we please. We refer to each of the num-

3

bers now available as a **real number,** and call this set of numbers the **real number system;** it consists of the *positive numbers,* the *negative numbers,* and *zero,* which is not called positive or negative. The word *real* is used with real numbers to permit contrast later with so-called *imaginary* numbers (considered on page 45).

ILLUSTRATION 2. -17, $-\frac{5}{3}$, 0, $\sqrt{3}$, and 25 are real numbers.

For contrast with **explicit numbers,** like -2, 5, and 0, number symbols such as x, y, and c will be called **literal numbers.** In this book, any single letter used without a qualifying description will represent a *real number.*

In arithmetic, the numbers are *unsigned,* and the signs "$+$" and "$-$" are used to indicate the operations of addition and subtraction. In the introduction of positive and negative numbers, we have used "$+$" and "$-$" differently, to denote *varieties of numbers.* However, as mentioned in Section 4, notational agreements in algebra lead to extended uses of "$+$" and "$-$" which are consistent with the notations of arithmetic.

2. Foundation for operations on real numbers

For any real numbers, we shall define their *sum* and their *product.* The computation of a sum is called *addition,* and of a product is called *multiplication.* As a first step, we agree that a sum or a product of numbers which are *positive or zero* has the same value in algebra as in arithmetic. All other sums and products, and notations for them, require new definitions.

In a product of given numbers, each of them is called a **factor** of their product. To indicate multiplication, we write the factors side by side, with a dot or "$\times$" between them (where the *cross* is not favored with literal numbers because it resembles x). In the case of literal factors without attached signs, we just write the letters side by side. Adjacent factors are separated by parentheses when the dot or cross is omitted between explicit factors. We agree that *insertion of a plus sign or a minus sign at the left of a number is equivalent to multiplying it by $+1$ or by -1, respectively.*

ILLUSTRATION 1. $6 \cdot 3 = 6(3) = 18$, where we read "6 *times* 3 *is* 18."

Hereafter, we agree that every number, explicit or literal, has an attached sign at the left, where "$+$" is understood if no sign is written. Then, to represent the sum of a set of numbers, we *take each number, with its attached sign written explicitly, and arrange the signed numbers in a line. Usually,* any plus sign at the left-hand end is omitted. In a sum, each number with its attached sign is called a **term** of the sum.

ILLUSTRATION 2. $(3 + a - 7)$ is the sum of 3, a, and -7.

From arithmetic, we know that the following Laws I–V are true for addition and multiplication when the numbers are positive or zero.

I. Multiplication is commutative, *or the product of two numbers is the same in whatever order they are multiplied. That is, $ab = ba$.*

II. Multiplication is associative, *or the product of three or more numbers is the same in whatever order they are grouped in multiplying.*

$$abc = (ab)c = (ac)b = a(bc).$$

III. Addition is commutative, *or the sum of two numbers is the same in whatever order they are added. That is, $a + b = b + a$.*

IV. Addition is associative, *or the sum of three or more numbers is the same in whatever order they are grouped in adding. That is,*

$$a + b + c = a + (b + c) = a + (c + b) = a + c + b = c + (a + b), \text{ etc.}$$

V. Multiplication is distributive with respect to addition, *or* *

$$a(b + c) = ab + ac.$$

In the real number system, we define the following products and sums, where $(-1) \times (+1)$ and $(-1) \times 0$ have been introduced previously.

$$(-1) \times (-1) = +1; \quad (-1) \times (+1) = -1; \tag{1}$$

$$(-1) \times 0 = 0; \quad -1 + 1 = 0; \quad -1 + 0 = -1. \tag{2}$$

Then, we define addition and multiplication for any real numbers as follows.

DEFINITION I. *In the addition or multiplication of real numbers, the result is that number obtained if each negative number $-P$ is rewritten $(-1)P$, and use is made of* (1), (2), *and Laws* I–V *as applied to positive numbers, zero, and -1.*

On the basis of Definition I, it is possible to show that Laws I–V apply when the numbers involved are any real numbers. We omit the proofs.

ILLUSTRATION 3. $(-4)(-5) = (-1)(4)(-1)(5) = (-1)(-1)(4 \cdot 5) = +20.$

ILLUSTRATION 4. The product of an *even* number of factors -1 is equal to $+1$, and of an *odd* number of factors -1 is equal to -1, because the factors can be grouped two at a time to yield $+1$. Thus,

$$(-1)(-1)(-1) = [(-1)(-1)](-1) = (+1)(-1) = -1.$$

ILLUSTRATION 5. Insertion of a plus sign before a number does not alter its value because $+a = (+1)(a) = a$. If $N \neq 0$, insertion of a minus sign before N changes it from negative to positive, or from positive to negative.

Thus, $\qquad (-1)(5) = -5; \quad -(-5) = (-1)(-1)(5) = +5.$

DEFINITION II. *The **negative** of a number N is $-N$.*

The negative of 0 is 0, because $-0 = 0$. If P is positive, its negative is $-P$. The negative of $-P$ is $-(-P) = (-1)(-1)P = +P$. Hence, we refer to P and $-P$ as *negatives*, each the negative of the other number.

* We read $a(b + c)$ as "*a times the quantity $b + c$.*"

DEFINITION III.   *The* **absolute value** *of a positive number or zero is the number itself.   The absolute value of a negative number is its negative.*

We use $|H|$ to represent the "*absolute value of H.*"   Thus,

$$|H| = H \text{ if } H \text{ is zero or positive;} \tag{3}$$

$$|H| = -H \text{ if } H \text{ is negative.} \tag{4}$$

ILLUSTRATION 6. $|0| = 0.$ $|-5| = -(-5) = 5;$ $\left|\dfrac{4}{3}\right| = \dfrac{4}{3}.$

3. Multiplication and division

To multiply a set of numbers means *to find their* **product.**

To compute a product, multiply the absolute values of the factors to find the absolute value of the product, and attach a plus *or a* minus *sign according as there are an* **even** *or an* **odd** *number of negative factors.   In particular:*

The product of two explicit numbers, neither zero, is **positive** *if the factors have* **like signs,** *and is* **negative** *if the factors have* **unlike signs.**

ILLUSTRATION 1. $(-4)(-3)(-2)(5) = -(4\cdot3\cdot2\cdot5) = -120.$

DEFINITION IV.   *To* **divide** *b by c, where $c \neq 0$, means to find x so that $b = cx$. Then, we call b the* **dividend,** *c the* **divisor,** *and x the* **quotient.**

In a complete foundation for the real number system with its operations at a more advanced level, it is shown that there exists a unique number x satisfying Definition IV.   When b is divided by c, we denote the quotient by $b \div c$, or b/c, or $\dfrac{b}{c}$, where each is read "*b divided by c.*"   Also, we call b/c a **fraction** and may read it "*b over c.*"   In b/c, we call b the **numerator** and c the **denominator,** or we may call b and c the **terms** of the fraction. Sometimes, we refer to b/c as the **ratio** of b to c.

ILLUSTRATION 2. $(36 \div 9) = 4$ because $36 = (4 \times 9)$.

ILLUSTRATION 3.   If $c \neq 0$, then $(0 \div c) = 0$ because $0 = (c \times 0)$.   That is, if 0 is divided by any number $c \neq 0$, the result is 0.

SUMMARY.   *Computation of $b \div c$, where $c \neq 0$.*

1. *Obtain the absolute value of the quotient by computing the quotient of the absolute values, $|b| \div |c|$.*

2. *If $b \neq 0$, give the result a* **plus** *sign or a* **minus** *sign according as b and c have* **like** *signs or* **unlike** *signs.*

ILLUSTRATION 4. $\dfrac{-40}{10} = -4$ because $-40 = -4(10)$; $\dfrac{-40}{-8} = +5.$

Multiplication and division are referred to as **inverse operations,** because multiplication and then division of a number b by c, or these operations in reverse order, leave b *unchanged.*

4. Addition and subtraction

To add a set of numbers means *to find their* **sum.**

ILLUSTRATION 1. *The sum of any number and its negative is equal to zero.* Thus, since $-1 + 1 = 0$,

$$N - N = (+1)N + (-1)N = N(+1 - 1) = N(0) = 0.$$

ILLUSTRATION 2. $-3 - 4 = (-1)3 + (-1)4 = (-1)(3 + 4) = -7.$

DEFINITION V. **To subtract** *c from b means to find a number* x *such that* $b = x + c$. *Then,* x *is called the* **difference** *of b and c.*

For any numbers b and c, we verify that

$$(b - c) + c = b - c + c = b + 0 = b.$$

Or, the number $x = b - c$ satisfies the statement of Definition V:

$$\text{to subtract } c \text{ from } b, \text{ add } -c \text{ to } b. \tag{1}$$

Hence, $(b - c)$ can be referred to as the result of *subtracting c from b*, or as the *difference of b and c*. Thus, the minus sign in $(b - c)$ can be thought of as indicating subtraction, as in arithmetic. However, we also refer to $(b - c)$ as the *sum* of b and $-c$.

We cultivate automatic reactions by the following rules.

$$\left\{ \begin{array}{l} \textit{To add two explicit numbers with } \textbf{like } \textit{signs, add} \\ \textit{their absolute values and attach their common sign.} \end{array} \right\} \tag{2}$$

$$\left\{ \begin{array}{l} \textit{To add two explicit numbers with } \textbf{unlike } \textit{signs, subtract} \\ \textit{the smaller absolute value from the larger and prefix the} \\ \textit{sign of that given number having the larger absolute value.} \end{array} \right\} \tag{3}$$

ILLUSTRATION 3. In any sum of explicit numbers, we may add the positive numbers and the negative numbers separately, and then apply (3).

$$-20 - 8 = -(20 + 8) = -28; \quad -20 + 8 = -(20 - 8) = -12.$$
$$-16 - (-7) + (-12) + 14 = -16 + 7 - 12 + 14 = -28 + 21 = -7.$$

To *subtract 75 from 20*, we compute

$$x = 20 - 75 = -55.$$

ILLUSTRATION 4. We may refer to $c - 3 - 5a + 7b$ simply as a *sum* or, to emphasize the minus signs, as an *algebraic sum*. The expression is the sum of the terms c, -3, $-5a$, and $7b$.

If c is added to b, and then is *subtracted* from the first sum, or if these operations are performed in reverse order, the operations cancel each other and b is obtained as the final result. Hence, addition and subtraction are referred to as **inverse operations.**

Note 1. We call addition, subtraction, multiplication, and division the **fundamental operations** of algebra.

Note 2. Since "+" may be inserted before any number without altering it, we could indicate the sum of 3, − 2, and − 5 by $3 + (− 2) + (− 5)$. In this way, we could say that a *plus sign* can be used to indicate *addition*. However, such a method is clumsy and unnecessary. To indicate a sum, we merely write the numbers in a *line* with their own signs attached. Thus, the sum of 3, − 2, and − 5 can be written simply $(3 − 2 − 5)$, which gives − 4.

5. Zero in the fundamental operations

We defined $b \div c$ with the stipulation that $c \neq 0$. It is desirable to see why this agreement was made. Suppose that $b \div 0$ were defined as some number d. Then $b = 0 \times d = 0$, which is impossible if $b \neq 0$. If $b = 0$, we have $0 = 0 \times d$, which is true for *any* number d, or $0 \div 0$ could represent *any number*, and *thus would be useless*. Hence, we *never use* 0 *as a divisor*, or **division by zero is not allowed.** However, no exception arises in dividing zero by other numbers, in adding or subtracting zero, or in multiplying by zero. Thus, if N is any number,

$$N \times 0 = 0; \quad N + 0 = N; \quad N − 0 = N; \quad \frac{0}{c} = 0 \; \textit{if } c \neq 0.$$

6. Signs of grouping

Parentheses, ( ), brackets, [ ], braces, { }, and the vinculum, ‾, are used to enclose terms whose sum is to act as a single number. In general, the word *parentheses* will refer to any of these symbols.

ILLUSTRATION 1. Doubt arises as to the meaning of $(9 − 6 \div 3)$. Does it mean $(9 − 6) \div 3$, which is equal to 1, or $9 − (6 \div 3)$, which is equal to $(9 − 2)$ or 7? Use of parentheses eliminates ambiguity.

A factor multiplying a sum within parentheses should be used to multiply each term of the sum, because of Law V on page 5.

ILLUSTRATION 2. $− 4(a − 2b) = − 4a − 4(− 2b) = − 4a + 8b.$

A sign "+" or "−" before an expression indicates multiplication by + 1 or − 1, respectively. Hence, we have the following rules.

I. *In removing or inserting parentheses preceded by a* **plus** *sign, rewrite the included terms* **unchanged.**

II. *In removing or inserting parentheses preceded by a* **minus** *sign, rewrite the included terms with their* **signs changed.**

ILLUSTRATION 3. $− (− 2 + 5x − y) = (− 1)(− 2 + 5x − y) = 2 − 5x + y.$

If a symbol of grouping encloses other symbols of grouping, remove them by removing the *innermost* symbol first, etc. Usually, we enclose parentheses within brackets; brackets within braces.

ILLUSTRATION 4. $− [3y − (2x − 5)] = − (3y − 2x + 5) = − 3y + 2x − 5.$

Two terms with the same literal part are called *similar terms*, or *like terms*. In a term such as 5*abc*, the explicit number is called the *numerical coefficient*, or just the *coefficient*. With a term involving a literal part, we never write the coefficient when it is 1. *To collect terms* means *to collect similar terms.* In this operation, we use (V) of page 5.

To collect similar terms, add their numerical coefficients and multiply the result by the common literal part.

ILLUSTRATION 5. $\qquad -9ab + ab = ab(-9+1) = -8ab.$

The difference of $(3a - 5y - 8)$ and $(3y - 2a - 6)$ is

$$(3a - 5y - 8) - (3y - 2a - 6) = 5a - 8y - 2.$$

EXERCISE 1

Compute the expression, if possible. Otherwise, remove any signs of grouping and collect similar terms.

1. $-(-5).$ 2. $0(-3).$ 3. $-4(-5-6).$ 4. $-7(-4)(6).$ 5. $(-4)(+3).$
6. $-4(-5)(6)(-3).$ 7. $-5(-3)(0)(-4).$ 8. $-1.57(-2.31).$
9. $(6-18)+3.$ 10. $6-(18+3).$ 11. $(7-3)(16-5-2).$
12. $-(2a - 5b + c).$ 13. $-2(8a - 3b - c).$ 14. $-2(x - y + 8).$
15. $3a + 8a.$ 16. $-5b + 7b.$ 17. $-13x - 5x.$
18. $-19ab + 5ab.$ 19. $-2cd + 8cd.$ 20. $5xy - 9xy.$
21. $2(a - 3b) - 5(b - 2a) + 3(-a - 3b).$
22. $5(x - 3y + 5) - 2(x + 2y - 4) - 3(-4x - y + 6).$
23. $6(2a - h - k) - 3(a - 4h + 5k) + 2(4h - 3a - k).$
24. $-[4a - (2a + 3)].$ 25. $-[2t + (3 - 4t)].$
26. $-(a-2) - [2a - (a-3)].$ 27. $a + [b + (a - b)].$
28. $9 - [z - (6 - 2z)].$ 29. $2r + [r - (s + 4r)].$
30. $x - [2x - (y + 3z)].$ 31. $2y - \{5 + [3 - 2(y-2)]\}.$
32. $-\{a - [a - (2a - 7)]\}.$ 33. $-\{2b - [6 - (3b - 4)]\}.$

Rewrite, with two terms at the right in parentheses preceded by a minus sign.

34. $-5 + 7a - 4b.$ 35. $-6a + 4b - c.$ 36. $6 - 3x - 4y.$
37. $2a - 3 + 5b - c.$ 38. $16 - 4a - b + 3c.$
39. State the absolute value of 17; -46; -33; $-\frac{3}{4}$; $-1.48.$
40. Read the symbol and specify its value: $|-36|$; $|-9|$; $|-\frac{5}{3}|$; $|-1.3|.$
41. Write the negative of 7; -4; $-\frac{2}{3}$; -8; 16.7; 0.

Write an expression for the quantity, remove parentheses, and collect terms.

42. Subtract the sum of $(3a - 2b)$ and $(2a + 5b)$ from $(-a - 5b).$

HINT. The result is equal to $(-a - 5b) - [(3a - 2b) + (2a + 5b)].$

43. Subtract the sum of $(3a - 7h)$ and $(5h - 6a)$ from $(2a - 3h).$
44. Multiply $(3a - 5y - 3)$ by 2, $(-5a + 7y - 5)$ by -3, and then add.

7. Real number scale and inequality relations

On a horizontal line, as in Figure 1, select a point O, called the *origin*, and let it represent the number 0. Select a unit of length for measuring distances on the line. Then, if p is a positive number, let it be represented by the point on the line which is at p units of distance from O to the right.

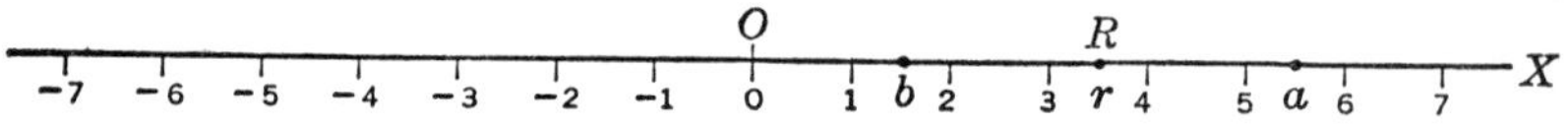

Fig. 1

Let the negative number $-p$ be represented by the point on the line at p units of distance from O to the left. Thus, all real numbers are identified with points on the line OX, and we call it a *real number scale*. If r is any real number, represented by R on OX, then r is the measure of the directed distance from O to R on the scale. This distance OR is considered *positive* or *negative* according as R is to the *right* or the *left* of O on OX. Hereafter, if r is any real number, we may refer to "*the point r*," meaning the point representing r on the scale.

DEFINITION VI. *To say that b is **less than** a, or that a is **greater than** b, means that b is to the **left** of a on the number scale.*

We use the inequality sign "$<$" for "*is less than*" and "$>$" for "*is greater than*." Thus,

$$\left\{ \begin{array}{l} \text{"}b < a\text{" means that } b \text{ is to the} \\ \text{left of } a \text{ on the number scale.} \end{array} \right. \tag{1}$$

ILLUSTRATION 1. We verify each of the following inequalities by plotting the two numbers on a number scale.

$$4 < 6. \qquad 0 < 8. \qquad -4 < 0. \qquad -6 < 5. \qquad -25 < -2.$$

To say that $p > 0$ is equivalent to saying that p is *positive*, because all numbers to the right of O in Figure 1 are positive. To say that $N < 0$ is equivalent to saying that N is *negative*.

We say that one number b is *numerically less* than a second number c in case *the absolute value of b is less than the absolute value of c*. To distinguish this relation from *ordinary* inequality, we sometimes place the word *algebraically* before *greater than* or *less than* when they are used in the ordinary sense.

ILLUSTRATION 2. 5 is *numerically* less than 9 because $|5| < |9|$. It is also true that 5 is *algebraically* less than 9, because $5 < 9$.

ILLUSTRATION 3. We see that -3 is numerically less than -7 because $|-3| = 3$ and $|-7| = 7$, and $3 < 7$. However, $-7 < -3$. Thus, -3 is *algebraically greater* than -7 but *numerically less* than -7. Any negative number is algebraically less than zero.

EXERCISE 2

Construct a real number scale and mark the locations of integers. Then, read each inequality and verify it on your scale.

1. $5 < 9.$ **2.** $0 < 7.$ **3.** $-3 < 0.$ **4.** $-3 < 8.$
5. $-5 < 2.$ **6.** $-7 < -4.$ **7.** $8 > -9.$ **8.** $-3 > -10.$

Decide which sign, $<$ or $>$, should be placed between the numbers.

9. $7, 9.$ **10.** $-2, 5.$ **11.** $0, 8.$ **12.** $-6, 0.$
13. $-3, 3.$ **14.** $-2, -7.$ **15.** $-9, 10.$ **16.** $7, 5.$
17. $7, 5.$ **18.** $8, -3.$ **19.** $-7, -9.$ **20.** $8, -10.$

Read the inequalities and check them.

21. $|-7| < |8|$ and $-7 < 8.$ **22.** $|4| < |9|$ and $4 < 9.$
23. $|-3| > |0|$ but $-3 < 0.$ **24.** $|-8| > 3$ but $-8 < 3.$

8. Rational and irrational numbers

On page 3, we observed that all numbers of arithmetic can be thought of in decimal forms, where we visualize an endless set of decimal places in each number. Then, the set of all real numbers can be defined as the set of *all decimals*, positive, negative, and zero.

DEFINITION VII. *A real number N is said to be a* **rational number** *if there exist integers p and q, where $q \neq 0$, such that $N = p/q$.*

If p is any integer, then $p = p/1$, and thus p is a rational number. Any rational number, not zero, can be written as a quotient of positive integers, or the negative of such a quotient.

ILLUSTRATION 1. $3, 5/7, -7/3,$ and 0 are rational numbers.

ILLUSTRATION 2. Any terminating decimal is a rational number. Thus, $35.78 = 3578/100.$ Also, on page 132, we shall show that any infinite repeating decimal is a rational number. Thus, $.222\cdots = 2/9.$ A rational number may be expressible as a terminating decimal; thus, $\frac{3}{4} = .75.$ If a rational number is not equal to a terminating decimal, by division we find that the number is equal to an infinite repeating decimal. For instance, $\frac{1}{6} = .1666\cdots$, which gives the sequence of terminating decimals

$$.1, \quad .16, \quad .166, \quad .1666, \quad \cdots, \tag{1}$$

and we call (1) the successive decimal approximations to $1/6$. We refer to $1/6$ as the **limit** of the sequence in (1).

DEFINITION VIII. *A real number is said to be an* **irrational number** *if it is not a rational number.*

The remarks in Illustration 2 lead to the conclusion that the rational numbers consist of all *terminating decimals* and all *infinite repeating decimals*. The irrational numbers consist of all *infinite nonrepeating decimals*.

ILLUSTRATION 3. If a number is described by general properties, a proof that it is rational or irrational may be difficult, even though we may have means for computing the number to any specified decimal place. Thus, an elaborate proof is necessary to show that π is irrational. Its value has been computed to hundreds of decimal places, and we find $\pi = 3.14159\cdots$. In Note 1 of the Appendix, it is proved that $\sqrt{2}$ is not rational; that is, no integers m and n exist such that $2 = m^2/n^2$. The successive decimal approximations to $\sqrt{2}$ are obtainable by the square root process of arithmetic.

Note 1. In a certain sense, which is discussed in advanced mathematics, there are "*more*" irrational numbers than rational numbers. On a number scale, as in Figure 1 on page 10, each point corresponds to just one real number. Both rational and irrational numbers are "*dense*" on the scale, in the sense that, between any two numbers (points) on the scale, there exist infinitely many numbers of each type.

9. Elementary operations on fractions

Suppose that each of a, b, c, and d is a *positive integer or* 0, with $b \neq 0$ and $d \neq 0$. Then, in arithmetic, the following equations are specified to be true as *definitions* of equality, multiplication, and addition, respectively, for the rational numbers a/b and c/d.

$$\frac{a}{b} = \frac{c}{d} \quad means\ that \quad ad = bc. \tag{1}$$

$$\frac{a}{b}\cdot\frac{c}{d} = \frac{ac}{bd}. \tag{2}$$

$$\frac{a}{b} + \frac{c}{d} = \frac{ad + bc}{bd}. \tag{3}$$

By use of the definitions given previously for the numbers of the real number system and for the operations in this system, it is possible to prove that (1), (2), and (3) remain true when a, b, c, and d are any real numbers, with $b \neq 0$ and $d \neq 0$. All of the following rules for the use of fractions grow out of (1), (2), and (3). Except in a few simple instances, we shall omit the proofs (in some cases very elaborate) of the preceding facts.

I. FUNDAMENTAL PRINCIPLE. *The value of a fraction is not altered if both numerator and denominator are multiplied (or divided) by the same number, not zero.* That is, if $k \neq 0$ and $b \neq 0$,

$$\frac{a}{b} = \frac{ka}{kb}. \tag{4}$$

Proof. Since $a(kb) = b(ka)$, it is seen that (4) is true because (1) is true. On reading (4) from right to left, it follows that *division* of both numerator and denominator by k on the right does not change the value of the fraction.

ILLUSTRATION 1.
$$\frac{5}{7} = \frac{5 \times 3}{7 \times 3} = \frac{15}{21}. \qquad \frac{36}{84} = \frac{36 \div 12}{84 \div 12} = \frac{3}{7}.$$

In particular, from (4), both numerator and denominator of a fraction **may** be multiplied by -1. Thus,

$$\frac{-3}{-4} = \frac{(-1)(-3)}{(-1)(-4)} = \frac{3}{4}.$$

II. *To divide one fraction by another, invert the divisor and multiply the dividend by this inverted divisor.*

$$\frac{a}{b} \div \frac{c}{d} = \frac{ad}{bc}. \tag{5}$$

Proof of (5). By Definition IV on page 6, the left-hand side of (5) represents a unique number x such that $(c/d)x = a/b$. By use of (2) and (4),

$$\frac{c}{d} \cdot \frac{ad}{bc} = \frac{acd}{bcd} = \frac{a}{b},$$

and hence (5) is true.

The following statement (III) is a consequence of (I), and (IV) is a verbal description of (2).

III. *To reduce a fraction to lowest terms, divide numerator and denominator by all of their common factors.*

IV. *To multiply one fraction by another, multiply the numerators for a new numerator, and the denominators for a new denominator.*

ILLUSTRATION 2.
$$\frac{\frac{4}{5}}{\frac{3}{7}} = \frac{4}{5} \cdot \frac{7}{3} = \frac{28}{15}. \qquad \frac{5acx}{7acy} = \frac{5x}{7y} \qquad \text{(divide out } ac\text{)}.$$

By use of the fact that any number N can be written as a fraction $N/1$, we obtain the following rule.

V. *To multiply a fraction by a number, multiply the numerator by the number. To divide a fraction by a number, multiply the denominator by the number.*

ILLUSTRATION 3.
$$c\left(\frac{a}{b}\right) = \frac{c}{1} \cdot \frac{a}{b} = \frac{ac}{b}. \qquad 7 \cdot \frac{5}{6} = \frac{35}{6}.$$

$$\frac{a}{b} \div c = \frac{a}{b} \div \frac{c}{1} = \frac{a}{b} \cdot \frac{1}{c} = \frac{a}{bc}. \qquad 4 \div (3\tfrac{2}{7}) = 4 \div \frac{23}{7} = \frac{4}{1} \cdot \frac{7}{23} = \frac{28}{23}.$$

If just the numerator, or denominator, of a fraction is multiplied by -1, the sign before the fraction must be *changed*. These actions are equivalent to multiplying by *two* factors -1, whose product is $+1$, and thus the value of the fraction is not altered.

ILLUSTRATION 4.
$$\frac{a-3}{2} = -\frac{(-1)(a-3)}{?} = -\frac{3-a}{2}.$$

EXERCISE 3

Express the result by use of a fraction in lowest terms without a minus sign in numerator or denominator.

1. $\dfrac{15}{18}$. **2.** $\dfrac{40}{72}$. **3.** $\dfrac{24}{45}$. **4.** $\dfrac{77}{121}$. **5.** $\dfrac{65}{39}$.

6. $\dfrac{-5}{3}$. **7.** $\dfrac{4}{-7}$. **8.** $\dfrac{-3}{-12}$. **9.** $\dfrac{-35}{15}$. **10.** $-\dfrac{78}{-26}$

11. $\dfrac{3}{5}\cdot\dfrac{4}{7}$. **12.** $\dfrac{4}{5}\cdot\dfrac{3}{8}$. **13.** $\left(2\tfrac{1}{7}\right)\cdot\left(\dfrac{21}{4}\right)$. **14.** $\dfrac{b}{2}\cdot\dfrac{8}{d}$.

15. $\dfrac{4}{5}\div\dfrac{2}{3}$. **16.** $\dfrac{22}{7}\div\dfrac{11}{5}$. **17.** $\dfrac{5}{6}\div\dfrac{15}{4}$. **18.** $\dfrac{21}{38}\div\dfrac{14}{57}$.

19. $7\left(\dfrac{3}{8}\right)$. **20.** $21\left(\dfrac{2}{7}\right)$. **21.** $\left(3\tfrac{4}{5}\right)\cdot\left(\dfrac{4}{3}\right)$. **22.** $\dfrac{8}{15}\cdot6\tfrac{2}{3}$.

23. $a\cdot\dfrac{5}{9}$. **24.** $\dfrac{3}{5}\cdot c$. **25.** $\dfrac{8}{15}\div2$. **26.** $\dfrac{3}{5}\div6$.

27. $15\div\dfrac{12}{7}$. **28.** $12\div\dfrac{24}{5}$. **29.** $\dfrac{3x}{4}\div1\tfrac{3}{4}$. **30.** $a\div\dfrac{2}{3}$.

31. $\dfrac{4cd}{16c}$. **32.** $\dfrac{21x}{28xy}$. **33.** $\dfrac{3hy}{6y}$. **34.** $\dfrac{27a}{6ad}$.

35. $\dfrac{-bc}{3c}$. **36.** $\dfrac{4a}{-3ad}$. **37.** $-\dfrac{-3}{12b}$. **38.** $-\dfrac{5ad}{-a}$.

39. $\dfrac{12}{7}\div15$. **40.** $\left(4\tfrac{5}{9}\right)\div\dfrac{x}{3}$. **41.** $\dfrac{14}{15}\div2a$. **42.** $\dfrac{ab}{6}\div b$.

43. $\dfrac{3}{5}\cdot\dfrac{2}{7}\cdot\dfrac{5}{4}$. **44.** $\dfrac{3x}{4}\cdot\dfrac{5y}{6}\cdot\dfrac{2z}{9x}$. **45.** $\dfrac{a}{b}\cdot\dfrac{2c}{d}\cdot\dfrac{3b}{5a}$.

46. $\dfrac{\frac{2}{5}}{\frac{4}{15}}$. **47.** $\dfrac{\frac{7}{3}}{\frac{4}{18}}$. **48.** $\dfrac{-\frac{8}{9c}}{\frac{4d}{5c}}$. **49.** $\dfrac{\frac{12a}{5b}}{\frac{8a}{15}}$. **50.** $\dfrac{-\frac{3}{a}}{\frac{12}{ax}}$.

51. $\dfrac{\frac{15}{7}}{6}$. **52.** $\dfrac{\frac{14}{5}}{10}$. **53.** $\dfrac{\frac{3h}{k}}{6}$. **54.** $\dfrac{\frac{4w}{9d}}{2w}$.

55. $6\div\dfrac{3}{2}$. **56.** $5\div\dfrac{4}{7}$. **57.** $5\div\dfrac{3}{10}$. **58.** $5d\div\dfrac{3d}{c}$.

59. $\dfrac{\frac{3}{15}}{7}$. **60.** $\dfrac{\frac{21}{14}}{9}$. **61.** $\dfrac{\frac{2a}{c}}{d}$. **62.** $\dfrac{\frac{5w}{15w}}{8}$. **63.** $\dfrac{2}{5}\cdot\dfrac{2}{5}\cdot\dfrac{2}{5}$.

64. $-\left(\dfrac{3}{4}\right)\left(-\dfrac{3}{4}\right)\left(-\dfrac{3}{4}\right)\left(-\dfrac{3}{4}\right)$. **65.** $\left(-\dfrac{1}{2}\right)\left(-\dfrac{1}{2}\right)\left(-\dfrac{1}{2}\right)$.

66. $\dfrac{\left(-\dfrac{2}{3}\right)\left(-\dfrac{5}{6}\right)\left(\dfrac{2}{7}\right)\left(-4\tfrac{1}{2}\right)\left(5\tfrac{3}{4}\right)}{\left(\dfrac{3}{5}\right)\left(2\tfrac{5}{8}\right)}$.

10. Positive integral exponents

By definition, if m is a positive integer, then $a^m = a \cdot a \cdot a \cdots a$, to m factors. We call a^m the **mth power** of the **base** a and m the **exponent** of the power. By definition, $a^1 = a$. Hence, when the exponent is 1, we shall usually omit it. We call a^2 the **square** of a and a^3 the **cube** of a. The following properties I–V of exponents are called **index laws.**

Note 1. Until later, any literal number occurring in an exponent will represent a positive integer.

I. *Law of exponents for multiplication:* $a^m a^n = a^{m+n}$.

Proof. 1. By definition, $\qquad a^m = a \cdot a \cdots a;$ $\qquad\qquad$ (*m factors*)

$\qquad\qquad\qquad\qquad\qquad\quad a^n = a \cdot a \cdot a \cdots a.$ $\qquad\qquad$ (*n factors*)

2. Hence, $\quad a^m a^n = (a \cdot a \cdots a)(a \cdot a \cdot a \cdots a) = a^{m+n}.$ $\quad$ [(*m + n*) *factors a*]

II. *Law for finding a power of a power:* $(a^m)^n = a^{mn}$.

Proof. 1. $\qquad\qquad\qquad (a^m)^n = a^m \cdot a^m \cdots a^m;$ $\qquad\qquad$ (*n factors a^m*)

(By Law I) $\qquad\qquad\qquad\quad = a^{m+m+\cdots+m}.$ $\qquad\qquad$ (*n terms m*)

2. Since $(m + m + \cdots + m)$ to n terms is equal to mn, $(a^m)^n = a^{mn}$.

III. *Laws of exponents for division:* if $a \neq 0$,

$$\frac{a^m}{a^m} = 1; \qquad \frac{a^m}{a^n} = a^{m-n} \text{ (if } m > n\text{)}; \qquad \frac{a^m}{a^n} = \frac{1}{a^{n-m}} \text{ (if } n > m\text{)}.$$

Proof, for the case $n > m$. By the definition of a^m and a^n,

$$\frac{a^m}{a^n} = \frac{\overset{1 \cdot 1 \cdots 1}{\cancel{a} \cdot \cancel{a} \cdots \cancel{a}}}{a \cdot a \cdots a \cdot \underset{1 \cdot 1 \cdots 1}{\cancel{a} \cdot \cancel{a} \cdots \cancel{a}}};$$

$\qquad\qquad\qquad\qquad\qquad\qquad\qquad$ (*m factors*)

$\qquad\qquad\qquad\qquad\qquad\qquad\qquad$ (*n factors*)

[(*n − m*) *factors a*] $\qquad = \dfrac{1}{a \cdot a \cdots a} = \dfrac{1}{a^{n-m}}.$

IV. *Law for finding a power of a product:* $\qquad (ab)^n = a^n b^n$.

Proof. $\qquad\qquad\qquad\qquad (ab)^n = ab \cdot ab \cdots ab;$ $\qquad\qquad$ (*n factors ab*)

(*n factors a and b*) $\qquad\qquad = (a \cdot a \cdots a)(b \cdot b \cdots b) = a^n b^n.$

Law IV extends to products of any number of factors. Thus,

$$(abc)^n = a^n b^n c^n.$$

V. *Law for finding a power of a quotient:* $\qquad \left(\dfrac{a}{b}\right)^n = \dfrac{a^n}{b^n}.$

Proof. $\qquad\qquad\qquad\qquad \left(\dfrac{a}{b}\right)^n = \dfrac{a}{b} \cdot \dfrac{a}{b} \cdots \dfrac{a}{b}$ $\qquad\qquad$ $\left(n \text{ factors } \dfrac{a}{b}\right)$

(*n factors a*)

(*n factors b*) $\qquad\qquad\qquad = \dfrac{a \cdot a \cdots a}{b \cdot b \cdots b} = \dfrac{a^n}{b^n}.$

ILLUSTRATION 1. $(-3)^3 = (-3) \cdot (-3) \cdot (-3) = -27.$

ILLUSTRATION 2. $\dfrac{a^5}{a^5} = 1. \qquad \dfrac{a^{10}}{a^2} = a^8. \qquad \dfrac{a^4}{a^7} = \dfrac{1}{a^3}.$

ILLUSTRATION 3. $\left(\dfrac{3}{2}\right)^4 = \dfrac{3^4}{2^4} = \dfrac{81}{16}. \qquad \left(\dfrac{4cd^2}{3x}\right)^2 = \dfrac{(4cd^2)^2}{(3x)^2} = \dfrac{16c^2d^4}{9x^2}.$

ILLUSTRATION 4. $\dfrac{-15a^3x^5}{10ax^9} = -\dfrac{3}{2} \cdot \dfrac{a^3}{a} \cdot \dfrac{x^5}{x^9} = -\dfrac{3a^{3-1}}{2x^{9-5}} = -\dfrac{3a^2}{2x^4}.$

An algebraic term is said to be **integral and rational** in certain literal numbers if it does not involve them, or if it is the product of positive integral powers of the literal numbers and a factor not involving them.

ILLUSTRATION 5.   The terms $\frac{1}{4}a^3$, 5, and $-16a^4b^2$ are integral and rational in a and b, while $3/x$ is *not* integral and rational in x.

11. Square roots

If $R^2 = A$, we call R a **square root** of A. If A is positive, then A is found to have two square roots, one positive and one negative, with equal absolute values. The positive square root is denoted by $+\sqrt{A}$ or simply $\sqrt{A}$, and the negative square root by $-\sqrt{A}$. Unless otherwise stated, "*the square root of A*" will refer to the *positive* square root of A,

ILLUSTRATION 1.   16 has the square roots ± 4, read "*plus and minus* 4," because $4^2 = 16$ and $(-4)^2 = 16$. We have $4 = \sqrt{16}$ and $-4 = -\sqrt{16}$.

If $A < 0$, a search for square roots of A leads to the introduction of imaginary numbers, as on page 45. Zero has just *one* square root, $\sqrt{0} = 0$, because $0^2 = 0$, and $a^2 \neq 0$ if $a \neq 0$. If $A > 0$, by the definition of $\sqrt{A}$,

$$(\sqrt{A})^2 = A. \tag{1}$$

Also, if $x > 0$, then $\sqrt{x^2} = x$. Since $\sqrt{A} > 0$ if $A > 0$, we obtain

$$\sqrt{x^2} = -x \text{ if } x \text{ is negative.} \tag{2}$$

ILLUSTRATION 2. $\sqrt{(-5)^2} = \sqrt{25} = 5. \qquad (\sqrt{198})^2 = 198.$

An integer is said to be a *perfect square* if it is the square of an integer. An integral rational term, or a quotient of integral rational terms, is said to be a perfect square if it is the square of some expression of the same type.

ILLUSTRATION 3. $25a^2b^4$ is a perfect square, because $25a^2b^4 = (5ab^2)^2$. Also, $25a^2b^4/16x^6$ is a perfect square because

$$\left(\dfrac{5ab^2}{4x^3}\right)^2 = \dfrac{25a^2b^4}{16x^6}.$$

Until otherwise specified, in any radical $\sqrt{A}$, we shall suppose that the numerical coefficients are positive, that all literal numbers represent positive numbers, and that A is a perfect square of one of the types previously mentioned. In such a perfect square, any exponent for a literal number is an *even* integer because, in squaring, exponents are multiplied by 2.

SUMMARY. *To find (or extract) the square root of an integral rational term which is a perfect square, divide each exponent by 2 and multiply by the square root of the numerical coefficient.*

ILLUSTRATION 4. $\qquad 16x^4y^8 = \sqrt{16}\sqrt{x^4y^8} = 4x^2y^4$, *because*

$$(4x^2y^4)^2 = 4^2x^4y^8 = 16x^4y^8.$$

We verify that

$$\sqrt{\frac{N}{D}} = \frac{\sqrt{N}}{\sqrt{D}} \qquad because \qquad \left(\frac{\sqrt{N}}{\sqrt{D}}\right)^2 = \frac{(\sqrt{N})^2}{(\sqrt{D})^2} = \frac{N}{D}.$$

Hence, *to obtain the square root of a fraction, find the square root of the numerator and of the denominator, and divide.*

ILLUSTRATION 5. $\qquad \sqrt{\frac{4}{25}} = \frac{\sqrt{4}}{\sqrt{25}} = \frac{2}{5}. \qquad \sqrt{\frac{a^2}{b^2}} = \frac{\sqrt{a^2}}{\sqrt{b^2}} = \frac{a}{b}.$

ILLUSTRATION 6. $\qquad \sqrt{\frac{100a^6}{9x^4y^8}} = \frac{\sqrt{100a^6}}{\sqrt{9x^4y^8}} = \frac{10a^3}{3x^2y^4}.$

If H and K are positive,

$$\sqrt{HK} = \sqrt{H}\sqrt{K} \qquad because \qquad (\sqrt{H})^2(\sqrt{K})^2 = HK.$$

Hence, if a radicand A is a product of perfect square factors, we may find $\sqrt{A}$ by multiplying the square roots of the factors. This method gives rise to details similar to those met in using the Summary.

ILLUSTRATION 7. $\qquad \sqrt{225} = \sqrt{9}\sqrt{25} = 3 \cdot 5 = 15.$

$$\sqrt{25x^2y^{10}} = \sqrt{25}\sqrt{x^2}\sqrt{y^{10}} = 5xy^5.$$

EXERCISE 4

If no literal number is involved, compute the expression. Otherwise, carry out the multiplication or division by the laws of exponents.

1. 4^3.	2. 10^2.	3. $(-1)^6$.	4. $(-5)^2$.	5. $(-2)^5$.
6. $(-3)^3$.	7. $(-10)^4$.	8. $(\frac{1}{3})^4$.	9. $(\frac{2}{5})^2$.	10. $(\frac{3}{4})^3$.
11. $(-\frac{1}{2})^3$.	12. $(\frac{1}{10})^4$.	13. -2^6.	14. -3^4.	15. $3(2^3)$.
16. $-2(-5)^3$.	17. $(2^2)^3$.	18. $(10^2)^4$.	19. $2^2 2^3$.	20. $[3(2^2)]^2$.
21. a^5a^4.	22. xx^3.	23. y^3y^7.	24. a^ha^{2k}.	25. uu^5.
26. bb^2b^9.	27. $(xy)^4$.	28. $(3x)^2$.	29. $(c^3)^5$.	30. $(a^2)^5$.
31. $(h^n)^4$.	32. $(x^{2n})^k$.	33. $(-\frac{3}{2})^3$.	34. $(2a^3)^3$.	35. $(a^2x)^3$.
36. $\left(\frac{c}{d}\right)^3$.	37. $\left(\frac{h}{2}\right)^5$.	38. $\left(\frac{3}{a}\right)^4$.	39. $\left(\frac{x^2}{y^3}\right)^2$.	40. $\left(\frac{a^3}{b^2}\right)^4$.
41. $\frac{y^3}{y}$.	42. $\frac{a^2}{a^8}$.	43. $\frac{x^3}{x^5}$.	44. $\frac{x}{x^4}$.	45. $\frac{a^6}{a^2}$.

46. $\dfrac{3^9}{3^7}$.   **47.** $\dfrac{2^3}{2^8}$.   **48.** $\dfrac{5r}{25r^2}$.   **49.** $\dfrac{x^2y^4}{xy^4}$.   **50.** $\dfrac{a^3b^8}{ab^9}$.

51. $(-a^3x^2)^4$.   **52.** $(x^2y^3)^5$.   **53.** $(-3x^2y)^3$.   **54.** $(-2wx^3)^4$.

55. $\left(\dfrac{2a}{3x}\right)^3$.   **56.** $\left(\dfrac{2h^2}{k^3}\right)^4$.   **57.** $\left(-\dfrac{3x}{yz}\right)^3$.   **58.** $\left(-\dfrac{x^2y^3}{2a}\right)^5$.

59. $-\dfrac{21a^2}{3a}$.   **60.** $-\dfrac{-2a^5}{-4a^2}$.   **61.** $-\dfrac{9b}{-27bc^3}$.   **62.** $\dfrac{5cd^3}{20c^2d}$.

63. $2x^2(5x^4)$.   **64.** $3y(2y^5)$.   **65.** $ab(3a^2)$.   **66.** $4y^2(2x^2y)$.

67. $-3ax^4(-2a^2x)$.   **68.** $5x^2y(-2xy^3)$.   **69.** $2a^3b^2(-49a^5b^2)$.

70. $-8m^3n(-2m^2n^3)$.   **71.** $4hr^2(-6h^4r)$.   **72.** $-6c^2d^3(-2cd)$.

73. $-5w(2-3w+4w^2)$.   **74.** $-3hk^2(h^2-4hk-2k^2)$.

Find the two square roots of the number, or the specified root.

75. 25.   **76.** 49.   **77.** 121.   **78.** 64.   **79.** $\tfrac{1}{9}$.   **80.** $\tfrac{1}{36}$.

81. $\sqrt{9}$.   **82.** $\sqrt{100}$.   **83.** $\sqrt{81}$.   **84.** $\sqrt{144}$.

85. $\sqrt{196}$.   **86.** $\sqrt{\tfrac{9}{4}}$.   **87.** $\sqrt{\tfrac{16}{25}}$.   **88.** $\sqrt{\tfrac{25}{9}}$.

89. $\sqrt{\tfrac{1}{81}}$.   **90.** $\sqrt{\tfrac{49}{64}}$.   **91.** $\sqrt{\tfrac{4}{81}}$.   **92.** $\sqrt{\tfrac{49}{100}}$.

93. $\sqrt{4z^8}$.   **94.** $\sqrt{16h^2}$.   **95.** $\sqrt{49z^6}$.   **96.** $\sqrt{9x^2y^4}$.

97. $\sqrt{64x^4w^6}$.   **98.** $\sqrt{16a^2b^3}$.   **99.** $\sqrt{49w^4x^4}$.   **100.** $\sqrt{121z^2}$.

101. $\sqrt{\dfrac{9}{a^2}}$.   **102.** $\sqrt{\dfrac{4}{x^2}}$.   **103.** $\sqrt{\dfrac{y^2}{16}}$.   **104.** $\sqrt{\dfrac{z^2}{25}}$.

105. $\sqrt{\dfrac{49}{w^4}}$.   **106.** $\sqrt{\dfrac{121}{y^6}}$.   **107.** $\sqrt{\dfrac{a^2}{y^4}}$.   **108.** $\sqrt{\dfrac{b^4}{w^8}}$.

109. $\sqrt{\dfrac{4x^2}{h^8}}$.   **110.** $\sqrt{\dfrac{a^4}{9x^2}}$.   **111.** $\sqrt{\dfrac{81a^2}{y^2z^2}}$.   **112.** $\sqrt{\dfrac{b^2x^4}{49z^4}}$.

113. $\sqrt{\dfrac{9a^2b^4}{c^6w^{10}}}$.   **114.** $\sqrt{\dfrac{9x^6}{4y^4z^2}}$.   **115.** $\sqrt{\dfrac{121a^6}{9b^4z^6}}$.   **116.** $\sqrt{\dfrac{100x^4}{9y^2z^6}}$.

Square each quantity.

117. $\left(\sqrt{\dfrac{37}{x}}\right)^2$.   **118.** $(\sqrt{142a})^2$.   **119.** $(\sqrt{yz^3})^2$.   **120.** $\left(\sqrt{\dfrac{659}{z}}\right)^2$.

12. Multiplication and division of polynomials

An algebraic sum is called a **monomial** if the sum has just *one* term, a **binomial** if there are just *two* terms, and a **trinomial** if there are just *three* terms. A sum of any number of terms is called a **polynomial**, although this name usually applies to a sum of *more than one term*. An **integral rational polynomial** is one where all terms are integral and rational. Unless otherwise stated, any polynomial to which we refer will be integral and rational in all literal numbers involved.

ILLUSTRATION 1. $(3x + 7ab)$ is a binomial. $(3x - 7y - 5)$ is a trinomial. Each of these sums is a polynomial.

To form the product of two polynomials, multiply one of them by each term of the other and collect similar terms.

ILLUSTRATION 2. $(2x - 3y)(x^2 - xy) = 2x(x^2 - xy) - 3y(x^2 - xy)$
$$= 2x^3 - 2x^2y - 3x^2y + 3xy^2 = 2x^3 - 5x^2y + 3xy^2.$$

ILLUSTRATION 3. $\qquad\qquad (x + 5)^2 = (x + 5)(x + 5)$
$$= x(x + 5) + 5(x + 5) = x^2 + 5x + 5x + 25 = x^2 + 10x + 25.$$

Before multiplying, if many terms are involved, arrange the polynomials in ascending (or descending) powers of one letter.

ILLUSTRATION 4. To multiply $(x^2 + 3x^3 - x - 2)(2x + 3)$:

$$
\begin{array}{l}
3x^3 +x^2 -x - 2 \\
(Multiply)2x + 3 \\
\hline
6x^4 + 2x^3 - 2x^2 - 4x \qquad (Multiplying\ by\ 2x) \\
9x^3 + 3x^2 - 3x - 6 \quad (Multiplying\ by\ 3) \\
\hline
(Add)6x^4 + 11x^3 +x^2 - 7x - 6 = product.
\end{array}
$$

When we defined $b \div c$, its *complete value* was called the *quotient*. Frequently, the word quotient does not refer to a complete quotient. In such a case, we may use the name *partial quotient*.

ILLUSTRATION 5. We find $259 \div 17 = 15\frac{4}{17}$; the complete quotient is $15\frac{4}{17}$. Also, we might say that the *quotient* (meaning *partial quotient*) is 15 and the remainder is 4. Then,

$$259 = (17 \times 15) + 4. \tag{1}$$

At any stage of the usual long division process in arithmetic, or algebra, the remainder and partial quotient satisfy

$$\frac{\text{dividend}}{\text{divisor}} = (\text{quotient}) + \frac{\text{remainder}}{\text{divisor}}, or \tag{2}$$

$$\text{dividend} = (\text{quotient})(\text{divisor}) + \text{remainder}. \tag{3}$$

Equation (1) is an illustration of (3), which will be called the *fundamental equation of division*.

To divide a polynomial by a single term, divide each term of the polynomial by the divisor and combine the results.

ILLUSTRATION 6. $\qquad \dfrac{4a^2b^4 - 8a^2b - 2b^2}{-2ab^3} = \dfrac{4a^2b^4}{-2ab^3} - \dfrac{8a^2b}{-2ab^3} - \dfrac{2b^2}{-2ab^3}$

$$= -2ab + \frac{4a}{b^2} + \frac{1}{ab}.$$

To divide one polynomial by another, first we *arrange them in descending powers of some common literal number.* Then, we carry out details similar to those of long division in arithmetic. If the final remainder is zero, we say that the division is *exact*.

EXAMPLE 1. Divide: $(4x^3 - 9x - 8x^2 + 7) \div (2x - 3)$.

SOLUTION. Arrange the dividend in descending powers of x. Then, since $(4x^3 \div 2x) = 2x^2$, this is the first term of the quotient; etc.

$$\begin{array}{r}
2x^2 - x - 6 \ \ (Quotient) \\
\hline
(Divisor)\ 2x - 3\ )\overline{\ 4x^3 - 8x^2 - 9x + 7}\ (Dividend) \\
\end{array}$$

$2x^2(2x - 3) \to$ (Subtract) $\dfrac{4x^3 - 6x^2}{}$

$[(- 2x^2) \div 2x] = - x.$ $- 2x^2 - 9x$

$- x(2x - 3) \to$ (Subtract) $\dfrac{- 2x^2 + 3x}{}$

$[(- 12x) \div 2x] = - 6.$ $- 12x + 7$

$- 6(2x - 3) \to$ (Subtract) $\dfrac{- 12x + 18}{}$

$- 11$ (Remainder)

Conclusion. From equation (2),

$$\frac{4x^3 - 8x^2 - 9x + 7}{2x - 3} = 2x^2 - x - 6 - \frac{11}{2x - 3}. \tag{4}$$

13. Products of binomials

In calculating products mentally, the following formulas are useful. They will be referred to as Types I–VI in this chapter. The student should verify each formula by multiplication.

ILLUSTRATION 1. $(a + b)^2 = (a + b)(a + b)$

$$= a(a + b) + b(a + b) = a^2 + 2ab + b^2.$$

I. $a(x + y) = ax + ay.$

II. $(x + y)(x - y) = x^2 - y^2.$

III. $(a + b)^2 = a^2 + 2ab + b^2.$

IV. $(a - b)^2 = a^2 - 2ab + b^2.$

V. $(x + a)(x + b) = x^2 + (ax + bx) + ab.$

VI. $(ax + b)(cx + d) = acx^2 + (adx + bcx) + bd.$

ILLUSTRATION 2. Type II states that *the product of the sum and the difference of two numbers is the difference of their squares.* Type III states that *the square of the sum of two numbers is equal to the sum of their squares, plus twice the product of the numbers.*

ILLUSTRATION 3. From Type III with $a = 3x$ and $b = 2y$,

$$(3x + 2y)^2 = (3x)^2 + 2(3x)(2y) + (2y)^2 = 9x^2 + 12xy + 4y^2.$$

In Types V and VI, we refer to $(ax + bx)$ and $(adx + bcx)$ as *the sum of the cross products.*

ILLUSTRATION 4. $(2x - 7h)(3x + 2h) = 6x^2 - 17hx - 14h^2,$

because the sum of cross products is $- 21hx + 4hx$, or $- 17hx$.

ILLUSTRATION 5. $(x^2 - 2y)(x^2 + 2y)(x^4 + 4y^2)$

$= [(x^2 - 2y)(x^2 + 2y)](x^4 + 4y^2) = (x^4 - 4y^2)(x^4 + 4y^2)$ (Type II)

$= (x^4)^2 - (4y^2)^2 = x^8 - 16y^4.$

ILLUSTRATION 6. $(-3x - 4)(-3x + 4) = -(4 + 3x)(4 - 3x)$

$= -(16 - 9x^2) = -16 + 9x^2.$

EXERCISE 5

Multiply and collect similar terms, without using Section 13.

1. $(3 - 5x^2)(2 + 3x^2).$ **2.** $(ay - 2z)(3ay + 4z).$

3. $(x - 3)(x^2 + 2x - 5).$ **4.** $(a - 4)(3a^2 - 2a + 1).$

5. $(2 + x)(3 - 4x - x^2).$ **6.** $(c + 2)(2c - 5 - 3c^2).$

7. $(3x^3 - 2x^2 + 5x - 7)(2x - 1).$ **8.** $(2y^3 - 4y + 5y^2 - 3)(y + 3).$

9. $(2a - 3)(3a + 5)(a - 2).$ **10.** $(x - a^k)(x^2 + a^k x + a^{2k}).$

11. $(x^n - 3y^k)(x^{2n} + 3x^n y^k + 9y^{2k}).$

12. $(x^4 + y^4 - x^3 y + x^2 y^2)(x^2 - 2xy - y^2).$

Express as a sum of fractions in lowest terms.

13. $(24a^3 b^5 - 36a^4 b^2) \div 16a^2 b^6.$ **14.** $(21x^3 y^2 - 28y^4) \div 14x^2 y.$

15. $\dfrac{6 - 2uv + 18u^3 v^3}{12u^4 v}.$ **16.** $\dfrac{x^2 y^5 - 3xy^3 + 2x^2 y^4}{6x^3 y^6}.$

Divide, and summarize as in (4) *on page* 20.

17. $(38 + d^2 - 12d) \div (d - 5).$ **18.** $(3x^2 - 5x - 8) \div (3x + 1).$

19. $(6u^2 - 13uv - 5v^2) \div (2u - 5v).$ **20.** $(8x^2 + 2xy - 3y^2) \div (4x + 3y).$

21. $(4x^6 + 5x^3 - 6) \div (4x^3 - 3).$ **22.** $(3a^2 - 7) \div (a - 5).$

23. $(x^3 + 4x^2 + x - 6) \div (x + 2).$ **24.** $(4x^3 - 8x^2 + 13x - 5) \div (2x - 1).$

25. $(4y^3 - 9y + 8y^2 - 7) \div (2y + 3).$

26. $(6y^3 - 17y^2 + 14y + 8) \div (3y - 1).$

27. $(8y^3 - 18y^2 - 6 + 11y) \div (4y^2 - 3y + 2).$

28. $(x^4 - 4x^3 + 3x^2 - 4x + 12) \div (x - 3).$

29. $(3x^{3h} + 3x^{2h} - 19x^h + 17) \div (x^h - 3).$

Expand and collect terms, performing as much of the work as possible mentally by use of (I)–(VI) *in Section* 13.

30. $(b - k)(b + k).$ **31.** $(h + k)^2.$ **32.** $(c + 4)(c - 4).$

33. $(x - 2y)(x + 2y).$ **34.** $(a - y)^2.$ **35.** $(8 - x)(8 + x).$

36. $(c - 3x)(c + 3x).$ **37.** $(3 + x)^2.$ **38.** $(y - 2)(y + 2).$

39. $(5 - 2y)(5 + 2y).$ **40.** $(3 + 2r)(3 - 2r).$

41. $(3x - 4z)(3x + 4z).$ **42.** $(a^2 - 3b)(a^2 + 3b).$

43. $(ab - 2)(ab + 2).$ **44.** $(a - 2)(a - 4).$

45. $(c + 3)^2.$ **46.** $(x + 5)^2.$ **47.** $(2z - w)^2.$

48. $(3x - 4y)^2.$ **49.** $[3(2a + b)]^2.$ **50.** $[2(x - 3y)]^2.$

51. $(3 + x)(2 + x)$.   **52.** $(2x + 5y)(- 2x - 5y)$.

53. $(x - 5)(x + 9)$.   **54.** $(x + 13)(x - 4)$.

55. $(a + 2b)(a + 3b)$.   **56.** $(w - 2z)(w + 5z)$.

57. $(2x + 3)(3x + 4)$.   **58.** $(3x - 5)(2x - 3)$.

59. $(4y - 3x)(2y - x)$.   **60.** $(2y + w)(y + 5w)$.

61. $(2y - 3)(3y + 5)$.   **62.** $(y - 3)(2y + 7)$.

Note 1. Sometimes, products of polynomials which are not binomials can be calculated by use of Types II–IV, after terms are grouped. Thus,

$$(c + 2d - 11a)(c + 2d + 11a)$$
$$= [(c + 2d) - 11a][(c + 2d) + 11a] \qquad \text{(Type II)}$$
$$= (c + 2d)^2 - (11a)^2 = c^2 + 4cd + 4d^2 - 121a^2,$$

where we used $(x - y)(x + y) = x^2 - y^2$ with $x = c + 2d$ and $y = 11a$.

63. $[(x + y) + 2]^2$.   **64.** $[(a - b) + 5]^2$.   **65.** $[3 - (2x - y)]^2$.

66. $(2 + a + w)^2$.   **67.** $(3x + y + 5)^2$.   **68.** $(x - 2y - 3)^2$.

69. $(2x - 3x^2 + 3y)^2$.   **70.** $[(x + y) - 3][(x + y) + 3]$.

71. $[(c + 2x) - 2][(c + 2x) + 2]$.   **72.** $[4 - (2a + b)][4 + (2a + b)]$.

73. $(a + w + 4)(a + w - 4)$.   **74.** $(a + b - x)(a + b + x)$.

75. $(3x + y - 2)(3x + y + 2)$.   **76.** $(3a - y + 4)(3a - y - 4)$.

77. Expand $(x + y + z)^2$ and state the result in words.

14. Terminology about factoring

In any reference to *factors*, two possible sets of factors are considered essentially the same if those of one set differ at most in signs from those of the other set.

An integer is said to be *prime* if it has no integer as a factor except itself or 1.

ILLUSTRATION 1.   2, 3, 5, 7, 11, etc.,   are prime numbers.

In our discussion of factoring, any literal expression involved, or any factor which is mentioned, will be an *integral rational polynomial*, with integers as coefficients. Such an expression will be called *prime* if it has no factor of similar type except itself or 1. No simple rule can be stated for determining whether or not an expression is prime. *To factor a polynomial* will mean to express it as a product of positive integral powers of distinct *prime* factors.

ILLUSTRATION 2. $4x^4 - 4b^2x^2 = 4x^2(x^2 - b^2) = 4x^2(x - b)(x + b)$.

ILLUSTRATION 3. We shall say that $(x - y)$ is prime although

$$x - y = (\sqrt{x} + \sqrt{y})(\sqrt{x} - \sqrt{y}),$$

because these factors are not integral and rational. Other prime expressions are $(x + y)$, $(x^2 + y^2)$, $(x^2 + xy + y^2)$, and $(x^2 - xy + y^2)$.

Each of (I)–(VI) of Section 13 on page 20 becomes a formula for factoring when read *from right to left*. Thus, (I) is the basis for removal of a common factor from a sum of terms.

I. $$ax + ay + az = a(x + y + z).$$

ILLUSTRATION 4. To remove the factor $2x^2y^3$ from $14x^3y^5$, first divide:

$$14x^3y^5 \div 2x^2y^3 = 7xy^2; \quad then, \quad 14x^3y^5 = 2x^2y^3(7xy^2).$$

Similarly, we remove the common factor $2xy^2$ below:

$$14x^3y^5 + 6xy^2 - 8x^2y^3 = 2xy^2(7x^2y^3 + 3 - 4xy).$$

II. *The difference of two squares is equal to the product of the sum and the difference of their square roots:*

$$x^2 - y^2 = (x - y)(x + y).$$

ILLUSTRATION 5. $x^2 - 9 = (x - 3)(x + 3).$

ILLUSTRATION 6. Observe that $25x^2 = (5x)^2$ and $9y^4 = (3y^2)^2$. Hence,

$$25x^2 - 9y^4 = (5x - 3y^2)(5x + 3y^2).$$

Perfect square trinomials:

III. $$a^2 + 2ab + b^2 = (a + b)^2;$$

IV. $$a^2 - 2ab + b^2 = (a - b)^2.$$

Note 1. In a perfect square trinomial, we notice that *two terms are perfect squares, and the third term is plus (or minus) twice the product of the square roots of the other terms.*

ILLUSTRATION 7. Since $4x^2 = (2x)^2$, $25y^2 = (5y)^2$, and $2(5y)(2x) = 20xy$,

$$4x^2 - 20xy + 25y^2 = (2x - 5y)^2. \qquad \text{(Type IV)}$$

Certain trinomials of the form * $gx^2 + hx + k$ can be factored by a trial and error method based on the formulas of Types V and VI.

EXAMPLE 1. Factor: $15x^2 + 2x - 8.$

SOLUTION. 1. We wish to find a, b, c, and d so that

$$(ax + b)(cx + d) = acx^2 + (ad + bc)x + bd = 15x^2 + 2x - 8.$$

2. Hence, $ac = 15$, $bd = -8$, and the sum of the cross products is $2x$. After various unsatisfactory trials, we finally select $a = 3$, $c = 5$, $b = -2$, and $d = 4$, and verify that

$$15x^2 + 2x - 8 = (3x - 2)(5x + 4).$$

If one prime factor is merely the *negative* of another, we do *not* consider them as distinct prime factors; we combine their powers into a single power of one of them.

---

* If g, h, and k were chosen at random, without a common factor, the trinomial would probably be prime. Later, we shall discuss a condition which g, h, and k satisfy when and only when the trinomial is *not* prime.

ILLUSTRATION 8.   In $(-x-2)(x+2) = -x^2 - 4x - 4$, we notice that $(-x-2) = -(x+2)$.   Hence, we write

$$-x^2 - 4x - 4 = -(x+2)(x+2) = -(x+2)^2.$$

Note 2.   The preceding factoring methods apply to polynomials in which the coefficients are any real numbers, not merely integers as in the illustrations.   The nature of the coefficients which we agree to allow in a polynomial and its factors affects our definition of a *prime* expression but not our general factoring procedure.

Preliminary grouping of terms may be of aid in factoring a polynomial.

ILLUSTRATION 9. $6 - 3x^2 - 8x + 4x^3 = (6 - 8x) - (3x^2 - 4x^3)$

$$= 2(3 - 4x) - x^2(3 - 4x) = (3 - 4x)(2 - x^2).$$

ILLUSTRATION 10. $a^2 - c^2 + b^2 - d^2 - 2ab - 2cd$

$$= (a^2 - 2ab + b^2) - (c^2 + 2cd + d^2) = (a - b)^2 - (c + d)^2$$

$$= [(a - b) - (c + d)][(a - b) + (c + d)]$$

$$= (a - b - c - d)(a - b + c + d).$$

EXERCISE 6

Factor.   If fractions occur, leave the factors in the form which arises most naturally by use of the standard methods.

1. $ax + ay$.
2. $ax - xw$.
3. $-ax + bx$.
4. $3ab + 2a - 5a^2$.
5. $-4at + t^2 - ct^3$.
6. $w^2 - z^2$.
7. $4x^2 - y^2$.
8. $9x^2 - 25z^2$.
9. $4a^2 - 9b^2$.
10. $1 - 25x^2$.
11. $9z^2 - \frac{1}{4}$.
12. $\frac{1}{9} - w^2$.
13. $25w^2 - c^2d^2$.
14. $36a^2b^2 - 64x^2$.
15. $4x^2 + 12x + 9$.
16. $a^2 - 4a + 4$.
17. $9x^4 - 6x^2 + 1$.
18. $25 - 10x + x^2$.
19. $a^2 + 4a + 4$.
20. $y^2 - 6y + 9$.
21. $d^2 + 2dy + y^2$.
22. $u^2 - 8u + 16$.
23. $a^2 - 14ab + 49b^2$.
24. $64 - 16ab + a^2b^2$.
25. $9a^2 - 30ab + 25b^2$.
26. $x^2 + 8x + 15$.
27. $a^2 - 8a + 12$.
28. $x^2 + 10x + 21$.
29. $z^2 - 5z - 6$.
30. $12 - 7y + y^2$.
31. $15 - 8x + x^2$.
32. $16 - 6a - a^2$.
33. $4 - 3y - y^2$.
34. $27 + 6w - w^2$.
35. $2x^2 + 7xy + 3y^2$.
36. $3a^2 + 8a + 5$.
37. $2x^2 + 3xy - 5y^2$.
38. $6x^2 + x - 15$.
39. $3u^2 + 7u - 6$.
40. $6 - 5u - 6u^2$.
41. $10x^2 + 11x + 3$.
42. $5a^2 - 12ab + 7b^2$.
43. $3a^2 - 10a + 7$.
44. $-12h^2 - 8h + 15$.
45. $-27x^2 + 3x + 2$.
46. $7 - 19x - 6x^2$.
47. $5a^2 + 14ab + 9b^2$.
48. $3x^2 + 7ax - 6a^2$.
49. $3x^2 + 5xy + 2y^2$.
50. $8w^2 + 14wz - 15z^2$.

51. $45x^2 - 8xy - 4y^2$.

52. $-5u^2 - 28uv + 12v^2$.

53. $8x^4 - 10x^3 + 3x^2$.

54. $2x^4 - x^3 - 6x^2$.

55. $-5c(r+s) + 2d(r+s)$.

56. $-2x(a+h) - 3y(a+h)$.

57. $3h(w-z) - (w-z)$.

58. $2x(h-2k) + 3hy - 6ky$.

59. $2cx + cy - 2dx - dy$.

60. $5ax + 2bx - 10ad - 4bd$.

61. $4hx - 4bh - 8cx + 8bc$.

62. $3bw - 3bz - 4aw + 4az$.

63. $(x^3 - 2x^2) - (x-2)$.

64. $(ax^3 + bx^2) - 4(ax+b)$.

65. $x^3 + 2x^2 + x + 2$.

66. $ax^2 + bx^2 + ad^2 + bd^2$.

67. $x^3 - 3x^2 + x - 3$.

68. $2x^2 - 4x + 1 - 8x^3$.

69. $64a^2 + 9c^2 - 48ac$.

70. $9(a+b)^2 + 12(a+b) + 4$.

71. $8a^2c - 18c^3$.

72. $x^4 - y^4$.

73. $81c^4 - 16d^4$.

74. $(n^2 - 4n + 4) - 16w^2$.

75. $4w^2 + 20w + 25 - 81z^2$.

76. $4a^2 + 12a + 9 - 25x^2$.

77. $y^2 + 2yz + z^2 - 4x^2$.

78. $9y^2 - (4x^2 + 20x + 25)$.

79. $9w^2 - 4a^2 - 4ab - b^2$.

80. $4h^2 - 9a^2 + 12a - 4$.

81. $4a^2 - 9z^2 - 6z - 1$.

82. $4x^2 + 4xy + y^2 - 9a^2 - 12at - 4t^2$.

83. $15 + (z+w) - 6(z+w)^2$.

84. $(a^2 + 2a)^2 + 2(a^2 + 2a) + 1$.

85. $6(x-y)^2 - 11(x-y) + 4$.

86. $10(z+w)^2 + 14(z+w) - 12$.

87. $20(x+y)^2 - 22w(x+y) + 6w^2$.

88. $(1+n)^2 - 4m(1+n) + 4m^2$.

15. Cube of a binomial

We verify that

$$(x+y)^3 = (x+y)^2(x+y) = (x^2 + 2xy + y^2)(x+y)$$
$$= x^3 + 2x^2y + xy^2 + x^2y + 2xy^2 + y^3.$$

On collecting terms we obtain (1) and, similarly, verify (2):

$$(x + y)^3 = x^3 + 3x^2y + 3xy^2 + y^3; \tag{1}$$
$$(x - y)^3 = x^3 - 3x^2y + 3xy^2 - y^3. \tag{2}$$

ILLUSTRATION 1. From (1), with $x = 2a$ and $y = b$,

$$(2a + b)^3 = (2a)^3 + 3(2a)^2(b) + 3(2a)(b)^2 + b^3$$
$$= 8a^3 + 12a^2b + 6ab^2 + b^3.$$

16. The sum and the difference of two like powers

By multiplication on the right in (1) and (2) below, we verify the factors of the sum, and of the difference, of two cubes.

$$a^3 - b^3 = (a - b)(a^2 + ab + b^2); \tag{1}$$
$$a^3 + b^3 = (a + b)(a^2 - ab + b^2). \tag{2}$$

ILLUSTRATION 1. By use of (1), read from right to left, with $b = 3$,

$$(a - 3)(a^2 + 3a + 9) = a^3 - 3^3 = a^3 - 27.$$

ILLUSTRATION 2.   From (2) with $a = 3x$ and $b = 2y$,

$$27x^3 + 8y^3 = (3x)^3 + (2y)^3$$
$$= (3x + 2y)[(3x)^2 - (3x)(2y) + (2y)^2]$$
$$= (3x + 2y)(9x^2 - 6xy + 4y^2).$$

ILLUSTRATION 3. $1 - 64x^3 = 1^3 - (4x)^3 = (1 - 4x)(1 + 4x + 16x^2).$

ILLUSTRATION 4. $y^6 - 19y^3 - 216 = (y^3 - 27)(y^3 + 8)$

$$= (y - 3)(y^2 + 3y + 9)(y + 2)(y^2 - 2y + 4).$$

An integral rational term is said to be a *perfect nth power* if it is the nth *power of an integral rational term.* In a perfect nth power, each exponent has n as a factor because, in raising a term to the nth power, each original exponent is multiplied by n.

ILLUSTRATION 5. $8a^6b^6$ *is a perfect cube,* $(2a^2b^2)^3.$

In factoring a sum $a^n \pm b^n$, where a^n and b^n are perfect nth powers, we start as in (3) and (4) below, when they apply.

$$\left\{ \begin{array}{l} \textit{If n is even, commence factoring } (a^n - b^n) \textit{ by} \\ \textit{recognizing it as the difference of two squares.} \end{array} \right\} \tag{3}$$

ILLUSTRATION 6. $x^6 - y^6 = (x^3)^2 - (y^3)^2 = (x^3 - y^3)(x^3 + y^3)$

$$= (x - y)(x^2 + xy + y^2)(x + y)(x^2 - xy + y^2).$$

ILLUSTRATION 7. $16a^4b^4 - 81 = (4a^2b^2)^2 - 9^2$

$$= (4a^2b^2 - 9)(4a^2b^2 + 9) = (2ab - 3)(2ab + 3)(4a^2b^2 + 9).$$

$$\left\{ \begin{array}{l} \textit{If n is odd and has 3 as a factor, commence factoring} \\ (a^n \pm b^n) \textit{ as a sum or a difference of two cubes.} \end{array} \right\} \tag{4}$$

ILLUSTRATION 8. $x^9 + y^9 = (x^3)^3 + (y^3)^3 = (x^3 + y^3)(x^6 - x^3y^3 + y^6)$

$$= (x + y)(x^2 - xy + y^2)(x^6 - x^3y^3 + y^6).$$

We have met special cases of the following facts (I)–(V). Any special case can be verified by dividing $(a^n \pm b^n)$ by the indicated linear factor, $(a + b)$ or $(a - b)$. General proofs of the facts will be met in Problem 13 on page 272. Factors obtained by (I)–(V) are not necessarily prime. Hence, the student should continue to emphasize (3) and (4) in place of (I)–(V).

I. *For every positive integer n, $(a^n - b^n)$ has $(a - b)$ as a factor. In other words, $(a^n - b^n)$ is exactly divisible by $(a - b)$; in the quotient, all coefficients are $+1$, and the sum of the exponents of a and b is $(n - 1)$ in each term.*

ILLUSTRATION 9. $a^4 - b^4 = (a - b)(a^3 + a^2b + ab^2 + b^3).$

II. *If n is even, $(a^n - b^n)$ has $(a + b)$ as a factor.*

ILLUSTRATION 10. $a^4 - b^4 = (a + b)(a^3 - a^2b + ab^2 - b^3).$

III. *If n is odd, $(a^n + b^n)$ has $(a + b)$ as a factor.*

ILLUSTRATION 11. $a^3 + b^3 = (a + b)(a^2 - ab + b^2)$.

IV. *If n is even, $(a^n + b^n)$ does not have either $(a + b)$ or $(a - b)$ as a factor.*

ILLUSTRATION 12. $(a^2 + b^2)$ and $(a^4 + b^4)$ are *prime*. $(a^6 + b^6)$ is *not* prime, but does not have either $(a + b)$ or $(a - b)$ as a factor:

$$a^6 + b^6 = (a^2 + b^2)(a^4 - a^2b^2 + b^4).$$

V. *When $(a^n + b^n)$ or $(a^n - b^n)$ has $(a + b)$ as a factor and is divided by $(a + b)$, the coefficients in the quotient are alternately $+ 1$ and $- 1$; the sum of the exponents of a and b is $(n - 1)$ in each term of the quotient.*

EXERCISE 7

Expand by use of formulas from Sections 15 and 16.

1. $(c + w)(c^2 - cw + w^2)$. **2.** $(3a - c)(9a^2 + 3ac + c^2)$.

3. $(u - v)(u^2 + uv + v^2)$. **4.** $(1 - 3x)(1 + 3x + 9x^2)$.

5. $(c + d)^3$. **6.** $(5 - y)^3$. **7.** $(y - 3x)^3$. **8.** $(c + 3b^2)^3$.

9. $(2 + y)^3$. **10.** $(2x + w)^3$. **11.** $(a - b^2)^3$. **12.** $(c - 6z^3)^3$.

Divide by long division, and check by Section 16.

13. $\dfrac{a^3 - h^3}{a - h}$. **14.** $\dfrac{x^3 + 8y^3}{x + 2y}$. **15.** $\dfrac{x^4 - y^4}{x - y}$. **16.** $\dfrac{x^5 + y^5}{x + y}$.

★*Find each result without using long division, by use of* (I) *and* (V) *of Section 16, and check by multiplication.*

17. $\dfrac{a^5 + y^5}{a + y}$. **18.** $\dfrac{u^8 - v^8}{u - v}$. **19.** $\dfrac{x^5 - 1}{x - 1}$. **20.** $\dfrac{z^5 - 32x^{10}}{z - 2x^2}$.

21. $(a^8 - 16b^4) \div (a^2 - 2b)$. **22.** $(243x^5 - 1) \div (3x - 1)$.

★*Factor each expression which is not prime.*

23. $d^3 - y^3$. **24.** $1 - v^3$. **25.** $z^3 + 1000$. **26.** $216x^3 - y^3z^3$.

27. $h^3 + z^3$. **28.** $27 - u^3$. **29.** $8x^3 - 125y^3$. **30.** $x^3 - 343y^3$.

31. $a^5 - c^5$. **32.** $y^4 - 81$. **33.** $h^9 + k^9$. **34.** $a^3 - 27x^6$.

35. $a^4 - w^4$. **36.** $32 + x^5$. **37.** $x^{16} - y^{16}$. **38.** $32x^{5k} - w^5$.

39. $4x^4 + 1$. **40.** $a^6 - 64$. **41.** $16x^4 - y^8$.

HINT for Problem 39. Add and subtract $4x^2$.

42. $16x^4 + y^4$. **43.** $4w^4x^4 + 81z^4$. **44.** $u^{3h} + v^3$.

17. Fractions in lowest terms

Whenever we make a reference to *factoring* in a fraction, it will be assumed that the numerator and denominator are integral rational polynomials with integral coefficients. The following method is justified by (III) on page 13.

SUMMARY. *Reduction of a fraction to lowest terms.*

1. *Factor the numerator and denominator.*

2. *Divide both numerator and denominator by all common factors.*

ILLUSTRATION 1. In the following fraction, we divide both numerator and denominator by $3x - 4y$ and indicate this by cancellation.

$$\frac{9x^2 - 16y^2}{3x^2 + 2xy - 8y^2} = \frac{(3x - 4y)(3x + 4y)}{(3x - 4y)(x + 2y)} = \frac{3x + 4y}{x + 2y}.$$

ILLUSTRATION 2. To make two factors below identical, multiply by -1 in the denominator, and hence place -1 before the fraction to compensate.

$$\frac{x^2 - 9}{12 + 2x - 2x^2} = \frac{(x - 3)(x + 3)}{2(3 - x)(2 + x)} = -\frac{(x - 3)(x + 3)}{2(x - 3)(2 + x)} = -\frac{x + 3}{2(x + 2)}.$$

ILLUSTRATION 3. To eliminate minus signs in the numerator below, multiply it by -1 and then multiply the fraction by -1 to compensate.

$$\frac{-a - x}{c} = -\frac{-1 \cdot (-a - x)}{c} = -\frac{a + x}{c}.$$

EXERCISE 8

Reduce to lowest terms in good form.

all divisible by 5

1. $\dfrac{75}{125}.$ 2. $\dfrac{76x^3y^5}{57x^5y^2}.$ 3. $\dfrac{39a^3b}{65a^4b^2}.$ 4. $\dfrac{96uv^6}{40uv^3}.$ 5. $\dfrac{78x^3y}{52x^3y^2}.$

6. $\dfrac{5(x + 2y)}{3(x + 2y)}.$ 7. $\dfrac{ay(u - v)}{cy(u - v)}.$ 8. $\dfrac{3c - 2d}{6c - 4d}.$ 9. $\dfrac{ax + 2ay}{2cx + 4cy}.$

10. $\dfrac{4ay - 2by}{2ax - bx}.$ 11. $\dfrac{au^2 - auy}{cu^2 - cuy}.$ 12. $\dfrac{x^2 - y^2}{2x - 2y}.$ 13. $\dfrac{4a^2 - b^2}{4a + 2b}.$

14. $\dfrac{cx + 3cy}{x^2 - 9y^2}.$ 15. $\dfrac{5x^2 - 20}{2x - 4}.$ 16. $\dfrac{9a^2 - z^2}{3ax - xz}.$ 17. $\dfrac{uvx - uwx}{cvx - cwx}.$

18. $\dfrac{x^2 + 3x - 10}{x^2 - 5x + 6}.$ 19. $\dfrac{a^2 + 2a - 3}{a^2 + 7a + 12}.$ 20. $\dfrac{18 - 3y - y^2}{12 - 4y - y^2}.$

21. $\dfrac{6 + 7x - 3x^2}{2 + 5x + 3x^2}.$ 22. $\dfrac{a^2 + 6ab + 9b^2}{a^2 - 9b^2}.$ 23. $\dfrac{12 - 5y - 2y^2}{2y^2 - 5y + 3}.$

24. $\dfrac{6 + 13u - 5u^2}{2 + 7u + 5u^2}.$ 25. $\dfrac{25a^2 - 30ab + 9b^2}{10a^3b - 6a^2b^2}.$ 26. $\dfrac{9x^2b - 4y^2b}{3x^2 - 13xy - 10y^2}.$

27. $\dfrac{5(x - y)}{15(y - x)}.$ 28. $\dfrac{3(2a - b)}{x(b - 2a)}.$ 29. $\dfrac{-2x - 2y}{(x + y)^2}.$ 30. $\dfrac{(u - 2v)^2}{4v - 2u}.$

31. $\dfrac{a^3 - b^3}{2a^2 - 2b^2}.$ 32. $\dfrac{ax + ay}{cx^3 + cy^3}.$ 33. $\dfrac{27x^3 - 8y^3}{3x^2z + xyz - 2y^2z}.$

34. $\dfrac{-5}{-20x}.$ 35. $\dfrac{-b(-c)}{-4ab}.$ 36. $\dfrac{-x - y}{5}.$ 37. $\dfrac{2a + 2b}{-3a - 3b}.$

18. Addition of fractions

To express a sum of fractions with a common denominator as a single fraction, *form the sum of the numerators, each enclosed in parentheses preceded by the sign of its fraction, and divide by the common denominator.* This procedure is based on (3) of page 12.

ILLUSTRATION 1. $\dfrac{8}{5} - \dfrac{3}{5} + \dfrac{9}{5} = \dfrac{8 - 3 + 9}{5} = \dfrac{14}{5}.$

ILLUSTRATION 2. $\dfrac{6}{11a} - \dfrac{5 - x}{11a} + \dfrac{3 - 2x}{11a} =$

$$\dfrac{6 - (5 - x) + (3 - 2x)}{11a} = \dfrac{6 - 5 + x + 3 - 2x}{11a} = \dfrac{4 - x}{11a}.$$

To change a fraction to an equal one having an additional factor in the denominator, multiply *both numerator and denominator* by this factor, in order to leave the value of the fraction unaltered. This operation is justified by (I) on page 12.

ILLUSTRATION 3. To change $\frac{3}{7}$ to 14ths, multiply numerator and denominator by 2 because $\frac{14}{7} = 2$:

$$\dfrac{3}{7} = \dfrac{3 \times 2}{7 \times 2} = \dfrac{6}{14}.$$

ILLUSTRATION 4. To change the following fraction to one where the denominator is $6a^3b$, multiply numerator and denominator by $2a^2b$, because $(6a^3b \div 3a) = 2a^2b$:

$$\dfrac{5 - x}{3a} = \dfrac{2a^2b(5 - x)}{2a^2b(3a)} = \dfrac{10a^2b - 2a^2bx}{6a^3b}.$$

The **degree** of an integral rational term in certain literal numbers is defined to be the sum of the exponents with which these numbers appear in the term. The degree of an integral rational polynomial is defined as the degree of its term of highest degree.

ILLUSTRATION 5. x^4yz^2 is of the 4th degree in x, 1st degree in y, and 7th degree in x, y, and z. $(x^3 + x^2 - 7)$ is of the 3d degree in x.

The **lowest common multiple** (LCM) of two or more integral rational polynomials* is defined as the polynomial of *lowest degree* in all the literal numbers, with *smallest* integral coefficients, which has each given polynomial as a factor. Two results for a LCM which differ only in sign will be considered essentially identical.

ILLUSTRATION 6. Since $6 = 2 \cdot 3$ and $20 = 2 \cdot 2 \cdot 5$, the LCM of 6 and 20 is $2 \cdot 2 \cdot 3 \cdot 5$ or 60. The LCM of $3a^2x^3$ and $20xy^4$ is $60a^2x^3y^4$. The LCM of

$$(2a^2 + 4a) \quad and \quad (3a + 6) \quad is \quad (6a^2 + 12a).$$

The **lowest common denominator** (LCD) of two or more fractions is the LCM of their denominators. To find a sum of fractions, we first change them, if necessary, to fractions having the LCD, as follows, and then combine the new fractions.

---

* In remarks about a LCM and related matters, we shall assume that the coefficients are integers in any polynomial involved. Some of the resulting methods extend to more general situations in a natural fashion.

To find the LCD, factor each denominator and form the product of all different prime factors, giving to each factor the largest exponent with which it appears in any denominator.

For each fraction, divide the LCD by the denominator and then multiply both numerator and denominator by the resulting quotient, to express the fraction as an equal one having the LCD.

As a partial check on the determination of a LCD, notice that it should contain each given denominator as a factor. Also, recall that any polynomial may be written as a fraction whose denominator is 1. Thus, $x = x/1$.

ILLUSTRATION 7. In the following fractions, the LCD is 30.

$$2 + \frac{3}{5} - \frac{2}{15} + \frac{7}{10} = \frac{2 \cdot 30}{1 \cdot 30} + \frac{3 \cdot 6}{5 \cdot 6} - \frac{2 \cdot 2}{15 \cdot 2} + \frac{7 \cdot 3}{10 \cdot 3} = \frac{95}{30} = \frac{19}{6}.$$

ILLUSTRATION 8. In the following fractions, the LCD is $15x^2y$.

$$\frac{2x}{3y} - 4x - \frac{6y}{5x^2y} = \frac{2x \cdot 5x^2}{3y \cdot 5x^2} - \frac{4x \cdot 15x^2y}{1 \cdot 15x^2y} - \frac{6y \cdot 3}{5x^2y \cdot 3}$$

$$= \frac{10x^3 - 60x^3y - 18y}{15x^2y}.$$

ILLUSTRATION 9. In the following addition, we change signs in the second denominator to exhibit identical literal factors in denominators:

$$\frac{5}{9c - 6d} + \frac{7}{4d - 6c} = \frac{5}{3(3c - 2d)} - \frac{7}{6c - 4d} = \frac{5}{3(3c - 2d)} - \frac{7}{2(3c - 2d)}$$

$$= \frac{(5 \cdot 2) - (7 \cdot 3)}{3 \cdot 2(3c - 2d)} = -\frac{11}{6(3c - 2d)}.$$

EXAMPLE 1. Express as a single fraction: $\quad \dfrac{4x}{x^2 - 9} - \dfrac{3x}{x^2 + x - 6}.$

SOLUTION. 1. $x^2 - 9 = (x - 3)(x + 3); \quad x^2 + x - 6 = (x + 3)(x - 2).$
Hence, LCD $= (x - 3)(x + 3)(x - 2).$

2. In the 1st fraction, $\qquad\qquad$ LCD $\div (x^2 - 9) = x - 2.$

3. In the 2d fraction, $\qquad\qquad$ LCD $\div (x^2 + x - 6) = x - 3.$

4. Multiply by $x - 2$ and by $x - 3$ in the corresponding fractions:

$$\frac{4x}{x^2 - 9} - \frac{3x}{x^2 + x - 6} = \frac{4x(x - 2)}{(x - 3)(x + 3)(x - 2)} - \frac{3x(x - 3)}{(x - 3)(x + 3)(x - 2)}$$

$$= \frac{4x(x - 2) - 3x(x - 3)}{(x - 3)(x + 3)(x - 2)} = \frac{x^2 + x}{(x - 3)(x + 3)(x - 2)}.$$

Note 1. The **highest common factor** (HCF) of two or more integral rational expressions is the expression of *highest degree*, with *largest* integral coefficients, which is a factor of each of the given expressions. Thus, the HCF of $6x^2y^3$ and $4xy^4$ is $2xy^3$. We use the HCF terminology rarely.

EXERCISE 9

Combine into a single fraction in lowest terms.

1. $\dfrac{2}{3} + \dfrac{b}{3} - \dfrac{a}{3}.$

2. $\dfrac{3}{7} - \dfrac{2a - 5b}{7}.$

3. $\dfrac{5}{3} - \dfrac{6 - 3a}{2}.$

4. $\dfrac{5}{8} - \dfrac{3}{4}.$

5. $\dfrac{3}{7} + \dfrac{9}{14}.$

6. $\dfrac{3r}{2} + \dfrac{s}{5}.$

7. $\dfrac{2}{9} - \dfrac{x - 2y}{3}.$

8. $\dfrac{3}{5} - \dfrac{5x - y}{2}.$

9. $4 - \dfrac{3a - b}{5}.$

10. $\dfrac{2x - 3}{5} - \dfrac{3 - 5x}{35}.$

11. $\dfrac{3 - 2x}{4} - \dfrac{4 - 5x}{6}.$

12. $3u - \dfrac{3 - 4u}{12}.$

13. $\dfrac{1}{4a} - \dfrac{5}{6}.$

14. $\dfrac{b}{3x^3} - \dfrac{c}{2x}.$

15. $\dfrac{h}{4k^2} - \dfrac{w}{3k}.$

16. $\dfrac{5}{hk} + \dfrac{3}{kr}.$

17. $\dfrac{3}{2x^2} - \dfrac{5}{7xy^3}.$

18. $\dfrac{4}{3a^2} - \dfrac{5y - 1}{5ab}.$

19. $\dfrac{3}{2xy} - \dfrac{4x - y}{4x^2y^3}.$

20. $\dfrac{3a}{2bc} - \dfrac{2 - 5b}{c^3} + 6.$

21. $3a - \dfrac{2 - 4a}{3a - 2} - \dfrac{a}{2}.$

22. $\dfrac{2 - x}{3x^2y} - \dfrac{4 - 3y}{2xy^2}.$

23. $\dfrac{3}{2(a - b)} - \dfrac{2}{5(a - b)}.$

24. $\dfrac{3}{7x + 7y} - \dfrac{2}{5(x + y)}.$

25. $\dfrac{4}{3x - 3y} - \dfrac{2}{5x - 5y}.$

26. $\dfrac{a}{a - b} - \dfrac{b}{a + b}.$

27. $\dfrac{2x}{3x - 2y} - \dfrac{3y}{3x + 2y}.$

28. $\dfrac{2x + 1}{2x + 3} - \dfrac{x + 2}{2 - 3x}.$

29. $\dfrac{x}{4x^2 - 1} + \dfrac{4}{6x - 3}.$

30. $-\dfrac{2x - 3}{6x + 6} - \dfrac{5}{3x}.$

31. $\dfrac{3}{2x - 4y} - \dfrac{5}{x^2 - 4y^2}.$

32. $\dfrac{3x}{2x + 2y} + \dfrac{4}{x^2 - y^2}.$

33. $\dfrac{5}{4x - x^2} + \dfrac{10}{3x^2 - 48}.$

34. $\dfrac{2a - n}{2a - 2n} + \dfrac{3a - 4n}{6n - 6a}.$

35. $\dfrac{a - 4}{2a - 4} + \dfrac{2 - 11a}{2 - a}.$

36. $\dfrac{5x}{x + 4} - \dfrac{4x^2 + 2x - 1}{x^2 + x - 12}.$

37. $\dfrac{2x + 1}{x^2 + 4x - 60} - \dfrac{2}{x - 6}.$

38. $\dfrac{1}{3n - 3} - \dfrac{n + 6}{n^2 + 3n - 4}.$

39. $\dfrac{a - 2}{a^2 - 16} - \dfrac{a + 2}{a^2 + 8a + 16}.$

40. $\dfrac{3x - 5x^2}{4x^2 + 12x + 9} - \dfrac{x - 3}{4x + 6}.$

41. $\dfrac{2a - 3}{2a^2 - 18} - \dfrac{4}{3a^2 - 11a + 6}.$

42. $\dfrac{4x^2 + 1}{4x^2 - 1} - \dfrac{1 + 2x}{2x - 1} - \dfrac{5x + 3}{2x + 1}.$

43. $\dfrac{x^2 + 5}{8x^3 - 27} - \dfrac{3x + 2}{2x - 3}.$

44. $\dfrac{3x^2}{x^4 - 4} + \dfrac{5x^2 - 3}{2x^4 + x^2 - 6}.$

45. $\dfrac{x + 5x^2}{x^3 - y^3} + \dfrac{3}{2x - 2y}.$

46. $\dfrac{x^2}{x^3 + 8} - \dfrac{2x}{x^2 - 2x + 4}.$

47. $\dfrac{2x^3 - 3}{2x^6 + 3x^3 - 2} - \dfrac{x^3 + 3}{x^6 - 4}.$

19. Multiplication and division of fractions

Before multiplying or dividing fractions, factor the numerators and denominators if possible.

ILLUSTRATION 1.
$$\frac{2x^2 + 7x - 15}{2x^2 - 3x - 14} \cdot \frac{2x^2 - 19x + 42}{8x - 12}$$

$$= \frac{(2x-3)(x+5)}{(2x-7)(x+2)} \cdot \frac{(2x-7)(x-6)}{4(2x-3)} = \frac{(x+5)(x-6)}{4(x+2)}.$$

A **simple fraction** is one without any fraction in its numerator or denominator. A **complex fraction** is one in which one or more fractions appear in the numerator and denominator.

ILLUSTRATION 2.
$$\frac{\dfrac{xy^2 - y^3}{x^3 + x^2y}}{\dfrac{x^2 - 2xy + y^2}{x^2 - xy - 2y^2}} = \frac{xy^2 - y^3}{x^3 + x^2y} \cdot \frac{x^2 - xy - 2y^2}{x^2 - 2xy + y^2}$$

$$= \frac{y^2(x - y)}{x^2(x + y)} \cdot \frac{(x - 2y)(x + y)}{(x - y)^2} = \frac{y^2(x - 2y)}{x^2(x - y)}.$$

ILLUSTRATION 3.
$$\frac{2x - 4}{x^2 - 5} \div (x - 2) = \frac{2x - 4}{x^2 - 5} \div \frac{x - 2}{1}$$

$$= \frac{2(x - 2)}{x^2 - 5} \cdot \frac{1}{x - 2} = \frac{2}{x^2 - 5}.$$

The **reciprocal** of a number H is defined as $1/H$.

ILLUSTRATION 4. The reciprocal of 3 is $\frac{1}{3}$; of $\frac{3}{4}$ is $1 \div \frac{3}{4} = \frac{4}{3}$. *The reciprocal of a fraction is the fraction inverted, because*

$$\frac{1}{\dfrac{a}{b}} = 1 \cdot \frac{b}{a} = \frac{b}{a}.$$

ILLUSTRATION 5. To *divide* a number N by H is equivalent to *multiplying by the reciprocal* of H, because

$$\frac{N}{H} = N \cdot \frac{1}{H}.$$

A *mixed expression* is one consisting of an integral rational part and of one or more fractions. It is desirable to combine any mixed expression into a single fraction before performing multiplication or division.

In reducing a complex fraction to a simple fraction, *change the numerator and denominator to simple fractions and then form their quotient.*

ILLUSTRATION 6.
$$\frac{1 + \dfrac{3}{5}}{2 - \dfrac{4}{3}} = \frac{\dfrac{5 + 3}{5}}{\dfrac{6 - 4}{3}} = \frac{\dfrac{8}{5}}{\dfrac{2}{3}} = \frac{8}{5} \cdot \frac{3}{2} = \frac{12}{5}.$$

ILLUSTRATION 7.
$$\frac{\dfrac{a-a^2}{a^2-1}}{\dfrac{a}{a+1}-a} = \frac{\dfrac{a-a^2}{a^2-1}}{\dfrac{a-a(a+1)}{a+1}} = -\frac{\dfrac{a-a^2}{a^2-1}}{\dfrac{a^2}{a+1}}$$

$$= -\frac{a(1-a)}{(a-1)(a+1)}\cdot\frac{a+1}{a^2} = -\frac{1-a}{a(a-1)} = \frac{1}{a}.$$

le by 5

divis

divis.

by

9

EXERCISE 10

Express the result as a simple fraction in lowest terms.

1. $\frac{3}{5}\cdot\frac{10}{9}$.
2. $\frac{15}{4}\cdot x$.
3. $\frac{8}{5}\div 6$.
4. $\frac{3}{5}\div\frac{6}{10}$.
5. $x\div\frac{3}{5}$.

6. The reciprocal of 5; of $-\frac{4}{7}$; of $3c/d$.

7. $\frac{2a-2x}{3c+9d}\cdot\frac{c+3d}{a-x}$.
8. $\frac{3x-6d}{b-5}\cdot\frac{ab-5a}{bx-3bd}$.
9. $\frac{hx-hy}{ab-ac}\cdot\frac{cw-bw}{3x-3y}$.

10. $(a^2-9b^2)\cdot\dfrac{5a}{ab-3b^2}$.
11. $(y^2-9)\cdot\dfrac{y+2}{y^2+3y}$.
12. $\dfrac{2a-ab}{4d-ad}\cdot\dfrac{4k-ak}{2c-bc}$.

13. $\dfrac{2x-2y}{6x+3y}\cdot\dfrac{4x^2-y^2}{(x-y)^2}$.
14. $\dfrac{h^2-9}{3x-3y}\cdot\dfrac{(x^2-y^2)}{h^2-6h+9}$.

15. $\dfrac{\dfrac{2x-6}{x^2+5xy}}{\dfrac{x^2-25y^2}{x^2-9}}$.
16. $\dfrac{\dfrac{u^2-v^2}{(a+3b)^2}}{\dfrac{cu-cv}{a^2+3ab}}$.
17. $\dfrac{\dfrac{a^2-b^2}{2a+3b}}{\dfrac{2a+2b}{4a^2-9b^2}}$.
18. $\dfrac{\dfrac{9y^2-1}{y^2-16}}{\dfrac{6y-2}{y^2+4y}}$.

19. $\dfrac{3x-bx}{5h-hx}\div\dfrac{3c-bc}{4w-wx}$.
20. $\dfrac{6x-4a}{4x^2-9y^2}\div\dfrac{2a-3x}{2x+3y}$.

21. $\dfrac{\dfrac{3x-1}{9x^2-1}}{4x+5}$.
22. $\dfrac{\dfrac{ax+bx}{b^2-a^2}}{3x}$.
23. $\dfrac{\dfrac{x^2-16}{x^2-4x}}{x-1}$.
24. $\dfrac{\dfrac{h^2-x^2}{ch-cx}}{5w}$.

25. $\dfrac{25-9x^2}{x+3}\div(5x-3x^2)$.
26. $\dfrac{a^2+2ab+b^2}{2a-3b}\div(b^2-a^2)$.

27. $\dfrac{2+\frac{7}{3}}{3-\frac{2}{5}}$.
28. $\dfrac{3+\frac{4}{5}}{2-\frac{5}{3}}$.
29. $\dfrac{3\frac{7}{15}}{7\frac{1}{3}}$.
30. $\dfrac{\frac{2}{7}-3}{\frac{4}{5}-2}$.

31. $\dfrac{\frac{3}{x}-\frac{2}{y}}{\frac{5}{x}+\frac{6}{y}}$.
32. $\dfrac{1-\frac{2}{3x}}{9-\frac{4}{x^2}}$.
33. $\dfrac{\frac{2}{y}-\frac{3}{x}}{\frac{4}{y^2}-\frac{9}{x^2}}$.
34. $\dfrac{1-\frac{3}{ab}}{b^2-\frac{9}{a^2}}$.

35. $\dfrac{100-\frac{9}{a^2b^2}}{2a+\frac{3}{5b}}$.
36. $\dfrac{1-\frac{4a}{2a+b}}{1-\frac{2a}{2a+b}}$.
37. $\dfrac{\frac{1}{4x}-\frac{x^3}{4}}{\frac{1}{2x}-\frac{x}{2}}$.
38. $\dfrac{ab-\frac{8}{a^2b^2}}{a^2-\frac{4}{b^2}}$.

39. $(b^2-a^2)\div\dfrac{a^2+2ab+b^2}{2a-3b}$.
40. $(ax+ay^2)\div\dfrac{x^2+2xy^2+y^4}{x-y^2}$.

41. $\left(1+\dfrac{4}{x-2}\right)\left(3-\dfrac{2}{x+2}\right)$.
42. $\left(y+\dfrac{2x}{3}\right)\div\left(\dfrac{9y}{x}-\dfrac{4x}{y}\right)$.

43. $\left(\dfrac{y^2}{x^2} - \dfrac{x}{y}\right) \div \left(\dfrac{1}{2y} - \dfrac{x}{2y^2}\right).$ **44.** $\left(1 - \dfrac{25d^2}{a^2}\right) \div \dfrac{ax + 5dx}{b - 9a}.$

45. $\left(y - 1 - \dfrac{6}{y}\right) \div \left(1 + \dfrac{2}{y} - \dfrac{15}{y^2}\right).$

20. Terminology for equations

An *equation* is a statement that two number expressions are equal. The two expressions are called the *sides* or *members* of the equation. An equation in which the members are equal for all permissible values of the literal numbers involved is called an **identical equation** or, for short, an **identity.** An equation which is not an identity is called a **conditional equation.**

ILLUSTRATION 1.   The equation $(a - b)^2 = a^2 - 2ab + b^2$ is an identity. The equation $x - 2 = 0$ is a conditional equation whose members are equal only when $x = 2$. The equation $x = x + 2$ is a conditional equation whose members are never equal for any value of x, because the equation is equivalent to $0 = 2$, which is a contradiction.

The word *equation* by itself will be used in referring to both identities and conditional equations, except where such usage would cause confusion. Usually, however, the word *equation* refers to a *conditional equation*. At times, to emphasize that some equation is an identity, we may use " $\equiv$ " instead of " $=$ " between the members. A conditional equation may be thought of as presenting a question: the equation asks for the values of certain literal number symbols, called **unknowns,** which make the two members equal. Some letters in an equation may represent known numbers.

An equation is *satisfied* by a set of values of the unknowns if the equation becomes an identity when these values are substituted for the unknowns. A **solution** of an equation is a set of values of the unknowns which satisfies the equation. A solution of an equation in a single unknown also is called a **root** of the equation. **To solve** an equation means *to find all of its solutions.* It is possible that an equation may have no solution, as in the case of $x = x + 2$ in Illustration 1.

ILLUSTRATION 2.   4 is a root of the equation $2x - 3 = 5$ because, when $x = 4$, the equation becomes $[2(4) - 3] = 5$, which is true.

Two equations are said to be *equivalent* if they have the same solutions. Certain operations leading to equivalent equations are developed by recollection of the following familiar facts:

A. *If the same number is added to (or subtracted from) equal numbers, the results are equal.*

B. *If equal numbers are multiplied (or divided) by the same number, not zero, the results are equal.*

EXAMPLE 1. Solve the equation:
$$\frac{x-4}{3} - \frac{x-3}{2} = \frac{3+x}{10} - 2. \qquad (1)$$

SOLUTION. 1. The LCD is 30. Multiply both sides by 30, observing that we have

$$30 \cdot \frac{x-4}{3} = 10(x-4); \qquad 30 \cdot \frac{x-3}{2} = 15(x-3); \qquad 30 \cdot \frac{3+x}{10} = 3(3+x):$$

$$10(x-4) - 15(x-3) = 3(3+x) - 60; \qquad (2)$$

$$-5x + 5 = 3x - 51. \qquad (3)$$

2. Subtract $3x$ and 5 from both sides:

$$-5x - 3x = -51 - 5; \qquad -8x = -56. \qquad (4)$$

3. Divide both sides by -8: $\qquad\qquad\qquad x = 7. \qquad (5)$

CHECK. Substitute $x = 7$ in the original equation.

Left-hand side: $\qquad\qquad \dfrac{7-4}{3} - \dfrac{7-3}{2} = \dfrac{3}{3} - \dfrac{4}{2} = 1 - 2 = -1.$

Right-hand side: $\qquad$ We again obtain -1. *This checks.*

Comment. Because of (B), **IF** (1) has any roots, *they also are solutions of* (2). Conversely, since we can pass from (2) back to (1) by dividing both sides of (2) by 30, it is equally true by (B) that *any solution of* (2) *also is a solution of* (1). Thus, (1) and (2) have the same solutions, or are *equivalent.* Similarly, (3) and (4) are equivalent on account of (A). Finally, (1) and (5) are equivalent. Hence, *without any check*, we are sure that $x = 7$ is a solution, and is the only solution of (1), provided that no errors were made in the details of our work.

Remarks as in the Comment can be made to justify the solution of any equation where we use operations of types (I) and (II) of the following Summary. In general, we aim to solve any given equation by passing from it through a sequence of equivalent equations, where the final equation can be solved easily. Sometimes, however, our methods will not yield equivalent equations and then special care must be exercised, as will be discussed in Section 22.

SUMMARY. *The following operations on an equation in one* * *unknown,* x, *yield an equivalent equation.*

I. *Addition (or subtraction) of the same number expression* † *on both sides of the equation.*

II. *Multiplication (or division) of both sides of the equation by the same number expression,* k, *provided that* k *is defined and* $k \neq 0$ *at all values permitted for the literal numbers in the sides of the given equation.*

* Or in several unknowns.
† Defined at all values allowed for the literal numbers in the equation.

Note 1. The student is advised to phrase all of his manipulations of an equation in terms of the fundamental operations of algebra, that is, at present, in terms of *addition, subtraction, multiplication,* and *division,* applied simultaneously to the two sides. Thus, instead of saying "**cancel**" a term which appears on both sides, say "*subtract*" the term from both sides. Instead of saying "**transpose** *a term from one side to the other with a change in sign,*" say "**subtract** *the term from both sides.*" Instead of stating, mechanically, "**change the signs** *on both sides,*" we may say "**multiply** *both sides by* − 1."

21. Linear equations

An **integral rational equation** is one in which each member is an integral rational polynomial in the unknowns. A **linear equation** in one unknown, x, or an equation of the *first degree* in x, is an integral rational equation which, by use of operation (I) on page 35, is equivalent to an equation of the form $ax = b$, where a and b represent known numbers and $a \neq 0$. To solve a linear equation in x, *first clear the equation of fractions,* if any, by multiplying both sides by the LCD of the fractions. Then, rearrange terms by use of (I) on page 35 to obtain an equivalent equation *where x appears only in one member,* with all other terms in the other member. By this process, an equivalent equation $cx = b$ is obtained, whose only solution is $x = b/a$. Thus, a linear equation in x has *just one root.* This method of solution was illustrated in Example 1 on page 35.

EXAMPLE 1. If a and b are known numbers, not zero, solve for x:

$$\frac{2x}{ab} - \frac{3}{a} = \frac{x}{2a}.$$

SOLUTION. The LCD is $2ab$. Hence, multiply both sides by $2ab$, noticing

$$2ab\left(\frac{2x}{ab}\right) = 4x; \qquad 2ab\left(\frac{3}{a}\right) = 6b; \qquad 2ab\left(\frac{x}{2a}\right) = bx.$$

We obtain $4x - 6b = bx;$

$$4x - bx = 6b; \qquad x(4 - b) = 6b; * \qquad x = \frac{6b}{4 - b}.$$

EXAMPLE 2. Solve for x if $a + b \neq 0$: $b(b + x) = a^2 - ax.$

SOLUTION. 1. Expand: $b^2 + bx = a^2 - ax.$

2. Add ax; subtract b^2: $ax + bx = a^2 - b^2.$

3. Factor: $x(a + b) = (a - b)(a + b).$

4. Divide by $(a + b)$: $x = a - b.$

---

* At this point, we assume that $4 - b \neq 0$, or $b \neq 4$. Otherwise, $0 = 6b$, which is impossible since $b \neq 0$, and would imply that the given equation has *no solution.* Similarly, in the exercises, the student will assume that letters representing known numbers are not allowed to take on values which make any denominator zero in the solution.

EXERCISE 11

Solve and check.

D by

6

1. $x - 3 = 5x + 7.$

2. $3x - 6 = 18 + 7x.$

3. $5 - 3y = 2 - 4y.$

4. $3 - 4x = -7 - 6x.$

5. $4z + 5 = 8 - 2z.$

6. $3y - 4 = 1 - 3y.$

7. $2(4 + x) = 8 + 3x.$

8. $5 - 4y = 5 - 5y.$

9. $6z + \frac{3}{4} = 5z + 2.$

10. $5x + \frac{1}{6} = 4x - \frac{1}{2}.$

11. $\frac{2}{3} - 5y = -3y - \frac{2}{15}.$

12. $5x - \frac{5}{4} = 3x + \frac{4\frac{1}{12}}.$

13. $5x - .55 = .33 - 3x.$

14. $.23 - z = .95 - 3z.$

15. $\frac{3h}{10} - h = \frac{3}{2} - \frac{h}{5}.$

16. $\frac{5x}{3} - 3 = \frac{3x}{4} + \frac{3x}{2}.$

17. $\frac{5y}{6} - 4 = \frac{2y}{3} - \frac{3y}{2}.$

18. $\frac{2x}{15} - \frac{x}{3} = \frac{x}{5} - \frac{6}{5}.$

19. $\frac{3x}{10} - \frac{5}{2} = \frac{x}{6} - \frac{1}{2}.$

20. $\frac{3y}{10} - \frac{y}{3} = \frac{3}{2} - \frac{y}{12}.$

21. $\frac{3x}{2} - \frac{3x}{5} = \frac{3}{5}.$

22. $\frac{4x}{9} - \frac{3}{5} = \frac{5x}{6} - \frac{13}{10}.$

23. $\frac{2y - 7}{3} = \frac{4 + y}{4}.$

24. $\frac{h - 2}{7} = \frac{h - 2}{6}.$

25. $2.3x - 2.4 = 1.6 - 1.7x.$

26. $2.5x - 3.7 = 13.5 - 1.8x.$

27. $\frac{z - 7}{2} = \frac{1 - z}{10}.$

28. $\frac{3w - 1}{6} - \frac{w + 1}{4} = 0.$

29. $.17x - .362 = .028 - .09x.$

30. $4.088 + .03x = 3x - .07.$

31. $\frac{4 - 2x}{3} = \frac{21}{12} - \frac{5x - 3}{4}.$

32. $\frac{3 - 4x}{3} = \frac{9}{5} - \frac{2x - 3}{5}.$

33. $\frac{5 - x}{6} = \frac{7}{6} - \frac{x - 2}{2}.$

34. $\frac{33}{10} + \frac{2x + 9}{5} = -\frac{3x - 5}{4}.$

35. $\frac{4x - 11}{6} = \frac{x - 5}{2} + \frac{7}{2}.$

36. $\frac{3h + 5}{6} - \frac{h - 2}{3} = 2.$

37. $\frac{3x - 4}{4} + \frac{5x - 4}{6} = \frac{11}{4} + \frac{x - 2}{3}.$

38. $\frac{5 - x}{3} + \frac{3 - 11x}{15} = 3 + \frac{1 - 2x}{5}.$

Solve for x, y, or z, whichever appears. The other letters represent numbers which, for the moment, are assumed to be known.

39. $2x - 5 = \frac{a}{3}.$

40. $ax - 3b = \frac{5a}{2}.$

41. $hx - 4 = \frac{cx}{3}.$

42. $bx - 3c = dx.$

43. $ax = 2 - 3x.$

44. $cx + d = bx.$

45. $2ay - 5c = 3by + 4a.$

46. $7x - d = 5ax + 8.$

47. $3x = \frac{c}{b}.$

48. $\frac{2x}{b} = a.$

49. $\frac{y}{2c} = d.$

50. $\frac{ax}{b} = \frac{c}{d}.$

51. $\frac{2b}{c} - \frac{3x}{a} = 0.$

52. $\frac{a^2 x}{3} - 2a^3 = 0.$

53. $\frac{A}{4} - \frac{3x}{BC} = 0.$

54. $\dfrac{x}{b} - 2x = 3.$ **55.** $5 - \dfrac{3x}{a} = \dfrac{2x}{3c}.$ **56.** $\dfrac{3x}{a} - \dfrac{x}{b} = 4.$

57. $\dfrac{ax}{7} + 2c = \dfrac{dx}{a} + 2.$ **58.** $\dfrac{cx}{3} - \dfrac{a}{2c} = \dfrac{2x}{c^2} - 1.$

59. $aby - m = bmy - a.$ **60.** $2by - 3ay = 4b^2 - 9a^2.$

61. $3z - 18 = az - 2a^2.$ **62.** $c^2y - ck = b^2y - bk.$

63. $25a^2x - 5ab = d^2x - bd.$ **64.** $4z - b^3 = 64 - bz.$

65. $2adx + 9c^2 + d^2 = 6cd + 6acx.$ **66.** $27 + ay - a^2y = a^3 - 6y.$

22. Operations not yielding equivalent equations

In operation (II) of the Summary on page 35, the multiplier or divisor of both sides of the equation was stated to be *different from zero* at all values of x allowed in the number expressions in the equation. If this condition is *not* met, the new equation obtained by operation (II) may *not* be equivalent to the given equation. Hence, the following warnings are important.

A. *If both sides of an equation in an unknown, x, are divided by a common factor* **involving x,** *the new equation obtained may have fewer roots than the original equation. In fact, if the factor is equal to zero at any value $x = c$, this is a root of the original equation but not necessarily a root of the new equation.*

ILLUSTRATION 1. By substitution, we verify that $x = 1$ and $x = 2$ are roots of $x^2 - 3x + 2 = 0.$ On dividing both sides by $(x - 2)$, we obtain

$$\frac{x^2 - 3x + 2}{x - 2} = 0, \quad or \quad \frac{(x - 2)(x - 1)}{x - 2} = 0, \quad or \quad x - 1 = 0,$$

which has *just one* root, $x = 1.$ The root $x = 2$ was lost by the division.

In solving algebraic equations, we usually avoid operations of Type **A** in order that roots may not be lost.

B. *If both members of an equation are multiplied by an expression* **involving the unknowns,** *the new equation thus obtained may have more solutions than the original equation.*

ILLUSTRATION 2. Consider the equation $x - 3 = 0.$ (1)

Multiply both sides by $(x - 2)$ in (1):

$$(x - 2)(x - 3) = 0 \quad or \quad x^2 - 5x + 6 = 0. \tag{2}$$

By substitution, we verify that (2) has the roots $x = 2$ and $x = 3$, whereas (1) has just the solution $x = 3$; the root $x = 2$ of (2) was brought in by the multiplier $(x - 2).$ If $x - 2 \neq 0$, we can state that, if (2) is true, then (1) is true as a consequence of dividing both sides of (2) by $(x - 2).$ But, when $x - 2 = 0$, we cannot argue that the truth of (2) implies the truth of (1), because we cannot divide by $(x - 2)$ in (2) to obtain (1).

A value of the unknown, such as $x = 2$ in Illustration 2, which satisfies a derived equation but *not* the original equation, is called an **extraneous root.** Whenever an operation of Type B is employed, *test all values obtained to reject extraneous roots, if any.*

EXAMPLE 1. Solve:
$$\frac{x}{x^2 - 1} - \frac{1}{x^2 - 1} + \frac{2}{x + 1} = 0.$$

SOLUTION. The LCD is $x^2 - 1$; multiply both sides by $x^2 - 1$:
$$x - 1 + 2(x - 1) = 0; \quad 3x = 3; \quad or \quad x = 1.$$

Test. Since $x = 1$ makes $x^2 - 1 = 0$ in the given denominators, $x = 1$ *cannot be accepted as a root* because division by zero is not admissible. Hence, 1 is an extraneous root and the given equation has *no root.*

EXAMPLE 2. Solve:
$$\frac{27}{z - 5} - \frac{8}{z + 2} = \frac{18}{z^2 - 3z - 10}. \qquad (3)$$

SOLUTION. LCD $= (z - 5)(z + 2)$. On multiplying by this on both sides of (3), we obtain
$$27(z + 2) - 8(z - 5) = 18, \quad or \quad z = -4. \qquad (4)$$

Test. When $z = -4$ in (3), we find $-3 + 4 = 1$, which checks.

Comment. Instead of substituting $z = -4$ in (3), we may check the fact that LCD $= 18 \neq 0$ at $z = -4$. Then, with $z = -4$, we recall that (3) would be obtained if *both sides of* (4) *are divided by the* LCD. Hence, by (II) on page 35, (3) is true at $z = -4$ because (4) is true.

EXERCISE 12

Solve and check.

1. $\dfrac{2}{3x} - \dfrac{3}{x} + \dfrac{5}{2x} = 1 - \dfrac{11}{6x}.$

2. $\dfrac{5}{6} - \dfrac{21}{5x} = \dfrac{5x - 2}{10x}.$

3. $\dfrac{1}{3} - 5 + \dfrac{2}{x} = \dfrac{6}{2x}.$

4. $\dfrac{10}{3x} = -\dfrac{29}{4} - \dfrac{3}{2x}.$

5. $\dfrac{7}{x - 2} = \dfrac{5}{x}.$

6. $\dfrac{2}{x - 3} = \dfrac{3}{x}.$

7. $2 - \dfrac{5x - 7}{2x + 2} = 0.$

8. $\dfrac{1 + 4t}{t - 1} - \dfrac{20t}{5t - 6} = 0.$

9. $\dfrac{2x - 5}{3x + 1} = \dfrac{2x - 6}{3x + 8}.$

10. $\dfrac{2t}{t - 2} = 2 + \dfrac{5}{t}.$

11. $\dfrac{1}{t + 1} = \dfrac{5}{4t + 2}.$

12. $\dfrac{4}{14 - 3h} = \dfrac{1}{1 - 2h}.$

13. $\dfrac{x}{3x + 3} = \dfrac{x + 3}{3x + 6}.$

14. $\dfrac{2}{t^2 + t} = \dfrac{1}{t^2 - 1}.$

15. $\dfrac{z + 3}{z + 1} = \dfrac{z^2 + 9z + 20}{z^2 - z - 2}.$

16. $\dfrac{1}{2x - 1} = 1 - \dfrac{8x - 6}{10x - 5}.$

17. $\dfrac{2x - 1}{1 + 3x} = \dfrac{2x^2 + x + 14}{3x^2 - 5x - 2}.$

18. $\dfrac{x}{.3 + x} - 1.1 = \dfrac{.3 - x}{.3 + x}.$

19. $\dfrac{1 + 2y}{y - 4} = \dfrac{4y^2 + 5y}{2y^2 - 7y - 4}.$

20. $\dfrac{1 + 3z}{2 + 3z} = \dfrac{6 + 6z^2}{6z^2 + z - 2}.$

21. $\dfrac{1 - y}{1 + y} - \dfrac{2}{1 - y} = \dfrac{4 - y}{1 + y}.$

22. $\dfrac{x + 6}{x - 2} - \dfrac{x + 3}{x - 10} = \dfrac{11}{x^2 - 12x + 20}.$

23. $\dfrac{2}{3z + 2} + \dfrac{2}{9z^2 - 4} = \dfrac{3z}{9z^2 - 4}.$

24. $\dfrac{z - 1}{z + 2} - \dfrac{4z - 3}{2z + 3} = \dfrac{7 - 2z^2}{2z^2 + 7z + 6}.$

25. $\dfrac{3}{w + 1} - \dfrac{5}{2w} = \dfrac{5 - 8w}{4w^2 + 4w}.$

26. In the Fahrenheit-centigrade equation, $5F = 9C + 160$, solve for C in terms of F. Then, use the formula to find C corresponding to the following values of F: (a) 32°; (b) 212°; (c) 80°.

23. Applications of linear equations

In applying equations to the solution of problems stated in words, we translate word descriptions into algebraic expressions.

EXAMPLE 1. $350 is to be divided between Jones and Smith so that Jones will receive $25 more than Smith. How much does Smith receive?

SOLUTION. Let x be the number of dollars which Smith receives. Then, Jones receives $(x + 25)$ dollars, and

$$x + (x + 25) = 350; \quad x = 162.50. \qquad \textit{Smith receives } \$162.50.$$

24. Percentage

The word *percent* is abbreviated by the symbol % and means *hundredths*. That is, if r is the value of $h\%$, then

$$h\% = \frac{h}{100} = r. \tag{1}$$

From equation (1), we obtain $h = 100r$; hence, to change a number r to percent form, we *multiply r by 100 and add the % symbol.*

ILLUSTRATION 1. $.0175 = 1.75\%.$ $\dfrac{18}{800} = \dfrac{9}{400} = .0225 = 2.25\%.$

If M is described by the relation $M = Nr$, where r is the ratio M/N, we sometimes say that M is expressed as a **percentage** of N, with r as the **rate** and N as the **base** for the percentage:

$$\textbf{M = Nr,} \quad \textit{or} \quad \textbf{percentage = (base)} \cdot \textbf{(rate);} \tag{2}$$

$$\textbf{r = }\frac{\textbf{M}}{\textbf{N}}, \quad \textit{or} \qquad \textbf{rate = }\frac{\textbf{percentage}}{\textbf{base}}. \tag{3}$$

ILLUSTRATION 2. To express 375 as a percentage of 500, we compute the rate $r = \frac{375}{500} = .75$. Hence, $375 = .75(500)$, or 375 is 75% of 500.

EXAMPLE 1. Find the number of residents in a city where 13% of the population, or 962 people, had influenza.

SOLUTION. Let P be the number of residents:

$$.13P = 962; \qquad P = \frac{962}{.13} = \frac{96,200}{13} = 7400.$$

25. Simple interest

Interest is income received from invested capital. The capital originally invested is called the **principal.** At any later time, the sum of the principal and the interest due is called the **amount.** The *rate of interest* is the ratio of the interest earned in one year to the principal. If r is the rate and P is the principal, then

$$r = \frac{\textbf{interest per year}}{P}; \tag{1}$$

$$\textbf{(interest for one year)} = \boldsymbol{Pr}. \tag{2}$$

In (1) and (2), r is to be thought of as a small decimal, perhaps to be expressed later in percent form. Thus, in (2), the interest can be referred to as *a percentage of the principal*, with r as the *rate*.

ILLUSTRATION 1. If \$1000 earns \$36.60 interest in one year, then

$$r = \frac{36.60}{1000} = .0366, \quad or \quad r = 3.66\%.$$

If interest is computed on the *original* investment during the *whole life* of a transaction, the interest earned is called **simple interest.** Suppose that P is invested at simple interest for t years at the rate r. Let I be the interest and F be the final amount at the end of the t years. Then, the interest for one year is Pr and, by definition, the simple interest for t years is $t(Pr)$ or Prt; that is,

$$I = \boldsymbol{Prt}. \tag{3}$$

Since *amount equals principal plus interest,*

$$F = \boldsymbol{P + I}. \tag{4}$$

From (3), $\qquad\qquad P + I = P + Prt = P(1 + rt),\ or$

$$F = \boldsymbol{P(1 + rt)}. \tag{5}$$

Note 1. Whenever we use a number symbol for a concrete quantity, in accordance with common practice the symbol will represent the *measure* of the quantity in terms of an appropriate unit. Thus, if it is known that the money unit is \$1, we may say *"let P represent the capital,"* meaning that it is $\$P$. However, if we wish to emphasize the money unit, we might say *"let $\$P$ represent the capital."* Our equations involve the *numbers* representing the measures of whatever concrete quantities are involved.

In (3) and (5), t represents the time expressed in years. If the time is described in *months*, we express it in years by assuming a year to contain 12 equal months. If the time is given in *days*, there are two varieties of interest used, **ordinary** and **exact simple interest.** In computing ordinary interest, we assume that a year contains 360 days, and 365 days in computing exact interest. In (5), P frequently is called the **present value** of F because, if P is invested today, the amount at the end of t years will be F.

Note 1. Unless otherwise specified, the word "*interest*" in this book will refer to *simple* interest, taken to mean *ordinary* interest if the time is specified in days.

ILLUSTRATION 2. If \$5000 is invested for 59 days at 5%,

the ordinary interest due is $\qquad$ $5000(.05)\frac{59}{360} = \$40.97;$

the final amount due is $\qquad$ $5000 + 40.97 = \$5040.97.$

EXAMPLE 1. Find the present value of \$1100 which is due at the end of $2\frac{1}{2}$ years, if money can be invested at 4%.

SOLUTION. We have $F = \$1100$, $r = .04$, and $t = 2\frac{1}{2}$. From (5),

$$1100 = P[1 + \tfrac{5}{2}(.04)]; \quad 1100 = P(1 + .10);$$

$$1.1P = 1100; \quad P = \frac{1100}{1.1} = \$1000.$$

EXERCISE 13

Solve by use of an equation.

1. A rope 75 feet long is cut into two pieces where one is 11 feet longer than the other. Find their lengths.

2. Find the dimensions of a rectangle where the altitude is four sevenths of the base and the perimeter is 330 feet.

3. Find two consecutive integers whose sum is 73.

4. Find two consecutive odd positive integers whose squares differ by 64.

5. One dimension of a rectangle is 4/5 of the other. Find the dimensions if the perimeter of the rectangle becomes 62 feet when each dimension is increased by 2 feet.

6. Change to decimal form: $4\frac{1}{4}\%$; 45%; 126.3%; $\frac{5}{12}\%$.

7. Change to percent form: .07; .0925; .0575; 1.35.

8. Compute 6% of \$300; $3\frac{1}{4}\%$ of \$256; 110% of \$1250.

9. Express 75 as a percentage of 200; 350 as a percentage of 200.

10. The average price of copper per pound in the United States was approximately \$.138 in 1926; \$.081 in 1931; \$.385 in 1956. Find the percent change in price from 1926 to 1931; from 1931 to 1956.

11. If 390 is 65% of x, find x. $\qquad$ 12. If 366 is 18% less than y, find y.

13. After selling 15% of a stock of radios, a merchant finds that he has 119 radios left. How large was the original stock?

14. In a certain state, the first $2500 of Smith's income is not taxed; on the next $5000 of income, the tax is 2%; on all income over $7500 the tax is 5%. If Smith pays a tax of $365, find his income.

Find the ordinary interest and the final amount.

15. On $5000 at 6% for 288 days.　　　**16.** On $4000 at .045 for 93 days.

Find the exact interest and the final amount.

17. On $3000 at .04 for 219 days.　　　**18.** On $10,500 at .05 for 75 days.

Solve by use of equations (3), (4), *and* (5) *of Section* 25.

19. Find the amount at the end of 8 months if $250 is invested at 8%.

20. At what rate will $1250 be the interest for 5 years on $10,000?

21. Find the principal if it earns $300 interest when invested for 120 days at $4\frac{1}{2}$% simple interest.

22. Find the principal if it earns $250 interest in $\frac{3}{4}$ year at 4%.

23. Find the present value of $5000 which is due at the end of 5 years, if the interest rate is 4%.

24. In purchasing golf clubs, a man is offered the choice of paying $45 cash or $50 at the end of 90 days. At what rate is he actually being charged interest if he chooses to pay at the end of 90 days?

Solve by use of an equation.

25. A merchant has some coffee worth 80¢ and some worth 90¢ per pound. How many pounds of each should he use to make 100 pounds of a mixture worth 88¢ per pound?

26. A grocer forms a mixture of 100 pounds of two kinds of nuts, worth 60¢ and 80¢ per pound, respectively. If the mixture is worth 65¢ per pound, how much of each variety was used?

27. How many gallons of a 60% solution of nitric acid should be added to 10 gallons of a 30% solution to obtain a 50% solution of the acid?

Note 1. When we say that a body is moving in a path at *constant speed*, we mean that the body passes over equal distances in any two equal intervals of time. Such motion is referred to as **uniform motion** *in the path.* The **speed** or **rate** of the body in its path is defined as *the distance traveled in one unit of time.* If *r* is the rate, and *s* is the distance traveled in *t* units of time, then $s = rt$.

28. An airplane flew 950 miles in $2\frac{1}{2}$ hours against a head wind blowing 30 miles per hour. How fast could the plane fly in still air?

29. An airplane leaves an aircraft carrier and flies south at 350 miles per hour. The carrier travels south at 25 miles per hour. If the wireless communication range of the airplane is 700 miles, when will it lose touch with the carrier?

30. With a wind velocity of 30 miles per hour, it takes an airplane as long to travel 840 miles with the wind as 660 miles against it. How fast can the airplane travel in still air?

31. An alloy of silver and copper weighs 28 ounces in air and 25 ounces in water, where copper loses $\frac{1}{9}$ of its weight and silver $\frac{1}{10}$ of its weight. How much of each metal is in the alloy?

32. One pound of an alloy of lead and nickel weighs 14.4 ounces in water, where lead loses $\frac{1}{11}$ of its weight and nickel $\frac{1}{9}$ of its weight. How much of each metal is in the alloy?

Note 2. In a lever problem, assume that the lever has negligible weight. Recall that, with a lever (or, as an elementary instance, a teeterboard), horizontal equilibrium under the force of gravity results if the following condition is satisfied: *the sum of all weights, multiplied by their respective distances from the point of support* (the *fulcrum*) *on one side of it, is equal to the similar sum on the other side.*

33. Two girls, weighing 75 pounds and 90 pounds, respectively, sit at the ends of a teeterboard 15 feet long. Where should the fulcrum be placed to balance the board?

34. A weight of 300 pounds is placed on a lever 10 feet from the fulcrum. How far from the fulcrum on the other side must a weight of 250 pounds be placed in order to give equilibrium?

35. Jones and Roberts together weigh 350 pounds. Find their weights if they balance a teeterboard when Jones sits 4 feet from the fulcrum on one side and Roberts is 3 feet from the fulcrum on the other side.

36. How many pounds of force must a man exert on one end of a 9-foot lever to lift a 250-pound rock on the other end, if the fulcrum is 2 feet from the rock?

Radicals and Exponents

26. Foundation for imaginary numbers

Suppose that P is positive. Then, by definition, R is a square root of the negative number $-P$ if and only if $R^2 = -P$. But, R^2 is positive or zero if R is a real number, and hence $-P$ can have *no real number R as a square root*. In particular, -1 has no real square root. Therefore, in order that negative numbers may have square roots, we define numbers of a new type.

Let the symbol $\sqrt{-1}$ be introduced as a new variety of number, called an *imaginary number*, with the property that

$$\sqrt{-1}\sqrt{-1} = -1. \tag{1}$$

We let $i = \sqrt{-1}$. Thus, by definition, $i \cdot i = -1$ or $i^2 = -1$. We expand the number system by joining i to the system of real numbers. In the new system, we agree that the operations of addition, subtraction, and multiplication will be applied to combinations of i and real numbers as if i were an ordinary real literal number, with $i^2 = -1$. Then,

$$(-i)^2 = i^2 = -1, \tag{2}$$

so that $-i$, as well as $+i$, is a square root of -1. Any positive integral power of i can be computed by use of $i^2 = -1$. In particular,

$$i^4 = (i^2)(i^2) = (-1)(-1) = 1. \tag{3}$$

ILLUSTRATION 1. $\qquad i^{13} = i^{12}i = (i^4)^3 i = (1^3)(i) = i.$

$$(3 + 5i)(4 + i) = 12 + 23i + 5i^2 = 12 + 23i - 5 = 7 + 23i.$$

If P is any positive number, we verify that, since $i^2 = -1$,

$$(i\sqrt{P})^2 = i^2 P = -P; \quad (-i\sqrt{P})^2 = i^2 P = -P.$$

Hence, $-P$ has the square roots $\pm i\sqrt{P}$. Hereafter, $\sqrt{-P}$ or $(-P)^{\frac{1}{2}}$ will represent the particular root $i\sqrt{P}$. Then, $-P$ has the two square roots $\pm \sqrt{-P} = \pm i\sqrt{P}$. Thus, we should proceed as follows in dealing with the square root of a negative number.

$$\sqrt{-P} = \sqrt{(-1) \cdot P} = \sqrt{-1}\sqrt{P} = i\sqrt{P}.$$

ILLUSTRATION 2. The square roots of -5 are $\pm i\sqrt{5}$.

ILLUSTRATION 3. $\sqrt{-4}\sqrt{-9} = (i\sqrt{4})(i\sqrt{9}) = 6i^2 = -6.$

If a and b are *real* numbers, we call $(a + bi)$ a **complex number,** whose *real part* is a and *imaginary part* is bi. If $b \neq 0$, we call $(a + bi)$ an **imaginary number.** A **pure imaginary number** is one whose real part is *zero;* that is, $(a + bi)$ is a pure imaginary if $a = 0$ and $b \neq 0$. Any real number a is thought of as a complex number in which the coefficient of the imaginary part is zero; that is, $a = a + 0i$. In particular, 0 means $(0 + 0i)$.

ILLUSTRATION 4. $(2 - 3i)$ is an imaginary number. The real number 6 can be thought of as $(6 + 0i)$.

Note 1. Unless otherwise stated, all literal numbers represent real numbers, except that hereafter i always will represent $\sqrt{-1}$. Any literal number in a radical $\sqrt{A}$ will be supposed *positive,* if this is possible.

EXERCISE 14

Express by use of the imaginary unit i.

1. $\sqrt{-4}$.   **2.** $\sqrt{-49}$.   **3.** $\sqrt{-36}$.   **4.** $\sqrt{-17}$.   **5.** $\sqrt{-\frac{1}{4}}$.

6. $\sqrt{-\frac{1}{9}}$.   **7.** $\sqrt{-\frac{36}{49}}$.   **8.** $\sqrt{-a^2}$.   **9.** $\sqrt{-4c^2}$.   **10.** $\sqrt{-\frac{121}{25}}$.

Specify the two square roots of the number.

11. -100.   **12.** $-\frac{4}{25}$.   **13.** -81.   **14.** $-\frac{25}{16}$.   **15.** -144.

Perform indicated operations and simplify by use of $i^2 = -1$.

16. i^7.   **17.** i^8.   **18.** i^5.   **19.** i^9.   **20.** i^{26}.   **21.** i^{15}.

22. $(2 - i)(2 + i)$.   **23.** $(2i + 3)(5i - 2)$.   **24.** $(3 + 4i)(2 + i)$.

25. $(5i + 2)^2$.   **26.** $(2i - 7)^2$.   **27.** $(8i - 3)^2$.   **28.** $(6 - 5i)^2$.

29. $\sqrt{-4}\sqrt{-144}$.   **30.** $\sqrt{-4}\sqrt{-49}$.   **31.** $\sqrt{-36}\sqrt{-25}$.   **32.** $(\sqrt{-4})^2$.

27. Roots of any order

We call R a *square root* of A if $R^2 = A$ and a *cube root* of A if $R^3 = A$. If n is any positive integer,

R is an nth root of A if $R^n = A$.   (1)

ILLUSTRATION 1. The only nth root of 0 is 0. 2 is a 5th root of 32 because $2^5 = 32$. -3 is a cube root of -27.

The following facts are proved in Chapter 14.

1. *Every real number A, not zero, has just n distinct nth roots, some or all of which may be imaginary numbers.*

2. *If n is **even,** every positive number A has just **two** real nth roots, one positive and one negative, with equal absolute values.*

3. *If n is **odd,** every real number A has just **one** real nth root, which is positive when A is positive and negative when A is negative.*

4. *If n is **even** and A is **negative,** all nth roots of A are imaginary numbers.*

If A is *positive*, its *positive* nth root is called the **principal nth root** of A. If A is *negative* and n is *odd*, the *negative* nth root of A is called its *principal nth root*. If A is *zero*, its only nth root, 0, is called the *principal nth root* of A.

ILLUSTRATION 2. The real 4th roots of 81 are ± 3, and $+3$ is the principal 4th root. The principal cube root of $+125$ is $+5$, and of -125 is -5. All 4th roots of -16 are imaginary numbers.

ILLUSTRATION 3. The real cube root of 8 is 2. It can be shown that 8 also has the imaginary cube roots $(-1 \pm \sqrt{-3})$, or $(-1 \pm i\sqrt{3})$.

The **radical** $\sqrt[n]{A}$, which we read "*the nth root of A*," is used to denote the *principal nth root* of A if it has a real nth root, and to denote any convenient nth root of A if all nth roots are imaginary. In $\sqrt[n]{A}$, the positive integer n is called the **index** or **order** of the radical, and A is called its **radicand**. When $n = 2$, we omit writing the index and use $\sqrt{A}$ instead of $\sqrt[2]{A}$ for the square root of A.

I. $\sqrt[n]{A}$ *is positive if A is positive.*

II. $\sqrt[n]{A}$ *is negative if A is negative and n is odd.*

III. $\sqrt[n]{A}$ *is imaginary if A is negative and n is even.*

ILLUSTRATION 4. $\sqrt[4]{81} = 3$; $\sqrt[3]{-8} = -2$; $\sqrt[4]{-8}$ is imaginary. The two real 4th roots of 16 are $\pm \sqrt[4]{16}$ or ± 2.

By the definition of an nth root,

$$(\sqrt[n]{A})^n = A. \tag{2}$$

ILLUSTRATION 5. $(\sqrt{3})^2 = 3$. $(\sqrt[7]{169})^7 = 169$. $(\sqrt[5]{2cd^3})^5 = 2cd^3$.

In this book, unless otherwise stated, if the index of a radical is an *even* integer, all literal numbers in the radicand not used as exponents represent positive numbers, and are such that the radicand is positive. With this agreement, for every positive integer n we have * $\sqrt[n]{a^n} = a$.

Recall that N is said to be a *rational* number if there exist integers p and q, where $q \neq 0$, such that $N = p/q$; if N is real and is not rational, then N is called an *irrational number*. If $\sqrt[n]{A}$ is rational, from (2) we find that A must be the nth power of a rational number, and hence also is rational. Moreover, if A is *not* the nth power of a rational number, it follows that $\sqrt[n]{A}$ is irrational.

ILLUSTRATION 6. $\sqrt{3}$ is irrational. $\sqrt[6]{64}$ is not irrational, because $\sqrt[6]{64} = \sqrt[6]{2^6} = 2$.

28. Elementary properties of radicals

The following results (I) and (II) were met earlier. To verify (III), (IV), and (V), we raise each side of each equality to the nth power.

_____

* If $a < 0$ and n is even, then $a^n > 0$ and the positive nth root of a^n is $-a$, or $\sqrt[n]{a^n} = -a$. This case is ruled out by the agreement above. For any a, $\sqrt[n]{a^n} = |a|$ if n is even.

I. $(\sqrt[n]{a})^n = a.$

II. $\sqrt[n]{a^n} = a.$ ($a > 0$ if n is even)

III. $\sqrt[n]{ab} = \sqrt[n]{a}\sqrt[n]{b}.$

IV. $\sqrt[n]{\dfrac{a}{b}} = \dfrac{\sqrt[n]{a}}{\sqrt[n]{b}}.$ ($b \neq 0$)

V. If m, n, and m/n are positive integers, $\sqrt[n]{a^m} = a^{\frac{m}{n}}.$

ILLUSTRATION 1. $\sqrt[3]{ab} = \sqrt[3]{a}\sqrt[3]{b};$ $\sqrt[3]{a^{12}} = a^{\frac{12}{3}} = a^4,$ because $(a^4)^3 = a^{12}.$

ILLUSTRATION 2. $\sqrt[4]{\dfrac{81}{16}} = \dfrac{\sqrt[4]{3^4}}{\sqrt[4]{2^4}} = \dfrac{3}{2}.$ $\sqrt[3]{\dfrac{125y^9}{8x^6}} = \dfrac{\sqrt[3]{5^3}\sqrt[3]{y^9}}{\sqrt[3]{2^3}\sqrt[3]{x^6}} = \dfrac{5y^3}{2x^2}.$

An algebraic expression is said to be **rational** in certain literal numbers if it can be expressed as a fraction whose numerator and denominator are integral rational polynomials in the literal numbers. If the expression is not rational in the letters, it is said to be **irrational** in them.

ILLUSTRATION 3. Since $x^3 - 2x = \dfrac{x^3 - 2x}{1}$, hence $(x^3 - 2x)$ is rational in x.

$\dfrac{x^3 - 3a^2}{x + a}$ is rational in a and x. $\sqrt{3x + y}$ is irrational in x and y.

In this chapter, unless otherwise stated, in any expression which is met, we shall assume that the coefficients are rational numbers. Then, a rational expression will be called a **perfect nth power** if the expression is the nth power of some rational expression. In particular, a rational number is a perfect nth power if the number is the nth power of a rational number. In a perfect nth power, the exponent of any prime literal factor has n as a factor because, in obtaining an nth power, each exponent is multiplied by n.

ILLUSTRATION 4. Since $32y^{15} = (2y^3)^5$, then $32y^{15}$ is a perfect 5th power: $\sqrt[5]{32y^{15}} = \sqrt[5]{(2y^3)^5} = 2y^3.$ By (II) and (III), $\sqrt[3]{8x^3y^9} = \sqrt[3]{8}\sqrt[3]{x^3}\sqrt[3]{y^9} = 2xy^3.$

EXERCISE 15

State the two square roots of the number.

1. 36.   **2.** 25.   **3.** 64.   **4.** 144.   **5.** $\frac{1}{16}$.   **6.** $\frac{9}{25}$.   **7.** .04.

State the principal square root of the number.

8. 64.   **9.** 121.   **10.** 100.   **11.** $\frac{1}{81}$.   **12.** $\frac{4}{49}$.   **13.** $\frac{25}{36}$.   **14.** $\frac{64}{9}$.

State the principal cube root of the number.

15. $-8.$ **16.** 27.   **17.** 125.   **18.** $-\frac{1}{27}$.   **19.** $-1.$ **20.** $-216.$

State the principal 4th root of the number.

21. 81.   **22.** 625.   **23.** $\frac{1}{16}$.   **24.** 10,000.   **25.** 256.   **26.** .0001.

Find the specified power of the radical or the indicated root.

27. $\sqrt{a^2}$, if $a < 0$.   28. $\sqrt{a^4b^2}$.   29. $\sqrt[3]{y^3}$.   30. $\sqrt[6]{3^6}$.

31. $\sqrt[3]{2^4}$.   32. $\sqrt[4]{81}$.   33. $(\sqrt{29})^2$.   34. $(\sqrt[5]{57})^5$.

35. $(\sqrt[3]{-19})^3$.   36. $(\sqrt[3]{3ab^3})^5$.   37. $\sqrt{81}$.   38. $\sqrt{49}$.

39. $\sqrt[3]{-8}$.   40. $\sqrt[3]{-27}$.   41. $\sqrt[3]{\frac{1}{8}}$.   42. $\sqrt[3]{\frac{1}{125}}$.

43. $\sqrt[3]{64}$.   44. $\sqrt[4]{16}$.   45. $\sqrt[4]{625}$.   46. $\sqrt[3]{-216}$.

47. $\sqrt[4]{10{,}000}$.   48. $\sqrt{900}$.   49. $\sqrt[3]{1000}$.   50. $\sqrt[5]{-1}$.

51. $\sqrt{y^8}$.   52. $\sqrt[3]{z^9}$.   53. $\sqrt[3]{x^6}$.   54. $\sqrt{4z^4}$.

55. $\sqrt[3]{8y^3}$.   56. $\sqrt[3]{27h^3}$.   57. $\sqrt{\frac{9}{16}}$.   58. $\sqrt{\frac{36}{49}}$.

59. $\sqrt[3]{\frac{8}{27}}$.   60. $\sqrt[4]{\frac{81}{16}}$.   61. $\sqrt[3]{\frac{27}{64}}$.   62. $\sqrt[3]{\frac{1000}{27}}$.

63. $\sqrt[5]{\frac{32}{243}}$.   64. $\sqrt[3]{8y^6}$.   65. $\sqrt[4]{16y^4}$.   66. $\sqrt[4]{81x^8}$.

67. $\sqrt[3]{-x^3}$.   68. $\sqrt[3]{-27x^3}$.   69. $\sqrt{y^4w^6}$.   70. $\sqrt[3]{a^9b^6}$.

71. $\sqrt[3]{8a^6y^9}$.   72. $\sqrt{.0625}$.   73. $\sqrt[3]{-8x^3y^{12}}$.   74. $\sqrt[5]{-32a^{10}}$.

75. $\sqrt{\dfrac{9a^4}{25y^8}}$.   76. $\sqrt[3]{\dfrac{216}{x^6b^3}}$.   77. $\sqrt[3]{\dfrac{-64}{a^6b^9}}$.   78. $\sqrt[4]{\dfrac{16x^4}{a^4b^8}}$.

29. Fractions, zero, and negative numbers as exponents

For certain purposes it is convenient to use powers with fractional exponents as substitutes for radicals. If fractional exponents are to obey the laws of exponents, then, for example, we should have $(a^{\frac{5}{3}})^3 = a^{3(\frac{5}{3})} = a^5$, and thus $a^{\frac{5}{3}}$ should be a cube root of a^5. Accordingly, if m and n are any positive integers, we *define* $a^{\frac{m}{n}}$ **to be the principal nth root of a^m**, or

$$a^{\frac{m}{n}} = \sqrt[n]{a^m}; \tag{1}$$

[*when* $m = 1$ *in* (1)] $\qquad a^{\frac{1}{n}} = \sqrt[n]{a}. \tag{2}$

When m/n is an integer, (1) is consistent with (V) on page 48.

ILLUSTRATION 1. $8^{\frac{1}{3}} = \sqrt[3]{8} = 2$. $(-8)^{\frac{1}{3}} = \sqrt[3]{-8} = -2$. $x^{\frac{8}{3}} = \sqrt[3]{x^8}$.

$\qquad 8^{\frac{2}{3}} = \sqrt[3]{8^2} = \sqrt[3]{64} = 4$. $(-8)^{\frac{2}{3}} = \sqrt[3]{(-8)^2} = \sqrt[3]{64} = 4$.

THEOREM I. $a^{\frac{m}{n}}$ *is the mth power of the nth root of a, or*

$$a^{\frac{m}{n}} = (\sqrt[n]{a})^m. \tag{3}$$

Proof. 1. $(\sqrt[n]{a})^m$ *is an nth root of a^m because*

$$[(\sqrt[n]{a})^m]^n = [(\sqrt[n]{a})^n]^m = (a)^m = a^m.$$

2. $(\sqrt[n]{a})^m$ in (3) and $\sqrt[n]{a^m}$ in (1) differ at most in sign, because each symbol represents a *real nth root* of a^m. Both symbols are *positive* if $a > 0$, and hence are equal. If $a < 0$, then by agreement n is *odd;* again, both symbols are *positive,* or both are *negative,* according as m is *even* or *odd.* Hence, $(\sqrt[n]{a})^m = \sqrt[n]{a^m}$ in all cases, or (3) is true.

From (1) and (3), *we have two means for computing $a^{m/n}$*.

ILLUSTRATION 2. By use of (3), $64^{\frac{5}{6}} = (\sqrt[6]{64})^5 = 2^5 = 32.$

If operations with a^0 are to obey the law of exponents for multiplication, then we should define a^0 so that

$$a^0 a^n = a^{0+n} = a^n, \quad or \quad a^0 a^n = a^n, \quad so\ that \quad a^0 = \frac{a^n}{a^n} = 1.$$

Hence, if $a \neq 0$, we *define a^0* as follows: $a^0 = 1.$ (4)

If a negative exponent is to obey the laws of exponents, and if p is any positive rational number, we should have $a^p a^{-p} = a^{p-p} = a^0 = 1.$ Hence, we *define a^{-p}* as follows when $a \neq 0$:

$$a^{-p} = \frac{1}{a^p}.$$ (5)

From (5), $a^p a^{-p} = 1$ so that, besides (5), we have $a^p = 1/a^{-p}$. That is, a^p and a^{-p} are *reciprocals*. As one consequence of this fact, we have the following result: In a fraction, any power which is a factor of one term (numerator or denominator) may be removed if the factor, *with the sign of its exponent changed*, is written as a factor of the other term.

ILLUSTRATION 3. $\dfrac{a}{bx^n} = \dfrac{ax^{-n}}{b}. \quad \dfrac{3a^{-2}b^3}{c^{-3}a^4} = \dfrac{3b^3c^3}{a^2a^4} = \dfrac{3b^3c^3}{a^6}.$

It can be proved that Laws I–V for integral exponents on page 15 apply when the exponents are allowed to be any rational numbers, positive, negative, or zero. Hereafter we shall make use of this result. *To simplify* an expression involving exponents will mean to apply Laws I–V and to eliminate zero or negative exponents, unless otherwise specified.

ILLUSTRATION 4. $(x^6)^{\frac{2}{3}} = x^4. \qquad x^{\frac{1}{4}}x^{\frac{2}{3}} = x^{\frac{1}{4}+\frac{2}{3}} = x^{\frac{11}{12}}.$

$$(-\tfrac{1}{125})^{-\frac{2}{3}} = [(-\tfrac{1}{5})^3]^{-\frac{2}{3}} = (-\tfrac{1}{5})^{-2} = \frac{1}{(-\frac{1}{5})^2} = \frac{1}{\frac{1}{25}} = 25.$$

EXERCISE 16

Find the value of the expression by changing to radical form, or by eliminating negative exponents.

1. $4^{\frac{1}{2}}$.	**2.** $36^{\frac{1}{2}}$.	**3.** $8^{\frac{1}{3}}$.	**4.** $27^{\frac{1}{3}}$.	**5.** 3^{-1}.
6. 8^{-1}.	**7.** 28^{-1}.	**8.** 35^0.	**9.** $144^{\frac{1}{2}}$.	**10.** $81^{\frac{1}{4}}$.
11. 5^{-2}.	**12.** 6^{-3}.	**13.** 4^{-3}.	**14.** $16^{\frac{1}{4}}$.	**15.** $32^{\frac{1}{5}}$.
16. $(\frac{1}{49})^{\frac{1}{2}}$.	**17.** $(\frac{1}{27})^{\frac{1}{3}}$.	**18.** $121^{\frac{1}{2}}$.	**19.** $216^{\frac{1}{3}}$.	**20.** $(-8)^{\frac{1}{3}}$.
21. $9^{-\frac{1}{2}}$.	**22.** $4^{-\frac{1}{2}}$.	**23.** $27^{-\frac{1}{3}}$.	**24.** $(\frac{1}{5})^{-1}$.	**25.** $(\frac{2}{3})^{-1}$.
26. $(\frac{2}{5})^{-2}$.	**27.** $(.04)^{\frac{1}{2}}$.	**28.** 750^0.	**29.** $(-2)^{-3}$.	**30.** $(-5)^{-2}$.
31. $(-1)^{\frac{1}{3}}$.	**32.** $1^{-\frac{1}{3}}$.	**33.** $(.36)^{\frac{1}{2}}$.	**34.** $(.0144)^{\frac{1}{2}}$.	**35.** $(-\frac{2}{5})^{-3}$.
36. $(-216)^{\frac{1}{3}}$.	**37.** $(64)^{-\frac{1}{2}}$.	**38.** $(-125)^{-\frac{1}{3}}$.	**39.** $(-.008)^{-\frac{1}{3}}$.	

Find the value of the symbol by use of formula (3), *page* 49.

40. $16^{\frac{3}{2}}$.   **41.** $36^{\frac{3}{2}}$.   **42.** $8^{\frac{4}{3}}$.   **43.** $144^{\frac{3}{2}}$.   **44.** $81^{\frac{3}{4}}$.

45. $125^{\frac{4}{3}}$.   **46.** $(\frac{1}{4})^{\frac{3}{2}}$.   **47.** $(\frac{25}{9})^{\frac{5}{2}}$.   **48.** $16^{\frac{5}{4}}$.   **49.** $(-8)^{\frac{2}{3}}$.

Express with positive exponents.

50. x^{-4}.   **51.** b^{-3}.   **52.** $y^{-5}x^{2}$.   **53.** $x^{-3}y$.   **54.** $x^{2}y^{-4}$.

55. $c^{2}y^{-3}$.   **56.** $5x^{-3}$.   **57.** $3y^{-2}z$.   **58.** $2xy^{-4}$.   **59.** $4x^{-3}y$.

Write without denominators by use of negative exponents.

60. $\dfrac{2}{y^{3}}$.   **61.** $\dfrac{3}{x^{5}}$.   **62.** $\dfrac{x}{4}$.   **63.** $\dfrac{y^{2}}{3}$.   **64.** $\dfrac{2a^{3}}{9y^{4}}$.   **65.** $\dfrac{5x^{\frac{1}{2}}}{y^{3}}$.

66. $\dfrac{2}{(1.02)^{4}}$.   **67.** $\dfrac{3}{(1.04)^{6}}$.   **68.** $\dfrac{A}{(1+x)^{3}}$.   **69.** $\dfrac{B}{(1+i)^{n}}$.

Express any radical as a power, and each fractional power as a radical.

70. $x^{\frac{1}{5}}$.   **71.** $z^{\frac{1}{3}}$.   **72.** $a^{\frac{5}{3}}$.   **73.** $b^{\frac{2}{3}}$.   **74.** $5a^{\frac{1}{4}}$.

75. $6x^{\frac{2}{5}}$.   **76.** $ax^{\frac{2}{3}}$.   **77.** $bx^{\frac{3}{4}}$.   **78.** $\sqrt[4]{x^{5}}$.   **79.** $\sqrt[3]{x^{7}}$.

80. $\sqrt[9]{y^{12}}$.   **81.** $\sqrt[5]{x^{10}}$.   **82.** $\sqrt[4]{a^{6}}$.   **83.** $(3a)^{\frac{3}{2}}$.   **84.** $(2x^{3})^{\frac{2}{3}}$.

Express without negative exponents; change to a fraction in lowest terms.

85. $2^{-1} - 3^{-1}$.   **86.** $4^{-1} + 5^{-2}$.   **87.** $2^{-3} + 4^{-2}$.   **88.** $a^{-1} + b^{-1}$.

89. $\dfrac{5^{-1}}{2^{-1}+3^{-1}}$.   **90.** $\dfrac{2^{-1}+3^{-2}}{4^{-1}}$.   **91.** $\dfrac{5(2^{-1})+6^{-1}}{3^{-1}+2^{-1}}$.   **92.** $\dfrac{a^{-1}}{b^{-1}+c^{-1}}$.

Simplify. Compute the expression, if convenient.

93. $a^{\frac{1}{3}}a^{3}$.   **94.** $x^{\frac{2}{3}}x^{\frac{3}{4}}$.   **95.** $y^{4}y^{0}y$.   **96.** $(x^{\frac{2}{3}})^{6}$.   **97.** $(2^{6})^{\frac{4}{3}}$.

98. $x^{0}x^{\frac{5}{4}}$.   **99.** $(3^{4})^{\frac{3}{2}}$.   **100.** $(4y)^{-2}$.   **101.** $(3x)^{-4}$.   **102.** $(a^{-2}y)^{2}$.

103. $\dfrac{a^{4}}{a^{\frac{3}{2}}}$.   **104.** $\dfrac{x^{2}}{x^{\frac{2}{3}}}$.   **105.** $\dfrac{a^{2}}{a^{\frac{5}{3}}}$.   **106.** $\dfrac{b^{-3}y^{4}}{b^{2}y^{-2}}$.   **107.** $\dfrac{x^{-2}y^{3}}{y^{-1}x^{4}}$.

108. $30(1.01)^{-4}$.   **109.** $5(1+r)^{-6}$.   **110.** $A(1+r)^{-n}$.   **111.** $(1+r)^{2}(1+r)^{-\frac{1}{3}}$.

112. $\left(\dfrac{2x^{2}}{3y^{\frac{1}{3}}}\right)^{3}$.   **113.** $\left(\dfrac{4y^{3}}{2a^{\frac{1}{4}}}\right)^{2}$.   **114.** $\left(\dfrac{8u^{3}}{27x^{6}}\right)^{\frac{1}{3}}$.   **115.** $\left(\dfrac{64a^{3}b^{6}}{125x^{6}}\right)^{\frac{2}{3}}$.

30. Elementary operations on radicals

In various operations where all radicals are of the same order, it may be convenient to maintain the radical form and use properties I, II, III, and IV of page 48, instead of changing to powers with fractions as exponents.

To remove a factor which is a perfect nth power from the radicand in a radical $\sqrt[n]{A}$, *use* $\sqrt[n]{ab} = \sqrt[n]{a}\sqrt[n]{b}$.

ILLUSTRATION 1. $\sqrt{147} = \sqrt{49\cdot3} = \sqrt{49}\sqrt{3} = 7\sqrt{3} = 7(1.732) = 12.124$.

$$\sqrt[5]{64a^{11}c^{9}} = \sqrt[5]{32}\sqrt[5]{2}\sqrt[5]{a^{10}}\sqrt[5]{a}\sqrt[5]{c^{5}}\sqrt[5]{c^{4}} = 2a^{2}c\sqrt[5]{2ac^{4}}.$$

The product or quotient of two radicals of the same order can be expressed as a single radical, by use of $\sqrt[n]{ab} = \sqrt[n]{a}\sqrt[n]{b}$ *and* $\sqrt[n]{a/b} = \sqrt[n]{a}/\sqrt[n]{b}$.

ILLUSTRATION 2. $2\sqrt{3}(5\sqrt{6}) = 10\sqrt{3}\sqrt{6} = 10\sqrt{18} = 10\sqrt{9}\sqrt{2} = 30\sqrt{2}.$

$$\frac{\sqrt{3}}{\sqrt{5}} = \sqrt{\frac{3}{5}}. \qquad \frac{\sqrt[3]{ab}}{\sqrt[3]{b^5}} = \sqrt[3]{\frac{ab}{b^5}} = \sqrt[3]{\frac{a}{b^4}} = \frac{\sqrt[3]{a}}{b\sqrt[3]{b}} = \frac{1}{b}\sqrt[3]{\frac{a}{b}}.$$

In simplifying a radical, $\sqrt[n]{A}$, if A involves fractions, first change A to a single fraction. In any operation on radicals, it is good style to obtain a final form where as few minus signs as possible remain in the radicands.

ILLUSTRATION 3. $\qquad \sqrt[3]{-5} = \sqrt[3]{-1}\sqrt[3]{5} = (-1)\sqrt[3]{5} = -\sqrt[3]{5}.$

$$\sqrt[3]{3a + \frac{5}{x^3}} = \sqrt[3]{\frac{3ax^3 + 5}{x^3}} = \frac{\sqrt[3]{3ax^3 + 5}}{x}.$$

Terms involving the same radical as a factor can be combined by factoring.

ILLUSTRATION 4. $\qquad\qquad 5\sqrt{3} + 2b\sqrt{3} = (5 + 2b)\sqrt{3}.$

$$(\sqrt{2} + \sqrt{3})(2\sqrt{2} + 5\sqrt{3}) = 2(\sqrt{2})^2 + 2\sqrt{2}\sqrt{3} + 5\sqrt{2}\sqrt{3} + 5(\sqrt{3})^2 =$$
$$4 + 2\sqrt{6} + 5\sqrt{6} + 15 = 19 + 7\sqrt{6}.$$

Note 1. The result $\sqrt{ab} = \sqrt{a}\sqrt{b}$ was obtained under the assumption that $a \geqq 0$ and $b \geqq 0$, and is not true when $a < 0$ and $b < 0$, as seen below. Thus, since $\sqrt{-P} = i\sqrt{P}$ if $P > 0$,

$$\sqrt{-4}\sqrt{-9} = i\sqrt{4}(i\sqrt{9}) = 6i^2 = -6. \tag{1}$$

Incorrectly, with unjustified use of $\sqrt{ab} = \sqrt{a}\sqrt{b}$,

$$\sqrt{-4}\sqrt{-9} = \sqrt{(-4)(-9)} = \sqrt{36} = 6, \tag{2}$$

because $\sqrt{36}$ represents the positive square root. Thus (2) shows that $\sqrt{ab} \neq \sqrt{a}\sqrt{b}$ when $a < 0$ and $b < 0$. Also, see problems 29–31, page 46.

31. Rationalization of denominators

To rationalize a denominator in a radical of order n, after the radicand has been expressed as a simple fraction, *multiply both numerator and denominator of the radicand by the simplest expression which will make the denominator a perfect nth power.* If the radical is a *square* root, we make the denominator a perfect *square;* if a *cube* root, we make the denominator a perfect *cube.*

ILLUSTRATION 1. $\qquad \sqrt{\dfrac{3}{7}} = \sqrt{\dfrac{3\cdot7}{7^2}} = \dfrac{\sqrt{21}}{7} = \dfrac{4.583}{7} = .655.$ (Table I)

ILLUSTRATION 2. $\qquad\qquad \sqrt[3]{\dfrac{3}{4}} = \sqrt[3]{\dfrac{3\cdot2}{4\cdot2}} = \dfrac{\sqrt[3]{6}}{\sqrt[3]{8}} = \dfrac{\sqrt[3]{6}}{2}.$

ILLUSTRATION 3. $\qquad\qquad \dfrac{\sqrt{3}}{\sqrt{5}} = \dfrac{\sqrt{3}}{\sqrt{5}}\cdot\dfrac{\sqrt{5}}{\sqrt{5}} = \dfrac{\sqrt{15}}{5}.$

If a denominator has the form $a\sqrt{b} - c\sqrt{d}$, we can rationalize it by multiplying by $a\sqrt{b} + c\sqrt{d}$.

Prove: $x^n, y^n \neq z^n$ where $n > 2$

ILLUSTRATION 4. $\dfrac{3\sqrt{2} - \sqrt{3}}{2\sqrt{2} - \sqrt{3}} = \dfrac{3\sqrt{2} - \sqrt{3}}{2\sqrt{2} - \sqrt{3}} \cdot \dfrac{2\sqrt{2} + \sqrt{3}}{2\sqrt{2} + \sqrt{3}} =$

$$\frac{6(\sqrt{2})^2 + (3-2)\sqrt{6} - (\sqrt{3})^2}{(2\sqrt{2})^2 - (\sqrt{3})^2} = \frac{9 + \sqrt{6}}{8 - 3} = \frac{9 + 2.449}{5} = 2.290.$$

EXERCISE 17

Simplify by removing perfect powers from the radicand.

1. $\sqrt{27}$.   2. $\sqrt{50}$.   3. $\sqrt{300}$.   4. $\sqrt[3]{32}$.   5. $\sqrt[3]{81}$.   6. $\sqrt[3]{108}$.

7. $\sqrt[3]{-5}$.   8. $\sqrt[3]{-40}$.   9. $\sqrt[3]{y^8}$.   10. $\sqrt[4]{z^{19}}$.   11. $\sqrt[4]{16z^6}$.

12. $\sqrt{18x^3y^4}$.   13. $\sqrt{75x^4y^9}$.   14. $\sqrt[5]{-x^6y^7}$.   15. $\sqrt[3]{-128a^9}$.

16. $\sqrt{\dfrac{81u^5}{25v^5}}$.   17. $\sqrt[4]{\dfrac{16a^2b^6}{81u^4v^5}}$.   18. $\sqrt[3]{\dfrac{-27x^3}{4y^6}}$.   19. $\sqrt[3]{-\dfrac{16a^7}{x^3y^4}}$.

20. $\sqrt{4x^2 + 4y^2}$.   21. $\sqrt{9x^2 + y^2}$.   22. $\sqrt[3]{a^3 + 3a^3b^3}$.

Replace the coefficient by an equivalent factor under the radical sign.

23. $3\sqrt{5a}$.   24. $2\sqrt{3x}$.   25. $3\sqrt[3]{x}$.   26. $3\sqrt[4]{ax}$.

Simplify and collect terms, exhibiting any common radical factor.

27. $3\sqrt{5} - 8\sqrt{5}$.   28. $3\sqrt{50} - 2\sqrt{18}$.   29. $\sqrt{150} - \sqrt{24}$.

30. $\sqrt{3}\sqrt{2}$.   31. $\sqrt[4]{5}\sqrt{2}$.   32. $\sqrt[3]{2}\sqrt[3]{12}$.   33. $\sqrt[3]{3}\sqrt[3]{27}$.

34. $(\sqrt{3})^2$.   35. $(\sqrt[3]{3})^3$.   36. $(2\sqrt{5})^2$.   37. $(3\sqrt[3]{2})^3$.

38. $\dfrac{\sqrt{15}}{\sqrt{3}}$.   39. $\dfrac{\sqrt{15x}}{\sqrt{3x}}$.   40. $\dfrac{\sqrt{2a}}{\sqrt{8c}}$.   41. $\dfrac{\sqrt[4]{44}}{\sqrt[4]{11}}$.

42. $\sqrt{5x}\sqrt{20x}$.   43. $\sqrt{y}\sqrt{3y}\sqrt{15y^3}$.   44. $\sqrt[3]{4x^2}\sqrt[3]{6x^2y^4}$.

45. $(5\sqrt{x-y})^2$.   46. $(3a\sqrt{2x} + y^2)^2$.   47. $(2a\sqrt[3]{b} + c)^3$.

48. $(3 - 2\sqrt{7})(2 + \sqrt{7})$.   49. $(\sqrt{3} - \sqrt{5})(\sqrt{3} + \sqrt{5})$.

50. $(\sqrt{5} - 2\sqrt{3})(2\sqrt{5} - \sqrt{3})$.   51. $(\sqrt{6} - 2\sqrt{3})(2\sqrt{6} + \sqrt{3})$.

Rationalize the denominator. Compute, by use of Table I if possible.

52. $\sqrt{\tfrac{1}{3}}$.   53. $\sqrt{\tfrac{1}{5}}$.   54. $\sqrt{\tfrac{2}{5}}$.   55. $\sqrt{\tfrac{5}{6}}$.   56. $\sqrt{\tfrac{3}{8}}$.   57. $\sqrt{\tfrac{5}{27}}$.

58. $\sqrt[3]{\tfrac{1}{4}}$.   59. $\sqrt[3]{\tfrac{1}{36}}$.   60. $\sqrt[3]{\tfrac{1}{9}}$.   61. $\sqrt[3]{\tfrac{3}{25}}$.   62. $\sqrt[3]{\tfrac{4}{25}}$.   63. $\sqrt[3]{\tfrac{3}{100}}$.

64. $\dfrac{1}{\sqrt{7}}$.   65. $\dfrac{1}{\sqrt{10}}$.   66. $\dfrac{5}{\sqrt{3}}$.   67. $\dfrac{3}{\sqrt[3]{36}}$.   68. $\dfrac{1}{\sqrt[3]{100}}$.   69. $\dfrac{\sqrt[3]{14}}{\sqrt[3]{63}}$.

70. $\sqrt[3]{-\tfrac{7}{1000}}$.   71. $\sqrt[3]{-.03}$.   72. $\sqrt[3]{-\tfrac{1}{25}}$.   73. $\sqrt[3]{-.128}$.

74. $\dfrac{1 - \sqrt{3}}{2 + \sqrt{3}}$.   75. $\dfrac{2\sqrt{5} - 2}{\sqrt{5} - 3}$.   76. $\dfrac{1}{2 + 3\sqrt{3}}$.

77. $\dfrac{2}{\sqrt{5} - \sqrt{3}}$.   78. $\dfrac{\sqrt{3} + 2\sqrt{2}}{3\sqrt{2} + 2\sqrt{3}}$.   79. $\dfrac{\sqrt{5} + \sqrt{2}}{3\sqrt{2} - \sqrt{5}}$.

80. $(\sqrt{7} - 2\sqrt{3}) \div (2\sqrt{3} + \sqrt{7})$.   81. $(\sqrt{5} + 2\sqrt{6}) \div (2\sqrt{6} - 3\sqrt{5})$.

82. $\sqrt{\dfrac{a}{2}}$.   83. $\sqrt{\dfrac{3x}{5}}$.   84. $\sqrt{\dfrac{2c}{a}}$.   85. $\sqrt{\dfrac{3x}{2y}}$.   86. $\sqrt{\dfrac{2a}{5b}}$.

87. $\sqrt[3]{\dfrac{c}{9}}$. 88. $\sqrt[3]{\dfrac{2d}{25}}$. 89. $\sqrt[3]{\dfrac{ab}{3c}}$. 90. $\sqrt[3]{\dfrac{3cd}{16x^2}}$. 91. $\sqrt[3]{\dfrac{c}{3d^2}}$.

92. $\sqrt{x^{-3}}$. 93. $\sqrt[4]{a^{-3}}$. 94. $\sqrt[3]{a^{-5}}$. 95. $\sqrt{x^2y^{-3}}$. 96. $\sqrt{\frac{1}{3}x^{-5}}$.

97. $\sqrt{\dfrac{a}{2} - \dfrac{5}{x}}$. 98. $\sqrt{\dfrac{3}{a} - \dfrac{4}{5b^2}}$. 99. $\sqrt{\dfrac{2}{x} + \dfrac{x}{2b}}$. 100. $\sqrt{4 + \dfrac{9}{25x^4}}$.

32. Operations on radicals by use of exponents

Any algebraic operations involving powers, roots, products, or quotients of radicals can be performed by expressing each radical as a power with a fraction as the exponent, and then simplifying by use of the laws of exponents. If a result in terms of powers with possibly fractional exponents is acceptable, practically all operations are simple to perform. We shall adopt this attitude in the following illustrations. Frequently, in advanced mathematics, the exponential form has advantages as compared to the radical form.

ILLUSTRATION 1. $\sqrt[3]{\sqrt[4]{3xy}} = [(3xy)^{\frac{1}{4}}]^{\frac{1}{3}} = (3xy)^{\frac{1}{12}} = 3^{\frac{1}{12}}x^{\frac{1}{12}}y^{\frac{1}{12}}$.

ILLUSTRATION 2. $(2\sqrt[3]{5x})^4 = 2^4[(5x)^{\frac{1}{3}}]^4 = 2^4 5^{\frac{4}{3}}x^{\frac{4}{3}}$.

ILLUSTRATION 3. $(\sqrt[3]{3})^6 = (3^{\frac{1}{3}})^6 = 3^2 = 9$.

ILLUSTRATION 4. $\dfrac{\sqrt[3]{4b^2x}}{\sqrt{3ab}} = \dfrac{4^{\frac{1}{3}}b^{\frac{2}{3}}x^{\frac{1}{3}}}{3^{\frac{1}{2}}a^{\frac{1}{2}}b^{\frac{1}{2}}} = \dfrac{4^{\frac{1}{3}}b^{\frac{1}{6}}x^{\frac{1}{3}}}{3^{\frac{1}{2}}a^{\frac{1}{2}}}$.

ILLUSTRATION 5. $\sqrt[8]{16x^2} = [(4x)^2]^{\frac{1}{8}} = (4x)^{\frac{1}{4}} = 4^{\frac{1}{4}}x^{\frac{1}{4}}$.

33. Changing from mixed fractional exponents to a radical form

Suppose that a product of powers involves fractional exponents. Then, we may express the product by use of a single radical, as follows:

1. *Express each exponent as an integer plus a fraction, and change these fractions to their* LCD — *say it is n.*

2. *Write the expression as the product of one factor involving only integral powers, and a second factor where all exponents are less than 1 and have the denominator n; then, change this factor to a radical of order n.*

ILLUSTRATION 1. $5y^{\frac{2}{3}}z^{\frac{5}{2}} = 5z^2y^{\frac{2}{3}}z^{\frac{1}{2}} = 5z^2y^{\frac{4}{6}}z^{\frac{3}{6}} = 5z^2(y^4z^3)^{\frac{1}{6}} = 5z^2\sqrt[6]{y^4z^3}$.

The following operations on radicals may arise:

I. *To find a power or a root of a radical.*

II. *To find the product or quotient of two radicals of different orders.*

III. *To reduce the order of a radical when possible.*

We may perform the preceding operations by use of fractional exponents. If desired, the final exponential form then can be changed to a radical form as indicated in (1) and (2) above. In any final radical, any denominator should be rationalized.

ILLUSTRATION 2. $\sqrt[6]{25w^4} = [(5w^2)^2]^{\frac{1}{6}} = (5w^2)^{\frac{1}{3}} = \sqrt[3]{5w^2}.$

$$\sqrt[5]{\sqrt[3]{u}} = (u^{\frac{1}{3}})^{\frac{1}{5}} = u^{\frac{1}{15}} = \sqrt[15]{u}.$$

$$\sqrt[3]{a^2}\sqrt[4]{a^3} = a^{\frac{2}{3}}a^{\frac{3}{4}} = a^{\frac{8}{12}}a^{\frac{9}{12}} = a^{\frac{17}{12}} = a\sqrt[12]{a^5}.$$

EXERCISE 18

Change to simplest radical form.

1. $a^{\frac{1}{3}}a^{\frac{1}{5}}.$ **2.** $x^{\frac{1}{3}}y^{\frac{1}{2}}.$ **3.** $3c^{\frac{2}{3}}.$ **4.** $3x^{\frac{5}{7}}.$ **5.** $2a^{\frac{3}{4}}b^{\frac{1}{3}}.$

6. $x^{\frac{1}{3}}b^{\frac{2}{5}}.$ **7.** $c^{\frac{2}{3}}b^{\frac{3}{2}}.$ **8.** $x^{\frac{1}{5}}y^{\frac{4}{3}}.$ **9.** $a^{\frac{3}{2}}y^{\frac{3}{4}}.$ **10.** $ax^{\frac{2}{3}}y^{\frac{5}{5}}.$

11. $3a^{\frac{7}{3}}b^{\frac{3}{2}}.$ **12.** $5x^{\frac{4}{5}}y^{\frac{7}{2}}.$ **13.** $a^2b^{\frac{7}{3}}.$ **14.** $x^{\frac{2}{7}}y^{\frac{9}{2}}.$ **15.** $xy^{\frac{3}{8}}z^{\frac{7}{4}}.$

Factor any integer involved. Express by use of fractional exponents. Place the final answer in radical form.

16. $\sqrt[8]{y^2}.$ **17.** $\sqrt[6]{z^3}.$ **18.** $\sqrt[4]{b^2}.$ **19.** $\sqrt[6]{u^4}.$ **20.** $\sqrt[10]{x^5}.$

21. $\sqrt[9]{a^6}.$ **22.** $\sqrt[12]{x^9}.$ **23.** $\sqrt[4]{4}.$ **24.** $\sqrt[6]{36}.$ **25.** $\sqrt[8]{25}.$

26. $\sqrt[6]{8}.$ **27.** $\sqrt[6]{49}.$ **28.** $\sqrt[9]{125}.$ **29.** $\sqrt[12]{27}.$ **30.** $\sqrt[15]{32}.$

31. $\sqrt[6]{16}.$ **32.** $\sqrt[6]{64}.$ **33.** $\sqrt[8]{4x^2}.$ **34.** $\sqrt[8]{16x^4}.$ **35.** $\sqrt[9]{27a^3}.$

Factor any integer involved. Express in a final exponential form and also in a final radical form with any denominator rationalized.

36. $(\sqrt{x})^4.$ **37.** $(\sqrt{a})^3.$ **38.** $(\sqrt{y})^5.$ **39.** $(\sqrt[3]{b})^4.$ **40.** $(\sqrt[3]{d})^2.$

41. $(\sqrt[4]{x})^3.$ **42.** $(\sqrt[4]{z})^6.$ **43.** $(\sqrt[4]{y})^8.$ **44.** $(\sqrt[3]{3})^4.$ **45.** $(\sqrt[5]{a})^4.$

46. $(\sqrt[3]{7})^5.$ **47.** $(\sqrt{3})^5.$ **48.** $(\sqrt{6})^7.$ **49.** $(\sqrt{2a})^3.$ **50.** $(\sqrt[3]{2a})^2.$

51. $(\sqrt{2x^5})^3.$ **52.** $(\sqrt[3]{5a})^4.$ **53.** $\sqrt[3]{\sqrt{x}}.$ **54.** $\sqrt{\sqrt[4]{a}}.$ **55.** $\sqrt[5]{\sqrt[3]{z}}.$

56. $\sqrt[3]{\sqrt[3]{x}}.$ **57.** $(2\sqrt{3})^4.$ **58.** $\sqrt[3]{\sqrt[4]{a^3}}.$ **59.** $\sqrt{\sqrt[5]{a^4}}.$ **60.** $\sqrt[4]{\sqrt[3]{a^8}}.$

61. $\sqrt[3]{x}\sqrt{x}.$ **62.** $\sqrt[4]{2}\sqrt{2}.$ **63.** $\sqrt[4]{y}\sqrt[3]{y}.$ **64.** $\sqrt[5]{x}\sqrt{x}.$

65. $\sqrt{5}\sqrt[3]{5}.$ **66.** $\sqrt[3]{3}\sqrt[4]{3}.$ **67.** $\sqrt[3]{x^2}\sqrt[4]{x^2}.$ **68.** $\sqrt[3]{a^2}\sqrt[4]{a^3}.$

69. $\sqrt[3]{3}\sqrt[4]{27}.$ **70.** $\sqrt[3]{2}\sqrt[5]{16}.$ **71.** $\sqrt[3]{4}\sqrt[4]{8}.$ **72.** $\sqrt[4]{\frac{4}{25}}.$

73. $\dfrac{\sqrt[3]{x}}{\sqrt{x}}.$ **74.** $\dfrac{\sqrt{a}}{\sqrt[4]{a}}.$ **75.** $\dfrac{\sqrt[3]{y}}{\sqrt{y}}.$ **76.** $\dfrac{\sqrt[4]{b}}{\sqrt{b}}.$ **77.** $\dfrac{\sqrt{5}}{\sqrt[4]{25}}.$

78. $\sqrt[4]{\frac{9}{25}}.$ **79.** $\sqrt[6]{\frac{8}{27}}.$ **80.** $\sqrt[3]{\frac{1}{4}x^{-5}}.$ **81.** $\sqrt[4]{\frac{1}{9}x^{-3}}.$ **82.** $\sqrt{x^{-5}}.$

83. $\sqrt{2} \div \sqrt[4]{2}.$ **84.** $\sqrt[4]{2} \div \sqrt[8]{16}.$ **85.** $\sqrt{6} \div \sqrt[4]{4}.$

86. $\sqrt[3]{cd^4} \div \sqrt{cd}.$ **87.** $\sqrt[4]{a^2d^3} \div \sqrt{ad}.$ **88.** $2\sqrt{xy} \div \sqrt[3]{xy^2}.$

89. $\sqrt[3]{81x^{-4}}.$ **90.** $\sqrt[6]{216}.$ **91.** $\sqrt[3]{\sqrt{27x^3}}.$ **92.** $\sqrt{4\sqrt[3]{9u^2}}.$

93. $\sqrt[3]{27\sqrt{8a^3}}.$ **94.** $\sqrt[6]{16y^{-8}}.$ **95.** $\sqrt{\sqrt[3]{8b^9}}.$ **96.** $\sqrt[9]{x^6\sqrt{8}}.$

97. $\sqrt{\sqrt[3]{4y^4}}.$ **98.** $\sqrt[3]{\sqrt{27x^3}}.$ **99.** $\sqrt{3}\sqrt[3]{3}\sqrt[4]{3}.$ **100.** $\sqrt{a^{-2} - y^{-4}}.$

101. $\sqrt[3]{y^{-3} + x^{-3}}.$ **102.** $\sqrt{\sqrt{\sqrt{x}}}.$ **103.** $\sqrt[3]{\sqrt[3]{\sqrt{a}}}.$ **104.** $\sqrt[5]{\sqrt[3]{\sqrt{8}}}.$

105. $(a\sqrt[3]{5})^4.$ **106.** $(\sqrt{ay^2})^3.$ **107.** $(d\sqrt[3]{6})^5.$ **108.** $\sqrt[6]{32}\sqrt[3]{4}.$

109. $\sqrt[6]{\dfrac{a^2}{b^3}}.$ **110.** $\sqrt[4]{\dfrac{c^6}{4b^2}}.$ **111.** $\sqrt[4]{\dfrac{64a^2}{9b^6}}.$ **112.** $\sqrt[4]{\dfrac{4c^2y^6}{9b^4}}.$ **113.** $\sqrt[6]{\dfrac{b^3a^3}{8x^3}}.$

EXERCISE 19
Review of Chapters 1 and 2

Compute the expression, leaving any fraction in lowest terms.

1. $-(-2)(-5)$.   **2.** $-3\,|-5\,|$.   **3.** $-(-3)(-4)(0)$.   **4.** $|\,7\times 0\,|$.

5. $\dfrac{-5}{7}$.   **6.** $\dfrac{-15}{-35}$.   **7.** $\dfrac{4}{7}\dfrac{14}{15}$.   **8.** $\dfrac{3}{5}\div\dfrac{6}{35}$.

9. $17\left(\dfrac{3}{7}\right)$.   **10.** $\dfrac{3}{8}\div 5$.   **11.** $7\div\dfrac{3}{4}$.   **12.** $\left(-\dfrac{3}{5}\right)^3$.

13. $\frac{2}{3}-\frac{7}{6}+\frac{10}{3}$.   **14.** $-4[3-(-5)+6]$.   **15.** $-2[3-(2-7)]$.

Insert the proper sign, $<$ or $>$, between the numbers.

16. 11 and 26.   **17.** -15 and -35.   **18.** 0 and -6.

19. Which one of -15 and 7 is numerically less than the other?

Perform indicated operations, removing any parentheses, and simplify to a convenient form.

20. $-2(3a-2b-c)$.   **21.** $-2[a-(3b+c)]$.   **22.** $-a^2(3a^3b-4ab^2)$.

23. $-2x^3y^4(3x-5y)$.   **24.** $3(2a-h)-2(3a-4h)$.

25. $3a-[2a-3(5-a)]$.   **26.** $-6(a-b)-2[4-2(a-3b)]$.

27. $\dfrac{cd^2}{7}\div c^3d^4$.   **28.** $\dfrac{10ab^3}{25a^2b^7}$.   **29.** $\dfrac{a^7}{a^3}$.   **30.** $\dfrac{-6c^3d^2}{24c^5d}$.

31. $(3x^2y^3)^4$.   **32.** $(-2a^2x^3)^3$.   **33.** $(5c^2d^3y)^4$.   **34.** $(\frac{1}{2}a^3b)^2$.

35. $\left(\dfrac{3a}{4x}\right)^2$.   **36.** $\left(\dfrac{c^2x}{-4a}\right)^3$.   **37.** $\left(\dfrac{-2}{3a^2}\right)^5$.   **38.** $\left(\dfrac{-3x}{4y}\right)^4$.

39. $\dfrac{2a^2h^3-5ah^4}{2a^2h^5}$.   **40.** $\dfrac{4y^3+8y^9}{-2y^7}$.   **41.** $\dfrac{4x^3-7x^2}{-2x^4}$.

42. $(2x+3)(2x-7)$.   **43.** $(2x-y)(3x-5y)$.

44. $(7x-3x^2)(2x-5x^3)$.   **45.** $(3+b)(9-3b+b^2)$.

46. $(3a-2b)^2$.   **47.** $(3h+4k)^2$.   **48.** $(3a-5b)(3a+5b)$.

49. $\dfrac{6-19x+21x^2-9x^3}{2-3x}$; use long division.

50. $\dfrac{2h-3}{5}-3-\dfrac{4h-7}{10}$.   **51.** $\dfrac{-2a}{3}+2-\dfrac{4a-7}{12}$.

52. $\dfrac{b}{2xy}-\dfrac{c}{3y^2}+\dfrac{d}{4x^2}$.   **53.** $\dfrac{2-3x}{4x^2y}-\dfrac{5-3y}{3xy^3}$.

54. $\dfrac{3-\dfrac{5}{3}}{2+\dfrac{4}{5}}$.   **55.** $\dfrac{1-\dfrac{5}{3a}}{a^2-\dfrac{25}{9}}$.   **56.** $\dfrac{27-\dfrac{b^3}{x^3}}{\dfrac{9x}{b}+3+\dfrac{b}{x}}$.

57. $\dfrac{3x-1}{2x-5}-\dfrac{2x+3}{3x-1}$.   **58.** $\dfrac{2a-b}{a^2-b^2}+\dfrac{5b}{b-a}$.

59. $\dfrac{3c-b}{c^2-b^2}+\dfrac{3b}{b-c}$.   **60.** $\dfrac{3y-2}{y-4}-\dfrac{2y-5}{3y+1}$.

Factor.

61. $y^2 - 25z^2$. **62.** $4z^2 - 9h^2k^2$. **63.** $z^2 - 8yz + 16y^2$.

64. $M^4 - 81y^4z^4$. **65.** $a^3 - 27b^3$. **66.** $8u^3 + 27v^3$.

67. $9y^2 + 12yz^2 + 4z^4$. **68.** $y^2 + y - 12$.

69. $z^2 + 4z - 21$. **70.** $6x^2 + x - 15$.

71. $2 - 12x^2 + 5x$. **72.** $4h^2 - 28hw + 49w^2$.

73. $5z^2 - 30wz + 45w^2$. **74.** $ab + 2bc + 3ad + 6cd$.

75. $2a^3 + 4a^2 - 2a - 4$. **76.** $(m + w)^2 + 4m + 4w + 4$.

77. $x^2 - a^2 - 6ab - 9b^2$. **78.** $x^2 + 4x + 4 - 9a^2$.

Find the value of the symbol or simplify it, using Table I *if desirable.*

79. 5^{-4}. **80.** $(-3)^{-2}$. **81.** $(-18)^0$. **82.** $216^{\frac{1}{3}}$. **83.** $8^{\frac{1}{2}}$.

84. $49^{\frac{3}{2}}$. **85.** $4^{-\frac{3}{2}}$. **86.** $(-125)^{\frac{2}{3}}$. **87.** $\sqrt{\frac{1}{6}}$. **88.** $\sqrt{\frac{4}{5}}$.

89. $(\sqrt{973})^2$. **90.** $(\sqrt[3]{17})^3$. **91.** $\sqrt{\frac{5}{16}}$. **92.** $\sqrt[3]{\frac{2}{9}}$. **93.** $\sqrt{\frac{27}{20}}$.

94. $\sqrt[3]{\frac{7}{25}}$. **95.** $9^{\frac{5}{2}}$. **96.** $(\frac{27}{20})^{\frac{1}{3}}$. **97.** $625^{\frac{1}{4}}$. **98.** $\sqrt{.003}$.

99. $\dfrac{2\sqrt{8}}{\sqrt{6}}$. **100.** $\dfrac{4\sqrt{15}}{\sqrt{45}}$. **101.** $\dfrac{\sqrt{5a}}{\sqrt{20a}}$. **102.** $\dfrac{1}{\sqrt[3]{-2}}$. **103.** $(-\frac{3}{16})^{\frac{1}{3}}$.

Express without radicals, and simplify by the laws of exponents. Then give the simplest radical form if fractional exponents remain.

104. $\sqrt[4]{x^5}$. **105.** $\sqrt[4]{h^7}$. **106.** $\sqrt{9u^7}$. **107.** $\sqrt[3]{16z^5}$. **108.** $\sqrt[3]{16u^7}$.

109. $\sqrt[4]{4h^2}$. **110.** $\sqrt[5]{32x^7}$. **111.** $\sqrt[4]{16y^2}$. **112.** $\sqrt[3]{(2ax^2)^2}$. **113.** $5x^{-3}$.

114. au^{-4}. **115.** $(3a^2)^{-3}$. **116.** $(5a^0b)^{-3}$. **117.** $(3cd^{\frac{2}{3}})^4$. **118.** $(a^3b^{\frac{4}{3}})^3$.

119. $\sqrt[3]{\sqrt{x^3}}$. **120.** $(ab^{-n})^k$. **121.** $\sqrt[3]{a}\sqrt[4]{a}$. **122.** $\sqrt{x^2}\sqrt[5]{x^3}$. **123.** $3^{\frac{1}{2}}\sqrt[3]{3}$.

124. $\left(\dfrac{2x^2}{4y^{\frac{1}{2}}}\right)^4$. **125.** $\left(\dfrac{27y^6}{8u^3}\right)^{\frac{2}{3}}$. **126.** $\left(\dfrac{49a^8}{4b^4c^8}\right)^{\frac{3}{2}}$. **127.** $\left(\dfrac{au^0}{4y^{\frac{2}{3}}}\right)^{\frac{1}{2}}$.

128. $\dfrac{\sqrt{8a^3u^5}}{\sqrt[3]{4a^5x^6}}$. **129.** $\dfrac{\sqrt[4]{4u^2v^2}}{\sqrt[4]{4uv^4}}$. **130.** $\left(\dfrac{u^xv^z}{2a^k}\right)^{-n}$. **131.** $\sqrt[h]{\dfrac{a^hz^k}{u^xv^y}}$.

132. $(3a^{-1} - b^{-3})^{-1}$. **133.** $2(a^{-2} + y^{-1})^{-1}$. **134.** $5(x^{-2} - 3y^{-2})^{-2}$.

Write without fractions by use of negative exponents.

135. $\dfrac{2ax^2}{u^5y^2}$. **136.** $\dfrac{cx^2}{3a^2y^3}$. **137.** $\dfrac{2b^2x}{3d^4}$. **138.** $\dfrac{cx^4}{4x^{\frac{1}{3}}}$. **139.** $\dfrac{2x}{5x + 3y}$.

Change to a simple radical form.

140. $\sqrt{80u^6}$. **141.** $\sqrt{90y^7}$. **142.** $\sqrt[5]{32uv^8}$. **143.** $\sqrt[3]{5x^{-6}}$. **144.** $\sqrt[3]{\frac{1}{8}x}$.

145. $\sqrt{\frac{3}{14}}$. **146.** $\sqrt{\frac{5}{8}}$. **147.** $\sqrt[3]{\frac{5}{32}}$. **148.** $6^{\frac{1}{2}}x^{\frac{1}{3}}$. **149.** $a^{\frac{1}{3}}b^{\frac{5}{2}}$.

150. $\dfrac{2\sqrt{3}}{\sqrt{3} - \sqrt{2}}$. **151.** $\dfrac{\sqrt{5} - 3}{2(5^{\frac{1}{2}}) + 2}$. **152.** $\sqrt[6]{729u^4x^6} - \sqrt[9]{u^6y^9}$.

153. $\sqrt[4]{a^2 + 6ab^2 + 9b^4}$. **154.** Prove that $\sqrt[m]{\sqrt[n]{P}} = \sqrt[mn]{P}$.

155. $\dfrac{3}{\sqrt[4]{25} - \sqrt[4]{9}}$. **156.** $\dfrac{2}{\sqrt{3} + 2\sqrt{5} - \sqrt{2}}$. **157.** $\dfrac{\sqrt{2x} - 3}{\sqrt{x - y} + \sqrt{2x}}$.

Introduction to Functions and Graphs

34. The origin of analytic geometry

In the year 1637, the French mathematician and philosopher René Descartes (1596–1650) established a landmark in the field of mathematics by publishing a book entitled *La Géométrie*. It brought into use the notion of the equation of a curve and related analytic methods in the study of plane geometry. Later, similar methods were extended to the field of geometry in space of three dimensions (solid geometry). The achievements of Descartes smoothed the road leading to the invention of the important mathematical discipline called *calculus* by Sir Isaac Newton (1642–1727) and Gottfried Wilhelm Leibniz (1646–1716), whose work appeared late in the 17th century. A large part of the present chapter is devoted to initial steps in the presentation of plane analytic geometry.

35. Directed line segments

In any remarks relating to analytic geometry, we shall be dealing with problems in a plane, and thus be in the field of *plane* analytic geometry. If we refer to a *line*, we shall mean a straight line. In this book, the word *length* or the *unqualified word distance* will refer to a *positive number* or *zero* which is the measure of some distance, along a line, in terms of a given unit of length.

A line l is said to be a *directed line* if it is agreed that one direction on l is called *positive*, with the opposite direction *negative*, as in Figure 2, page 59. Directed distances on l in the corresponding directions will be positive and negative, respectively, and a direction is assigned to each line segment on l. To indicate that a segment is directed or traced *from a point A to B on l*, the segment is named AB. Then, we define the *value* of AB as the *directed distance from A to B*. Thus, if A and B coincide, $AB = 0$. If AB has *positive direction*, the value of AB is *positive* and is equal to the *length* of the segment. If AB has *negative direction*, the value of AB is the *negative of the length* of

AB. In any case, the absolute value of AB is equal to the length of AB:

$$| AB | = \text{(length of segment } AB\text{)}. \tag{1}$$

If a segment is directed *from B to A*, we refer to the segment, and also to its value, as BA. Since AB and BA have opposite directions,

$$AB = -BA \quad or \quad AB + BA = 0. \tag{2}$$

ILLUSTRATION 1. In Figure 2, the positive direction is indicated on the line by an arrowhead (common usage); then

$$AB = -2; \qquad BA = 2;$$
$$| AB | = | BA | = 2.$$

Fig. 2

The student already has met directed line segments in the familiar representation of real numbers on a linear scale, as in Figure 3. If x is any real number, we associate it with that point P on the scale for which $x = OP$, with OP taken as positive or negative according as P is to the right or the left, respectively, from O. On the real number scale OX in Figure 3, we call O the **origin** and x the **coordinate** of P. We shall use "$P:(x)$" to abbreviate "*point P with coordinate x.*"

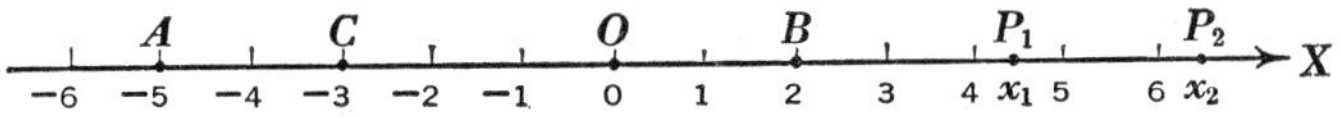

Fig. 3

For any three points A, B, and C on a directed line, as in Figures 4 and 5, it can be seen that

$$AB + BC = AC. \tag{3}$$

In (3), if we think of the *value* of each segment as *the measure of travel in a specified direction*, then (3) simply states the fact that travel *from A to B*, followed by travel *from B to C*, is equivalent to travel *from A to C*.

Fig. 4 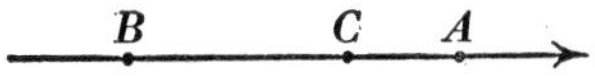   Fig. 5

ILLUSTRATION 2. In Figure 3, $AB = 7$, $BC = -5$, and $AC = 2$. We verify that $7 + (-5) = 2$, as stated in (3).

THEOREM I. *If* * $P_1:(x_1)$ *and* $P_2:(x_2)$ *are on a number scale, then*

$$P_1P_2 = x_2 - x_1; \tag{4}$$

$$\text{(length of } P_1P_2\text{)} = | P_1P_2 | = | x_2 - x_1 |. \tag{5}$$

Proof of (4). In Figure 3, $OP_1 = x_1$, $OP_2 = x_2$, $P_1O = -OP_1$. On applying (3) to (P_1, O, P_2) in that order, we obtain

$$P_1P_2 = P_1O + OP_2 = OP_2 - OP_1 = x_2 - x_1.$$

* We read "$P_1:(x_1)$" as "$P,1$ *with coordinate* $x,1$," or simply "$P,1,x,1$."

Note 1. Sometimes we shall use $\overline{AB}$ instead of $|AB|$ for the length of AB.

Illustration 3. In Figure 3 on page 59, the coordinates of B and C are 2 and -3, respectively. From (4), $BC = -3 - 2 = -5$; the distance between B and C is $\overline{BC} = |BC| = |-3 - 2| = 5$.

Note 2. If no agreement is made as to positive and negative directions on a line l, it is said to be *undirected.* Then, all distances measured on l are undirected and positive, and it is immaterial whether we use AB or BA for a segment
of l with A and B as end points. In this case,
the value of either AB or BA is the *length* of AB.

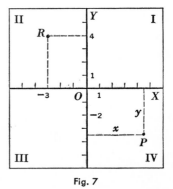
Fig. 6

Let b and c be real numbers, as indicated on the scale in Figure 6. On page 10, we agreed that the statement "*b is less than c,*" or $b < c$, means that *b is to the left of c* on the scale. Then, the *value* of the *directed segment from* b *to* c on the scale is *positive*, because the segment is directed to the *right.* That is, $(c - b)$ is *positive.* Hence,

$$\text{"} b < c \text{" means that } (c - b) \text{ is positive.} \tag{6}$$

Illustration 4. $-5 < 2$ because -5 is to the left of 2 on the number scale, and also because $2 - (-5) = 7$, which is positive.

36. Rectangular coordinates

In the plane involved, we draw two perpendicular lines, each called a *coordinate axis*, with one axis, OX, horizontal and the other, OY, vertical in the typical Figure 7. We agree that the axes and lines parallel to them will be directed lines, with the positive direction to the right on horizontal lines and upward
on vertical lines. Assign a unit of length *on
each axis;* on it, establish a number scale with
0 as the origin. We agree that distances in the
plane will be measured *horizontally* in terms of
the unit on OX, and *vertically* in terms of the
unit on OY, where these units are **not necessarily equal.** The intersection O of the axes
is called the **origin** of coordinates. Then, if
P is any point in the plane, we present the
following definitions.

Fig. 7

I. *The horizontal coordinate, or* **abscissa,** *of P is the directed perpendicular distance x from the vertical axis OY to P.*

II. *The vertical coordinate, or* **ordinate,** *of P is the directed perpendicular distance y from the horizontal axis OX to P.*

The abscissa and ordinate of P together are called its *rectangular coordinates.*

We use "$P:(x, y)$" to mean "P *with coordinates* (x, y)." We read "$P:(x, y)$" as "P, x, y." The axes divide the plane into four **quadrants,** numbered I, II, III, and IV, counterclockwise from OX.

ILLUSTRATION 1. To plot $R:(-3, 4)$, erect a perpendicular to OX at $x = -3$ and go 4 units upward to reach R, in Figure 7.

37. Distance formula

The *projection* of a point P on a line l is defined as the foot of the perpendicular from P to l.

ILLUSTRATION 1. In Figure 7, the projection of $R:(-3, 4)$ on OX is $(-3, 0)$ and on OY is $(0, 4)$. The projection of any point $P:(x, y)$ on OX is $(x, 0)$ and on OY is $(0, y)$.

Note 1. If A and B are any two points, at present "AB" will refer to the *segment* AB of the line through A and B.

Now, suppose that a *single unit* of length has been assigned, for measurement of *all distances* in a coordinate plane, in Figure 8. Let $P_1:(x_1, y_1)$ and $P_2:(x_2, y_2)$ be given points. Figure 8 shows the projections M_1 and N_1 of P_1, and M_2 and N_2 of P_2 on the coordinate axes, with the associated values of one coordinate of each projection.

THEOREM II. *In a coordinate plane where* **a single unit of length is used** *for measuring all distances, the distance d between $P_1:(x_1, y_1)$ and $P_2:(x_2, y_2)$, or the length of P_1P_2, is given by the formula*

$$d = |P_1P_2| = \sqrt{(x_2 - x_1)^2 + (y_2 - y_1)^2}. \tag{1}$$

Proof. 1. In Figure 8, let H be the intersection of perpendiculars to OY through P_1, and to OX through P_2. Then, in triangle P_1HP_2,

$$(P_1P_2)^2 = (P_1H)^2 + (HP_2)^2. \tag{2}$$

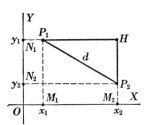

Fig. 8

2. From (4) on page 59,

$$P_1H = M_1M_2 = x_2 - x_1;$$
$$HP_2 = N_1N_2 = y_2 - y_1.$$

Hence, we obtain

$$d^2 = (P_1P_2)^2 = (x_2 - x_1)^2 + (y_2 - y_1)^2. \tag{3}$$

On extracting square roots we obtain (1).

Note 2. Since $|P_1P_2| = |P_2P_1|$, and also because (1) involves *squares* of differences, the *order* of P_1, P_2 in (1) is immaterial. In (1), $|P_1P_2|$ can be rewritten merely P_1P_2 if P_1P_2 is undirected.

ILLUSTRATION 2. From (1) with $x_1 = 2$, $x_2 = -3$, etc., the distance between $A:(2, -8)$ and $B:(-3, 4)$ is

$$AB = \sqrt{(-3 - 2)^2 + [4 - (-8)]^2} = \sqrt{25 + 144} = 13.$$

The distance d of $P:(x, y)$ from the origin $O:(0, 0)$ is called the **radius vector** of P and is found from (1):

$$d = \sqrt{x^2 + y^2}. \tag{4}$$

EXAMPLE 1. Find the point on OX equidistant from $A:(5, 4)$ and $B:(-2, 3)$ in a plane where a single unit of length has been assigned for measurement of all distances.

SOLUTION. 1. Let the unknown point be $P:(x, 0)$, in Figure 9. Then $PA = PB$. This occurs if and only if $(PA)^2 = (PB)^2$.

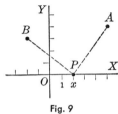

From (1),

$$(PA)^2 = (5 - x)^2 + 4^2; \tag{5}$$

$$(PB)^2 = (x + 2)^2 + 3^2. \tag{6}$$

Fig. 9

2. From (5) and (6),

$$25 - 10x + x^2 + 16 = x^2 + 4x + 4 + 9.$$

Therefore, $14x = 28$ or $x = 2$. The point is $P:(2, 0)$.

EXERCISE 20

1. Mark $A:(2)$, $B:(-3)$, $C:(-6)$, and $D:(-8)$ on a number scale and compute AB, DC, BC, $|BC|$, and DA.

Plot the points on a number scale. Find AB, BC, and AC by use of (4) on page 59, and check $AB + BC = AC$. Also, compute $(|AB| + |BC|)$ and $|AC|$.

2. $A:(-7)$; $B:(-3)$; $C:(-1)$.   3. $A:(9)$; $B:(-1)$; $C:(-5)$.

4. $A:(9)$; $B:(-8)$; $C:(0)$.   5. $A:(-5)$; $B:(7)$; $C:(2)$.

Verify each inequality of type $b < c$ by computing $(c - b)$ and also by plotting b and c on a number scale.

6. $3 < 17$.   7. $-25 < -4$.   8. $-16 < 0$.   9. $-12 < 5$.

Find the other vertex of a rectangle with the given vertices.

`9. $(3, 4)$; $(-5, 4)$; $(3, -1)$.   11. $(-2, -1)$; $(3, -1)$; $(3, 2)$.

12. A line l through $(-2, -1)$ is perpendicular to OY. What is true about the ordinates of all points on l?

13. Describe and construct the locus of a point $P:(x, y)$ for which (a) the abscissa is -3; (b) the ordinate is -4.

The following problems refer to an xy-plane where a single unit of length is used in measuring all distances.

Find the distance between the points or an expression for it.

14. $(1, 2)$; $(4, 6)$.   15. $(5, 0)$; $(0, 12)$.   16. $(3, 7)$; $(-6, 7)$.

17. $(7, 2)$; $(2, 14)$.   18. $(-1, -3)$; $(2, 1)$.   19. (x, y); $(3, -4)$.

20. Prove that the triangle with the vertices $(-2, 8)$, $(-1, 1)$, and $(3, 3)$ is isosceles.

Prove that the triangle with the given vertices is equilateral.

21. $(-2, 0)$; $(8, 0)$; $(3, 5\sqrt{3})$.   **22.** $(0, 2)$; $(0, -6)$; $(4\sqrt{3}, -2)$.

23. Prove that the following points are the vertices of a right triangle: $(-1, -1)$; $(1, 0)$; $(-2, 6)$.

24. Prove that $(-2, 4)$, $(-4, 1)$, $(6, 2)$, and $(4, -1)$ are the vertices of a parallelogram.

25. Find y if $(-3, y)$ is equidistant from $(-3, 2)$ and $(5, 6)$.

26. Find a point on OX equidistant from $(-1, 1)$ and $(3, 5)$.

38. Variables and constants

A **variable** is a symbol, such as x, or y, etc., which may represent any particular thing which we choose to designate from a specified set of things. Then, this set of things is called the **range** of the variable.

ILLUSTRATION 1. We may use x to represent any person in the United States. Then, its population is the range for the variable x.

Hereafter, in this book, the range for any variable will be a corresponding set of numbers, unless otherwise specified. If x is a variable whose range is S, then x may take on as its value any one of the numbers in S, and we may refer to x as the *general number* of S.

ILLUSTRATION 2. Let S represent the set of all numbers from 2 to 5, inclusive. If x represents any number in S, then $2 \leq x \leq 5$. Also, we can state that S consists of all numbers u such that $2 \leq u \leq 5$. In other words, the letter, x or u, used to denote the general number of S is of no importance.

In a given discussion, a **constant** is a number symbol having a *fixed value*. A constant may be an explicit number, such as 3, $-\frac{5}{2}$, etc. Or, a constant may be a number symbol such as b, c, etc., which by agreement has a fixed value in the discussion. If desired, a constant may be thought of as a variable whose range consists of just one number.

ILLUSTRATION 3. In the formula $A = \pi r^2$ for the area, A, of a circle of radius r, if we think of all circles, then r and A are variables, and π is a constant.

Note 1. If we choose, we may use the word **variable** *instead of* **unknown** as met on page 34. Thus, we may refer to an equation *in a single variable*, x; a *solution* of the equation is a value of x which satisfies the equality.

39. Graph of an equation in two variables

A **solution** of an equation in two variables x and y is a pair of corresponding values of x and y which satisfy the equation. Usually, an equation in x and y has infinitely many solutions.

ILLUSTRATION 1. In $3x - 5y = 15$, if $x = 0$ then $-5y = 15$ or $y = -3$; hence $(x = 0, y = -3)$ is a solution. Another solution is $(x = 8\frac{1}{3}, y = 2)$.

If each real solution (x, y) of an equation in the variables x and y is taken as the coordinates of a point in a plane provided with a system of xy-coordinates, the resulting points usually will make up one or more curves. This leads to the following terminology.

DEFINITION I.   *The* **graph,** *or* **locus,** *of an equation in two variables x and y is the set of all points whose coordinates (x, y) satisfy the equation.*

To graph an equation will mean *to draw its graph.* To obtain it, we may substitute values for either variable in the equation and compute the corresponding values of the other variable, to form a table of representative solutions (x, y). The graph then is drawn through the points having the coordinates in the table. In graphing an equation in x and y, usually we shall employ the horizontal axis for x and the vertical axis for y.

ILLUSTRATION 2.   To graph $3x - 5y = 15$, we form the following table of solutions by substituting $x = 0$, then $y = 0$, and other values of x or of y. We plot the solutions $(-5, -6)$, etc., in Figure 10, and join the points by a smooth curve, which is seen to be a straight line, l.

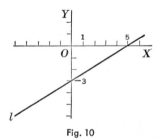

Fig. 10

$x =$	-5	-2	0	5	6
$y =$	-6	$-4\frac{1}{5}$	-3	0	$\frac{3}{5}$

A **linear equation,** or an equation of the 1st degree, in variables x and y is of the form $Ax + By + C = 0$, where A and B are constants not both zero. In Figure 10, we illustrated the fact that, in an xy-plane where the units on the axes need *not* be equal, *the graph of a linear equation in x and y is a straight line.* To obtain it for a given equation, it is advisable to compute *three solutions* of the equation, although just two points determine a line.

The **x-intercepts** of a graph in an xy-plane are the values of x at the points where the graph meets the x-axis; the **y-intercepts** are the values of y where the graph meets the y-axis. Intercepts are useful in graphing.

SUMMARY.   *To obtain the intercepts of the graph of an equation in x and y.*

   1. *To find the x-intercepts, place $y = 0$ and solve for x.*

   2. *To find the y-intercepts, place $x = 0$ and solve for y.*

ILLUSTRATION 3.   To graph $3x - 5y = 15$, we place $x = 0$ and find $y = -3$, the y-intercept. The x-intercept is $x = 5$. The graph, in Figure 10, passes through $(0, -3)$ and $(5, 0)$.

ILLUSTRATION 4.   We may look upon $x - 8 = 0$ as a linear equation in x and y where y has the coefficient zero. Then, the graph of $x - 8 = 0$ in an xy-plane has an x-intercept, $x = 8$, but no y-intercept because we cannot have $x = 0$ in a solution. Hence, the graph is the line perpendicular to the x-axis where $x = 8$. Also, we could look upon $x - 8 = 0$ as an equation in a *single* variable, x; then, the graph of $x - 8 = 0$ on simply an x-axis would be the *single point* where $x = 8$, the only solution of the equation. The *context* should always show what viewpoint is involved.

ILLUSTRATION 5. To graph the equation $y - x^2 + 2x + 1 = 0$, we first solve for y to obtain $y = x^2 - 2x - 1$; then we assign values to x and compute y to form the following table of solutions (x, y). The graph is a curve called a **parabola,** in Figure 11.

$x =$	-2	0	1	2	4
$y =$	7	-1	-2	-1	7

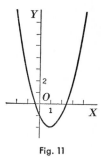

Fig. 11

ILLUSTRATION 6. The equation

$$x^2 + 5y^2 + 6 = 0, \quad or \quad x^2 + 5y^2 = -6,$$

has no real solution (x, y) because x^2 and y^2 are positive or zero for all real x and y, and hence $x^2 + 5y^2 \neq -6$ for any real point (x, y). Therefore, the equation $x^2 + 5y^2 + 6 = 0$ has no graph.

40. The equation of a locus

An equation of a locus in an xy-plane is an equation in x and y whose graph is the given locus.

ILLUSTRATION 1. An equation of the locus of a point $P:(x, y)$ which is two units to the right of the y-axis is $x = 2$.

In terminology from page 34, two equations in variables x and y are called *equivalent* if they have the same solutions, and hence the *same graph.* For instance, if one equation can be obtained by multiplying both sides of another by a constant, the equations are equivalent. If we can find one equation for a locus, then we can write infinitely many equivalent equations for it. As a rule, we refer to the particular one of these equations with which we deal as **THE** equation of the locus.

ILLUSTRATION 2. The locus of $3x - 5y = 15$ is the line l in Figure 10, page 64. This line also is the locus of $6x - 10y = 30$.

Either the *equation of a locus* in an xy-plane or the *locus of an equation* in x and y is determined by the following conditions.

I. *If $P:(x, y)$ is on the locus, the coordinates (x, y) of P satisfy the equation.*

II. *If $P:(x, y)$ is not on the locus, the coordinates (x, y) of P do not satisfy the equation.*

Sometimes we may refer to an equation by giving it *the name of its graph.*

ILLUSTRATION 3. In Figure 11, we observe the *parabola* $y = x^2 - 2x - 1$.

EXERCISE 21

Graph each equation in the variables x and y.

1. $4x - 3y = 12$, by use of solutions where $x = 0$, $y = 0$, and $x = -5$.

2. $3x + 2y = 6$.   3. $x - 2y = 8$.   4. $4x + 5y + 20 = 0$.

5. $3x + 2y = 0$.   6. $5x = 3y$.   7. $3x - 4 = 0$.

8. $x - y = 0$.   9. $2y + 7 = 0$.   10. $x + 2y = 0$.

Write the equation of the line satisfying the condition.

11. Parallel to the y-axis with the x-intercept 7.

12. Parallel to the x-axis with the y-intercept -4.

13. Perpendicular to the x-axis with the x-intercept -2.

Graph the equation, with $x = 2$ used in the table of values.

14. $y = x^2 - 4x - 5$.   15. $y = 3 + 4x - x^2$.   16. $y - x^2 = 7 - 4x$.

Graph the equation, with $y = 1$ used in the table of values.

17. $x = y^2 - 2y + 3$.   18. $2x + 3y^2 = 6y + 4$.

19. Make verbal statements to show that $3x^2 + y^2 + 5 = 0$ has no graph.

20. If $(x = 2, y = -3)$ is a solution of $2x + ky = 3k$, find k.

41. Slope of a line

Consider a nonvertical line l in an xy-plane, where the units on the co-ordinate axes **need not be equal.** If we move on l from $P_1:(x_1, y_1)$ to a second point $P_2:(x_2, y_2)$, the change in the ordinate is $(y_2 - y_1)$ and in the abscissa is $(x_2 - x_1)$. The characteristic property which distinguishes a line from all other types of curves is that the ratio $(y_2 - y_1)/(x_2 - x_1)$ remains the same, regardless of the locations of P_1 and P_2 on l. Thus, in Figure 12, from similar right triangles,

$$\frac{y_2 - y_1}{x_2 - x_1} = \frac{y_2' - y_1'}{x_2' - x_1'}. \tag{1}$$

We call $\langle y_2 - y_1)/(x_2 - x_1)$ the *rate of change of y with respect to x* as we move on l from any first point P_1 to a distinct second point P_2, and give this rate a *name:*

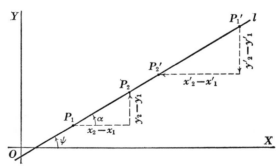

Fig. 12

DEFINITION II. *The **slope** of a **nonvertical line*** *in an xy-plane is the ratio of the change in the vertical coordinate to the change in the horizontal coordinate as we move on l from any first point to a distinct second point.*

If m is the slope of a line l, and if $P_1:(x_1, y_1)$ and $P_2:(x_2, y_2)$ are distinct points on l then, by Definition II,

$$m = \frac{y_2 - y_1}{x_2 - x_1}. \tag{2}$$

ILLUSTRATION 1. To find the slope of the line through $A:(2, -5)$ and $B:(-3, 4)$, use (2) either with A as P_1 and B as P_2, or with B as P_1 and A as P_2:

$$m = \frac{4 - (-5)}{-3 - 2} = -\frac{9}{5}, \quad or \quad m = \frac{-5 - 4}{2 - (-3)} = -\frac{9}{5}.$$

The slope of a line l is *positive* if, colloquially, l slopes *upward* to the right, and *negative* if l slopes *downward* to the right. If l is *horizontal*, the slope of l is zero. If l is *vertical*, l is said to have *no slope*.

By the nature of (2), it is seen that two lines l and L in an xy-plane are *parallel if and only if l and L have the same slope.*

Note 1. Under our present assumption that the units of length on the x-axis and y-axis are *not necessarily equal*, we have *no present basis for discussing perpendicularity of lines, or the angles formed by two lines.*

To say that two or more points are **collinear** means that they lie *on a line*. Three points A, B, and C are collinear if and only if the slopes of the lines through A and B and through B and C are equal.

EXAMPLE 1. Prove that $A:(2, 3)$, $B:(-4, 6)$, and $C:(-2, 5)$ are collinear.

SOLUTION. From (2), the slope of line AB is $-\frac{1}{2}$ and of line AC also is $-\frac{1}{2}$. Hence, A, B, and C are collinear.

EXERCISE 22

Draw the line through the points and compute its slope.

1. (2, 3), (7, 10).   **2.** (-2, 4), (4, -3).   **3.** (-4, -7), (-3, -4).
4. (1, 4), (5, 6).   **5.** (0, -3), (-2, 5).   **6.** (6, -4), (2, -3).

Prove by use of slopes, if possible, that AB and CD are parallel, or that they are not parallel.

7. $A:(3, 5)$, $B:(1, 1)$, $C:(-2, 1)$, $D:(-1, 3)$.
8. $A:(-1, -2)$, $B:(-2, -4)$, $C:(2, -5)$, $D:(0, -2)$.
9. $A:(2, 5)$, $B:(1, 2)$, $C:(2, -4)$, $D:(3, -4)$.
10. $A:(2, 3)$, $B:(6, 6)$, $C:(-1, -4)$, $D:(-5, -7)$.
11. $A:(2, -3)$, $B:(2, -7)$, $C:(1, 3)$, $D:(4, -2)$.

12. Prove by use of slopes that the points $(-2, 1)$, $(-1, -2)$, $(2, 2)$, and $(3, -1)$ are the vertices of a parallelogram.

13. In an xy-plane where a single unit is used for all distances, prove that the following points are the vertices of a rhombus (a parallelogram with sides of equal length): $(1, -1)$, $(2, 3)$, $(5, 0)$, $(6, 4)$.

Prove that the points are collinear.

14. $(2, 3)$, $(3, 5)$, $(1, 1)$.   **15.** $(-2, 1)$, $(0, 2)$, $(4, 4)$.

Find x, or y, given that the points are collinear.

16. $(3, 4)$, $(2, 6)$, $(x, 3)$.   **17.** $(3, -2)$, $(1, -3)$, $(2, y)$.

42. Standard equations for a line in an xy-plane

In the study of loci of a given type, in analytic geometry, it is desirable to derive standard equations for the typical locus, corresponding to special features of its situation.   At present, we illustrate this procedure for lines.

ILLUSTRATION 1.   If the x-intercept of a vertical line l is a, the equation of l is $x = a$.   If the y-intercept of a horizontal line l is b, the equation of l is $y = b$.   Thus we have the following standard forms.

Line parallel to OX: $y = b$.   Line parallel to OY: $x = a$.

Point-slope form.   *The line through P_1: (x_1, y_1) with slope m has the equation*

$$y - y_1 = m(x - x_1). \tag{1}$$

Proof.   1. If $x = x_1$ and $y = y_1$, then (1) is satisfied.   Hence, P_1: (x_1, y_1) is on the graph of (1).

2. In Figure 13, let l be the line through P_1 with slope m.   Then, if P: (x, y) is on l and different from P_1, the slope of P_1P is m. From Section 41, applied to P_1P,

Fig. 13

$$\frac{y - y_1}{x - x_1} = m, \quad or \quad y - y_1 = m(x - x_1). \tag{2}$$

3. If P: (x, y) is *not* on l then segment P_1P does *not* have slope m and the pair (x, y) does *not* satisfy (2), or (1).   Hence, (1) is the equation of l because (1) *is* true if P: (x, y) is on l and is *not* true if P: (x, y) is *not* on l.

ILLUSTRATION 2.   The equation of the line with slope 3 through $(2, -5)$ is obtained from (1) with $m = 3$, $x_1 = 2$, and $y_1 = -5$.

$$y + 5 = 3(x - 2) \quad or \quad y - 3x = -11.$$

Two-point form.   *The line l through two distinct points P_1: (x_1, y_1) and P_2: (x_2, y_2), not on a vertical line, has the equation*

$$y - y_1 = \frac{y_2 - y_1}{x_2 - x_1}(x - x_1). \tag{3}$$

Proof.   From (2) on page 67, the slope of l is $(y_2 - y_1)/(x_2 - x_1)$; with this value for m, then (1) gives (3).

ILLUSTRATION 3. The equation of the line through $(2, 3)$ and $(-3, 5)$ is obtained from (3) with $(2, 3)$ as P_1 and $(-3, 5)$ as P_2 (or vice versa):

$$y - 3 = \frac{5 - 3}{-3 - 2} (x - 2) \quad or \quad 5y + 2x = 19.$$

If $x_1 = x_2$, equation (3) does not apply, and P_1P_2 is vertical; then, without (3), the equation of P_1P_2 is $x = x_1$.

ILLUSTRATION 4. The line through $(3, -5)$ and $(3, 8)$ is $x = 3$.

Note 1. To find a line will mean *to find an equation of the line.*

EXAMPLE 1. Find the line through $(2, -3)$ with the y-intercept -1.

SOLUTION. The line l goes through $(0, -1)$ on the y-axis. From (3) with $P_1: (2, -3)$ and $P_2: (0, -1)$, the line l has the equation

$$y + 3 = \frac{-1 + 3}{0 - 2} (x - 2) \quad or \quad y + x + 1 = 0.$$

The intercept form. *If $a \neq 0$ and $b \neq 0$, the line with x-intercept a and y-intercept b has the equation*

$$\frac{x}{a} + \frac{y}{b} = 1. \tag{4}$$

Proof. Points $A: (a, 0)$ and $B: (0, b)$ are on the specified line. From the two-point form, the equation of AB is

$$y - 0 = \frac{b - 0}{0 - a} (x - a) = -\frac{b}{a} (x - a); \quad or \quad \frac{b}{a} x + y = b. \tag{5}$$

On dividing both sides in (5) by b we obtain (4).

ILLUSTRATION 5. The equation of the line with x-intercept 3 and y-intercept -5 is

$$\frac{x}{3} + \frac{y}{-5} = 1 \quad or \quad 5x - 3y = 15.$$

Slope-intercept form. *The line with slope m and y-intercept b is*

$$y = mx + b. \tag{6}$$

Proof. Point $B: (0, b)$ is on the line. From (1), the equation of the line through B with slope m is

$$y - b = m(x - 0) \quad or \quad y = mx + b. \tag{7}$$

ILLUSTRATION 6. The equation of the line with slope -3 and y-intercept 5 is $y = -3x + 5$.

In an equation $Ax + By + C = 0$, where $B \neq 0$, we can always change the equation to the form (6) *on solving for y in terms of x,* and then *by inspection* obtain the slope and y-intercept of the graph of the given equation.

ILLUSTRATION 7. By inspection, and comparison with (6), the graph of $y = 3x - 7$ is a line with slope 3 and y-intercept -7.

ILLUSTRATION 8. To obtain the slope-intercept form of $3x + 2y - 8 = 0$, solve for y in terms of x:

$$2y = - 3x + 8 \quad or \quad y = - \tfrac{3}{2}x + 4.$$

Hence, $3x + 2y - 8 = 0$ is the equation of a line with slope $- \tfrac{3}{2}$ and y-intercept 4.

43. General equation of the first degree

Any equation of the first degree in two variables x and y can be written in the form $Ax + By + C = 0$, where A and B are not both zero, which we call the *general linear equation* in x and y.

THEOREM III.   *The graph of any linear equation in x and y is a line.*

Proof. 1. If $B \neq 0$, we can solve $Ax + By + C = 0$ for y:

$$y = -\frac{A}{B} x - \frac{C}{B}. \tag{1}$$

This is the equation of a line with slope $- A/B$ and y-intercept $- C/B$.

2. If $B = 0$, then $A \neq 0$ and $Ax + By + C = 0$ becomes

$$Ax = - C \quad or \quad x = -\frac{C}{A}.$$

This is the equation of a vertical line. Hence, in *all* cases the locus of the equation $Ax + By + C = 0$ is a *line*.

THEOREM IV.   *(Converse of Theorem* III.) *Any line in the xy-plane has an equation linear in x and y.*

Proof. If a line l is vertical, with x-intercept a, the equation of l is $x = a$, which is linear in x and y. If l is not vertical, it has a slope m and y-intercept b. Then, the equation of l is $y = mx + b$. Hence, any line has an equation linear in x and y.

EXERCISE 23

Write the equation of the line satisfying the conditions.

1. Horizontal; y-intercept $- 5$.   2. Vertical; x-intercept 4.
3. Slope 3; y-intercept 2.   4. Slope $- 2$; y-intercept $- 3$.
5. x-intercept 2; y-intercept 3.   6. x-intercept $- 1$; y-intercept 4.
7. Slope $- \tfrac{2}{3}$; y-intercept 4.   8. Slope $\tfrac{13}{5}$; y-intercept $- 2$.

Find the line through the given points, or through the given point with the given slope m or intercept a or b.

9. $(2, - 4)$; $m = 5$.   10. $(1, 3)$; $m = - 2$.   11. $(3, 0)$; $m = - \tfrac{1}{4}$.
12. $(- 1, 3)$; $m = 0$.   13. $(0, 0)$; $m = \tfrac{2}{3}$.   14. $(1, 5)$; $(3, 7)$.
15. $(0, 3)$; $(- 1, 3)$.   16. $(- 2, 3)$; $(1, 4)$.   17. $(3, - 2)$; $(5, 0)$.
18. $(- 1, 3)$; $(- 1, 7)$.   19. $(- 1, 3)$; $b = - 3$.   20. $(2, - 5)$; $a = 4$.

Write the equation of the line in the slope-intercept form, to find the slope and y-intercept.

21. $2x + 3y = 6$.   **22.** $3x + 4y = -2$.   **23.** $5x = 12y + 6$.

24. $3x + 5y = 15$.   **25.** $6x + 10 = 5y$.   **26.** $x = 4y - 5$.

Write the equation of the line through C parallel to AB.

27. $A:(2, 5)$, $B:(1, 3)$, $C:(-2, 7)$.   **28.** $A:(1, -2)$, $B:(4, 7)$, $C:(5, 9)$.

Prove that the points are on a line and find its equation.

29. $(2, 3)$, $(3, 5)$, $(1, 1)$.   **30.** $(1, -6)$, $(-3, -5)$, $(-7, -4)$.

44. The concept of a function

If x and y are variables, and it is said that "*y is a function of x,*" this brings to mind the existence of some rule assigning values of y corresponding to given values of x. We shall make this terminology precise.

DEFINITION III. *Let D be a given set of numbers. Suppose that, for each number x in D, some rule specifies just one corresponding number y and let R be the set of all of these values of y. Then, the whole set of ordered* pairs of numbers (x, y) is called a* **function,** *F, whose* **domain** *is D and* **range** *is R.*

In Definition III, x and y are variables with the ranges D and R, respectively, and each value of y is called a *value of the function*. We call x the **independent variable** and y the **dependent variable**. Frequently we shall refer to the dependent variable *as if it were the function*, or we shall say that †

$$y \text{ is a function of } x. \tag{1}$$

Thus, to say that *y is a function of x* means that x and y are variables such that *to each value of x there corresponds just one value of y*. In Definition III, we refer to F as a function of a *single variable*, x, because the domain D is a set of *single numbers*.

ILLUSTRATION 1. The table on page 72 gives the number of four-year bachelor's degrees, y, in thousands granted by colleges in the United States in various years, t. The table exhibits a function F consisting of the set of ten pairs of numbers (1940, 187), (1942, 185), etc. The *domain* of F is the set (1940, 1942, $\cdots$, 1955, 1956); the *range* of F is the set (187, 185, $\cdots$, 287, 311). We say that *the number of bachelor's degrees is a function of the time.* In Figure 14 on page 72, each pair (t, y) is plotted as a point. These ten dots give *a picture of the whole function F,* called the *graph* of F. For such a graph, usually consecutive dots would be joined by line segments, as shown by broken lines in Figure 14.

---

* We refer to the pairs as being *ordered* because we designate the 1st place for a number from D and the 2d place for a number from R. Sets are discussed on page 303.

† We can consider (1) as an abbreviation for "*y is the general value of a function F corresponding to the general number x in the domain of F.*"

$t =$	1940	1942	1944	1946	1948	1950	1952	1954	1955	1956
$y =$	187	185	126	136	271	432	330	293	287	311

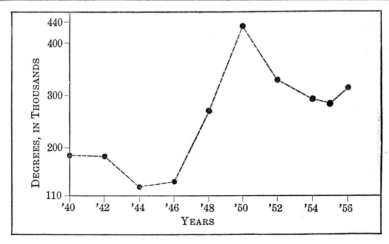

Fig. 14

Any formula in terms of a variable x defines a function whose general value is given by the formula. Illustration 1 shows that a function may be defined by its tabulated values, without a formula being available.

ILLUSTRATION 2. In Definition III, if $y = k$, a constant, for all x, we say that F is a *constant function;* its range is the *single number* k.

ILLUSTRATION 3. We may refer to "*the function* $(x^2 + 7x)$," or we may say "$(x^2 + 7x)$ *is a function of* x," as a special case of (1) with $(x^2 + 7x)$ used in place of y. When $x = 2$, the value of the function is $(4 + 14)$ or 18.

ILLUSTRATION 4. Let D be the set of all real numbers x, and let F be the function whose value is $(\frac{3}{5}x - 3)$ at any value x. Let $y = \frac{3}{5}x - 3$. Then, F consists of the set of infinitely many pairs (x, y), a few of which are in the following table; the whole set of pairs (x, y) is the same as the set of all solutions of the equation $y = \frac{3}{5}x - 3$. Hence, in an xy-plane, if each pair (x, y) is taken as the coordinates of a point, the locus of all of these points is the graph of the equation $y = \frac{3}{5}x - 3$, or is the line AB through the points from the table, as in Figure 15. We call AB the *graph* of F. This graph is a picture of *the whole set of pairs* (x, y) which form F.

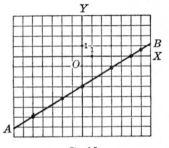

Fig. 15

$x =$	-5	0	3	5	6
$y =$	-6	-3	$-1\frac{1}{5}$	0	$\frac{3}{5}$

In Illustrations 1 and 4, we have met special cases of the following terminology, where we use the notation of Definition III.

DEFINITION IV. *In an xy-plane, the* **graph** *of a function F of a single variable, x, is the set of all points whose coordinates (x, y) form pairs of corresponding values of x and the function.*

Note 1. Unless otherwise stated, whenever a formula involving variables is introduced, we understand that the variables may take on just those values for which the expression has a well-defined meaning.

ILLUSTRATION 5. We refer to $\dfrac{3x^2 + 5x - 7}{x - 4}$ as a function of x, or say that the formula defines a function of x, and infer that the range of x consists of all real numbers *except* 4, because the denominator is zero when $x = 4$.

To graph a function defined by a formula in a variable, x, *place y equal to the formula and graph the resulting equation.*

ILLUSTRATION 6. To graph the function $(\frac{3}{5}x - 3)$, we let $y = \frac{3}{5}x - 3$, and then graph this equation, as in Illustration 4.

ILLUSTRATION 7. Let D be the set (0, 1, 2, 3, 4, 5, 6, 7, 8, 9, 10, 11, 12, 13). Let F be the function such that, for any number x in D, the value, y, of F is the *largest integral multiple of 2 which is at most equal to x.* Thus, if $x = 0$, then $y = 0$; if $x = 5$, then $y = 4$; etc. The range, R, of F is seen to be (0, 2, 4, 6, 8, 10, 12). In Figure 16, x and y are plotted on parallel scales, and the correspondence between the numbers in D and those in R is shown by arrows. F consists of fourteen pairs (0, 0), (1, 0), (2, 2), (3, 2), $\cdots$, (11, 10), (12, 12), (13, 12). A graph of F would consist of *fourteen points.* Figure 16 shows why a function F may be called *a law of correspondence between points x in the domain of F and points y in its range.*

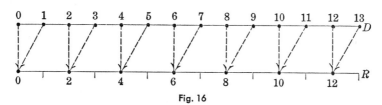

Fig. 16

Note 2. Usually, in graphing a function in a coordinate plane, we use the *horizontal axis* for values of the *independent variable.*

Note 3. In the description of a function F, the letters used for the independent and dependent variables are of no importance. Thus, suppose that F is defined by stating that, for every number x in the domain, the value, y, of F is $y = 3x - 5$. The same function is defined by saying that, for every number u in the domain, the value, v, of F is $v = 3u - 5$.

Note 4. In Definition III, since *just one* value of y corresponds to each value of x, we say that a function, as thus described, is **single-valued.** If the definition is altered by saying that *one or more values of y* correspond to each value of x, the function as thus defined may be **many-valued.** Occasionally, we shall find it convenient to bring a many-valued function into focus. However, except where otherwise stated, the word *function* in this text will refer to a *single-valued function.*

★*Note 5.* In Definition III, if we change the word *number* to *object*, the definition describes a function F whose domain D is a set of *objects, of any specified variety,* and whose range is a second set of *objects.* Thus, D might consist of a *set of people,* and y, with range R, might be the *color of the eyes of the general person x of D.* Functions of this nature are important but, in this book, except when otherwise indicated, the domain and range of any function will consist of *numbers,* as specified in Definition III.

45. Functions defined by equations

Suppose that two variables x and y are related by an equation which determines just one value of y for each value of x. Then, the equation defines y as a function, F, of the independent variable x. In the typical case, we may obtain a formula for the values of F by solving the equation for y in terms of x. The pairs of numbers which form F are the set of all solutions (x, y) of the equation. Hence, in an xy-plane, **the graph of the equation is identical with the graph of the function defined by the equation,** because each graph is the set of all points whose coordinates (x, y) form solutions of the equation. Similarly, an equation in x and y may define x *as a function of y.*

ILLUSTRATION 1. From $3x - 5y = 15$, on solving for y, we obtain

$$y = \tfrac{3}{5}x - 3; \quad similarly, \quad x = \tfrac{5}{3}y + 5. \tag{1}$$

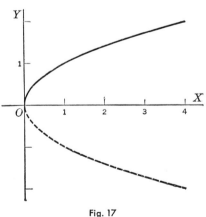

Fig. 17

Thus, $3x - 5y = 15$ defines y as a function of x, and also x as a function of y. The graph of $3x - 5y = 15$ is the graph of the function $(\tfrac{3}{5}x - 3)$, as given in Figure 15 on page 72.

ILLUSTRATION 2. The equation $y^2 = x$ defines x as a single-valued function of y; the graph of this function (or of the equation $y^2 = x$) is the parabola in Figure 17. From $y^2 = x$, we obtain $y = + \sqrt{x}$ or $y = - \sqrt{x}$. Thus, the equation $y^2 = x$ defines y as a function of x which is *two-valued* when $x > 0$ and is *single-valued* only at $x = 0$. The values of this many-valued function consist of the values of the *two single-valued functions* $y = \sqrt{x}$ and $y = -\sqrt{x}$, whose graphs are the upper half and the lower half (broken curve), respectively, in Figure 17. The graph of the many-valued function consists of the graphs of the two corresponding single-valued functions. This discussion indicates how we sometimes avoid dealing with a many-valued function by considering two or more corresponding single-valued functions. Hereafter, the word *function* again will refer to a *single-valued function* except when otherwise indicated.

EXERCISE 24

In each of Problems 1 and 2, state the range, R, of the function F; write the complete set of pairs of numbers which form F; construct a graph of F in an xy-plane; also prepare a diagram like Figure 16 on page 73 to show all correspondences between numbers in the domain D and range R. The units need not be equal on the scales for D and R.

1. F has the domain (1, 2, 3, 4, 5, 6, 7, 8, 9, 10) and the value of F for any number x in the domain is x^2.

2. F has the domain $(1, 2, 3, \cdots, 15)$; the value of F for any number x in the domain is the largest integral multiple of 3 which is less than or equal to x.

3. The table gives the number of Ph.D. degrees in mathematics granted by universities in the United States for the indicated years. Graph the number of degrees as a function of the time.

YEAR	1949	1950	1951	1952	1953	1954	1955	1956	1957
DEGREES	126	160	184	206	241	227	250	235	214

4. The weight of a cubic foot of dry air at an atmospheric pressure of 29.92 inches of mercury, under various temperatures, is given in the table, where weight is in pounds, and temperature is in degrees Fahrenheit. Graph the weight of air as a function of the temperature.

TEMP.	0°	12°	32°	52°	82°	112°	152°	192°	212°
WEIGHT	.0864	.0842	.0807	.0776	.0733	.0694	.0646	.0609	.0591

5. The table gives the United States Department of Labor wholesale price index number for various years. An index k means that the average price was $k\%$ of the average in 1947–49. Graph the index number as a function of the time. The 1958 entry is the value in March, 1958.

YEAR	'48	'49	'50	'51	'52	'53	'54	'55	'56	'57	'58
k	104	99	103	115	112	110	110	111	114	118	120

Graph the function F whose values, for any real number x, are given by the formula.

6. $3x - 2$.   **7.** $-2x + 5$.   **8.** $x - 7$.   **9.** 12.

10. Graph the function $(x^2 + 6x - 5)$, with $x = -3$ used in the table of values.

11. Graph the function $(4x - x^2 + 3)$, with $x = 2$ used in the table of values.

By solving for y, and then for x, obtain a formula for the function of x, and also for the function of y defined by the equation.

12. $4x + 3y = 12$.   **13.** $2x + y = 7$.   **14.** $3x - 6y = 7$.

15. Solve for y to obtain the function of x defined by $2y + 2x^2 - 4x = 5$. Then graph the function, with $x = 1$ used in the table of values.

46. Functional notation

We have used a single letter, say y, for the general value of a function F. A second notation for its values now will be introduced.

DEFINITION V. *The value of a function F corresponding to the general number x in the domain of F is represented by* $F(x)$*, read* **F of x**. *Also, if c is any particular value of x, then*

$$F(c) \text{ represents the value of } F(x) \text{ at } x = c. \qquad (1)$$

We refer to a symbol such as $F(x)$ or $F(c)$ as *functional notation.* In $F(x)$, we call x the *argument* of the symbol. We may refer to "*a* **function** * $F(x)$*,*" which means "*a function F of a single variable, to be named x.*" When the symbol $F(x)$ enters in an equation or in an expression representing a number, $F(x)$ means *the value of F at x in the domain.*

ILLUSTRATION 1. We may refer to "*the function* $F(x) = 3x^2 + x - 5$," meaning that the values of a function F are defined by the formula. We read $F(-1)$ as "*F of* -1" or "*F at* -1." We obtain

$$F(-1) = 3 - 1 - 5 = -3; \quad F(2) = 12 + 2 - 5 = 9; \quad F(0) = -5.$$

We may use any convenient letters, such as G, f, g, H, K, W, etc., to represent functions and thus have symbols such as $G(x), f(x), g(x)$, etc. We may refer to "*a function* $y = G(x)$," meaning that the general value of a function G is to be represented by either y or $G(x)$ as we please.

ILLUSTRATION 2. If $f(x) = 5x^2 + 2$ and $g(y) = 4/y$, then

$$[f(3)]^2 = [5(9) + 2]^2 = 47^2 = 2209, \quad f(x)g(x) = (5x^2 + 2)\left(\frac{4}{x}\right) = 20x + \frac{8}{x};$$

$$f(g(y)) = 5(g(y))^2 + 2 = 5\left(\frac{4}{y}\right)^2 + 2 = \frac{80}{y^2} + 2;$$

$$f(x + 3) = 5(x + 3)^2 + 2 = 5x^2 + 30x + 47; \quad f(3x) = 5(3x)^2 + 2 = 45x^2 + 2.$$

---

* This word always should be placed before "$F(x)$" when it is used as a symbol for the function. Otherwise, $F(x)$ represents the general value of the F function.

47. Functions of two or more variables

Let x and y be variables which are free to assume any pair of values (x, y) in a certain set, D, of pairs of numbers. We can represent D as a set of points (x, y) in an xy-plane. Suppose that, to each point (x, y) in the range D, there corresponds a certain number z, and let R be the set of all values thus obtained for z. Then, the resulting set of ordered triples of numbers $(x, y; z)$ is said to form a *function F of two independent variables, x and y*, where the domain of F is the set of pairs (x, y) in D, and the range of F is R. We call z the dependent variable, and extend the functional notation by writing $z = F(x, y)$, read "*F of (x, y).*" Similarly, we may deal with a function F of three (or more) independent variables.

ILLUSTRATION 1. We may refer to "*a function $z = F(x, y)$,*" meaning that z will represent the general value in the range of a function F of two independent variables, to be denoted by (x, y). If

$$F(x, y) = 3x^2y + 8x + 5y^2, \quad then \quad F(2, -3) = -36 + 16 + 45 = 25.$$

Note 1. Hereafter, unless otherwise stated, in any reference to a *function* we shall mean a *function of a single variable*.

EXERCISE 25

If $f(x) = 2x + 3$, find the value of the symbol.

1. $f(2)$. **2.** $f(-3)$. **3.** $f(-2)$. **4.** $f(\frac{1}{2})$. **5.** $[f(-4)]^2$.

If $g(z) = 2z^4 - 3z^2$, find the value of the expression.

6. $g(-3)$. **7.** $3g(5)$. **8.** $g(-\frac{1}{2})$. **9.** $g(2c)$. **10.** $g(\sqrt{x+y})$.

If $F(x, y) = 3y^2 + 2x - xy$, find the value of the symbol.

11. $F(3, 2)$. **12.** $F(-1, 3)$. **13.** $F(a, b)$. **14.** $F(c, d^2)$.

15. If $h(u) = 2u + 3$ and $g(v) = v^3 - 2$, find $h(2)g(3)$; $h(3)$; $h(2)/g(-1)$; $h(g(x))$; $3h(x) + g(x)$.

16. If $f(x) = x^2 + 2x - 1$, find $f(h)$; $f(3h)$; $f(x + 2)$; $f(x + h)$; $f(4x)$.

17. If $H(x) = x^3$, find $H(2 + k)$; $H(2x)$; $H(x - 3)$.

18. If $F(x) = x^2$ and $G(x) = 2x - 1$, and if x is a variable with the range $(1, 2, 3, 4, 5)$, (a) write out the complete set of *pairs of numbers* which form the function G; (b) write out the set of pairs of numbers which form the function $H(x) = F(x) + G(x)$.

48. Polynomials in one variable

If n is a nonnegative integer, an *integral rational function* of degree n or a **polynomial** of degree n in a variable x is a function $f(x)$ of the form

$$f(x) = a_0x^n + a_1x^{n-1} + a_2x^{n-2} + \cdots + a_{n-1}x + a_n, \qquad (1)$$

where $a_0 \neq 0$. If $n = 0$, then $f(x) = a_n$, a constant function of x. If $n = 1$, then $f(x)$ is called a *linear function* of x, and can be thought of in the form

(linear function) $\qquad\qquad f(x) = mx + b, \qquad (m \neq 0).$ $\qquad\qquad$ (2)

If $n = 2$ in (1), $f(x)$ is called a *quadratic function* of x, and is of the form

(quadratic function) $\qquad\qquad f(x) = ax^2 + bx + c, \qquad (a \neq 0).$ $\qquad$ (3)

In (1), $f(x)$ is called a *cubic function* if $n = 3$ and a *quartic function* if $n = 4$; if $n > 4$, we shall merely say that $f(x)$ is a polynomial of degree n.

ILLUSTRATION 1. $(3x - 5)$ is a linear function of x, and $(4x^2 - 5x + 7)$ is a quadratic function of x.

If $A \neq 0$ and $B \neq 0$, the *linear equation* $Ax + By + C = 0$ defines y as a *linear function* of x, and also defines x as a *linear function* of y. A special case of these facts was met in Illustration 1 on page 74.

Let F be a function of the independent variable x and let $y = F(x)$. Then, the graph of F in an xy-plane can be described as the set of *all points with coordinates* $(x, F(x))$, or (x, y) with $y = F(x)$. In other words,

$$\left\{ \begin{array}{l} \textit{to graph a function } F(x), \textit{ we let} \\ y = F(x) \textit{ and then graph this equation.} \end{array} \right\} \qquad (4)$$

The graph of a function $(mx + b)$ in an xy-plane is the graph of the linear equation $y = mx + b$ and hence is *a line with slope m and y-intercept b.* In particular, with $m \neq 0$, **the graph of the linear function $(mx + b)$ is a line,** as just described.

ILLUSTRATION 2. The graph of the function $(3x - 5)$ is the graph of the equation $y = 3x - 5$, which is a line with slope 3 and y-intercept -5.

In Note 3 of the Appendix, it is proved that **the graph of any quadratic function is a curve called a parabola.**

EXAMPLE 1. Graph the function $f(x) = x^2 - 2x - 3$.

SOLUTION. Let $y = x^2 - 2x - 3$. We assign values to x and compute y, as in the following table. The parabola through these points, in Figure 18, is the graph of the function. The lowest point, V, of the parabola is called its *vertex.* At V, $y = -4$. This ordinate is the *smallest* or **minimum value** of f, and hence V is called the **minimum point** of the graph. The vertical line through V is called the *axis* of the parabola. It is *symmetric* to its axis, because *any chord* (such as AC) *of the parabola perpendicular to the axis is bisected by it.* The *equation of the axis,* through V, in Figure 18 is $x = 1$. This parabola is **concave** *upward* (open upward). The curve bends *counterclockwise* if we travel on it from left to right.

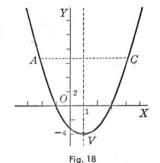

Fig. 18

x	-3	-2	0	1	2	4	5
y	12	5	-3	-4	-3	5	12

ILLUSTRATION 3. The graph of $y = -x^2 + 2x + 3$ would be a parabola concave downward, and its vertex V would be called the **maximum point** of the curve. The value of y at V would be called the **maximum value** of the function $(-x^2 + 2x + 3)$.

The following results are proved in Note 3 of the Appendix.

SUMMARY. *Concerning the* **graph of a quadratic function,**

$$y = ax^2 + bx + c.$$

1. *The graph is a parabola, with its axis perpendicular to the x-axis, which is concave* **upward** *or* **downward** *according as a is* **positive** *or* **negative.**

2. *At the parabola's vertex,* $x = -b/2a.$ *This value of x gives the function its* **minimum** *or its* **maximum** *value according as a is* **positive** *or* **negative.** *The equation of the axis of the parabola is* $x = -b/2a.$

ILLUSTRATION 4. In Figure 18, at V, $\qquad x = -(-2)/2 = 1.$

In constructing a table of values for graphing $y = ax^2 + bx + c$, it is convenient to proceed as follows.

Compute $x = -b/2a$, *and then the corresponding value of y to obtain the coordinates of the vertex.*

If the value $x = -b/2a$ *is convenient, form the table by using pairs of values of x where, in each pair, the values are equidistant from the vertex, on either side. The values of y corresponding to any pair will be equal. If the value* $x = -b/2a$ *is inconvenient, choose values of x arbitrarily.*

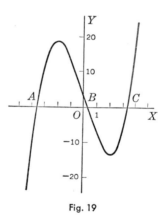

Fig. 19

ILLUSTRATION 5. In Example 1, the abscissa of V is $x = 1$. Then, we selected $x = 1 \pm 1$, or $x = 2$ and $x = 0$; $x = 1 \pm 3$, or $x = 4$ and $x = -2$; etc. The corresponding pairs of values of y are equal.

ILLUSTRATION 6. $(x^3 - 12x + 3)$ is a polynomial of the 3d degree in x, or a **cubic function** of x. We let $y = x^3 - 12x + 3$ and compute the following table of values. The graph of the polynomial is shown in Figure 19.

WHEN $x =$	-4	-3	-2	-1	0	1	2	3	4
THEN $y =$	-13	$+12$	$+19$	$+14$	$+3$	-8	-13	-6	$+19$

ILLUSTRATION 7. From the equation $2y - 2x^2 + 4x + 3 = 0$, we obtain

$$y = x^2 - 2x - \tfrac{3}{2}, \qquad\qquad (6)$$

or the equation defines y as a quadratic function of x. Hence, the graph of the equation is a parabola with its axis perpendicular to the x-axis.

EXERCISE 26

In a coordinate plane, the units on the axes need not be the same.
Graph the function f whose general value f(x) is given.

1. $f(x) = 2x + 3.$ **2.** $f(x) = -3x + 5.$ **3.** $f(x) = -7.$ **4.** $f(x) = 5.$

For each quadratic function, (a) find the coordinates of the vertex of its graph and the equation of its axis; (b) graph the function in an xy-plane; (c) state the maximum or minimum value of the function.

5. $x^2.$ **6.** $x^2 - 4x + 7.$ **7.** $-3x^2 - 6x + 5.$ **8.** $4x^2 + 5.$
9. $-x^2.$ **10.** $x^2 + 6x + 5.$ **11.** $-2x^2 + 8x + 3.$ **12.** $8x - 2x^2.$

In an xy-plane where the x-axis is horizontal, graph the given equation, which expresses x as a quadratic function of y. Employ the Summary on page 79, with the roles of x and y interchanged (thus, the parabola's axis is horizontal; at the vertex, $y = -b/2a$; etc.). State the maximum or the minimum of x.

13. $x = 4y^2 + 2.$ **14.** $x = 2y^2 + 8y - 6.$ **15.** $x = -y^2 + 6y - 8.$

16. Graph the function $f(x) = 3x^2 - 2x^3 + 12x - 6$ by use of $f(-2), f(-1), f(0), f(1), f(2),$ and $f(3).$

17. Graph the function $f(x) = x^3 - 3x^2 - 24x - 7$ by use of $f(-4), f(-3), f(-2), f(-1), f(0), f(3), f(4),$ and $f(5).$

18. Graph the function $f(x) = x^3$ by use of $f(-2), f(-1), f(-\frac{1}{2}), f(0), f(\frac{1}{2}), f(1),$ and $f(2).$

19. Graph the function $f(x) = x^3 - 3x^2 + 3x + 4$ by use of $f(-1), f(0), f(\frac{1}{2}), f(1), f(\frac{3}{2}), f(2),$ and $f(3).$

20. Without expanding, graph the quartic function $f(x) = x^2(x - 2)^2$ by use of $f(-2), f(-\frac{1}{2}), f(0), f(\frac{1}{2}), f(1), f(\frac{3}{2}), f(2), f(\frac{5}{2}),$ and $f(4).$

Solve for x or for y, whichever occurs only to the first degree; then graph the resulting quadratic function, of x or y, with the x-axis horizontal in either case.

21. $2x^2 - 8x + 9 - 2y = 0.$ **22.** $3x - 12y^2 + 36y - 17 = 0.$

★*Solve by introducing a single unknown x, and then finding the maximum or the minimum of a quadratic function of x.*

23. Divide 40 into two parts whose product is a maximum.

24. Find the dimensions of the rectangular field of maximum area which can be enclosed with 400 feet of fence.

25. Find two numbers whose sum is 15, if the sum of the squares of the numbers is a minimum.

26. In forming a trough with a rectangular cross section and open top, a sheet of tin, 20 inches wide, is bent upward along each side. Find the dimensions of the cross section with the largest possible area.

27. One side of a rectangular field is along the bank of a river. For the other sides, 400 feet of fencing is available. Find the dimensions of the field, to obtain the maximum area.

Quadratic Equations in One Variable

49. Pure quadratic equations

We recall * that an *integral rational equation* is one in which each member is an integral rational polynomial in the variables. An integral rational equation in x is said to be of *degree n* (> 0) if the equation can be written in the form $f(x) = 0$, where $f(x)$ is a polynomial of degree n in x. The solutions or roots of the equation are those *numbers on the range for x* which cause the value of $f(x)$ to be zero. Hereafter, in referring to *an equation of degree n,* we shall mean an *integral rational equation of degree n.* An equation of the 2d degree in x is called a **quadratic equation** in x, and can be written in the form

$$ax^2 + bx + c = 0, \tag{1}$$

where a, b, and c are constants and $a \neq 0$. We call (1) a *complete quadratic equation* if $b \neq 0$, and a *pure quadratic equation* if $b = 0$.

ILLUSTRATION 1. $3x^2 - 5x + 7 = 0$ is a complete quadratic equation and $5x^2 - 7 = 0$ is a pure quadratic in x.

To solve a pure quadratic equation in x, clear of fractions if necessary, solve for x^2, and then extract square roots.

EXAMPLE 1.   Solve: $7y^2 = 18 + 3y^2$.

SOLUTION. 1. $7y^2 - 3y^2 = 18$; $4y^2 = 18$; $y^2 = \frac{9}{2}$.

2. Hence the values of y satisfying the equation are the square roots of $\frac{9}{2}$. Extract square roots and use Table I:

$$y = \pm \sqrt{\frac{9}{2}} = \pm \sqrt{\frac{9 \cdot 2}{2 \cdot 2}} = \pm \frac{3}{2}\sqrt{2} = \pm \tfrac{3}{2}(1.414) = \pm 2.121.$$

Note 1. If the coefficients in a quadratic equation are explicit numbers, and if a radical occurs in any solution which is a real number, usually compute decimal values of the solutions by use of Table I. If it is desired to check such a solution, substitute the *radical* form instead of the approximate decimal value, unless otherwise directed by the instructor.

* See terminology introduced in Section 21 on page 36.

Example 2. Solve: $2y^2 + 35 = -5y^2$.

Solution. $7y^2 = -35$; $y^2 = -5$.   Hence, $y = \pm \sqrt{-5} = \pm i\sqrt{5}$.

Example 3. Solve for x: $a^2x^2 + b^2 = abx^2 + a^2$.

Solution. 1. $a^2x^2 - abx^2 = a^2 - b^2$,   or $x^2(a^2 - ab) = a^2 - b^2$.

2. Divide by $(a^2 - ab)$ and reduce to lowest terms:

$$x^2 = \frac{a^2 - b^2}{a^2 - ab} = \frac{(a - b)(a + b)}{a(a - b)}; \quad or \quad x^2 = \frac{a + b}{a}.$$

3. Extract square roots: $x = \pm\sqrt{\dfrac{a + b}{a}} = \pm \dfrac{\sqrt{a(a + b)}}{a}.$

Note 2.   In the solutions of Examples 1–3, we used a new operation on both sides of an equation, that is, *the extraction of square roots*, and assumed that this led to equivalent equations.   Let $A^2 = B^2$ represent any equation in a single * variable, x; we assume that A^2 and B^2 are expressions where at least one involves x.   Assume that A^2 and B^2 are either positive or negative on the range of x.   Plainly, $A^2 = B^2$ is equivalent to $A^2 - B^2 = 0$, or

$$(A - B)(A + B) = 0, \tag{2}$$

where A is either of the two square roots of A^2 while B and $-B$ are the *two square roots* of B^2.   A product of real numbers or pure imaginary numbers is zero *if and only if one of the factors of the product is zero.*†   Hence, the values of x which satisfy (2) consist of all values of x satisfying

$$A - B = 0 \quad or \quad A + B = 0, \tag{3}$$

which can be combined as $A = \pm B$, read "*A is equal to* $+ B$ *or* $- B$."   Hence, the equation $A^2 = B^2$ is equivalent to the *two equations* obtained *by extracting square roots on both sides, with the double sign $\pm$ used then on just one ‡ side.* This justifies our future extraction of square roots in solving equations.

50. Solution of an equation by factoring

We mentioned above that a product of two or more numbers is equal to zero if and only if at least one of the factors is zero.   The preceding fact is the basis for the following method.

Summary.   *Solution of an equation in x by use of factoring.*

1. *Transpose terms to obtain zero as one member, and thus have the equation in the form $f(x) = 0$.*

2. *Factor $f(x)$ if possible.   Then, place each factor equal to zero and solve.*

---

* The conclusions to be reached apply also to equations in any number of variables.
† The absolute value of a product of real numbers is the product of their absolute values, and thus is zero *if and only if one of the factors of the original product is zero.*   In Chapter 14, this result will be extended to factors which are complex numbers.
‡ The equations $- A = \pm B$ are equivalent to $A = \pm B$, because multiplication of both sides by -1 changes one form into the other.

EXAMPLE 1. Solve: $6 - 5x - 6x^2 = 0.$ (1)

SOLUTION. 1. Multiply both sides by -1, for later convenience:

$$6x^2 + 5x - 6 = 0.$$

2. Factor: $(3x - 2)(2x + 3) = 0.$ (2)

3. Equation (2) is true if and only if $3x - 2 = 0$ *or* $2x + 3 = 0.$

4. If $3x - 2 = 0$, then $3x = 2$; $x = \frac{2}{3}$ is one solution.

5. If $2x + 3 = 0$, then $2x = -3$; $x = -\frac{3}{2}$ is a second solution.

EXAMPLE 2. Solve: $4x^2 + 20x + 25 = 0.$

SOLUTION. 1. Factor: $(2x + 5)^2 = 0$;   *or* $(2x + 5)(2x + 5) = 0.$

2. If $2x + 5 = 0$, then $x = -\frac{5}{2}$. Since each factor gives the same value
for x, we agree to say that the equation has *two equal roots*.

From page 38, recall that, in solving an equation, if both sides are divided
by *an expression involving the variables*, solutions may be *lost*.

EXAMPLE 3. Solve: $5x^2 = 8x.$

SOLUTION. 1. Subtract $8x$: $5x^2 - 8x = 0$; $x(5x - 8) = 0.$

2. Hence, $x = 0$ or $5x - 8 = 0$; the solutions are 0 and $\frac{8}{5}$.

INCORRECT SOLUTION. Divide both sides of $5x^2 = 8x$ by x: $5x = 8.$
Then, incorrectly, we obtain $x = \frac{8}{5}$ as the only solution. In this incorrect
solution, the root $x = 0$ was lost on dividing by x.

EXAMPLE 4. Solve for x: $2a^2x^2 + 3abx - 2b^2 = 0.$

SOLUTION. 1. Factor: $(2ax - b)(ax + 2b) = 0.$

2. If $2ax - b = 0$,   *then* $2ax = b$; $x = \dfrac{b}{2a}.$

3. If $ax + 2b = 0$,   *then* $ax = -2b$; $x = -\dfrac{2b}{a}.$

EXERCISE 27

Solve for x or y or z. All other letters represent positive constants.

1. $3x^2 = 48.$ **2.** $5x^2 = 45.$ **3.** $x^2 = -4.$ **4.** $9x^2 = -4.$

5. $4x^2 = -25.$ **6.** $3x^2 = 2.$ **7.** $7x^2 = 5.$ **8.** $10x^2 = 3.$

9. $9z^2 = a.$ **10.** $4y^2 = b.$ **11.** $2ax^2 = b.$ **12.** $3bx^2 = 5.$

13. $4x^2 + 49 = 0.$ **14.** $45x^2 + 36 = 0.$ **15.** $63 + 14z^2 = 0.$

16. $9x^2 = 5 - 4x^2.$ **17.** $\frac{1}{3}x^2 - \frac{8}{15} = \frac{1}{5}x^2.$ **18.** $\frac{1}{5}x^2 - \frac{3}{4} = \frac{1}{2}x^2.$

19. $4ay^2 - 9b = 4b^2.$ **20.** $abx^2 + c^2 = b^2 + acx^2.$

21. $az^2 + \frac{1}{3}b^3 = \frac{1}{3}a^3 + bz^2.$ **22.** $\frac{1}{4}ax^2 = \frac{1}{2}bx^2 + bc.$

23. Solve $S = \frac{1}{2}gt^2$ for t.   **24.** Solve $A = \pi r^2$ for r.

If possible, solve for x or w or z by factoring.

25. $x^2 - 3x = 10.$ **26.** $y^2 - 5y = 14.$ **27.** $x^2 + x = 12.$

28. $x^2 + 3x = 28.$ **29.** $21x = 14x^2.$ **30.** $9x^2 - 144 = 0.$

31. $3x^2 - 7x = 0.$ **32.** $6x^2 = 15x.$ **33.** $5x^2 - 9x = 0.$

34. $16x^2 = 24x - 9.$ **35.** $25y^2 = 20y - 4.$ **36.** $x^2 + 6x = -9.$

37. $4y^2 + 4y = -1.$ **38.** $3x^2 + 2 = -7x.$ **39.** $2x^2 + 7x = -6.$

40. $10x + 3 + 8x^2 = 0.$ **41.** $12 - 5x^2 - 17x = 0.$

42. $6x^2 - 19x + 15 = 0.$ **43.** $16x^2 + 40x + 25 = 0.$

44. $8 - 22x + 15x^2 = 0.$ **45.** $15 - 7w - 4w^2 = 0.$

46. $2ax^2 + bx = 0.$ **47.** $3bw^2 = 2aw.$ **48.** $x^2 - ax = 6a^2.$

49. $3x^2 - bx = 2b^2.$ **50.** $4x^2 - ax = 3a^2.$ **51.** $x^2 + 4a^2 = 4ax.$

52. $3c^2z^2 - bcz = 2b^2.$ **53.** $3a^2w^2 - 7aw = 6.$ **54.** $9a^2 + x^2 = 6ax.$

55. $25a^2w^2 + 20abw + 4b^2 = 0.$ **56.** $6ax^2 - bc = 3cx - 2abx.$

57. $(x - 2)(2x + 3)(3x - 5) = 0.$ **58.** $x(x^2 - 4)(x + 5) = 0.$

59. $3x^3 - 2x^2 - 5x = 0.$ **60.** $4w^3 - 4w^2 + w = 0.$

61. $(x - 3)(x + 2) = 14.$ **62.** $(2x + 1)(x - 3) = 9.$

63. $\dfrac{5}{x + 4} - \dfrac{3}{x - 2} = 4.$ **64.** $\dfrac{2}{x - 1} - \dfrac{3}{2x + 5} = \dfrac{5}{3}.$

51. The quadratic formula

A binomial $(x^2 + px)$ becomes a *perfect square* if we add *the square of one half of the coefficient of x, or $p^2/4$*. Then,

$$x^2 + px + \frac{p^2}{4} = \left(x + \frac{p}{2}\right)^2. \tag{1}$$

ILLUSTRATION 1. To make $x^2 - 7x$ a perfect square, add $(\frac{7}{2})^2$, or $\frac{49}{4}$:

$$x^2 - 7x + \tfrac{49}{4} = (x - \tfrac{7}{2})^2. \tag{2}$$

The general quadratic equation

$$ax^2 + bx + c = 0, \tag{3}$$

where $a \neq 0$, can be solved by the following method of completing a square.

SOLUTION of (3). Subtract c: $ax^2 + bx = -c.$

Divide by a: $x^2 + \dfrac{b}{a} x = -\dfrac{c}{a}.$

Complete a square on the left by adding $(b/2a)^2$ to both sides:

$$x^2 + \frac{b}{a}x + \left(\frac{b}{2a}\right)^2 = \frac{b^2}{4a^2} - \frac{c}{a}, \quad or \quad \left(x + \frac{b}{2a}\right)^2 = \frac{b^2 - 4ac}{4a^2}.$$

Extract square roots, obtaining two equations equivalent to (3), as emphasized in Note 2 on page 82:

$$x + \frac{b}{2a} = \pm\frac{\sqrt{b^2 - 4ac}}{2a}.$$

Subtract $\dfrac{b}{2a}$: $x = -\dfrac{b}{2a} \pm \dfrac{\sqrt{b^2 - 4ac}}{2a}. \tag{4}$

Hence, if a, b, and c are any real numbers, with $a \neq 0$, we have proved that (3) is equivalent to (4), and thus has just two solutions, as follows:

$$x = \frac{-b \pm \sqrt{b^2 - 4ac}}{2a}. \tag{5}$$

We call (5) the **quadratic formula.** To employ (5) for a given equation, first clear the equation of fractions if necessary, write it in the standard form (3), and substitute the values of a, b, and c in (5).

ILLUSTRATION 2. To solve $2x^2 - 4x + 5 = 0$, we notice that $a = 2$, $b = -4$, and $c = 5$. Hence, from the quadratic formula,

$$x = \frac{4 \pm \sqrt{16 - 40}}{4} = \frac{4 \pm \sqrt{-24}}{4} = \frac{4 \pm 2i\sqrt{6}}{4} = \frac{2 \pm i\sqrt{6}}{2}.$$

ILLUSTRATION 3. The solutions of $3x^2 - 6x - 2 = 0$ are

$$x = \frac{-(-6) \pm \sqrt{(-6)^2 - 4 \cdot 3 \cdot (-2)}}{6} = \frac{6 \pm 2\sqrt{15}}{6} = \frac{3 \pm 3.873}{3},$$

or $x = 2.291$ and $x = -.291$. Table I was used.

EXAMPLE 1. Solve for x: $\qquad\qquad x^2 - 3ex + 5dx - 15de = 0.$

SOLUTION. 1. Group terms in x: $\qquad\qquad x^2 + x(-3e + 5d) - 15de = 0.$

2. In the standard notation, $a = 1$, $b = -3e + 5d$, and $c = -15de$.

Hence, $\qquad\qquad x = \dfrac{-(-3e + 5d) \pm \sqrt{(5d - 3e)^2 - 4(-15de)}}{2}.$

The radicand is $25d^2 + 30de + 9e^2$, or $(5d + 3e)^2$, and thus

$$x = \frac{-(-3e + 5d) \pm (5d + 3e)}{2};$$

$$x = \frac{3e - 5d + 5d + 3e}{2} = 3e \quad or \quad x = \frac{3e - 5d - 5d - 3e}{2} = -5d.$$

Note 1. In deriving the quadratic formula, we showed that an equation of the 2d degree in x has *just two roots* (possibly identical). This result is a special case of Theorem II on page 274, which states that an equation of degree n in a single variable has *just n roots*, with repetitions of values possible among them.

EXERCISE 28

Solve for x by completing a square, as in solving (3), *page 84.*

1. $x^2 + 3x - 4 = 0.$ 2. $x^2 - 2x = 24.$ 3. $x^2 + 2 = 4x.$
4. $2x^2 - 5 = x.$ 5. $4x^2 + 12x + 9 = 0.$ 6. $3x^2 - 5 = 14x.$

Solve for x, y, z, or w by the quadratic formula.

7. $2x^2 - 10 = x.$ 8. $6x^2 - x = 12.$ 9. $3x^2 + x = 4.$
10. $9x^2 + 4 = 12x.$ 11. $8x - 4x^2 = 1.$ 12. $6y + 1 = -6y^2.$

13. $1 = 12x - 9x^2$.

14. $81z^2 + 4 = 0$.

15. $25y^2 + 9 = 0$.

16. $2y^2 - 2y = 3$.

17. $9x^2 + 7 = 6x$.

18. $8x^2 + 7 = -8x$.

19. $15x^2 - x = 28$.

20. $4x^2 + 4x = -19$.

21. $27 + 6z = -2z^2$.

22. $4w^2 + 8w = -5$.

23. $2x^2 + .3x = .35$.

24. $x^2 - 4x = 32$.

25. $25x^2 + 20x = -4$.

26. $48 = 12x - 9x^2$.

27. $3w^2 = 9 + 2w$.

28. $4x^2 = 8x + 59$.

29. $2x^2 = 2x - 3$.

30. $15x^2 + 22x = 48$.

31. $9x^2 + 28 = 30x$.

32. $2x^2 + 10x = -13$.

33. $9x^2 + 14 = 24x$.

34. $12x^2 + 8x = 15$.

35. $10x^2 + x = 21$.

36. $16x^2 = 24x + 19$.

37. $6x^2 + 7dx = 5d^2$.

38. $ky + 3k^2 - 2y^2 = 0$.

39. $ax^2 + 2dx - 3c = 0$.

40. $2bx^2 + cx - 3a = 0$.

41. $4x^2 - 4ax + a^2 - 3b^2 = 0$.

42. $2kx^2 - 5x + 3k = 0$.

Note 1. Any quadratic equation in a single variable, x, may be solved by the quadratic formula. However, unless otherwise directed, a pure quadratic should be solved simply by extracting square roots, and a complete quadratic should be solved by factoring, if factors are easily recognized. Otherwise, a quadratic should be solved by use of the quadratic formula.

Solve for x or y or z by the most convenient method.

43. $28 - y^2 = -3y$.

44. $3x - x^2 = -40$.

45. $9x^2 + 16 = 24x$.

46. $14x^2 + x = 3$.

47. $9x^2 - 16 = 6x$.

48. $3x^2 + 3 = 4x$.

49. $6 - 10x^2 = 11x$.

50. $8x = 19 - 16x^2$.

51. $6x^2 = 13x + 28$.

52. $1 = 12x - 36x^2$.

53. $5y^2 = 4 - 3y^2$.

54. $3x^2 = 7x$.

55. $4y^2 = 12y - 17$.

56. $(x - 1)(x + 3) = 3$.

57. $25z^2 + 1 = 10z$.

58. $4x^2 = 16x - 61$.

59. $4x^2 = 4x - 37$.

60. $16y^2 + 8y = 15$.

61. $x^2 + 3cx + ax + 3ac = 0$.

62. $ax^2 + 2abx - cx = 2bc$.

63. Solve for y in terms of x: $6y^2 - 8xy = 9y - 3x - 2x^2$.

64. Solve for x in terms of y: $x^2 - 3x + 2xy + 7y = 3y^2 + 4$.

65. Solve for x in terms of y in Problem 63.

66. Solve for y in terms of x in Problem 64.

Solve each problem by introducing an equation in just one unknown.

67. Separate 27 into two parts whose product is 92.

68. The base of a triangle is 4 feet shorter than its altitude, and the area of the triangle is 126 square feet. Find the base and the altitude.

69. Find two consecutive integers whose product is 506.

70. Find the length of a side of an equilateral triangle whose altitude is 3 feet shorter than a side.

71. Find the side of a square whose diagonal is 5 feet longer than a side.

72. An airplane flew 660 miles with the wind, and then took 40 minutes longer for the return flight against this wind. If the plane flies 200 miles per hour in still air, find the speed of the wind.

52. Graphical solution of an equation

At a point where the graph of a function $f(x)$ meets the x-axis, we have $f(x) = 0$. This remark leads us to a method for obtaining approximate values of the real roots of $f(x) = 0$.

SUMMARY. *Graphical method to obtain the real roots, if any, of an equation in one variable, x.*

1. *Transpose terms, to write the equation in the form $f(x) = 0$.*
2. *Graph the function $f(x)$, that is, graph the equation $y = f(x)$.*
3. *The x-intercepts of the graph are the real roots of $f(x) = 0$.*

In graphing a quadratic function, we have no license to alter it by multiplication. However, before solving a quadratic equation in x graphically, we may, if desired, clear of fractions; divide out any common factor; make the coefficient of x^2 positive in the final form. The last operation would cause the resulting graph to be concave upward.

If the roots of $f(x) = 0$ are *imaginary*, this would be indicated by the fact that the graph of $f(x)$ would *not* meet the x-axis.

In order to solve a quadratic equation

$$ax^2 + bx + c = 0 \tag{1}$$

graphically, that is, to obtain its real roots, if any, or to show that the roots are imaginary, we graph the following related equation in two variables (x, y):

$$y = ax^2 + bx + c. \tag{2}$$

I. *The parabola (2) cuts the x-axis in two points if and only if (1) has unequal real roots.*

II. *The parabola touches the x-axis in just one point, or is tangent to the x-axis, if and only if the roots of (1) are equal.*

III. *The parabola does not meet the x-axis, if and only if (1) has imaginary roots.*

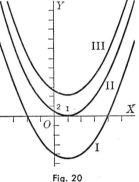

Fig. 20

ILLUSTRATION 1. To solve $x^2 - 2x - 8 = 0$ graphically, we graph the equation $y = x^2 - 2x - 8$, by the method of page 79. The graph is the parabola (I) in Figure 20, which shows that the roots of the given equation are $x = 4$ and $x = -2$. Similarly, we solve $x^2 - 2x + 1 = 0$ by use of (II) in Figure 20; the equation is seen to have equal roots $x = 1$, since the parabola is tangent to the x-axis where $x = 1$. To solve $x^2 - 2x + 5 = 0$ graphically, we draw the graph of $y = x^2 - 2x + 5$, which is (III) in Figure 20; this curve does not meet the x-axis and hence $x^2 - 2x + 5 = 0$ has imaginary roots.

EXERCISE 29

Find the real roots of the equation graphically.

1. $3x - 7 = 0$.
2. $x^2 - 6x = 0$.
3. $x^2 + 8x = 0$.
4. $x^2 + 2x - 3 = 0$.
5. $x^2 + 4x + 4 = 0$.
6. $x^2 + 6x + 12 = 0$.
7. $x^2 - 2x + 4 = 0$.
8. $4x^2 + 9 = 12x$.
9. $x = 6 - 2x^2$.
10. $4x - x^2 = 1$.
11. $1 = 8x - 4x^2$.
12. $x^2 + 6x + 7 = 0$.
13. $\frac{1}{3}x^2 - x + \frac{5}{6} = 0$.
14. $\frac{2}{3}z^2 - \frac{4}{3}z = 1$.
15. $4x^2 - 4x = 7$.
16. $\frac{1}{6}x^2 = \frac{4}{3}x - 4$.
17. $x^2 + x + \frac{1}{4} = 0$.
18. $x^2 + 2x + 2 = 0$.

19. Draw the parabola $y = x^2 - 6x + 9$. Then, by use of auxiliary lines parallel to the x-axis, solve the following equations graphically.

$$x^2 - 6x + 9 = 0; \qquad x^2 - 6x + 9 = 5; \qquad x^2 - 6x + 2 = 0.$$

53. Character of the roots

Let r and s represent the roots of $ax^2 + bx + c = 0$, where the constants a, b, and c are real numbers and $a \neq 0$. Then, from the quadratic formula, we may let

$$r = \frac{-b + \sqrt{b^2 - 4ac}}{2a}; \qquad s = \frac{-b - \sqrt{b^2 - 4ac}}{2a}. \qquad (1)$$

If $b^2 - 4ac = 0$, then $r = s = -b/2a$. If $b^2 - 4ac > 0$, then $\sqrt{b^2 - 4ac}$ is *real* and *not zero;* hence, r and s are *real and unequal*, because one root involves $+\sqrt{b^2 - 4ac}$ and the other involves $-\sqrt{b^2 - 4ac}$. If $b^2 - 4ac < 0$, then the radical in (1) is *imaginary*, and the roots are *imaginary and unequal.* The preceding possibilities, and corresponding facts, are listed below.

THE ROOTS OF $ax^2 + bx + c = 0$	THE VALUE OF $b^2 - 4ac$	THE GRAPH OF $ax^2 + bx + c$
real and unequal	$b^2 - 4ac > 0$	cuts x-axis in two points
real and equal	$b^2 - 4ac = 0$	is tangent to x-axis
imaginary and unequal	$b^2 - 4ac < 0$	does not touch x-axis

If a, b, and c are *rational numbers*, the roots r and s are *rational* if and only if $\sqrt{b^2 - 4ac}$ is real and is a *rational number*, or *the roots are* **rational** *if and only if* $(b^2 - 4ac)$ *is a* **perfect square.**

We shall call $b^2 - 4ac$ the **discriminant** of the *quadratic equation* $ax^2 + bx + c = 0$, or of the *quadratic function* $ax^2 + bx + c$. As soon as we know the value of $b^2 - 4ac$, we can tell the general character of the roots of the equation without solving it, and the general nature of the graph of the function without graphing it.

Before computing the discriminant of a quadratic equation, simplify it by clearing of fractions and combining terms.

ILLUSTRATIONS OF THE USE OF THE DISCRIMINANT

EQUATION	DISCRIMINANT	HENCE, THE ROOTS ARE
$4x^2 - 3x + 5 = 0$	$(-3)^2 - 4 \cdot 4 \cdot 5 = -71$	*imaginary; unequal*
$4x^2 - 4x + 1 = 0$	$(-4)^2 - 4 \cdot 4 = 0$	*real; equal; rational*
$4x^2 - 3x - 5 = 0$	$(-3)^2 + 4 \cdot 4 \cdot 5 = 89$	*real; unequal; irrational*
$x^2 - 2x - 3 = 0$	$(-2)^2 - 4(-3) = 16 = 4^2$	*real; unequal; rational*

EXAMPLE 1. State what you can learn about the graph of the quadratic function $-3x^2 + 5x - 6$ *without* graphing.

SOLUTION. 1. The discriminant of the function is $25 - 72 = -47$.

2. Hence, the graph would not touch the x-axis. We notice that the coefficient of x^2 is negative. Thus, the graph is a parabola with its axis perpendicular to the x-axis, concave downward. Since the graph does not touch the x-axis, the parabola lies entirely below the x-axis.

EXAMPLE 2. Find the values of k for which the following equation in x has equal roots: $\qquad kx^2 + 2x^2 - 3kx + k = 0.$

SOLUTION. 1. Group in standard form: $\qquad (k+2)x^2 - 3kx + k = 0.$

Hence, the standard coefficients are $a = k + 2$, $b = -3k$, and $c = k$.

2. If the roots are equal, the discriminant $b^2 - 4ac$ is zero:

$\qquad discriminant = (-3k)^2 - 4(k+2)(k) = 0;\quad or\quad 5k^2 - 8k = 0.$

3. Hence, $\qquad k(5k - 8) = 0;\quad k = 0\quad or\quad k = \frac{8}{5}.$

If two imaginary numbers differ only in the *signs of the coefficients of their imaginary parts*, then the given numbers are called **conjugate imaginary numbers,** and either is the *conjugate* of the other.

ILLUSTRATION 1. The conjugate of $(3 + 5i)$ is $(3 - 5i)$.

When the roots of a quadratic equation are imaginary, *these roots are conjugate imaginary numbers*, because the imaginary parts come from $\pm \sqrt{b^2 - 4ac}$ in the quadratic formula.

ILLUSTRATION 2. The roots of $x^2 + 4x + 5 = 0$ are

$$x = \frac{-4 \pm \sqrt{16 - 20}}{2} = -2 \pm i,\ conjugate\ imaginaries.$$

54. Factored form of a quadratic function

We have seen that, sometimes, a quadratic equation $f(x) = 0$ can be solved by first factoring the function $f(x)$. Now, we shall find that this process can be reversed, and that we can obtain factors for $f(x)$ by first solving the equation $f(x) = 0$.

THEOREM I. *If r and s are the roots of $ax^2 + bx + c = 0$, then*

the sum of the roots is equal to $-\dfrac{b}{a}$, $\qquad r + s = -\dfrac{b}{a};$ $\qquad$ (1)

the product of the roots is equal to $\dfrac{c}{a}$, $\qquad rs = \dfrac{c}{a}.$ $\qquad$ (2)

Proof. From $\qquad r = \dfrac{-b + \sqrt{b^2 - 4ac}}{2a}$ *and* $\quad s = \dfrac{-b - \sqrt{b^2 - 4ac}}{2a},$

we obtain $\qquad\qquad\qquad\qquad r + s = \dfrac{-2b}{2a} = -\dfrac{b}{a};$

$$rs = \frac{-b + \sqrt{b^2 - 4ac}}{2a} \cdot \frac{-b - \sqrt{b^2 - 4ac}}{2a};$$

$$rs = \frac{(-b)^2 - (b^2 - 4ac)}{4a^2} = \frac{4ac}{4a^2} = \frac{c}{a}.$$

ILLUSTRATION 1. For $3x^2 - 5x + 7 = 0$, we find $r + s = \frac{5}{3}$ and $rs = \frac{7}{3}$.

THEOREM II. *If r and s are the roots of $ax^2 + bx + c = 0$, then*

$$ax^2 + bx + c = a(x - r)(x - s). \qquad (3)$$

Proof. $\qquad\qquad ax^2 + bx + c = a\left(x^2 + \dfrac{b}{a}x + \dfrac{c}{a}\right)$

[From (1) and (2)] $\qquad = a[x^2 - (r + s)x + rs] = a(x - r)(x - s).$

By use of (3), we can form a quadratic equation having specified roots, with the constant a in (3) chosen to suit our convenience.

ILLUSTRATION 2. A quadratic equation whose roots are 5 and -3 is

$$(x + 3)(x - 5) = 0, \quad or \quad x^2 - 2x - 15 = 0. \qquad\qquad [a = 1 \text{ in } (3)]$$

ILLUSTRATION 3. A quadratic equation whose roots are $\frac{1}{2}(2 \pm 3i)$ is

$$a[x - \tfrac{1}{2}(2 + 3i)][x - \tfrac{1}{2}(2 - 3i)] = 0.$$

To eliminate fractions, we use $a = 4 = 2 \cdot 2$, and group terms to exhibit the *sum* and *difference* of two numbers. Finally, we use $i^2 = -1$.

$$2\left(x - \frac{2 + 3i}{2}\right) \cdot 2\left(x - \frac{2 - 3i}{2}\right) = (2x - 2 - 3i)(2x - 2 + 3i) = 0;$$

$$[(2x - 2) - 3i][(2x - 2) + 3i] = 0, \quad or \quad (2x - 2)^2 - 9i^2 = 0;$$
$$4x^2 - 8x + 4 + 9 = 0, \quad or \quad 4x^2 - 8x + 13 = 0.$$

EXAMPLE 1. Factor $6x^2 - 23x + 20$ by first solving an equation.

SOLUTION. 1. Solve $6x^2 - 23x + 20 = 0$ by the quadratic formula:

$$x = \frac{23 \pm \sqrt{49}}{12} = \frac{23 \pm 7}{12}; \quad x = \frac{5}{2} \quad or \quad x = \frac{4}{3}.$$

2. From (3), $\qquad 6x^2 - 23x + 20 = 6(x - \tfrac{5}{2})(x - \tfrac{4}{3}) = (2x - 5)(3x - 4).$

Formula (3) states that *any quadratic function of x can be expressed as a product of factors which are linear in x.* However, these factors involve *rational, irrational,* or *imaginary* numbers according as the roots *r* and *s* have corresponding characters. In particular, the facts about rational roots prove the following result.

If a, b, and c are rational numbers, with a ≠ 0, $ax^2 + bx + c$ can be expressed as a product of real linear factors with rational coefficients when and only when the discriminant $b^2 - 4ac$ is a perfect square.

ILLUSTRATION 4. To determine whether or not $12x^2 + 12x - 105$ has linear factors with rational coefficients, we compute the

$$discriminant = 12^2 + 48(105) = 5184 = 72^2. \qquad \text{(Table I)}$$

Hence, $12x^2 + 12x - 105$ can be factored as specified. By the method of Example 1, we find

$$12x^2 + 12x - 105 = (6x - 15)(2x + 7).$$

EXERCISE 30

Compute the discriminant and tell the character of the roots, without solving.

1. $y^2 - 7y + 10 = 0$.   2. $9x^2 + 12x + 4 = 0$.   3. $25x^2 + 1 = -10x$.

4. $x^2 + 2x - 2 = 0$.   5. $4x^2 + 4x = 3$.   6. $1 = 2x - 2x^2$.

7. $3x^2 - 5x + 7 = 0$.   8. $5x^2 + 1 = 2x$.   9. $3 + 5x^2 = 0$.

Solve graphically; check the graph by computing the discriminant.

10. $x^2 - 4x = 6$.   11. $x^2 + 7 = 4x$.   12. $4x^2 + 4x = 1$.

Compute the discriminant of the function and, without graphing, state all facts which you can learn about its graph.

13. $4x^2 - 12x + 9$.   14. $3x^2 - 4x$.   15. $4x^2 + 5x + 7$.

16. $2x^2 - 3x - 5$.   17. $-3x^2 + 5x - 7$.   18. $-3x^2 - 2x + 4$.

By use of the discriminant, find the values of the constant k for which the equation in the variable x will have equal roots.

19. $4x^2 - 3kx + 1 = 0$.   20. $x^2 - kx^2 - 5kx - 3k = 0$.

21. $kx^2 + 3kx + 5 = 0$.   22. $kx + x^2 + kx^2 - 2x = 4$.

Find the values of the constant k for which the graph of the function of x will be tangent to the x-axis.

23. $5x^2 - 2kx + k$.   24. $x^2 - 3x - k - kx$.

With x as the variable, find the sum and the product of the roots without solving the equation.

25. $x^2 + 3x - 5 = 0$.   26. $5x = 2x^2 + 7$.   27. $3x^2 = 4x - 6$.

28. $2 - 5x = 2x^2$.   29. $4 - 3x = 7x^2$.   30. $13 - 2x^2 = 0$.

31. $cx^2 - dx = h$.   32. $ax^2 = 2x + b$.   33. $3x^2 = cx - a$.

34. $3x^2 + 2x - ax + c = 0$.   35. $3x^2 + bx^2 - 5x + d = 0$.

Form a quadratic equation with integral coefficients having the given roots.

36. $-2; \; 5.$ **37.** $\frac{3}{4}; \; -2.$ **38.** $-\frac{3}{7}; \; -\frac{2}{3}.$ **39.** $\pm 3\sqrt{2}.$

40. $\pm 3i.$ **41.** $\pm \frac{3}{4}i.$ **42.** $\frac{5}{6}; \; \frac{5}{6}.$ **43.** $\pm \sqrt{-20}.$

44. $-3 \pm i.$ **45.** $3 \pm 5i.$ **46.** $-\frac{2}{3} \pm \frac{2}{3}i.$ **47.** $2 \pm 3\sqrt{2}.$

48. $\frac{1}{2}(3 \pm 2\sqrt{2}).$ **49.** $\frac{1}{5}(-3 \pm 4i).$ **50.** $d \pm 3bi.$

Find the value of the constant h under the given condition about the solutions for the unknown x.

51. One root is -2: $2hx^2 - 4x + 3h = 0.$

52. The sum of the roots is -3; $3hx^2 - 2x + 5xh = 3.$

    Hint. From (1) on page 90, $\dfrac{2 - 5h}{3h} = -3.$

53. The sum of the roots is 2: $2x^2 - hx^2 + 4x + 5h = 0.$

54. The product of the roots is -4: $2hx^2 + 3x^2 + 4x - 5h = 0.$

55. The product of the roots is 8: $3x^2 + 5x + 3h - 5 = 0.$

★*Factor, after solving a related equation by the quadratic formula.*

56. $12x^2 + x - 35.$ **57.** $27x^2 - 57x - 40.$ **58.** $12x^2 - 61x + 60.$

59. $30x^2 - 19x - 140.$ **60.** $30 - 19x - 28x^2.$ **61.** $24x^2 + 101x + 70.$

★*Without factoring, or solving any equation, determine whether or not the function has real linear factors with rational coefficients.*

62. $12x^2 - 7x - 10.$ **63.** $9x^2 + 6x + 7.$ **64.** $12x^2 - 11x - 36.$

65. $16x^2 - 16x + 13.$ **66.** $45x^2 - 33x - 70.$ **67.** $25x^2 - 30x - 3.$

★*Prove the following theorems about roots of $ax^2 + bx + c = 0$, where $a \neq 0$.*

68. If one root is the negative of the other, then $b = 0$.

69. If $b = 0$, then one root is the negative of the other.

Note 1. Problem 69 is the *converse* of Problem 68. If the words *and conversely* had been added to Problem 68, this would have required us to prove both theorems as now stated in the two problems.

70. If $b = 0$ and $c = 0$, then both roots are zero, *and conversely.*

71. If a and c are opposite in sign, then one root is positive and one is negative, *and conversely.*

72. If a and c are opposite in sign, the roots are real and unequal.

55. Equations in quadratic form

An equation in a variable x is said to be in the *quadratic form* in a certain function of x in case, after substitution of a new variable, y, for the general value of this function, the equation becomes a *quadratic in y*. Equations in quadratic form can be solved by use of methods applicable to quadratic equations, with supplementary details.

Note 1. Hereafter, unless otherwise specified in directions given by the text or the instructor, solutions of equations may be left in *radical form*, without substitution of decimal values from Table I.

EXAMPLE 1. Solve: $\qquad x^4 - 5x^2 + 6 = 0.$ $\qquad$ (1)

SOLUTION. 1. The equation is in the quadratic form in x^2 because, if we let $y = x^2$, the equation becomes $y^2 - 5y + 6 = 0$.

2. Without using y, we factor in (1):

$$(x^2 - 3)(x^2 - 2) = 0. \qquad (2)$$

If $x^2 - 3 = 0$, then $x = \pm \sqrt{3}$; if $x^2 - 2 = 0$, then $x = \pm \sqrt{2}$. Hence, (1) has four solutions, $\pm \sqrt{3}$ and $\pm \sqrt{2}$.

EXAMPLE 2. Solve: $\qquad 2x^{-4} - x^{-2} - 3 = 0.$ $\qquad$ (3)

SOLUTION. 1. Let $y = x^{-2}$. Then, $y^2 = x^{-4}$ and (3) becomes

$$2y^2 - y - 3 = 0, \quad or \quad (2y - 3)(y + 1) = 0. \qquad (4)$$

Hence, the solutions of (4) are $y = -1$ and $y = \frac{3}{2}$.

2. If $y = -1$, then $\quad x^{-2} = -1; \quad \dfrac{1}{x^2} = -1; \quad x^2 = -1, \quad or \quad x = \pm i$.

3. If $y = \dfrac{3}{2}$, then $\quad x^{-2} = \dfrac{3}{2}; \quad \dfrac{1}{x^2} = \dfrac{3}{2}; \quad x^2 = \dfrac{2}{3}; \quad x = \pm \dfrac{1}{3}\sqrt{6}$.

Hence, (3) has the solutions $\pm i$ and $\pm \frac{1}{3}\sqrt{6}$.

Comment. We could solve (3) by factoring without using y. Thus,

$$2x^{-4} - x^{-2} - 3 = (2x^{-2} - 3)(x^{-2} + 1) = 0; \quad x^{-2} = -1 \quad or \quad x^{-2} = \frac{3}{2}.$$

EXAMPLE 3. Solve: $\qquad (x^2 + 3x)^2 - 3x^2 - 9x - 4 = 0.$ $\qquad$ (5)

INCOMPLETE SOLUTION. 1. Group terms:

$$(x^2 + 3x)^2 - 3(x^2 + 3x) - 4 = 0.$$

2. Let $y = x^2 + 3x$. Then, $y^2 - 3y - 4 = 0$; the solutions here are $y = 4$ and $y = -1$. Finally, we would obtain the four roots of (5) by solving

$$x^2 + 3x = 4 \quad and \quad x^2 + 3x = -1.$$

In solving an equation of the form $x^k = A$ where k is a positive integer greater than 2, we agree at present that we desire only *real* solutions *unless otherwise specified*. The real solutions, if any, of $x^k = A$ are the real kth roots of A, as discussed on page 46.

EXAMPLE 4. Obtain *all* roots by use of factoring: $\qquad 8x^3 + 125 = 0.$

SOLUTION. 1. Factor: $\qquad (2x + 5)(4x^2 - 10x + 25) = 0.$

2. Hence, $\qquad 2x + 5 = 0, \quad or \quad 4x^2 - 10x + 25 = 0.$

3. The solutions are

$$x = -\tfrac{5}{2} \quad and \quad x = \tfrac{1}{8}(10 \pm \sqrt{100 - 400}) = \tfrac{5}{4} \pm \tfrac{5}{4}i\sqrt{3}.$$

EXAMPLE 5. Find the four 4th roots of 625.

SOLUTION. 1. If x is any 4th root of 625, then $x^4 = 625$.

2. Solve for x: $\qquad\qquad\qquad\qquad x^4 - 625 = 0$;

$$(x^2 - 25)(x^2 + 25) = 0; \quad x^2 = 25 \quad or \quad x^2 = -25.$$

Hence, $x = \pm 5$ and $x = \pm 5i$ are the desired 4th roots of 625.

In this section the student has met further illustrations of the truth of the theorem that *an integral rational equation of degree n in a single variable x has exactly n roots* (we admit the possibility that some of the roots may be equal). Also, we have seen illustrations of the related fact that, if n is a positive integer, every number $H \neq 0$ has exactly n distinct nth roots, some or all of which may be imaginary (to be proved on page 265).

EXERCISE 31

Solve for x or y or z. Factor, or change to a quadratic in a new variable.

1. $x^4 - 3x^2 + 2 = 0$.   **2.** $x^4 = 5x^2 - 4$.   **3.** $x^4 - 8x^2 + 16 = 0$.

4. $4x^4 + 9 = 13x^2$.   **5.** $x^4 = 13x^2 - 36$.   **6.** $4x^4 - 5x^2 + 1 = 0$.

7. $y^4 - 2y^2 - 3 = 0$.   **8.** $z^4 + z^2 = 12$.   **9.** $x^4 - 16 = 0$.

10. $16z^4 - 81 = 0$.   **11.** $8y^6 + 7y^3 = 1$.   **12.** $x^6 + 27 = 28x^3$.

13. $36x^{-4} = 13x^{-2} - 1$.   **14.** $4 - 29y^{-2} + 25y^{-4} = 0$.

15. $9x^{-4} + 5x^{-2} - 4 = 0$.   **16.** $6y^{-4} - 7y^{-2} - 5 = 0$.

17. $27y^6 - 35y^3 + 8 = 0$.   **18.** $(x^2 + 2x)^2 - 2(x^2 + 2x) = 3$.

19. $(2x^2 - x)^2 = 4(2x^2 - x) - 3$.   **20.** $(x^2 + 2x)^2 - 3x^2 - 6x = 18$.

21. $x^4 - 2x^3 + x^2 - 3x^2 + 3x - 18 = 0$.

★*Find all roots.*

22. $x^3 - 8 = 0$.   **23.** $8x^3 = 27$.   **24.** $x^3 + 64 = 0$.   **25.** $81x^4 = 16$.

26. $625x^4 - 81 = 0$.   **27.** $125 + 8y^3 = 0$.   **28.** $27 + 125x^3 = 0$.

★*Find the three cube roots of each number.*

29. -8.   **30.** 125.   **31.** -1.   **32.** 1.   **33.** $\frac{1}{8}$.   **34.** $-\frac{1}{27}$.

★*Find the four 4th roots of each number.*

35. 1.   **36.** 16.   **37.** 625.   **38.** 81.   **39.** $\frac{16}{81}$.   **40.** $\frac{81}{256}$.

56. Irrational equations

Let $M = N$ represent any equation. On squaring both sides, we obtain $M^2 = N^2$, which is equivalent to $M = N$ and $M = -N$. Hence, the solutions of $M^2 = N^2$ consist of all solutions of $M = N$ together with those of $M = -N$.

ILLUSTRATION 1. $x = 5$ is the only root of $\qquad\qquad x - 3 = 2$. $\qquad$ (1)

On squaring both sides, we obtain $\qquad\qquad\qquad\qquad (x - 3)^2 = 4$. $\qquad$ (2)

On solving (2) for x we find $\quad x - 3 = \pm 2; \quad$ hence, $\quad x = 5 \quad or \quad x = 1$.

Therefore, (2) has the root $x = 1$ besides the root $x = 5$ of (1).

If an operation on an equation in x produces a new equation which is satisfied by values of x which are not roots of the given equation, we name such values (as on page 39) **extraneous roots.** From the preceding discussion, we observe that, if both members of an equation are *squared*, extraneous roots *may* be introduced. The statement just made is true also if both members are raised to any integral power.

ILLUSTRATION 2. In Illustration 1, $x = 1$ is an extraneous root.

An *irrational equation* is one in which the variables occur under radical signs or in expressions with fractional exponents.

EXAMPLE 1. Solve for x in the following equations (a) and (b).

(a) $2x - 2 = \sqrt{2x^2 + 4}.$	(b) $2x - 2 = -\sqrt{2x^2 + 4}.$
SOLUTION. 1. Square both sides: $$4x^2 - 8x + 4 = 2x^2 + 4.$$ 2. $2x^2 - 8x = 0;\ 2x(x - 4) = 0;$ $$x = 0 \quad or \quad x = 4.$$ TEST. Substitute $x = 0$ in (a): Does $0 - 2 = \sqrt{4}$? Or, does $$-2 = 2?\ \textbf{No.}$$ Substitute $x = 4$ in (a): Does $8 - 2 = \sqrt{36}$? **Yes.** $x = 0$ is *not*, and $x = 4$ *is* a root.	SOLUTION. 1. Square both sides: $$4x^2 - 8x + 4 = 2x^2 + 4.$$ 2. $2x^2 - 8x = 0;\ 2x(x - 4) = 0;$ $$x = 0 \quad or \quad x = 4.$$ TEST. Substitute $x = 0$ in (b): Does $0 - 2 = -\sqrt{4}$? **Yes.** Substitute $x = 4$ in (b): Does $8 - 2 = -\sqrt{36}$? Or, does $$6 = -6?\ \textbf{No.}$$ $x = 4$ is *not*, and $x = 0$ *is* a root.

Comment. We met the extraneous roots 0 in solving (a) and 4 in solving (b). The test of the values obtained in Step 2 in either solution was necessary in order to *reject* these extraneous roots. The necessity for the test is shown also by the fact that, although (a) and (b) are *different equations*, all distinction between them is lost after squaring.

SUMMARY. *Solution of an equation involving radicals.*

1. *Transpose the most complicated radical to one member and all other terms to the other side.*

2. *If the most complicated radical is a square root, square both members; if a cube root, cube both members; etc.*

3. *Repeat Steps 1 and 2 with the effort to eliminate all radicals involving the unknowns. Then, solve the resulting equation.*

4. *Test each value obtained in Step 3 by substitution in the given equation to determine which values are roots.*

Note 1. Recall that, if A is positive, then $\sqrt{A}$ or $A^{\frac{1}{2}}$ represents the *positive* square root of A, and $\sqrt[n]{A^m}$ or $A^{\frac{m}{n}}$ represents only the *principal* nth root of A^m.

EXAMPLE 2. Solve: $(x-2)^{\frac{1}{2}} - \sqrt{2x+5} = 3.$

SOLUTION. 1. $\sqrt{x-2} = 3 + \sqrt{2x+5}.$

2. Square: $x-2 = 9 + 6\sqrt{2x+5} + 2x + 5.$

3. Simplify: $-x - 16 = 6\sqrt{2x+5}.$

4. Square: $x^2 + 32x + 256 = 36(2x+5);$

$$x^2 - 40x + 76 = 0; \quad (x-38)(x-2) = 0.$$

Possible roots of the given equation are $x = 38$ and $x = 2$.

TEST. Substitute $x = 2$ and $x = 38$ in the original equation:

$x = 2$: does $\sqrt{2-2} - \sqrt{4+5} = 3$, or does $-3 = 3$? **No.**

$x = 38$: does $\sqrt{38-2} - \sqrt{76+5} = 3$, or does $6 - 9 = 3$? **No.**

Hence, neither $x = 2$ nor $x = 38$ is a root. Thus, there are *no solutions.*

★EXAMPLE 3. Find all real roots of $y^{\frac{3}{2}} = 8$.

SOLUTION. $(y^{\frac{3}{2}})^2 = 8^2 = (2^3)^2 = 2^6,$ *or* $y^3 = 2^6;$ $y = (2^6)^{\frac{1}{3}} = 2^2 = 4.$

Since $y^{\frac{3}{2}}$ represents the positive square root of y^3, a test of $y = 4$ in $y^{\frac{3}{2}} = 8$ shows that $y = 4$ is a solution.

EXERCISE 32

Solve for x or y or z. Assume that no radical is imaginary valued.

1. $\sqrt{2-3x} = 4.$ 2. $\sqrt{3+2x} = 5.$ 3. $\sqrt{x+4} = -1.$

4. $\sqrt{2x-1} = -3.$ 5. $\sqrt[3]{3+4z} = 3.$ 6. $\sqrt[3]{3x-1} = 2.$

7. $\sqrt[3]{3-2y} = 2.$ 8. $\sqrt[4]{2z+5} = 1.$ 9. $(2+3x)^{\frac{1}{2}} = 4.$

10. $(3+2x)^{\frac{1}{3}} = -2.$ 11. $7x = 3\sqrt{2}.$ 12. $(3x-1)^{\frac{1}{2}} = -4.$

13. $5\sqrt{2} + 3z = 0.$ 14. $\sqrt{3x} + 3 = 2x.$ 15. $5x^2 + x\sqrt{3} = 0.$

16. $\sqrt[3]{z^2 + 2z} = 2.$ 17. $\sqrt[4]{y^2 - 6y} = 2.$ 18. $3y\sqrt{2} - 4y^2 = 0.$

19. $\sqrt{x+5} - 1 = \sqrt{x}.$ 20. $\sqrt{3x+1} = \sqrt{x} - 1.$

21. $\sqrt{2x-2} - \sqrt{4x+3} = 2.$ 22. $\sqrt{7-4x} - \sqrt{3-2x} = 1.$

23. $\sqrt{3+3x} + 3\sqrt{x-1} = 6.$ 24. $\sqrt{3+2x} - (3-2x)^{\frac{1}{2}} = \sqrt{2x}.$

25. $\sqrt{3-x} - \sqrt{3+3x} = 2\sqrt{3x-2}.$ 26. $\sqrt{3x+2a} = 3\sqrt{x} - \sqrt{2a}.$

27. $\sqrt{2x} + \sqrt{6x+4b} = 2\sqrt{4x+b}.$ 28. $\sqrt{2z-a} + \sqrt{4z+3a} = \sqrt{5a}.$

29. $l = \pi r \sqrt{r^2 + y^2}.$

★*Find all real roots. If the equation is in quadratic form, solve by changing to a quadratic in a new variable.*

30. $4x^{\frac{2}{3}} + 7x^{\frac{1}{3}} = 2.$ 31. $2z = 7z^{\frac{1}{2}} - 3.$ 32. $3x + 2\sqrt{x} = 1.$

SOLUTION *of Problem* 30. Let $y = x^{\frac{1}{3}}$. Then $y^2 = x^{\frac{2}{3}}$, and we obtain $4y^2 + 7y - 2 = 0$, whose solutions are $y = -2$ and $y = \frac{1}{4}$. From $y = -2$, we find $-2 = \sqrt[3]{x}$ and hence $x = -8$. If $y = \frac{1}{4}$, then $x = \frac{1}{64}$.

33. $8y - 2y^{\frac{1}{2}} = 3.$ 34. $2x^{\frac{1}{2}} = 7x^{\frac{1}{4}} - 6.$ 35. $3x^{\frac{1}{2}} = 13x^{\frac{1}{4}} - 4.$

36. $3x^{\frac{2}{3}} = 20 - 7x^{\frac{1}{3}}.$ 37. $4x^{\frac{2}{3}} = 12x^{\frac{1}{3}} - 9.$ 38. $2x^{\frac{2}{3}} = 15 - 7x^{\frac{1}{3}}.$

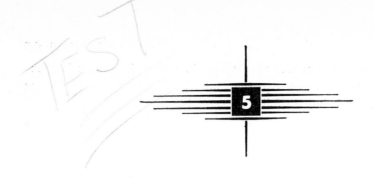

Systems of Equations

57. Solution of a system of two linear equations

In dealing with a system of equations in certain variables, if our objective is *the solution of the system*, sometimes we shall refer to the *variables* as *unknowns*. Then, we look upon each equation as a relation between *unknown values of the variables*, where we seek to find these unknowns. Whenever we speak of the graph of one of the equations, clarity demands that we refer to the literal numbers as variables.

A *solution* of a system of two equations in two variables x and y is a pair of values (x, y) which satisfy both equations. If a system has a solution, we say that the system is, or its equations are, **consistent.** If a system has no solution, we say that the equations of the system are **inconsistent,** or that it is an inconsistent system.

To solve a system of equations means to find all of its solutions. To solve a system of two equations in the variables x and y graphically, we *graph the two equations on the same coordinate system.* Then, the real solutions of the system are the sets of coordinates (x, y) of the points of intersection, if any, of the graphs. The graphs do not intersect when and only when (a) all solutions of the system are imaginary, or (b) the system has no solution, real or imaginary.

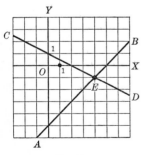

Fig. 21

EXAMPLE 1. Solve graphically:

$$\begin{cases} x - y = 5, & (1) \\ x + 2y = 2. & (2) \end{cases}$$

SOLUTION. 1. In Figure 21, AB is the graph of (1) and CD is the graph of (2). Hence, the point of intersection, E, of AB and CD is the only point whose coordinates satisfy both equations.

2. E has the coordinates $(4, -1)$. Hence, $(x = 4, y = -1)$ is the only solution of the system. These values check in (1) and (2). As a rule, however, a graphical solution gives only approximate results.

97

Usually a system of two linear equations in two variables has just one solution and the graphs of the equations intersect in just one point, as was the case in Example 1, but the following special cases occur.

A. *The graphs of the equations are parallel lines if and only if the system has no solution, and thus the equations are* **inconsistent.**

B. *The graphs of the equations are the same line if and only if each solution of either equation is also a solution of the other equation, and hence the system has infinitely many solutions. In this case the equations are* **consistent** *and also are said to be* **dependent** *equations.*

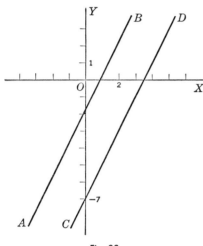

Fig. 22

EXAMPLE 2. Solve graphically:

$$\begin{cases} 6x - 3y = 5, & (3) \\ 2x - y = 7. & (4) \end{cases}$$

SOLUTION. 1. The graph of (3) is AB, and the graph of (4) is CD in Figure 22. (The graphs *appear* to be parallel, but *this must be proved.*)

2. In the slope-intercept form, (3) becomes $y = 2x - \frac{5}{3}$, and (4) becomes $y = 2x - 7$. Both graphs have slope 2, and hence are *parallel*, but *not identical*. Therefore, the system has no solution, or (3) and (4) are *inconsistent.*

We may solve a system of two linear equations by elimination, by addition or subtraction, as follows.

1. *In each equation, multiply both members, if necessary, by a properly chosen number in order to obtain two equations in which the coefficients of one of the unknowns have the same absolute value. Then add, or subtract, corresponding sides of the two new equations so as to eliminate one unknown.*

2. *Solve the equation, just obtained, for the unknown in it; substitute the result in one of the given equations to find the other unknown.*

EXAMPLE 3. Solve for x and y:

$$\begin{cases} 4x + 5y = 6, & (5) \\ 2x + 3y = 4. & (6) \end{cases}$$

SOLUTION. 1. Multiply in (5) by 3: $12x + 15y = 18.$ (7)

2. Multiply in (6) by 5: $10x + 15y = 20.$ (8)

3. Subtract, (8) from (7): $2x = -2; \quad x = -1.$ (9)

4. On substituting $x = -1$ in (6) we obtain

$$3y = 4 + 2 \quad or \quad y = 2.$$

5. The solution of the system is $(x = -1, y = 2)$.

↯2/

EXAMPLE 4. Solve for x and y:
$$\begin{cases} ax + by = e, & (10) \\ cx + dy = f. & (11) \end{cases}$$

SOLUTION. 1. Multiply by d in (10): $\qquad adx + bdy = de.$ $\qquad (12)$

Multiply by b in (11): $\qquad bcx + bdy = bf.$ $\qquad (13)$

Subtract, (13) from (12): $\qquad x(ad - bc) = de - bf.$ $\qquad (14)$

Assume that $ad - bc \neq 0$, and divide by $ad - bc$ in (14):

$$x = \frac{de - bf}{ad - bc}. \qquad (15)$$

2. By similar steps, $\qquad y = \dfrac{af - ce}{ad - bc}.$

Note 1. In the solution of each of the preceding examples, we applied operations on the given equations in a system to obtain new equations. We have assumed implicitly that *the new systems thus obtained have the same solutions as*, or *are equivalent to*, *the given system.* Let us investigate this matter. Suppose that $(A = B, C = D)$ represent a given system, in two variables (x, y) for concreteness. On multiplying both sides of the first equation by $k \neq 0$, and of the second by $h \neq 0$, we obtain $(kA = kB, hC = hD)$. If we subtract corresponding sides of these equations, we find

$$kA - hC = kB - hD. \qquad (16)$$

Now, consider the system consisting of (16) together with any one of the given equations, say $A = B$. If the numbers (x, y) satisfy $(A = B, C = D)$, then certainly (x, y) satisfy $[(16)$ *and* $A = B]$. Conversely, if (x, y) satisfy $[A = B$ *and* $(16)]$, then (x, y) satisfy

$$kA = kB, \quad and \quad kA - hC = kB - hD. \qquad (17)$$

On subtracting the sides of the equation at the right in (17) from the corresponding sides of $kA = kB$, we obtain $hC = hD$, equivalent to $C = D$. Thus, *any solution of* (17) *satisfies* $(A = B, C = D)$. Hence, the given system is equivalent to (17). All of our details in the preceding solutions were of the type just considered, that is, by *elimination*, by addition or subtraction, we replaced one equation of a given system by a new equation, like (16). Hence, our method involved *replacing a given system by an equivalent system.* Our final results in each example MUST be *the only solution*, and it *does not require verification or testing*, except as a means to check the details of our work. Moreover, if our process should lead to an equation (16) which gives a contradiction such as $10 = 0$, the preceding remarks show that the original system has no solution, or the equations are inconsistent. If (16) should be equivalent to the identity $0 = 0$, which then could be paired with $A = B$ as in (17), this would show that every solution of $A = B$ satisfies $C = D$, or the equations $A = B$ and $C = D$ are dependent.

EXERCISE 33 *

Solve the system graphically; if the graphs seem to be parallel, prove this fact by use of slopes. Also, solve the system algebraically.

1. $\begin{cases} x - y = 1, \\ y + 2x = -3. \end{cases}$
   2. $\begin{cases} y + x = 2, \\ 2y - x = -5. \end{cases}$
   3. $\begin{cases} y - 2x = 1, \\ 3y + 4x = 23. \end{cases}$

4. $\begin{cases} 2y - 3x = 0, \\ 4y + 3x = -18. \end{cases}$
   5. $\begin{cases} 3x + 8 = 0, \\ 6x + 7y = 5. \end{cases}$
   6. $\begin{cases} 5y - 3 = 0, \\ 10y + 3x = 4. \end{cases}$

7. $\begin{cases} 2y - 5x = 10, \\ 2y - 2x = 3. \end{cases}$
   8. $\begin{cases} 2x - 3y = 0, \\ 5x + 7y = 0. \end{cases}$
   9. $\begin{cases} 3x + 5y = 2, \\ 2x - 3y = -5. \end{cases}$

10. $\begin{cases} x + 2y = 4, \\ 3x - y = 6. \end{cases}$
    11. $\begin{cases} 2x - y = 3, \\ 2y - 4x = 5. \end{cases}$
    12. $\begin{cases} 3 = 2x - 3y, \\ 4x - 6 = 6y. \end{cases}$

13. $\begin{cases} x + y = 1, \\ 2x + 2y = 7. \end{cases}$
    14. $\begin{cases} 3x - 4y = 5, \\ 6x - 8y = 3. \end{cases}$
    15. $\begin{cases} x - 5y = 2, \\ 10y - 2x + 4 = 0. \end{cases}$

Note 1. Hereafter, *to solve* a system of equations will mean to solve *algebraically* unless otherwise stated.

Clear of fractions if necessary and solve the system.

16. $\begin{cases} \frac{3}{2}x = 2 + \frac{5}{4}y, \\ \frac{1}{2}x = \frac{3}{2} - \frac{5}{3}y. \end{cases}$
    17. $\begin{cases} \frac{9}{2}x - 4y = -3, \\ \frac{4}{3}x - \frac{1}{2}y = \frac{7}{6}. \end{cases}$

18. $\begin{cases} 5y + 3x = 3.45, \\ 4y - \frac{5}{2}x + .67 = 0. \end{cases}$
    19. $\begin{cases} \frac{3}{2}y - 5x = 5, \\ 7x - \frac{5}{2}y + 9 = 0. \end{cases}$

20. $\begin{cases} \dfrac{u - 4}{u - 1} = \dfrac{w + 2}{w + 1}, \\[2mm] \dfrac{u - 5}{u - 6} = \dfrac{w + 5}{w + 4}. \end{cases}$
    21. $\begin{cases} \dfrac{y - 2x + 2}{x + 3y + 3} + \dfrac{1}{5} = 0, \\[2mm] \dfrac{3x + y + 2}{y + 4x + 9} - \dfrac{7}{11} = 0. \end{cases}$

Solve for x and y, or for v and w.

22. $\begin{cases} 3ax + 2y = 2, \\ ax + 2y = 1. \end{cases}$
    23. $\begin{cases} av + b^2w = 2, \\ b^2v + aw = 2. \end{cases}$
    24. $\begin{cases} 6hx + y = 2h, \\ 2kx - 3y = k. \end{cases}$

25. $\begin{cases} 2av - 2w = 2 + b, \\ av + 2w = 1 - b. \end{cases}$
    26. $\begin{cases} cx - dy = c^2 + d^2, \\ x + y = 2c. \end{cases}$

27. $\begin{cases} v + 2bw = a^2 + b^2, \\ v - bw = a^2 - b^2. \end{cases}$
    28. $\begin{cases} 2ax + 3by = ab, \\ x - 3by = 3ab + 2b. \end{cases}$

Solve by introducing unknown literal numbers and obtaining a system of equations involving them.

29. The sum of the digits is 9 in a certain positive integer having two digits. If the digits are reversed, the new number is 9 less than three times the original number. Find it.

   HINT. If t is the tens' digit and u is the units' digit, the integer is equal to $(10t + u)$ and, with digits reversed, becomes $(10u + t)$.

---

* If the class is to solve systems of three linear equations, it is suggested that the simple triangular method of page 341 be taught at this time.

30. Workmen A and B complete a job if A works for 2 days and B works for 3 days, or if both work for $2\frac{2}{5}$ days. How long would it take each man to do the job alone?

HINT. If the job can be done by A alone in x days and by B alone in y days then, in 1 day, A does $(1/x)$th and B does $(1/y)$th of the job. Hence, $(2/x) + (3/y) = 1$; etc. Then, let $u = 1/x$, $v = 1/y$, solve for (u, v) and finally obtain (x, y).

31. At present John's age is 30% of his father's age. Twenty years from now, John's age will be 58% of his father's age. How old are John and his father now?

32. A motorboat can travel 15 miles per hour downstream and 9 miles per hour upstream on a certain river. Find the rate of its current and the rate at which the boat can travel in still water.

33. How much of a 40% solution of alcohol and how much of an 80% solution should be mixed to give 40 gallons of a 50% solution?

34. We wish to obtain a 40% solution of nitric acid by mixing a 20% solution and a 70% solution of the acid. What percentages of the final solution should be taken from the 20% and 70% solutions?

35. An alloy contains 20% silver and 30% lead. How much silver and how much lead should be added to 100 pounds of the alloy in order to obtain an alloy containing 25% silver and $33\frac{1}{3}$% lead?

36. When A and B both work, they can paint a certain house in 8 days. Also, they could paint this house if A worked 12 days and B worked 6 days. How long would it take each to paint the house alone?

37. An airplane, flying with the wind, took 2 hours for a 1000-mile flight, and $2\frac{1}{2}$ hours for the return flight. Find the speed of the wind and the speed of the airplane in still air.

58. Graphs of quadratic equations in two variables

A *quadratic equation* in two variables x and y is an integral rational equation of the 2d degree, and hence can be written

$$ax^2 + bxy + cy^2 + dx + ey + f = 0, \tag{1}$$

where a, b, c, d, e, and f are constants and at least one of a, b, and c is *not zero*. In analytic geometry, it is proved that, if (1) is satisfied by any real values of x and y, the graph of (1) in an xy-plane (where the units on the axes need not be equal) is of one of the following types: an **ellipse**, Figure 23, page 102, with a **circle** as a special case; a **hyperbola**, Figure 24, page 102; a **parabola; two lines,** which may coincide; **a single point.** Any locus of one of these types is called a **conic** because, except for two distinct parallel lines, all of the types can be obtained as plane sections of a (double) right circular cone (see Note 3 in the Appendix). We shall consider graphing (1) only in special cases, as mentioned later.

ILLUSTRATION 1. An *ellipse* has two *axes of symmetry*, *AB* and *CD* in Figure 23, where the longer, *AB*, and shorter, *CD*, are called the **major axis** and the **minor axis,** respectively. Any chord, *EF*, perpendicular to one of the axes is bisected by it. Also, the intersection *H* of these axes is a *center of symmetry* for the ellipse, and is called its **center.** That is, in Figure 23, any chord *KE* through *H* is bisected at *H*. *If the major and minor axes are equal, the ellipse is a circle.*

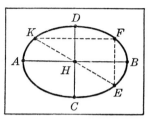

Fig. 23

ILLUSTRATION 2. A hyperbola consists of two separated parts, *AB* and *CD* in Figure 24, of infinite extent, each of which is called a **branch** of the curve. It has two *axes of symmetry*, *MN* and *PQ*, and their intersection, *H*, is a *center of symmetry* for the curve. Corresponding to any hyperbola, there exist two characteristic lines called **asymptotes,** passing through the center of the hyperbola, and indicated by the broken lines in Figure 24. By moving far enough out on either branch, we may approach an asymptote as closely as we please, but never reach it.

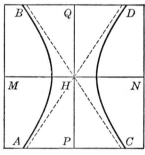

Note 1. Usually, in graphing, we shall not assume that the units for distance on the two coordinate axes are equal. Wherever equality is essential, this fact will be mentioned. Then, it also will be assumed that the same unit is used for distance in all directions; thus, (1) of page 61 will be available.

Fig. 24

CASE I. **Circle.** *If the units on the axes are equal and $r > 0$, the graph of $x^2 + y^2 = r^2$ is a circle with radius r and center at the origin. Or, if A and C have the same sign, the graph of $Ax^2 + Ay^2 = C$ is a circle with center at the origin and radius $\sqrt{C/A}$.*

Proof for Case I. In Figure 25, let the same unit be used for all distances. If $P:(x, y)$ is any point in the plane, then

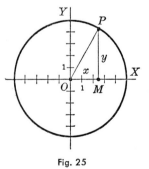

$$\overline{OP}^2 = \overline{OM}^2 + \overline{MP}^2, \quad or \quad \overline{OP}^2 = x^2 + y^2. \quad (2)$$

Thus, $P:(x, y)$ is on the graph of $x^2 + y^2 = r^2$ if and only if $\overline{OP}^2 = r^2$, or P is on the circle with radius r and center at O. Hence, this circle is the graph of $x^2 + y^2 = r^2$.

ILLUSTRATION 3. If the units on the axes are equal, the graph of $x^2 + y^2 = 25$ is a circle with center at $(0, 0)$ and radius $r = 5$.

Fig. 25

ILLUSTRATION 4. Suppose that the units on the coordinate axes are equal. Then, to graph $3x^2 + 3y^2 = 5$, first divide by 3, and obtain $x^2 + y^2 = \frac{5}{3}$; recognize that the graph is a circle with radius $r = \sqrt{\frac{5}{3}} = \frac{1}{3}\sqrt{15}$.

CASE II. **Ellipse.** *If A, B, and C have the* **same sign,** *then* $Ax^2 + By^2 = C$ *represents an ellipse with center at the origin and with the coordinate axes as axes of symmetry.*

Note 2. If the units on the coordinate axes are unequal and $A \neq B$, the ellipse of Case II may be a circle.

EXAMPLE 1.   Graph $4x^2 + 9y^2 = 36.$ (3)

SOLUTION. 1. From Case II, the graph is an ellipse.

2. *The intercepts.* If $y = 0$ in (3) then $x = \pm 3$, which are the x-intercepts and give $(\pm 3, 0)$ on the graph in Figure 26. If $x = 0$ in (3) then $y = \pm 2$, which are the y-intercepts and give $(0, \pm 2)$ on the graph. If merely a roughly approximate graph were sufficient, we could now sketch the ellipse through the four intercept points, with a smooth rounded shape at A and B, as in Figure 26.

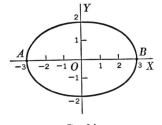

3. *To obtain a more accurate graph,* compute solutions (x, y) by use of (4), below, as given in the following table, and plot the corresponding points as a basis for the ellipse in Figure 26.

Fig. 26

$y = \frac{2}{3}\sqrt{9 - x^2}$	$x =$	-3	-2	0	2	3
	$y =$	0	1.5	2	1.5	0
$y = -\frac{2}{3}\sqrt{9 - x^2}$	$x =$	-3	-2	0	2	3
	$y =$	0	-1.5	-2	-1.5	0

Comment. On solving (3) for y, we obtain $y^2 = \frac{1}{9}(36 - 4x^2)$; then, on extracting square roots, we find

(a) $y = +\frac{2}{3}\sqrt{9 - x^2}$ *or*   (b) $y = -\frac{2}{3}\sqrt{9 - x^2}.$ (4)

In (4), the radicand $(9 - x^2)$ is *negative* if $x^2 > 9$ or if $|x| > 3$. Hence, for *real* values of y, we must have $|x| \leq 3$, or $-3 \leq x \leq 3$, which thus is the range for x. From (4), equation (3) defines two values of y for each value of x where $|x| < 3$, and just one value, $y = 0$, when $x = \pm 3$. That is, (3) defines y as a *two-valued* function of x, except that y is *single-valued* at $x = \pm 3$. All values of y are obtained from the values of the *two single-valued functions* of x in (4). The graph for (a) is the *upper half* of the ellipse in Figure 26, and for (b) is the *lower half.* Similarly, from (3), $x = \pm \frac{3}{2}\sqrt{4 - y^2}$, which gives *two single-valued functions* of y, whose graphs are, respectively, the right-hand and the left-hand halves of the ellipse.

CASE III. **A single point.** *If A and B have the same sign, the graph of the equation $Ax^2 + By^2 = 0$ is just one point, the origin.*

ILLUSTRATION 5. The graph of $3x^2 + 4y^2 = 0$ is just the origin, $(x = 0, y = 0)$, because the equation is equivalent to $x^2 = 0$ and $y^2 = 0$, since each term in the equation is nonnegative.

CASE IV. **Two straight lines.** *If the left-hand side of (1) can be written as the product of real linear factors, the graph of (1) consists of the graphs of the equations obtained on placing each factor separately equal to zero.*

ILLUSTRATION 6. The equation $(3x - y + 3)(x + y - 7) = 0$ gives

$$3x - y + 3 = 0 \quad or \quad x + y - 7 = 0. \tag{5}$$

Hence, the graph of the given equation consists of the *two lines* whose equations are in (5).

ILLUSTRATION 7. To graph $9x^2 - 4y^2 = 0$, we first factor:

$$(3x - 2y)(3x + 2y) = 0; \quad hence,$$

$$3x - 2y = 0 \quad or \quad 3x + 2y = 0.$$

Thus, the graph of $9x^2 - 4y^2 = 0$ consists of the graph of $3x - 2y = 0$ and the graph of $3x + 2y = 0$, which give the broken lines AB and CD, respectively, in Figure 28, on page 105.

ILLUSTRATION 8. If $A \neq 0$, the graph of $Ax^2 = 0$, or $A \cdot x \cdot x = 0$, is the two lines $x = 0$ and $x = 0$, which give the y-axis *twice*. Thus, the graph of $Ax^2 = 0$ is thought of as *two coincident lines*.

CASE V. **Hyperbola, with the coordinate axes as asymptotes.** *If $k \neq 0$, the graph of $xy = k$ is a hyperbola in quadrants I and III if $k > 0$, and in quadrants II and IV if $k < 0$.*

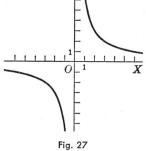

Fig. 27

ILLUSTRATION 9. By use of the following table of values, we verify that the graph of $xy = 6$ is the hyperbola in Figure 27. We cannot have $x = 0$ or $y = 0$ on the graph because then $xy = 6$ becomes $0 = 6$. This remark checks the fact that the hyperbola does not meet its asymptotes.

$x =$	1	2	3	6	0	-1	-2	-3	-6
$y =$	6	3	2	1	*no value*	-6	-3	-2	-1

CASE VI. **Hyperbola symmetric to the coordinate axes.** *If A and B have opposite signs and $C \neq 0$, the graph of $Ax^2 + By^2 = C$ is a hyperbola. An equation for its asymptotes is $Ax^2 + By^2 = 0$, which is obtained on replacing C by zero in the given equation.*

EXAMPLE 2. Graph $9x^2 - 4y^2 = 36.$ (6)

SOLUTION. 1. *The intercepts.* If $y = 0$ in (6), the x-intercepts are found to be $x = \pm 2$, giving $(\pm 2, 0)$ on the graph. If $x = 0$, then $-4y^2 = 36$ or $y^2 = -9$; hence, y is imaginary and there are no y-intercepts, or the graph does not meet the y-axis.

2. *The equation of the asymptotes* is obtained on replacing 36 by 0 in (6), which gives $9x^2 - 4y^2 = 0,$ or $(3x - 2y)(3x + 2y) = 0,$ or

$$3x - 2y = 0 \quad and \quad 3x + 2y = 0. \quad (7)$$

The asymptotes AB and CD in Figure 28 are the graphs of the equations in (7).

3. *To obtain a quick, approximate graph* of (6), sketch each branch of the hyperbola through the corresponding x-intercept point, G or H, with the curve drawn smoothly to approach the asymptotes as guides.

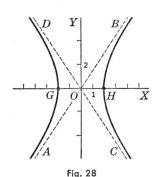

Fig. 28

4. To obtain a more accurate graph, first solve (6) for x:

$$x = \pm \tfrac{2}{3}\sqrt{y^2 + 9}. \quad (8)$$

Compute solutions (x, y) for (6) by substituting values of y in (8):

$y =$	-6	-3	0	3	6
$x =$	± 4.5	± 2.8	± 2	± 2.8	± 4.5

Then, sketch the branches through the points given by the table.

CASE VII. **Parabola.** *If a quadratic equation in x and y does not involve y^2 or xy, the equation defines y as a quadratic function of x, and hence the graph of the equation is a parabola whose axis is perpendicular to the x-axis. If the equation does not involve x^2 or xy, then x is defined as a quadratic function of y, and the graph is a parabola whose axis is perpendicular to the y-axis.*

EXAMPLE 3. Determine the nature of the graph of

$$4y - 3x^2 + 5x - 7 = 0. \quad (9)$$

SOLUTION. The equation is linear in y. Hence, solve for y:

$$y = \tfrac{3}{4}x^2 - \tfrac{5}{4}x + \tfrac{7}{4}, \quad (10)$$

and y *is a quadratic function of x.* Thus, the graph of (9) is a parabola whose axis is perpendicular to the x-axis; the parabola is concave upward because, in (10), $\tfrac{3}{4} > 0$. The graph could be found as on page 79.

CASE VIII. **No locus.** *If A and B have the* **same sign** *and C has the* **opposite sign,** *then $Ax^2 + By^2 = C$ has no graph.*

ILLUSTRATION 10. The equation $3x^2 + 4y^2 = -7$ has no real solutions, and hence no graph, because the left-hand side is never negative. Then, the "*graph*" may be said to be "*imaginary*."

SUMMARY. *For graphing quadratic equations of the following types.*

1. **Circle:** $Ax^2 + Ay^2 = C$, with C/A *positive. Find the radius* $\sqrt{C/A}$ *and draw the circle with compasses.* (**Equal units** *on the coordinate axes.*)

2. **Ellipse:** $Ax^2 + By^2 = C$, *with* A, B, C of **one sign.** *Find the x-intercepts and y-intercepts, and then draw a well-rounded curve through the intercept points.*

3. **Two straight lines:** $Ax^2 + By^2 = 0$, *where* A *and* B *have* **opposite signs.** *Factor* $Ax^2 + By^2$ *and obtain two equivalent linear equations whose graphs are the desired lines.*

4. **Hyperbola:** $Ax^2 + By^2 = C$, *where* $C \neq 0$, *while* A *and* B *have* **opposite signs.** *Graph as follows:*

  Try to find x-intercepts and y-intercepts (one set imaginary).

  Write $Ax^2 + By^2 = 0$, *the equation of the asymptotes; plot them.*

  Sketch each branch through an intercept point on an axis, to approach the asymptotes.

5. **Parabola:** *the equation does not involve* x^2 *and* xy, *or does not involve* y^2 *and* xy. *Solve for that variable which enters only to the first degree; graph the resulting quadratic function as on page 79.*

EXERCISE 34

By inspection, name the graph. Then, graph the equation.

1. $x^2 + y^2 = 9$.   2. $xy = 4$.   3. $xy = -6$.   4. $4x^2 - 25y^2 = 0$.

5. $4x^2 + 4y^4 = 9$.   6. $3x^2 + 5y^2 = 0$.   7. $2 + 3x^2 + y^2 = 0$.

8. $4x^2 + 25y^2 = 100$.   9. $4x^2 - y^2 = 16$.   10. $9y^2 - 4x^2 = 36$.

11. $y = x^2 - 6x + 7$.   12. $3y + 6x^2 + 12x - 7 = 0$.

13. $x = y^2 + 4y - 3$.   14. $3y^2 - 2x + 4 = 0$.

15. $(x - 2y)(3x - y - 6) = 0$.   16. $36 - x^2 - 9y^2 = 0$.

17. $3x^2 - 4xy - 4y^2 = 0$.   18. $5x^2 + 13xy - 6y^2 = 0$.

19. $(x - 1)^2 + 3(y + 2)^2 = 0$.   20. $(x - y)(x + 2y)(3x - y - 1) = 0$.

21. $(x - 3y)(x + 3y) = 9$.   22. $(3y - x)(3y + x) = 9$.

59. Graphical solution of systems involving quadratics

We recall the remarks about the solution of a system of two equations in two variables on page 97.

EXAMPLE 1. Solve graphically:

$$\begin{cases} x^2 - 2y^2 = 1, & (1) \\ x^2 + 4y^2 = 25. & (2) \end{cases}$$

SOLUTION. In Figure 29, the graph of (1) is the hyperbola, and the graph of (2) is the ellipse. Any point on the hyperbola has coordinates satisfying (1), and any point on the ellipse has coordinates satisfying (2). Hence, both equations are satisfied by the coordinates of A, B, C, and D, where the ellipse and hyperbola intersect. The pairs of coordinates are the four solutions of $[(1), (2)]$:

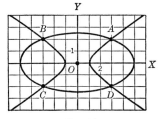
Fig. 29

$$A:(x = 3,\ y = 2);$$
$$B:(x = -3,\ y = 2);$$
$$C:(x = -3,\ y = -2);$$
$$D:(x = 3,\ y = -2).$$

EXERCISE 35

Solve graphically.

1. $\begin{cases} x^2 + y^2 = 16, \\ y - 2x = 3. \end{cases}$

2. $\begin{cases} x + 2y = 3, \\ x^2 + y^2 = 9. \end{cases}$

3. $\begin{cases} x^2 - y^2 = 4, \\ x + y = 1. \end{cases}$

4. $\begin{cases} 4y^2 - x^2 = 16, \\ 3 = y - x. \end{cases}$

5. $\begin{cases} 4x^2 + y^2 = 16, \\ y^2 - 4x^2 = 4. \end{cases}$

6. $\begin{cases} 4x^2 + y^2 = 9, \\ 4x^2 + 4y^2 = 25. \end{cases}$

7. $\begin{cases} x^2 - 4y^2 = 4, \\ xy = 2. \end{cases}$

8. $\begin{cases} x^2 + y^2 = 1, \\ 4x^2 + y^2 = 9. \end{cases}$

9. $\begin{cases} x^2 + y^2 = 9, \\ x^2 - 9y^2 = 9. \end{cases}$

10. $\begin{cases} x^2 - xy - 12y^2 = 0, \\ x^2 + 4y^2 = 4. \end{cases}$

11. $\begin{cases} x = 2y^2 - 8y + 9, \\ xy = 12. \end{cases}$

60. Algebraic solution of a simple system

Hereafter, *to solve* a system will mean *to solve it algebraically*, unless otherwise specified. If a system of two equations in two variables consists of *one linear equation* and *one quadratic equation*, they will be called a **simple system**. Usually it will have either (1) *two distinct real solutions*, (2) *two identical real solutions*, or (3) *two imaginary solutions*. These possibilities correspond, respectively, to the following geometrical situations: the straight line, which is the graph of the linear equation, (1) *may intersect the conic which is the graph of the quadratic equation in two distinct points;* (2) *may be tangent to the conic;* (3) *may not intersect the conic.*

SUMMARY. *Solution of a system of one linear and one quadratic equation.*

1. *Solve the linear equation for a first unknown in terms of the other, say for y in terms of x, and substitute the result in the quadratic equation, in order to eliminate the first unknown.*

2. *Solve the equation just obtained for the second unknown.*

3. *For each value of the second unknown, find the corresponding value of the first unknown by substitution* **in the linear equation.**

EXAMPLE 1. Solve:
$$\begin{cases} 4x^2 - 6xy + 9y^2 = 63, & \text{(1)} \\ 2x - 3y = -3. & \text{(2)} \end{cases}$$

SOLUTION. 1. Solve (2) for x:
$$x = \frac{3y - 3}{2}. \qquad \text{(3)}$$

2. Substitute (3) in (1) to eliminate x:

$$4\left(\frac{3y - 3}{2}\right)^2 - 6y\left(\frac{3y - 3}{2}\right) + 9y^2 = 63. \qquad \text{(4)}$$

$y^2 - y - 6 = 0;$ $(y - 3)(y + 2) = 0;$ $y = 3$ *or* $y = -2.$

3. In (3), if $y = 3,$ then $x = 3;$ if $y = -2,$ then $x = -\frac{9}{2}.$

4. The solutions are $(x = 3, y = 3)$ *and* $(x = -\frac{9}{2}, y = -2).$

Note 1. Each solution of a system of two equations in x and y should be plainly indicated as a pair of values, as in Example 1.

61. Solution of a system of two quadratic equations

A system of two quadratic equations in two variables usually has *four solutions*, real or imaginary. In particular, there may be four distinct real solutions, as observed in certain problems on page 107. In general, the algebraic solution of a system of two quadratic equations in two variables may be expected to involve the solution of an equation of degree 4 in one variable, and other difficulties beyond the level of this course. We shall discuss only simple types of systems of two quadratic equations.

Note 1. In advanced algebra it is proved that, in general, *a system of two integral rational equations in x and y, in which one equation is of degree m and the other of degree n, has mn solutions.* With $m = 2$ and $n = 2$, the theorem leads us to expect 2×2 or 4 solutions.

An elementary type of system consisting of *two quadratics* is one in which each equation is of the form $ax^2 + by^2 = c$, where a, b, and c are constants. Such an equation is said to be *linear in x^2 and y^2*, because the substitution $u = x^2$ and $v = y^2$ would lead to an equation linear in u and v. A system of the preceding type can be solved by methods of elimination, as used with systems of linear equations.

EXAMPLE 1. Solve:
$$\begin{cases} x^2 + y^2 = 25, & \text{(1)} \\ x^2 + 2y^2 = 34. & \text{(2)} \end{cases}$$

SOLUTION. 1. Multiply by 2 in (1): $2x^2 + 2y^2 = 50.$ (3)

2. Subtract, (2) from (3): $x^2 = 16;$ $x = \pm 4.$

3. Substitute $x^2 = 16$ in (1): $16 + y^2 = 25;$ $y^2 = 9;$ $y = \pm 3.$

4. Hence, if x is either $+4$ or -4, we obtain as corresponding values $y = +3$ and $y = -3$, and there are *four* solutions of the system:

$(x = 4, y = 3);$ $(x = -4, y = 3);$ $(x = 4, y = -3);$ $(x = -4, y = -3).$

#22

EXERCISE 36

Solve (a) graphically and (b) algebraically.

1. $\begin{cases} x^2 + y^2 = 25, \\ x + y = 1. \end{cases}$

2. $\begin{cases} x - 2y = 3, \\ x^2 + 4y^2 = 4. \end{cases}$

3. $\begin{cases} u^2 + v^2 = 25, \\ 3u - 4v = 25. \end{cases}$

4. $\begin{cases} x^2 + y^2 = 4, \\ 9x^2 + y^2 = 9. \end{cases}$

5. $\begin{cases} 9x^2 + y^2 = 36, \\ x^2 + y^2 = 36. \end{cases}$

6. $\begin{cases} y^2 - 4x^2 = 16, \\ 9x^2 + 9y^2 = 4. \end{cases}$

Solve algebraically for (x, y) or (u, v).

7. $\begin{cases} 4x^2 + y^2 = 25, \\ 2x + y - 7 = 0. \end{cases}$

8. $\begin{cases} 5uv = 4v + u, \\ u + 4v = 5. \end{cases}$

9. $\begin{cases} x^2 - 4y^2 = 16, \\ 5x - 6y = 16. \end{cases}$

10. $\begin{cases} 5u - 2v = 6, \\ 4u^2 + 4u - v^2 - 4v = 12. \end{cases}$

11. $\begin{cases} 4x^2 + y^2 = 14, \\ 2x^2 = y^2 - 8. \end{cases}$

12. $\begin{cases} x^2 - 4y^2 = 4, \\ 2x^2 + 4y^2 = 11. \end{cases}$

13. $\begin{cases} 2u^2 + 3v^2 = 12, \\ 3u^2 - 4v^2 = 1. \end{cases}$

14. $\begin{cases} 5x^2 + 2y^2 = 6, \\ 2x^2 - 3y^2 = 10. \end{cases}$

15. $\begin{cases} 6x^2 + 5y^2 = 17, \\ 3x^2 - 4y^2 = 2. \end{cases}$

16. $\begin{cases} 3u^2 + 4v^2 = 21, \\ 9u^2 + 8v^2 = 54. \end{cases}$

17. $\begin{cases} 2x + 3y + 9 = 0, \\ 2xy + 9y + 4x = 3. \end{cases}$

18. $\begin{cases} 4y - 3x = 1, \\ 2x^2 - 8y^2 + 3x + 2y = 2. \end{cases}$

19. $\begin{cases} xy + x^2 + 2y = 3, \\ 3x - 2y + 2 = 0. \end{cases}$

20. $\begin{cases} 4x^2 + 9y^2 = 2a^2 + 2b^2, \\ 2x - 3y = 2a. \end{cases}$

62. Reduction to simpler systems

We say that a given system of equations in certain variables is *equivalent* to two or more other systems in case their solutions consist of all solutions of the given system. We shall discuss methods for obtaining equivalent systems of types more simple than a given system, under various conditions.

Consider a system of equations in x and y in which one equation can be written in the form $f(x, y) = 0$, where $f(x, y)$ *can be expressed as a product of linear factors.* Then, the given system is equivalent to a set of simpler systems, in each of which *one equation is obtained by placing a linear factor of $f(x, y)$ equal to zero.*

EXAMPLE 1. Solve:
$$\begin{cases} x^2 + y^2 = 14, & (1) \\ x^2 - 3xy + 2y^2 = 0. & (2) \end{cases}$$

SOLUTION. 1. Factor in (2): $\qquad (x - 2y)(x - y) = 0. \qquad (3)$

Thus, (2) is satisfied if either

$$x - 2y = 0 \quad or \quad x - y = 0. \qquad (4)$$

2. Hence, (1) and (2) are satisfied if and only if x and y satisfy one of the following simple systems.

$$\text{I.} \begin{cases} x^2 + y^2 = 14, \\ x - y = 0. \end{cases} \qquad \text{II.} \begin{cases} x^2 + y^2 = 14, \\ x - 2y = 0. \end{cases}$$

3. On solving (**I**) by the method of Section 60, we obtain two solutions:
$(x = \sqrt{7}, y = \sqrt{7})$ and $(x = -\sqrt{7}, y = -\sqrt{7})$. From (**II**),

$$(x = \tfrac{2}{5}\sqrt{70},\ y = \tfrac{1}{5}\sqrt{70}); \qquad (x = -\tfrac{2}{5}\sqrt{70},\ y = -\tfrac{1}{5}\sqrt{70}).$$

Comment. System $[(1), (2)]$ *is equivalent to* (I) and (II). In obtaining them, we say that we have reduced the solution of $[(1), (2)]$ to the solution of *two simple systems.*

A system in which *all terms involving the variables are of the second degree* can sometimes be solved by use of the equation we obtain on **eliminating the constant terms** from the original system.

EXAMPLE 2. Solve:
$$\begin{cases} x^2 + 3xy = 28, & (5) \\ xy + 4y^2 = 8. & (6) \end{cases}$$

INCOMPLETE SOLUTION. 1. *Eliminate the constants.*

Multiply by 2 in (5): $\qquad\qquad\qquad\qquad 2x^2 + 6xy = 56.$ $\qquad\qquad$ (7)

Multiply by 7 in (6): $\qquad\qquad\qquad\qquad 7xy + 28y^2 = 56.$ $\qquad\qquad$ (8)

Subtract, (8) from (7): $\qquad\qquad\quad 2x^2 - xy - 28y^2 = 0,\ or$ $\qquad$ (9)

$$(2x + 7y)(x - 4y) = 0. \qquad\qquad (10)$$

2. By reversing the preceding steps, we see that, if (10) and (7) are satisfied by values (x, y), then (8) also is satisfied. Or, if (10) and (8) are satisfied, then (7) also is satisfied. That is, to find the solutions of $[(5), (6)]$, we may solve an *equivalent system* obtained on *replacing either given equation by* (10). We decide to solve $[(6), (10)]$:

$$[xy + 4y^2 = 8, \qquad (2x + 7y)(x - 4y) = 0.]$$

3. As in Example 1, $[(6), (10)]$ is equivalent to the following systems:

$$\textbf{I.}\ \begin{cases} xy + 4y^2 = 8, \\ 2x + 7y = 0. \end{cases} \qquad \textbf{II.}\ \begin{cases} xy + 4y^2 = 8, \\ x - 4y = 0. \end{cases}$$

We solve (I) and (II) separately by the method of Section 60 and find the following four solutions for $[(5), (6)]$:

From (I): $\quad (x = -14, y = 4); \quad (x = 14, y = -4).$

From (II): $\quad (x = 4, y = 1); \quad (x = -4, y = -1).$

Comment. In a system such as $[(5), (6)]$ where all terms are of the second degree, instead of eliminating the constants, we may commence solving by using the so-called *homogeneous substitution* $y = wx$. This gives two new equations in the unknowns w and x, where it is easy to eliminate x, by dividing corresponding sides of the two equations. Then, we would find the values of w, then the values of x, and finally the corresponding values of y by use of $y = wx$.

Sometimes, by combinations of the equations in a given system, we may obtain an equation of lower degree, or an equation which is equivalent to two or more equations of lower degree. In such a case, we may be able to reduce the solution of the given system to the solution of one or more simpler systems. The method of *ingenious devices* is the only rule which can be specified in solutions of the preceding nature.

★EXAMPLE 3. Solve:
$$\begin{cases} x^3 + y^3 = 27, & (11) \\ x + y = 3. & (12) \end{cases}$$

INCOMPLETE SOLUTION. 1. Factor in (11):
$$(x + y)(x^2 - xy + y^2) = 27. \tag{13}$$

2. Divide each side of (13) by the corresponding side of (12):
$$x^2 - xy + y^2 = 9. \tag{14}$$

3. Hence, (x, y) satisfies [(11), (12)] if and only if (x, y) satisfies
$$\begin{cases} x + y = 3, & (15) \\ x^2 - xy + y^2 = 9. & (16) \end{cases}$$

The student should complete the solution by solving [(15), (16)] by the method of Section 60.

★EXAMPLE 4. Solve:
$$\begin{cases} x^2 + xy + y^2 = 20, & (17) \\ xy = 5. & (18) \end{cases}$$

INCOMPLETE SOLUTION. Add sides in (17) and (18):
$$x^2 + 2xy + y^2 = 25, \quad or \quad (x + y)^2 = 25, \; or \tag{19}$$
$$x + y = 5 \quad and \quad x + y = -5. \tag{20}$$

Hence, (19) is equivalent to the two linear equations in (20), and system [(17), (18)] is equivalent to the following two simple systems:
$$\begin{cases} x + y = 5, \\ xy = 5. \end{cases} \qquad \begin{cases} x + y = -5, \\ xy = 5. \end{cases}$$

EXERCISE 37

Solve algebraically and graphically.

1. $\begin{cases} x^2 + y^2 = 25, \\ (3x - 4y)(4x + 3y) = 0. \end{cases}$

2. $\begin{cases} x^2 + y^2 = 169, \\ (5x - 12y)(12x + 5y) = 0. \end{cases}$

Solve by reducing to simpler systems.

3. $\begin{cases} 2x^2 - 3xy + y^2 = 0, \\ 2x^2 = 3xy - 4. \end{cases}$

4. $\begin{cases} 7x^2 - 3xy = 40, \\ 3x^2 + xy - 2y^2 = 0. \end{cases}$

5. $\begin{cases} 2x^2 + 3xy = 14, \\ xy + 2y^2 = 4. \end{cases}$

6. $\begin{cases} 2x^2 + 5xy + 3y^2 = 5, \\ 2x^2 + xy = 2. \end{cases}$

7. $\begin{cases} u^2 + uz + 10z^2 = 22, \\ uz - 2z^2 = -6. \end{cases}$

8. $\begin{cases} x^2 + 2xy = 1, \\ 2x^2 + 8y^2 = 5. \end{cases}$

9. $\begin{cases} 26u^2 + 17uz = 30, \\ z^2 + 5uz + 6u^2 = 10, \end{cases}$

10. $\begin{cases} y^2 + 3xy = 2, \\ 9x^2 + 2y^2 = 9, \end{cases}$

11. $\begin{cases} x^2 + 3y^2 = 7, \\ x^2 - xy + 4y^2 = 10. \end{cases}$ **12.** $\begin{cases} u^2 + 2uv = 21, \\ 2uv + v^2 = 16. \end{cases}$

13. $\begin{cases} 3x^2 - 13xy - 10y^2 = 0, \\ (y - 2)(2x + y - 3) = 0. \end{cases}$ **14.** $\begin{cases} (2x - y)(2x + y)(2x - 3y) = 0, \\ (2x - 2y + 1)(x + y - 1) = 0. \end{cases}$

HINT. Find a set of equivalent linear systems.

★*Solve by any convenient method.*

15. $\begin{cases} u + v = 2, \\ u^3 + v^3 = 8. \end{cases}$ **16.** $\begin{cases} x - 2y = 2, \\ x^3 - 8y^3 = 98. \end{cases}$ **17.** $\begin{cases} x^2 + 4y^2 = 13, \\ xy = 3. \end{cases}$

18. $\begin{cases} x^2 + 2xy + 4y^2 = 7, \\ x^3 - 8y^3 = 35. \end{cases}$ **19.** $\begin{cases} x^2y - 4xy^2 = 12, \\ x - 4y = 4. \end{cases}$

20. $\begin{cases} x^2 - 2xy + y^2 = 1, \\ 3x - 2xy + 3 = 0. \end{cases}$ **21.** $\begin{cases} u^2 - 4uv + 4v^2 = 1, \\ 9u^2 + 3uv + v = 1. \end{cases}$

22. $\begin{cases} x^2 + y^2 + 2x + 2y = 18, \\ xy + x + y = 7. \end{cases}$ **23.** $\begin{cases} 4x^2 + 8x + 4y^2 + 8y = 17, \\ 2xy = -3. \end{cases}$

HINT. The equations are said to be **symmetrical** *in x and y* because the equations are unaltered if x and y are interchanged. In such a case, the solution can be obtained conveniently by substituting $x = u + v$ and $y = u - v$, then solving for (u, v), and finally obtaining (x, y) by use of the equations of the substitution.

24. $\begin{cases} 2x^2 = 6xy - 5z - 2, \\ x - y + z = 1, \\ 4x + 2y + z = 16. \end{cases}$ **25.** $\begin{cases} 9x^2 + 4y^2 + 3z^2 = 3, \\ y^2 - 6x^2 = 6z^2 - 3, \\ z^2 - y^2 - x^2 = 2. \end{cases}$

26. $\begin{cases} 3u^3 - 2v^3 = 8, \\ 4v^3 - 3u^3 = 8. \end{cases}$ **27.** $\begin{cases} x^{\frac{2}{3}} + 3y^{\frac{2}{3}} = 28, \\ x^{\frac{2}{3}} - x^{\frac{1}{3}}y^{\frac{1}{3}} + 4y^{\frac{2}{3}} = 40. \end{cases}$

★*Find the value of the real constant k so that the graphs of the equations are tangent. Check by graphing.*

28. $\begin{cases} y = x^2 - 4x + 9, \\ y + kx = 8. \end{cases}$ **29.** $\begin{cases} 3x^2 + 4y^2 = 48, \\ x + ky = 8. \end{cases}$ **30.** $\begin{cases} x^2 + y^2 = 9, \\ kx - y = 4. \end{cases}$

★*Find an expression for c in terms of the other constants if the graphs of the equations in the variables x and y are tangent.*

31. $\begin{cases} 4x^2 + 9y^2 = 36, \\ y = mx + c. \end{cases}$ **32.** $\begin{cases} y = mx + c, \\ a^2x^2 - b^2y^2 = a^2b^2. \end{cases}$

Ratio, Proportion, and Variation

63. Ratio and proportion

Recall that the **ratio** of one number a to a second number b is the quotient $\dfrac{a}{b}$. The ratio of a to b sometimes is written $a:b$. A ratio is a fraction, and any fraction can be described as a ratio:

$$a:b = \frac{a}{b}. \tag{1}$$

The ratio of two concrete quantities has meaning only if they are of the same kind. Their ratio is the quotient of their measures in terms of the same unit.

ILLUSTRATION 1. The ratio of 3 feet to 5 inches is $\frac{36}{5}$.

A **proportion** is a statement that two ratios, or fractions, are equal. The proportion $a:b = c:d$ is read "a *is to* b *as* c *is to* d," and we say that the four numbers a, b, c, and d *form a proportion.*

$$a:b = c:d \quad \textit{means that} \quad \frac{a}{b} = \frac{c}{d}. \tag{2}$$

In a proportion $a:b = c:d$, the first and fourth numbers, a and d, are called the **extremes,** and the second and third, b and c, are called the **means** of the proportion.

ILLUSTRATION 2. To solve the proportion $x:(25 - x) = 3:7$, we first change it to fractional form, and then solve the resulting equation by use of standard methods:

$$\frac{x}{25 - x} = \frac{3}{7}; \quad 7x = 75 - 3x; \quad 10x = 75; \quad \textit{hence,} \quad x = 7.5.$$

EXAMPLE 1. Divide 36 into two parts with the ratio $3:7$.

SOLUTION. 1. Let x and y be the parts; then $\qquad x + y = 36. \qquad (3)$

2. Also, $x:y = 3:7$, or $\dfrac{x}{y} = \dfrac{3}{7}$. Hence, $\qquad 7x = 3y. \qquad (4)$

3. On solving the system [(3), (4)] we obtain $(x = 10.8, y = 25.2)$.

113

Note 1. If two triangles (or polygons of any number of sides) are similar, then (a) *the ratio of any two sides* * *of one triangle is equal to the ratio of the corresponding sides of the other triangle,* and (b) *the area of one triangle is to the area of the other as the square of any side of the first triangle is to the square of the corresponding side of the other triangle.*

EXAMPLE 2. The sides of a triangle are 12, 8, and 15 inches long. In a similar triangle, the longest side is 40 inches long. Find the other sides.

SOLUTION. 1. Let x and y be the lengths in inches of the sides of the similar triangle corresponding to those sides which are 8 and 12 inches long in the first triangle. Then,

$$y : 12 = 40 : 15 \quad or \quad \frac{y}{12} = \frac{40}{15}; \tag{5}$$

$$x : 8 = 40 : 15 \quad or \quad \frac{x}{8} = \frac{40}{15}. \tag{6}$$

2. On solving (5) and (6) we find $y = 32$ inches and $x = 21\frac{1}{3}$ inches.

Note 2. In the past, a considerable technical vocabulary concerning proportions was met in mathematical literature, particularly in some parts of geometry. The modern tendency is to consider such terminology unimportant, and to base all actions about proportions on the usual properties of the corresponding equations, such as (2).

EXERCISE 38

Express each ratio as a fraction and simplify.

1. $\frac{3}{7} : \frac{5}{21}$.   **2.** $\frac{15}{2} : \frac{35}{4}$.   **3.** $a^2b^5 : a^3b^2$.   **4.** $cx^3 : cx^5$.

Find the ratio of the quantities, or solve the equation.

5. 80 pounds to 300 ounces.   **6.** 32 days to 140 hours.

7. 29 pints to 12 quarts.   **8.** 35 miles to 3570 yards.

9. $2 : (5 - 3x) = 5 : 2$.   **10.** $x : (2x - 5) = 6$.   **11.** $2 : x = x : 8$.

12. $(2 - y) : (3 + 2y) = 4 : 3$.   **13.** $(2x - 1) : 3x = 2 : 5$.

14. $(2x - 1) : (1 + 4x) = (1 - 4x) : (2x + 3)$.

Solve by writing proportions.

15. A line 20 inches long is divided into two parts whose lengths have the ratio 3 : 7. Find the lengths of the parts.

16. Divide 80 into two parts such that the ratio of one part, decreased by 4, to the other part, decreased by 8, is 1 : 3.

17. The sides of a triangle are 10, 9, and 15 inches long. In a similar triangle, the longest side is 21 inches long. Find the other sides.

18. A triangle whose base is 18 inches long has an area of 280 square inches. Find the area of a similar triangle whose base is $6\frac{1}{4}$ feet long.

---

* The word "*sides*" here means the "*measures of the sides*" in terms of some prescribed unit of length.

19. The sides of a polygon are 6, 10, 20, and 24 inches long. If the shortest side is reduced by 2 inches, what reductions should be made in the other sides to obtain a similar polygon?

20. The area of a quadrilateral is 64 square feet and its shortest side is 10 feet long. Find the area of a similar quadrilateral whose shortest side is 15 feet long.

21. The area of a quadrilateral is 200 square feet and its longest side is 20 feet long. Find the length of the longest side of a similar polygon whose area is 400 square feet.

22. A basketball player is 6 feet 8 inches tall. How far should he stand from a light which is 15 feet above ground, in order to cast a shadow 25 feet long?

23. Find the coordinates of the point on the y-axis which divides the line segment from $(0, -4)$ to $(0, 20)$ internally in the ratio 5 : 7.

If $a : x = x : b$, then x is called a **mean proportional** *between a and b. If $a : x = x : b$, then $x^2 = ab$ or $x = \pm \sqrt{ab}$; or, if neither a nor b is zero, there are two mean proportionals between a and b. Find the mean proportionals between each of the following pairs of numbers.*

24. 27 and 3. 25. 9 and 9. 26. -2 and -8.
27. 6 and 216. 28. $\frac{1}{4}$ and $\frac{1}{64}$. 29. $2a^3$ and $4a$.
30. y^2 and x^{-4}. 31. -4 and 64. 32. -3 and 27.

64. Language of variation

Consider any set of related variables, where we regard one of them as a function of the others. Then, particularly in applied mathematics, we meet a convenient vocabulary, called the *language of variation*, for describing some of the most simple functions.

Direct variation. *Let y be a function of x. Then, we say that*

$$\left. \begin{array}{l} y \text{ is proportional to } x, \text{ or} \\ y \text{ varies directly as } x, \text{ or} \\ y \text{ is directly proportional to } x, \text{ or} \\ y \text{ varies as } x, \end{array} \right\} \tag{1}$$

in case there exists a constant $k \neq 0$ such that, for every value of x, the corresponding value of y is given by $y = kx$.

In $y = kx$, we call k the **constant of proportionality,** or the **constant of variation.** From $y = kx$, we obtain $k = y/x$. Or, if y is proportional to x, *the ratio of corresponding values of y and x is a constant.* Conversely, if this ratio is a constant, then y is proportional to x, because the equation $k = y/x$ leads to $y = kx$.

ILLUSTRATION 1. The circumference C of a circle varies directly as the radius r, because $C = 2\pi r$, where the constant of proportionality is 2π.

Then, $2\pi = C/r$, or the ratio of the circumference to the radius is 2π for any circle. In $C = 2\pi r$, C and r are *measures* in terms of the *same unit of length*. If r were a measure in feet and C a measure in inches, the statement that "C *varies directly as* r" still would be true, but then $C = 24\pi r$, where the constant of proportionality is 24π. This illustrates the fact that, when x and y are measures in assigned units, statements (1) can be made, when true, *without knowledge of the units*, whereas the value of k in $y = kx$ cannot be learned until the units are specified.

ILLUSTRATION 2. If y is proportional to x^2, then $y = kx^2$.

If y is any function of x, then y may be expected to change in value when the value of x changes. But, we do not say that y *varies as* x except when y is the simple linear function $y = kx$.

Inverse variation. *Let y be a function of x. Then, we say that*

$$\left. \begin{array}{l} y \text{ varies inversely as } x, \text{ or} \\ y \text{ is inversely proportional to } x, \end{array} \right\} \tag{2}$$

in case there exists a constant $k \neq 0$ such that, for every value of x, the corresponding value of y is given by $y = \dfrac{k}{x}.$

From $y = k/x$, we obtain $xy = k$, or *the product of corresponding values of x and y is a constant.* If y varies inversely as x, then likewise x varies inversely as y, because the equation $xy = k$ leads to both of the equations

$$y = \frac{k}{x} \quad and \quad x = \frac{k}{y}.$$

ILLUSTRATION 3. The time t necessary for a train to go a given distance s varies inversely as the speed r of the train because $t = s/r$. The constant of proportionality here is s.

Joint variation. *Let z be a function of x and y. Then, we say that*

$$\left. \begin{array}{l} z \text{ varies jointly as } x \text{ and } y, \text{ or} \\ z \text{ is directly proportional to } x \text{ and } y, \text{ or} \\ z \text{ is proportional to } x \text{ and } y, \text{ or} \\ z \text{ varies as } x \text{ and } y, \end{array} \right\} \tag{3}$$

in case z is proportional to the product xy, or $z = kxy$, where $k \neq 0$ is a constant of proportionality.

Notice that the significance of the word "*and*" in (3) is that x *and y are multiplied*, in the final relation $z = kxy$.

Any of the types of variation may be combined.

ILLUSTRATION 4. To say that z varies *directly* as x and y and *inversely* as w^3 means that $z = \dfrac{kxy}{w^3}.$

ILLUSTRATION 5. If $P = 10x^2y/z^3$, then P varies directly as x^2 and y, and inversely as z^3.

Suppose that certain variables are related by a variation equation, with an unknown constant of proportionality, k. Then, if one set of corresponding values of the variables is given, we can find k by substituting the values in the variation equation.

EXAMPLE 1. If y is proportional to x and w^2, and if $y = 36$ when $x = 2$ and $w = 3$, find y when $x = 3$ and $w = 4$.

SOLUTION. 1. We are given that $y = kw^2x$, where k is unknown.

2. To find k, substitute $(y = 36, x = 2, w = 3)$ in $y = kw^2x$:

$$36 = k(3^2)(2); \quad 36 = 18k \quad or \quad k = 2. \tag{4}$$

3. From Step 1, $\qquad\qquad\qquad y = 2w^2x. \tag{5}$

4. Substitute $(x = 3, w = 4)$ in (5):

$$y = 2 \cdot 16 \cdot 3 = 96.$$

Notice that the following steps were taken in Example 1.

1. *The variation statement was translated into an equation involving an unknown constant of proportionality.*

2. *The unknown constant was found by substituting given data.*

3. *The value of the constant of proportionality was substituted in the equation of variation, and this equation was used to obtain the value of one variable by use of given values of the other variables.*

Useful information may be obtained from an equation of variation even when the constant of proportionality cannot be found. This fact is responsible for many uses of the language of variation in the applications of mathematics in various fields.

EXAMPLE 2. The kinetic energy of a moving body is proportional to the square of its speed. Find the ratio of the kinetic energy of an automobile traveling at 50 miles per hour to the kinetic energy of the automobile traveling at 20 miles per hour.

SOLUTION. 1. Let E be the energy, and v the speed in miles per hour. Then, $E = kv^2$, where k is a constant of proportionality.

2. Let E_1 be the energy at 20 miles per hour, and E_2 the energy at 50 miles per hour. Then,

$$E_1 = k(20)^2 \quad or \quad E_1 = 400k; \tag{6}$$

$$E_2 = k(50)^2 \quad or \quad E_2 = 2500k. \tag{7}$$

3. From (6) and (7),

$$\frac{E_2}{E_1} = \frac{2500k}{400k} = \frac{25}{4} = 6\tfrac{1}{4}, \quad or \quad E_2 = (6\tfrac{1}{4})E_1.$$

EXERCISE 39

Introduce letters if necessary and express the relation by an equation.

1. W varies directly as u and inversely as v^3.
2. K is proportional to x^2 and y, and inversely proportional to z^3.
3. V varies as x and y, and is inversely proportional to w.
4. R varies jointly as $\sqrt{u}$, v, and $z^{\frac{3}{2}}$.
5. Z varies inversely as x^2, y^3, and $w^{\frac{1}{3}}$.
6. $(z - 3)$ is proportional to $(x + 5)$.
7. The area of a triangle is proportional to its base.
8. The volume of a sphere is proportional to the cube of its radius.
9. The volume of a specified quantity of a gas varies inversely as the pressure applied to it, if the temperature remains unchanged.
10. The weight of a body above the surface of the earth varies inversely as the square of the distance of the body from the earth's center.
11. The maximum safe load of a horizontal beam of a given material, supported at the ends, varies directly as the breadth and the square of the depth, and inversely as the distance between the supports.

By employing the data, obtain an equation relating the variables, with an explicit value for any associated constant which arises.

12. H is proportional to x^3, and $H = 20$ if $x = 2$.
13. W is inversely proportional to $\sqrt{y}$, and $w = 10$ if $y = 9$.
14. Z varies directly as x and y, and inversely as u^2; $Z = 30$ when $x = 5$, $y = 4$, and $u = 2$.

Find the specified quantity by use of an equation of variation.

15. If w is proportional to u, and if $w = 5$ when $u = 4$, find w when $u = 8$.
16. If v is inversely proportional to x and y, and if $v = 20$ when $x = 2$ and $y = 8$, find v when $x = 4$ and $y = 10$.
17. The distance fallen by a body, starting from a position of rest in a vacuum near the earth's surface, is proportional to the square of the time occupied in falling. If a body falls 256 feet in 4 seconds, how far will it fall in 11 seconds?
18. The force of a wind blowing on a certain surface varies directly as the area of the surface and the square of the speed of the wind. When the speed is 30 miles per hour, the force is 4 pounds per square foot of area. Find the force on 100 square feet of area when the speed is 50 miles per hour.
19. The power available in a jet of water varies jointly as the cube of the water's speed, and the cross-section area of the jet. If the power is 125 foot-pounds when the speed is 10 feet per second, and the area is 18 square inches, find the power when the speed is 6 feet per second and the area is 10 square inches.

20. The kinetic energy E of a moving mass is proportional to the mass and the square of the speed. If $E = 2500$ foot-pounds when a body of mass 64 pounds is moving at a speed of 50 feet per second, find E when a body of mass 40 pounds has a speed of 200 feet per second.

21. Kepler's third law concerning the motions of the planets in the solar system states that the square of the time for a planet to make a circuit of the sun is proportional to the cube of the planet's mean distance from the sun. The mean distances from the sun are approximately 93 million miles for the earth and 141 million miles for Mars. Find the time in years for one circuit of the sun by Mars.

22. See Problem 9. A certain amount of gas at a pressure of 50 pounds per square inch has a volume of 800 cubic feet. What is the pressure, if the gas is compressed to a volume of 200 cubic feet?

23. If y is proportional to x, and if $y = 8$ when $x = 4$, graph y as a function of x. Make a statement about the change in the value of y if $x > 0$ and x increases from a given value (a) by 200%; (b) by 30%.

24. Repeat Problem 23 if y is inversely proportional to x.

25. See Problem 11. If the maximum safe load is 2000 pounds for a beam 5 inches wide and 10 inches deep, with supports 12 feet apart, find the maximum load for a beam which is 4 inches wide and 8 inches deep, with supports 10 feet apart.

26. For the first beam involved in Problem 25, how far apart may the supports be placed if the load is to be 4000 pounds?

27. The approximate speed of a stream of water, necessary to move a round object, is proportional to the product of the square roots of the object's diameter and specific gravity. If a speed of 11.34 feet per second is needed to move a stone whose diameter is 1 foot and specific gravity is 4, how large a stone with specific gravity 6 can be moved by a stream whose speed is 22.68 feet per second?

28. The pressure of a given quantity of gas varies directly as the absolute temperature T and inversely as the volume V. At what temperature, with $V = 200$ cubic inches, will the pressure be three times that which exists when $T = 300°$ and $V = 500$ cubic inches?

29. Under given conditions with artificial light, the time of exposure necessary to photograph an object varies as the square of its distance from the light, and inversely as its candle power. If the exposure is .01 second when the light is 6 feet away, find the distance for the light if its candle power is doubled and the exposure is .02 second.

30. Newton's *Law of Gravitation* states that the force with which each of two masses of m pounds and M pounds attracts the other varies directly as the product of the masses and inversely as the square of the distance between the masses. Find the ratio of the force of attraction when two masses are 10^6 miles apart to the force when they are 10^5 miles apart.

EXERCISE 40
Review of Chapters 3–6

Any graph involved is assumed to be drawn in an xy-plane.
Find the x- and y-intercepts of the graph of the equation.

1. $3x - 5y = 20.$ **2.** $y = x^2 - 2x - 3.$ **3.** $x + 3 = 0.$ **4.** $y - 2 = 0.$

Find the slope and y-intercept of the line whose equation is given.

5. $2x + 3y - 5 = 0.$ **6.** $3y + 8x = 0.$ **7.** $4x - 2y = 7.$

Write an equation for the line satisfying the conditions.

8. Through $(4, -5)$ with slope $-\frac{1}{2}.$ **9.** Through $(-2, -4)$ and $(1, 5).$

10. Slope -3 and y-intercept 5.   **11.** x-intercept 2 and y-intercept $-3.$

12. Through $(2, -3)$ parallel to the line $2x - 5y = 4.$

' 13. Find the distance between the points $(5, -7)$ and $(2, 3)$ in an xy-plane where a single unit is used for measuring all distances.

14. Prove that the points $(2, -1)$, $(4, 2)$, and $(6, 5)$ are collinear.

15. If $f(x) = 2x^2 - 5x^{-3}$, find $f(-2)$; $f(3)$; $f(a^2b)$; $[f(2)]^2$; $f(x + 2).$

16. Let F be that function of a single variable, x, with the domain $(1, 2, 3, 4, 5, 6, 7, 8, 9)$, for which $F(x)$ is *the largest perfect square integer* which is at most as large as x. (a) Find the range of F. (b) Write the whole set of ordered pairs of numbers which form F. (c) Draw a diagram like Figure 16 on page 73 to show the correspondence between the domain and the range of F. (d) Let $y = F(x)$ and then draw a graph of F in an xy-plane.

Draw a graph of the function whose values are defined by the formula.

17. $2x - 3.$ **18.** $7.$ **19.** $-3x + 5.$ **20.** $x^2 - 6x + 7.$

21. Draw a graph of the function $f(x) = 9x - 3x^2 - x^3 - 5$ by use of $f(-3)$, $f(-2), f(-1), f(0), f(1), f(2), f(3),$ and $f(5).$

Solve the equation by the most convenient method.

22. $3x^2 = 20 - 2x^2.$ **23.** $8x^2 - 2x = 15.$ **24.** $4x^2 + 12x + 34 = 0.$

Without solving, find the nature of the roots of the equation.

25. $3x^2 - 5x = 7.$ **26.** $2x^2 + 7x = -9.$ **27.** $6x^2 + 11x - 35 = 0.$

28. Factor $(6x^2 + 11x - 35)$ by first solving an equation.

29. Solve $4x^2 - 12x + 7 = 0$ by use of (a) the quadratic formula; (b) the method of completing a square; (c) a graphical method.

Find the value of the constant k to satisfy the given condition.

30. The roots of $9x^2 - 2kx + 1 = 0$ are equal.

31. The graph of $y = 4x^2 - 12x + k$ is tangent to the x-axis.

32. The product of the roots of the equation $2x^2 - 8x + 3k = 0$ is 4.

33. The sum of the roots of the equation $3kx^2 - 2x = 8$ is 2.

34. Solve the equation $(2 - x) : 3 = (4 + 2x) : 2.$

35. Form a quadratic equation with the roots (a) 2 and -5; (b) $(2 \pm \frac{1}{3}i\sqrt{3})$.

Solve the system graphically and also algebraically. If both equations are linear, and if they are inconsistent, prove this fact by use of slopes.

36. $\begin{cases} 2x - 2y = 7, \\ 2x + 4y = -5. \end{cases}$
37. $\begin{cases} 3x + 2y = 5, \\ 6x + 4y = 9. \end{cases}$
38. $\begin{cases} x^2 + y^2 = 169, \\ x - y = 7. \end{cases}$

39. $\begin{cases} 8x^2 + y^2 = 14, \\ 4x^2 = y^2 - 8. \end{cases}$
40. $\begin{cases} x^2 + y^2 = 14, \\ (x + y)(x + 2y) = 0. \end{cases}$

41. Discuss the graph of $3x^2 + 4y^2 + 7 = 0$; of $2x^2 + (y - 1)^2 = 0$.

42. ·Graph the equations in the same xy-plane:
$$4x^2 - y^2 = 16; \qquad y^2 - 4x^2 = 16; \qquad y^2 - 4x^2 = 0.$$

43. Introduce literal numbers, and state the following fact by an equation: The lifting force exerted by the atmosphere on the wings of an airplane in flight is proportional to the area of the wings and the square of the airplane's air speed.

44. If H is proportional to x and inversely proportional to $\sqrt[3]{y}$, and if $H = 4$ when $x = 3$ and $y = 8$, find H if $y = 27$ and $x = 5$.

45. The electrical resistance of a wire of given material varies as its length and inversely as the square of the diameter. If a wire 300 feet long and .05 inch in diameter has a resistance of 30 ohms, (a) find the resistance of a wire which is 1000 feet long and .02 inch in diameter; (b) find the length of a wire whose resistance is 20 ohms and diameter is .03 inch.

Solve for x and y.

46. $\begin{cases} 4x^2 + 3y^2 = 7, \\ 2x^2 - xy + 2y^2 = 5. \end{cases}$
47. $\begin{cases} 2x^2 + xy - 6y^2 = 0, \\ (x + 3)(x + y - 1) = 0. \end{cases}$

48. Find the minimum value of the function $(2x^2 - 8x - 7)$.

49. Recall Problem 43. An airplane of an old model has an air speed of 250 miles per hour. In order to obtain three times the lifting force of the old model, a new plane is designed whose wing area is twice that in the old plane. What air speed (to the nearest mile) should be planned for the new plane?

Find all values of x, real or imaginary, which are solutions.

50. $3\sqrt{2 + x} - \sqrt{4x + 1} = 3.$
51. $2\sqrt{x + 1} - 2\sqrt{x} = 1.$

52. $3x^4 - x^2 - 10 = 0.$
53. $y^6 + 19y^3 - 216 = 0.$

54. Find all fourth roots of 625.

Certain Finite Series

65. Arithmetic progressions

A **sequence** of things is a set of things arranged in a definite order. An **arithmetic progression**, abbreviated **A.P.**, is a sequence of numbers called *terms*, each of which, after the first, is derived from the preceding one by *adding* to it a fixed number called the **common difference.**

ILLUSTRATION 1. In the arithmetic progression 9, 6, 3, 0, -3, $\cdots$, the common difference is -3. The 6th term would be -6.

Let b be the 1st term and d be the common difference in an A.P. Then, the 2d term is $b + d$; the 3d term is $b + 2d$; the 4th term is $b + 3d$. In each of these terms, the coefficient of d is 1 less than the number of the term. The nth term is the $(n - 1)$th after the 1st term and is obtained after d has been added $(n - 1)$ times. Hence, if l represents the nth term,

$$l = b + (n - 1)d. \tag{1}$$

Let S be the sum of the A.P. involved in (1). The first term is b; the common difference is d; the last term is l; the next to the last term is $l - d$, etc. On writing the sum of the n terms, forward and backward, we obtain

$$S = b + (b + d) + (b + 2d) + \cdots + (l - 2d) + (l - d) + l; \tag{2}$$

$$S = l + (l - d) + (l - 2d) + \cdots + (b + 2d) + (b + d) + b. \tag{3}$$

In (2), the three dots "$\cdots$" may be read "*and so forth up to.*" On adding corresponding sides of (2) and (3), we obtain

$$2S = (b + l) + (b + l) + (b + l) + \cdots + (b + l) + (b + l) + (b + l),$$

where there are n terms $(b + l)$. Hence, $2S = n(b + l)$ or

$$S = \frac{n}{2}(b + l). \tag{4}$$

Note 1. The sum of a sequence of numbers is called a *series*. If the sequence consists of just a finite number of numbers, their sum is called a *finite series*. In equation (4), we obtained a formula for the sum of a finite arithmetic series.

EXAMPLE 1. Find the sum of the A.P. $8 + 5 + 2 + \cdots$ *to twelve terms.*

SOLUTION. First obtain l from (1) with $b = 8$, $d = -3$, and $n = 12$:

$$l = 8 + 11(-3) = -25; \quad \textit{from (4)}, \quad S = 6(8 - 25) = -102.$$

On substituting $l = b + (n - 1)d$ in (4), we obtain

$$S = \frac{n}{2}\,[2b + (n - 1)d]. \tag{5}$$

We call b, d, l, n, and S the **elements** of the general A.P. The elements are related by (1), (4), and (5).

EXAMPLE 2. Find d and S in an A.P. where $b = 2$, $l = 402$, and $n = 26$.

SOLUTION. 1. From (4), $S = 13(404) = 5252.$

2. From (1), $402 = 2 + 25d; \quad \text{hence}, \quad d = 16.$

EXERCISE 41

Does the sequence form an arithmetic progression?

1. 3, 7, 11, 15.   **2.** 15, 17, 20, 22.   **3.** 23, 20, 17.   **4.** 35, 32, 30, 28.

Find the value of k for which the sequence forms an A.P.

5. 3, 8, k.   **6.** 25, 21, k.   **7.** 15, k, 13.   **8.** k, 17, 23.

HINT. If b, h, and w form an A.P., then $h - b = w - h$.

Find the specified term of the A.P. *by use of a formula.*

9. Given terms: 4, 7, 10; find the 50th term.

10. Given terms: -5, -8, -11; find the 29th term.

11. Given terms: 3, $3\frac{1}{4}$, $3\frac{1}{2}$; find the 83d term.

Find the last term and the sum of the A.P. *by use of formulas.*

12. 8, 13, 18, $\cdots$ *to* 15 *terms.*   **13.** 13, 8, 3, $\cdots$ *to* 17 *terms.*

14. 3, 5, 7, $\cdots$ *to* 41 *terms.*   **15.** 2.06, 2.02, 1.98, $\cdots$ *to* 33 *terms.*

16. 9, 6, 3, $\cdots$ *to* 28 *terms.*   **17.** 5, $4\frac{1}{2}$, 4, $\cdots$ *to* 81 *terms.*

Certain of b, d, l, n, and S are given. Find the other elements.

18. $b = 10$, $l = 410$, $n = 26$.   **19.** $b = 27$, $l = 11$, $d = -\frac{1}{4}$.

20. $b = 4$, $l = 72$, $n = 18$.   **21.** $b = 50$, $l = 0$, $d = -\frac{5}{2}$.

22. Find the 45th term in an A.P. where the 3d term is 7 and $d = \frac{1}{3}$.

23. Find the sum of all even integers from 10 to 380 inclusive.

24. Find the sum of all odd integers from 15 to 361 inclusive.

25. Find the sum of all positive integral multiples of 5 less than 498.

Note 1. The 1st term, b, and the last term, l, in an A.P. are called its *extremes*, and the other terms are called *arithmetic means* between b and l. An order *to insert k arithmetic means* between b and l implies that we are to find a sequence of k numbers which, when inserted between b and l, complete an A.P. with b and l as the extremes.

Insert the specified number of arithmetic means.

26. Five, between 13 and -11.   **27.** Four, between 23 and 16.

Hint *for Problem 26.* The means will complete an A.P. of 7 terms with $b = 13$ and $l = -11$. First find d from $l = b + (n-1)d$; then compute the intermediate terms between b and l.

28. Seven, between 4 and 8.   **29.** Eight, between $\frac{3}{4}$ and $6\frac{3}{4}$.

Note 2. When a *single* arithmetic mean is inserted between two numbers, it is called **THE** *arithmetic mean* of the numbers. Thus, if A is the arithmetic mean of b and c, we have the arithmetic progression b, A, c, and then $A - b = c - A$, or $2A = b + c$. Hence,

$$A = \tfrac{1}{2}(b + c). \tag{1}$$

Find the arithmetic mean of the numbers.

30. 8, 46.   **31.** 16, 54.   **32.** $-20, -59$.   **33.** $-16, 20$.   **34.** x, y.

35. A man invests \$800 at the beginning of each year for 15 years at 4% simple interest. Find the accumulated value of his investments at the end of 15 years if no interest has been withdrawn.

36. The bottom rung of a ladder is 26 inches long and each other rung is one half inch shorter than the rung below it. If the ladder has 20 rungs, how many feet of wood were used in making the rungs?

37. In a pile of logs, each layer contains one more log than the layer above, and the top layer contains just one log. If there are 105 logs in the pile, how many layers are there?

38. If an object falls from rest in a vacuum near sea level, then, approximately, the distance fallen in the 1st second is 16 feet, and in each succeeding second the object falls 32 feet farther than in the preceding second. How far does the object fall in 20 seconds?

39. A contractor has agreed to pay a penalty if he uses more than a specified length of time to finish a certain job. The penalties for excess time are \$25 for the 1st day and, thereafter, \$5 more for each day than for the preceding day. If he pays a total penalty of \$4050, how many excess days did he need to finish the work?

40. A mountain climber ascends 1000 feet in the first hour, and 100 feet less in each succeeding hour than in the preceding hour. When will he be 5400 feet above his starting point?

Find the total money paid by the debtor in discharging his debt.

41. *Debtor borrows* \$6000. Pays, at the end of each year for 12 years, \$500 of the principal and simple interest at 4% on all principal left unpaid during the year.

42. *Debtor borrows* \$15,000. Pays, at the end of each year for 15 years, \$1000 of the principal and simple interest at 5% on all principal left unpaid during the year.

66. Geometric progressions

A **geometric progression** (abbreviated **G.P.**) is a sequence of numbers called *terms*, each of which, after the first, is obtained by *multiplying* the preceding term by a fixed number called the **common ratio.** The common ratio is equal to the *ratio of any term, after the first, to the one preceding it.*

ILLUSTRATION 1. In the G.P. $(16, -8, +4, -2, \cdots)$, the common ratio is $-\frac{1}{2}$; the 5th term would be $(-\frac{1}{2})(-2) = +1$.

To determine whether or not a sequence of numbers forms a G.P., we *divide* each number by the one which precedes it. All of these ratios are equal if the terms form a G.P. In particular, if (a, b, c) form a G.P., then $b/a = c/b$.

ILLUSTRATION 2. If $(a, 10, 50)$ form a G.P., then $\dfrac{10}{a} = \dfrac{50}{10}$, or $a = 2$.

If the terms of a G.P. are *reversed*, the terms will form a G.P. whose common ratio is the *reciprocal* of the ratio for the given G.P.

ILLUSTRATION 3. In the G.P. $(4, 8, 16, 32)$, the common ratio is 2. When the terms are reversed, we have $(32, 16, 8, 4)$, where the ratio is $\frac{1}{2}$.

ILLUSTRATION 4. The G.P. (a, ar, ar^2, ar^3) has the common ratio r, whereas the G.P. (ar^3, ar^2, ar, a) has the common ratio ar^2/ar^3 or $1/r$.

Let a be the 1st term and r be the common ratio in a G.P. Then, the 2d term is ar; the 3d term is ar^2. In each of these terms, the exponent of r is 1 less than the number of the term. Similarly, the 8th term is ar^7. The nth term is the $(n-1)$th after the 1st and hence is found by multiplying a by $(n-1)$ factors r, or by r^{n-1}. Hence, if l represents the nth term,

$$l = ar^{n-1}. \tag{1}$$

ILLUSTRATION 5. If $a = 3$ and $r = 2$, the 7th term is $3(2^6) = 192$.

Let S be the sum of the first n terms of the G.P. considered in (1). The terms are $(a, ar, ar^2, \cdots, ar^{n-2}, ar^{n-1})$, where ar^{n-2} is the $(n-1)$th term. Hence,

$$S = a + ar + ar^2 + \cdots + ar^{n-2} + ar^{n-1}; \tag{2}$$

$$Sr = ar + ar^2 + ar^3 + \cdots + ar^{n-1} + ar^n; \tag{3}$$

in (3) we multiplied both sides of (2) by r. On subtracting each side of equation (3) from the corresponding side of (2), we obtain

$$S - Sr = a - ar^n, \tag{4}$$

because each term, except ar^n, on the right in (3) cancels a corresponding term in (2). From (4), we find $S(1 - r) = a - ar^n$, or

$$S = \frac{a - ar^n}{1 - r}. \tag{5}$$

Since $l = ar^{n-1}$, then $rl = ar^n$. Hence, from (5),

$$S = \frac{a - rl}{1 - r},$$ (6)

which is particularly useful when l is given. From (5),

$$S = a\frac{1 - r^n}{1 - r}.$$ (7)

EXAMPLE 1. Find the sum of the G.P.   2, 6, 18, $\cdots$ to six terms.

SOLUTION. $n = 6$; $a = 2$; $r = 3$. From (5),

$$S = \frac{2 - 2 \cdot 3^6}{1 - 3} = \frac{2 - 1458}{-2} = 728.$$

When a sufficient number of the elements (a, r, n, l, S) are given, we find the others by use of (1), (5), and (6).

EXAMPLE 2. If $S = 750$, $r = 2$, and $l = 400$, find n and a.

SOLUTION. 1. From (6), $750 = \frac{a - 800}{1 - 2}$; hence, $a = 50$.

2. From $l = ar^{n-1}$, $400 = 50(2^{n-1})$; $2^{n-1} = \frac{400}{50} = 8$;

$2^{n-1} = 2^3$; hence, $n - 1 = 3$, or $n = 4$.

EXAMPLE 3. Find an expression for the sum

$$(1.04)^3 + (1.04)^5 + (1.04)^7 + \cdots + (1.04)^{21}.$$ (8)

SOLUTION. 1. Since $(1.04)^5 \div (1.04)^3 = (1.04)^2$, etc., the terms in (8) form a G.P. with

$$a = (1.04)^3,   r = (1.04)^2,   and   l = (1.04)^{21}.$$ (9)

2. It is not necessary to find the number of terms, n. From (6),

$$S = \frac{(1.04)^3 - (1.04)^2(1.04)^{21}}{1 - (1.04)^2} = \frac{(1.04)^3 - (1.04)^{23}}{1 - (1.04)^2}.$$

The 1st term, a, and last term, l, of a G.P. are called its *extremes*. The other terms are called *geometric means* between a and l. To insert k geometric means between a and l, means to find a sequence of k numbers which, when placed between a and l, give a G.P. with a and l as the extremes. We shall ask only for real-valued means.

EXAMPLE 4. Insert two geometric means between 6 and 16/9.

SOLUTION. After the means are inserted they will complete a G.P. of 4 terms with $a = 6$ and $l = 16/9$. We shall find the ratio r and then the desired terms of the G.P. From $l = ar^{n-1}$ with $n = 4$,

$$\tfrac{16}{9} = 6r^3;   r^3 = \tfrac{8}{27};   r = \sqrt[3]{\tfrac{8}{27}} = \tfrac{2}{3}.$$

The G.P. is $(6, 4, \tfrac{8}{3}, \tfrac{16}{9})$. The geometric means are 4 and $\tfrac{8}{3}$.

EXERCISE 42

Write the first four terms of the G.P. for the data.

1. $a = 3, r = 5.$ **2.** $a = 2, r = -3.$ **3.** $a = 64, r = -\frac{1}{2}.$

If the terms form a G.P., write two more terms for it.

4. 3, 12, 48.   **5.** 15, $-\frac{15}{2}, \frac{15}{4}.$ **6.** 81, $-27, 9.$ **7.** 0, 1, 3, 9.

8. $a, au, au^2.$ **9.** $(1.03)^4, (1.03)^7, (1.03)^{10}.$

10. $\sqrt{1.02}, 1.02, (1.02)^{\frac{3}{2}}.$ **11.** $(1.01)^{-8}, (1.01)^{-6}, (1.01)^{-4}.$

Find x if the numbers form a G.P.

12. 3, 18, $x.$ **13.** $x, 7, 28.$ **14.** 9, $x, 81.$ **15.** $x, -6, 30.$

By use of a formula, find the specified term of the G.P. without finding intermediate terms.

16. 6th term of 2, 6, 18.   **17.** 9th term of 3, $-6, 12.$

18. 8th term of 28, 14, 7.   **19.** 8th term of 7, $-\frac{7}{2}, \frac{7}{4}.$

Find the last term and the sum of the G.P. by use of formulas.

20. 4, $-12, 36,$ *to 6 terms.*   **21.** 18, $-1.8, .18,$ *to 9 terms.*

22. $\frac{1}{64}, -\frac{1}{32}, \frac{1}{16},$ *to 8 terms.*   **23.** 2, $2a, 2a^2,$ *to 10 terms.*

Find the sum of the G.P. by a formula, without finding other terms.

24. $32 + 16 + 8 + \cdots + \frac{1}{64}.$ **25.** $4 + 12 + 36 + \cdots + 4(729).$

Find the missing elements of the G.P.

26. $r = 10, a = .0001, l = 1000.$ **27.** $a = 5, l = -1215, S = -910.$

28. $a = 512, r = \frac{1}{2}, l = 1.$ **29.** $a = 972, r = \frac{1}{3}, l = \frac{4}{3}.$

Find the specified term of the G.P. without finding its first term.

30. The 10th term, if the 7th term is 4 and $r = 3.$

31. The 14th term, if the 9th term is 250 and $r = .1.$

Insert the specified number of geometric means.

32. Six, between 1 and 128.   **33.** Three, between $\frac{1}{16}$ and 10,000.

34. Six, between .3 and 3,000,000.   **35.** Four, between $\frac{2}{3}$ and 162.

If x and y are of the same sign, and if a single geometric mean G of the same sign is inserted between x and y, then G is called **THE** *geometric mean of x and y; thus, (x, G, y) form a G.P. Find the geometric mean of the numbers.*

36. $\frac{1}{9}, 81.$ **37.** $\frac{1}{4}, 36.$ **38.** $x, y.$ **39.** $-4, -25.$

Find an expression for the sum by use of a progression formula, and simplify the exponents. Use (6) on page 126, when convenient.

40. $1 + (1.02) + (1.02)^2 + \cdots + (1.02)^{44}.$

41. $1 + (1.04) + (1.04)^2 + \cdots + (1.04)^{63}.$

42. $(1.03)^3 + (1.03)^4 + (1.03)^5 + \cdots + (1.03)^{21}.$

43. $(1.02)^5 + (1.02)^8 + (1.02)^{11} + \cdots + (1.02)^{50}.$

44. $(1.05)^{-18} + (1.05)^{-16} + (1.05)^{-14} + \cdots + (1.05)^{-2}.$

67. Applications of progressions

When a sequence of terms is suspected of forming an A.P., compute the explicit values of the first few terms to verify the existence of a common difference. If the sequence is suspected of forming a G.P., write the first few terms, *without computation*, in a form which will *exhibit any factor which enters to successive powers*.

In a problem where it is inferred that a progression enters, first we must decide whether an A.P. or a G.P. occurs. Then, we should specify the values of corresponding elements of the progression. Finally, formulas for progressions should be employed to obtain the unknown elements, which yield the solution of the problem.

EXAMPLE 1. A ball is dropped from a height of 100 feet. On each rebound, the ball rises to one half of the height from which it last fell. What distance has the ball traveled up to the instant it hits the ground for the 12th time?

PARTIAL SOLUTION. The first few distances traveled are as follows:

1st *fall*, 100′; 1st *rise and* 2d *fall*, $2(\frac{1}{2})(100′)$; 2d *rise and* 3d *fall*, $\frac{1}{2}(100′)$.

The total distance, in feet, is equal to 100 plus the sum of the G.P.

$$100, \tfrac{1}{2}(100), \tfrac{1}{4}(100), \cdots, \textit{to eleven terms.}$$

MISCELLANEOUS EXERCISE 43

Solve by use of formulas for progressions.

1. A man piles 150 logs in layers so that the top layer contains 3 logs and each lower layer has one more log than the layer above. How many logs are in the lowest layer?

2. The path of each swing, after the first, of a pendulum bob is .9 as long as the preceding swing. If the first swing is 25 inches long, how far does the bob travel on the first 5 swings?

3. In a lottery, the 1st ticket drawn will pay the holder 10¢ and each succeeding ticket twice as much as the preceding one. Find the total amount paid on the first 12 tickets drawn.

4. If none of your ancestors appears in more than one line of descent, how many ancestors have you had in the generations since the discovery of America in 1492 by Columbus? Assume that each generation covers approximately 33 years.

5. Total prize money of $1480 is to be divided among 8 contestants so that the lowest will receive $10 and each other a fixed amount more than the preceding person. What prize money goes to the leader?

6. A contractor agreed that, if his job was not done by a certain date, he would pay $100 for the 1st day of delay and, for each succeeding day, $5 more than for the preceding day. How many days after the stipulated date did he use, if his penalty was $1080?

7. An investment in an oil acreage paid a man, in each year after the 1st year, three times as much as in the preceding year. If the investment paid $45,375 in the first five years, how much did it pay in the 1st year and in the 5th year?

8. The following problem appeared in a book by the Hindu mathematician BHĀSKARA about A.D. 1150. "In an expedition to seize his enemy's elephants, a king marched 2 yojanas the first day. Say, intelligent calculator, with what increasing size of daily march did he proceed, since he reached his foe's city, a distance of 80 yojanas, in a week?"

9. Find an expression for the sum of the first n positive odd integers.

10. Prove that the squares of the terms of a G.P. also form a G.P. Then, state a more general theorem of the same nature.

11. Find an A.P. of four terms whose sum is 10, if the sum of their squares is 70.

12. Prove that the reciprocals of the terms of a G.P. form a G.P.

13. If $y = 3x + 7$, find the sum of the values of y corresponding to the successive integral values $x = 1, 2, 3, \cdots, 40$.

14. If $y = ax + b$, prove that the successive values of y, corresponding to the successive integral values of x, form an A.P.

15. Suppose that $r \neq 1$, $a \neq 0$, and $n_1, n_2, \cdots, n_k$ are a sequence of k integers. Prove that, if $a, ar^{n_1}, ar^{n_2}, \cdots, ar^{n_k}$ form a G.P., then $0, n_1, n_2, \cdots, n_k$ form an A.P.

Note 1. If P is the value of a quantity *now*, and if its value increases at the rate i (a decimal) per year, then the new value at the end of one year is $(P + Pi)$, or $P(1 + i)$. That is, *the value at the end of any year is $(1 + i)$ times the value at the end of the preceding year.* The values at the ends of the years form a G.P. whose common ratio is $(1 + i)$. If A is the value at the end of n years, then

$$A = P(1 + i)^n. \tag{1}$$

This formula is referred to as the **compound interest law** because, if a principal P is invested now at the rate i, compounded annually, the amount A at the end of n years will be $P(1 + i)^n$. In all of the following problems, it will be assumed that any *rate* is *constant*. In texts on the mathematics of investment, convenient tables are available for use with (1).

Find compact expressions for the results in Problems 16 and 17.

16. If 200 units of a commodity are consumed in a first year, and if the annual rate of increase in consumption is 5%, (a) what amount is consumed in the 8th year; (b) in the first 15 years?

17. A corporation will sell $2,000,000 worth of products this year, and sales are expected to increase at the rate of 5% per year. Find the total anticipated sales in the first 10 years.

18. The population of a city increased from 262,440 to 400,000 in 4 years. Find the rate of increase per year.

19. A piece of property was purchased 3 years ago for $8100 and its value now is $19,200. Find the annual rate at which the value increased.

20. The value of a certain quantity *decreases* at the rate w (a decimal) per year. If H is the value now, and K is the value at the end of n years, prove that $K = H(1 - w)^n$. This formula is the basis for computing depreciation charges in business under the so-called *constant-percentage* method. Also, the formula is met under the name of the *law of compound discount* in the mathematics of investment.

21. An airplane was purchased for $33,750 and its value three years later was $10,000. Find the rate per year at which the value depreciated.

Note 2. A sequence of numbers is said to form a *harmonic* * *progression* if their reciprocals form an *arithmetic progression.* To insert k harmonic means between two numbers, first insert k arithmetic means between the *reciprocals of the numbers;* the reciprocals of the arithmetic means are the harmonic means.

★*Insert the specified number of harmonic means.*

22. Four, between $\frac{1}{3}$ and $\frac{1}{13}$.   **23.** Five, between $\frac{1}{2}$ and $\frac{1}{26}$.

24. Four, between $\frac{5}{3}$ and $\frac{5}{11}$.   **25.** Four, between $\frac{3}{7}$ and $\frac{3}{17}$.

★*If (c, H, d) form a harmonic progression, then H is called* **THE** *harmonic mean of c and d. Find the harmonic mean of the numbers.*

26. $\frac{1}{2}$, $\frac{1}{18}$.   **27.** 4, 8.   **28.** $-6, 5$.   **29.** 6, 12.   **30.** x and y.

★68. Geometric progressions with infinitely many terms

Let S_n represent the sum of the progression $a, ar, ar^2, \cdots, ar^{n-1}$. Then, by (5) on page 125,

$$a + ar + ar^2 + \cdots + ar^{n-1} = S_n = \frac{a}{1-r} - \frac{ar^n}{1-r}. \tag{1}$$

Now, let us consider an endless geometric progression,

$$a, ar, ar^2, \cdots \text{ to infinitely many terms.} \tag{2}$$

We shall call (2) an *infinite* G.P. We shall develop a meaning for the notion of the *sum* of (2) if $|r| < 1$, that is, if $-1 < r < 1$.

ILLUSTRATION 1. Consider the infinite geometric progression

$$1, \frac{1}{2}, \frac{1}{4}, \cdots, \frac{1}{2^{n-1}}, \cdots \text{ to infinitely many terms.} \tag{3}$$

In (3), $r = \frac{1}{2}$; *the nth term is* $\frac{1}{2^{n-1}}$; $1 - r = \frac{1}{2}$; $ar^n = \frac{1}{2^n}$.

---

* Suppose that a set of strings of the same diameter and substance are stretched to uniform tension. If the lengths of the strings form a harmonic progression, a harmonious sound results if two or more strings are caused to vibrate at one time. This fact accounts for the name *harmonic progression.*

By (1), $\qquad 1 + \dfrac{1}{2} + \dfrac{1}{4} + \dfrac{1}{8} + \cdots + \dfrac{1}{2^{n-1}} = S_n = 2 - \dfrac{1}{2^{n-1}}.$ $\qquad$ (4)

If n grows larger, without limit, the term $1/2^{n-1}$ grows smaller, and is as near to zero as we please, if n is sufficiently large. Thus, if $n = 65$,

$$\frac{1}{2^{n-1}} = \frac{1}{2^{64}} = \frac{1}{18,446,744,073,709,551,616},$$

which is practically zero. Hence, in (4), S_n will be as near to $(2 - 0)$ as we please for all values of n which are sufficiently large. To summarize this statement we say that, *as n becomes infinite, S_n approaches the* **limit 2,** and we call 2 the *sum* of the progression $1, \frac{1}{2}, \frac{1}{4}, \frac{1}{8}, \cdots$ *to infinitely many terms.* We sometimes use "$n \to \infty$" to abbreviate "*n becomes infinite.*" Then, our conclusion can be written briefly *limit* $S_n = 2$.
$$\underset{n \to \infty}{}$$

We return to (2), with $|r| < 1$. Then, as $n \to \infty$, the absolute value of the numerator ar^n in (1) grows smaller, and is as near to zero as we please for all values of n sufficiently large. Hence, from (1) we see that, as $n \to \infty$, the value of S_n approaches

$$\left(\frac{a}{1-r} - \frac{0}{1-r} \right), \quad or$$

$$\underset{n \to \infty}{limit}\ S_n = \frac{a}{1-r}. \qquad (5)$$

This limit of the sum of n terms, as n becomes infinite, is called the **sum** of the geometric progression with infinitely many terms. If S represents this sum, then $\qquad\qquad\qquad\qquad S = \dfrac{a}{1-r}.$ $\qquad$ (6)

Thus, **if $|r| < 1$,** we agree to write

$$(a + ar + ar^2 + \cdots \textit{ to infinitely many terms}) = \frac{a}{1-r}. \qquad (7)$$

Note 1. Recognize that S in (6) is *not a sum in the ordinary sense,* but is *the limit of the sum of n terms as n grows large without bound.*

ILLUSTRATION 2. By use of (7), with $a = 5$ and $r = \frac{1}{2}$,

$$\left(5 + \frac{5}{2} + \frac{5}{4} + \cdots \textit{ to infinitely many terms} \right) = \frac{5}{1 - \frac{1}{2}} = 10.$$

Practically, this means that, by adding enough terms, we can obtain as close to 10 as we may desire. Thus, $S_{11} = 9\frac{1019}{1024}$.

An expression of the form

$$u_1 + u_2 + u_3 + \cdots \textit{ to infinitely many terms} \qquad (8)$$

is called an **infinite series.** Accordingly, the expression on the left in (7) is referred to as the *infinite geometric series.*

In any infinite series such as (8), let S_n represent the sum of the first n terms. Then, we say that the series *has a sum S*, and call the series a **convergent infinite series** which *converges* to S, in case *the limit of S_n is S as n becomes infinite.* If S_n has no limit as n becomes infinite, we say that the series is **divergent,** or *diverges.* In this section we have proved that the infinite geometric series in (7) has a sum, or *converges,* when $|r| < 1$. When $|r| \geq 1$, the series is divergent, or *does not have a sum,* because in this case S_n in (1) does not approach a limit as $n \to \infty$. Thus, for the G.P. $(1, 2, 4, \cdots)$ where $r = 2$, we find that S_n increases beyond all bounds as $n \to \infty$.

★69. Infinite repeating decimals

Any infinite repeating decimal can be interpreted as a symbol for *the sum of an infinite geometric series,* as in the following example. The sum of the resulting series can be computed by the method of Section 68, and, in all cases, *the result will be a rational number.*

EXAMPLE 1. Find a rational number equal to the infinite repeating decimal $.5818181 \cdots$.

SOLUTION. Because of the meaning of the decimal notation,

$$.5818181 \cdots = .5 + .081 + .00081 + \cdots \text{ to infinitely many terms,}$$

where we notice that $(.081 + .00081 + \cdots)$ is an infinite geometric series with $a = .081$, and $r = .01$. By use of (7) in Section 68,

$$.081 + .00081 + .0000081 + \cdots = \frac{.081}{1 - .01} = \frac{.081}{.99} = \frac{9}{110}.$$

Hence, $.5818181 \cdots = .5 + \frac{9}{110} = \frac{5}{10} + \frac{9}{110} = \frac{32}{55}.$

We recall that any terminating decimal is a rational number. Thus, $3.583 = 3583/1000$. Also, by the method of Example 1, we conclude that **any infinite repeating decimal is a rational number.** On the other hand, let m/n be any rational number, where m and n are integers and $n \neq 0$. Then, in arithmetic, we met illustrations of the fact that, when the division $m \div n$ is carried out in decimal form, we obtain either a terminating decimal or an infinite repeating decimal. The preceding remarks yield the following conclusion:

Any decimal which terminates, or is an infinite repeating decimal, is a rational number and, conversely, any rational number is equal to a decimal of one of the preceding types.

In other words, the set of *all rational numbers,* in their decimal forms, is the set of *all decimals which terminate or are infinite repeating decimals.* This result then gives a proper background for the definition of the *irrational numbers* as the set of *all infinite nonrepeating decimals.* Each of these is the sum of an infinite series, as discussed in more advanced mathematics.

★EXERCISE 44

Find the sum of the infinite geometric series by the established formula.

1. $5 + \frac{5}{3} + \frac{5}{9} + \cdots$.

2. $16 + 4 + 1 + \frac{1}{4} + \cdots$.

3. $15 + \frac{15}{2} + \frac{15}{4} + \cdots$.

4. $6 - 3 + \frac{3}{2} - \frac{3}{4} + \cdots$.

5. $1 - \frac{1}{5} + \frac{1}{25} - \cdots$.

6. $1 - \frac{1}{4} + \frac{1}{16} - \cdots$.

7. $1 + .01 + .0001 + \cdots$.

8. $.8 + .08 + .008 + \cdots$.

Find a rational number, in the form m/n where m and n are integers, which is equal to the infinite repeating decimal, where the repeating part is written three times.

9. $.222\cdots$.

10. $.555\cdots$.

11. $.666\cdots$.

12. $.999\cdots$.

13. $.1666\cdots$.

14. $.8333\cdots$.

15. $.090909\cdots$.

16. $.272727\cdots$.

17. $.212121\cdots$.

18. $.2333\cdots$.

19. $3.111\cdots$.

20. $2.666\cdots$.

21. $.363636\cdots$.

22. $.234234234\cdots$.

23. $10.060606\cdots$.

24. $242.424\cdots$.

25. $16.2162162\cdots$.

26. $26.06060\cdots$.

27. $.142857142857142857\cdots$.

28. $.076923076923076923\cdots$.

29. Let m and n be positive integers, with $m < n$. Prove that, if the division $m \div n$ is carried out in decimal form, we obtain either a terminating decimal or an infinite repeating decimal.

70. Expansion of a positive integral power of a binomial

By multiplication, we obtain the following results:

$$(x + y)^1 = x + y;$$
$$(x + y)^2 = x^2 + 2xy + y^2;$$
$$(x + y)^3 = x^3 + 3x^2y + 3xy^2 + y^3;$$
$$(x + y)^4 = x^4 + 4x^3y + 6x^2y^2 + 4xy^3 + y^4.$$

We see that, if $n = 1, 2, 3$, or 4, *the expansion of $(x + y)^n$ contains $(n + 1)$* **terms** *with the following properties:*

I. *In any term the sum of the exponents of x and y is n.*

II. *The first term is x^n, and in each other term the exponent of x is 1 less than in the preceding term.*

III. *The second term is $nx^{n-1}y$, and in each succeeding term the exponent of y is 1 more than in the preceding term.*

IV. *If the coefficient of any term is multiplied by the exponent of x in that term and if the product is divided by the number of that term, the quotient obtained is the coefficient of the next term.*

ILLUSTRATION 1. In $(x + y)^4$, the 3d term is $6x^2y^2$. By Property IV, we obtain $(6 \cdot 2) \div 3$, or 4, as the coefficient of the 4th term.

V. *The coefficients of terms equidistant from the ends are the same.*

We shall assume that Properties I to V are true if n is any positive integer. The theorem which justifies this assumption is called the **binomial theorem,** to be proved on page 301.

EXAMPLE 1. Expand $(c + w)^7$.

SOLUTION. 1. By use of Properties I, II, and III, we obtain

$$(c + w)^7 = c^7 + 7c^6w + \quad c^5w^2 + \quad c^4w^3 + \quad c^3w^4 + \quad c^2w^5 + \quad cw^6 + w^7,$$

where spaces are left for the unknown coefficients.

2. By Property IV, the coefficient of the third term is $(7 \cdot 6) \div 2$, or 21; that of the fourth term is $(21 \cdot 5) \div 3$, or 35.

3. By Property V, we obtain the other coefficients; hence,

$$(c + w)^7 = c^7 + 7c^6w + 21c^5w^2 + 35c^4w^3 + 35c^3w^4 + 21c^2w^5 + 7cw^6 + w^7.$$

EXAMPLE 2. Expand $\left(2a - \dfrac{w}{3}\right)^6$, or $\left[(2a) + \left(-\dfrac{w}{3}\right)\right]^6$.

SOLUTION. We use Properties I to V with $x = 2a$ and $y = -\dfrac{w}{3}$:

$$\left(2a - \frac{w}{3}\right)^6 = (2a)^6 + 6(2a)^5\left(-\frac{w}{3}\right) + 15(2a)^4\left(-\frac{w}{3}\right)^2 + 20(2a)^3\left(-\frac{w}{3}\right)^3$$

$$+ 15(2a)^2\left(-\frac{w}{3}\right)^4 + 6(2a)\left(-\frac{w}{3}\right)^5 + \left(-\frac{w}{3}\right)^6, \quad or$$

$$\left(2a - \frac{w}{3}\right)^6 = 64a^6 - 64a^5w + \frac{80}{3}a^4w^2 - \frac{160}{27}a^3w^3 + \frac{20}{27}a^2w^4 - \frac{4}{81}aw^5 + \frac{w^6}{729}.$$

Note 1. Suppose that n is a positive integer. Then, the symbol $n!$ is read "n *factorial*" and is an abbreviation for *the product of all integers from* 1 *to n inclusive.* If $n = 0$, we define $n! = 1$; that is, $0! = 1$. Thus, $5! = 1 \cdot 2 \cdot 3 \cdot 4 \cdot 5 = 120$.

By use of properties (I)–(IV), we obtain

$$\left. \begin{aligned} (x + y)^n &= x^n + nx^{n-1}y + \frac{n(n - 1)}{2!}\,x^{n-2}y^2 + \cdots \\ &+ \frac{n(n - 1) \cdots (n - r + 1)}{r!}\,x^{n-r}y^r + \cdots + y^n. \end{aligned} \right\} \tag{1}$$

The general term involving $x^{n-r}y^r$ in (1) can be verified by successive applications of (IV). We shall prove that this general term is correct on page 301. We refer to (1) as the **binomial formula.** By use of the expression for the term in (1) involving $x^{n-r}y^r$, we can write any term of (1) without writing the other terms.

ILLUSTRATION 2. The term involving y^4 in the expansion of $(x + y)^7$ is

$$\frac{7 \cdot 6 \cdot 5 \cdot 4}{4!}\,x^3y^4 \quad or \quad 35x^3y^4.$$

Note 2. The following array is called *Pascal's Triangle.* The rows give the coefficients in the successive positive integral powers of $(x + y)$. To

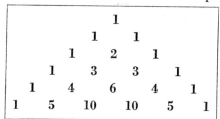

form any row after the second, we first place 1 at the left; the 2d number is the sum of the 1st and 2d numbers in the preceding row; the 3d number in the new row is the sum of the 2d and 3d numbers in the preceding row; etc. This triangle was known to Chinese mathematicians in the early fourteenth century.

EXERCISE 45

Expand each power by use of Properties I *to* V.

1. $(a + b)^5$.
2. $(c - d)^6$.
3. $(x - y)^8$.
4. $(c + 3)^5$.
5. $(2 + a)^4$.
6. $(x - 2a)^7$.
7. $(3b - y)^6$.
8. $(2c + 3d)^3$.
9. $(a + b^2)^3$.
10. $(c^3 - 3d)^4$.
11. $(a^2 - b^2)^6$.
12. $(c - x^3)^5$.
13. $(x - \frac{1}{2})^5$.
14. $(1 - a)^8$.
15. $(\sqrt{x} - \sqrt{y})^6$.
16. $(x^{\frac{1}{4}} + a)^5$.
17. $(-a + y^{-2})^4$.
18. $(z^{-3} - x)^5$.
19. $(x^{\frac{1}{2}} - 2a^{-1})^4$.

Find only the first three terms of the expansion. All letters used in exponents represent positive integers.

20. $(a + 12)^{15}$.
21. $(c - 3)^{25}$.
22. $(a^2 + b^3)^{20}$.
23. $(1 + 2a)^{10}$.
24. $(1 - .1)^{22}$.
25. $(1 + .2)^{12}$.
26. $(1 - \sqrt{2})^{12}$.
27. $(1 - 3x^3)^{18}$.
28. $(2x - a^2)^{30}$.
29. $(x^{\frac{1}{2}} + b)^{14}$.
30. $(a^{-1} + 3)^{26}$.
31. $(x - a^{-2})^{11}$.
32. $(x - y)^n$.
33. $(a + x)^k$.
34. $(x^2 - y)^m$.
35. $(w^2 + z)^h$.

Compute the power correct to three decimal places by using only as many terms as necessary in a binomial expansion.

36. $(1.01)^8$.
37. $(1.02)^9$.
38. $(1.03)^{11}$.
39. $(1.01)^{20}$.

HINT. $(1.01)^8 = (1 + .01)^8 = 1 + 8(.01) + 28(.01)^2 + \cdots$.

Find only the specified term without finding other terms.

40. Term involving y^6 in the expansion of $(x + y)^8$.
41. Term involving x^5 in the expansion of $(u + x)^{11}$.
42. Term involving y^4 in the expansion of $(x - y)^{10}$.
43. Term involving z^7 in the expansion of $(y - z)^9$.

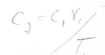

Trigonometric Functions of Angles

71. The objectives of trigonometry

Trigonometry is that field of mathematics which deals with the properties and applications of certain functions, called *trigonometric functions*, whose domain is the set of all * real numbers, where these numbers can be interpreted as *the measures of angles*. Trigonometry arose in connection with numerical applications in astronomy and surveying, where relations involving the angles in plane and spherical triangles are involved. The numerical applications of trigonometry remain important. However, with the discovery of calculus, there arose a new large field of usefulness for the trigonometric functions, not associated with their numerical applications. Trigonometric functions and their analytical properties (as contrasted to their numerical applications) are essential for a large part of calculus.

72. Directed angles

In elementary geometry, an *angle* was thought of as a ready-made figure, and the measure of an angle always was a positive number or zero. It is convenient now to add a dynamic concept to the figure for an angle.

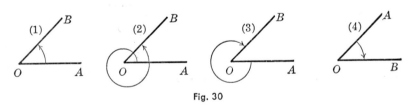

Fig. 30

Suppose that a ray, issuing from a point O in a plane, rotates in the plane about O in either a clockwise or a counterclockwise direction from an initial position OA to a terminal position OB, as for various cases in Figure 30. Then, this *rotation* is said to generate an angle AOB whose **initial side is**

---

* With a few exceptions, to be mentioned later, for certain functions.

136

OA, **terminal side** is *OB*, and **vertex** is *O*. To measure the amount of rotation, suppose that *O* is placed at the center of a circle of radius *r*, as in Figure 31. Let *s* be the directed distance measured along the arc *AB* which is traced on the circle as *OA* revolves into the position *OB*, where *s* is taken

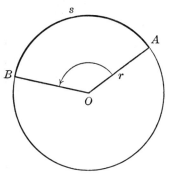

positive or negative according as the rotation was *counterclockwise or clockwise*, respectively. The circumference of the circle is equal to $2\pi r$. If $s > 0$ and $s:2\pi r = 1:360$, we define the value of $\angle AOB$ to be **1 degree**, written 1°. That is, as a unit for measuring the amount of rotation, 1° is 1/360 *of a complete revolution of OA counterclockwise.* In degree measure, the value,* θ, of any $\angle AOB$, placed as in Figure 31, is defined by

Fig. 31

$$\theta = \frac{s}{2\pi r} (360) \; degrees. \tag{1}$$

Thus, we have agreed that $\angle AOB$ has a **positive value** if the rotation is **counterclockwise** ($s > 0$), and a **negative value** if the rotation is **clockwise** ($s < 0$). If $\angle AOB$ consists of a complete revolution counterclockwise, then $s = 2\pi r$ in (1) and $\theta = 360°$. We shall introduce other units of angular measurement later in the text.

The description of an angle is incomplete until we are told its *sense (clockwise or counterclockwise)* and the amount of rotation used in forming the angle. In a figure, we may show the rotation by a curved arrow.

ILLUSTRATION 1. In Figure 30 on page 136, the configuration *AOB* is the same in each diagram. In (1), $\angle AOB = 45°$. In (2), a complete revolution is indicated besides 45°; $\angle AOB = 360° + 45° = 405°$. In (3), the rotation is 45° less than 360°, clockwise; $\angle AOB = -315°$. In (4), $\angle AOB = -45°$.

Note 1. The angular unit 1° is subdivided as in elementary geometry. Thus, we define *one minute*, 1′, as 1/60 of 1°, and *one second*, 1″, as 1/60 of 1′.

SUMMARY. *An* **angle** *is* **an amount of rotation,** *which may be represented geometrically as the rotation of any ray about its end point from an initial position, called the initial side of the angle, to a terminal position, called the terminal side. The measure of the rotation in terms of any specified unit is called the* **value** *of the angle.* **This value will be taken as a symbol for the angle** *when desired.*

ILLUSTRATION 2. Any positive angle between 0° and 90° is called an *acute angle.* Any positive angle between 90° and 180° is called an *obtuse angle.* An angle of 90° is called a *right angle*, and an angle of 180° is called a *straight angle.*

---

* Usually we shall employ Greek letters to represent angles. The letters α, β, γ, θ, and ϕ are called *alpha, beta, gamma, theta*, and *phi*, respectively.

Any number of complete revolutions, clockwise or counterclockwise, may be added to any of the rotations in Figure 30 on page 136 without altering the initial and terminal sides of the angles. Thus, we see that infinitely many positive and negative angles of unlimited absolute values correspond to any given pair of sides for the angles.

Note 2. If at any time an angle is shown by merely *drawing two half-lines* radiating from the vertex, without indicating the amount of rotation and sense, it will be assumed that the angle has *positive* measure, at most 180°. Thus, if an angle is indicated as in Figure 32, we infer that the angle has positive measure, about 130° in Figure 32. In other words, with no visible indication of the initial and terminal sides, or the amount of rotation involved, we return to the attitude of elementary geometry and assume that the angle's measure is positive or zero and at most 180°. Thus, in any triangle, each angle will be considered to have a positive measure.

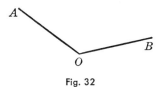

Fig. 32

73. Standard position of an angle

We shall say that an angle θ is in its *standard position* on a coordinate system if the vertex of θ is at the origin and the initial side of θ lies on the positive part of the horizontal axis.

ILLUSTRATION 1. To place 240° in standard position in Figure 33, imagine rotating OX about O through 240° counterclockwise to find the terminal side: $\gamma = 240°$. Similarly, we construct $\alpha = -60°$ and $\theta = 30°$ in standard positions.

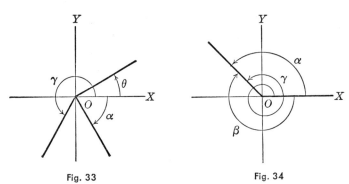

Fig. 33   Fig. 34

We shall say that an angle θ is *in a certain quadrant* if the terminal side of θ falls *inside* that quadrant when θ is in its standard position. If the terminal side of θ falls *on a coordinate axis*, then θ is not said to lie in any quadrant, but is called a **quadrantal angle.**

ILLUSTRATION 2. In Figure 33, θ is in quadrant I and γ is in quadrant III. Angles between $-180°$ and $-270°$ are in quadrant II. Obtuse angles lie in quadrant II. Examples of quadrantal angles are $0°$, $90°$, $360°$, $-90°$, $-180°$.

Two or more angles are said to be **coterminal** if their terminal sides coincide after the angles are placed in their standard positions.

ILLUSTRATION 3. In Figure 34 on page 138, α, β, and γ are coterminal.

EXERCISE 46

Sketch the angle in standard position and indicate the angle by an arrow. Give two coterminal angles, one positive and one negative, and indicate them by arrows.

1. 45°.	**2.** 90°.	**3.** 120°.	**4.** $-210°$.	**5.** $-60°$.
6. 150°.	**7.** $-270°$.	**8.** $-315°$.	**9.** $-180°$.	**10.** $-90°$.
11. 270°.	**12.** 420°.	**13.** 495°.	**14.** $-390°$.	**15.** 0°.
16. 135°.	**17.** $-225°$.	**18.** 870°.	**19.** 1050°.	**20.** $-1200°$.

74. Trigonometric functions of any angle

Let θ represent any angle, positive, negative, or zero. Place θ in its standard position on a coordinate system and let $P:(x, y)$ be any point other than the origin O on the terminal side of θ, as in Figure 35. With AP perpendicular to OX, we have a right triangle OAP, called a **reference triangle** for θ, in which $OA = x$, $AP = y$, and $OP = r$, the radius vector (positive) of P. Then, we form the ratios

$$\frac{AP}{OP} \text{ or } \frac{y}{r}, \quad \frac{OA}{OP} \text{ or } \frac{x}{r}, \quad \frac{y}{x}, \quad \frac{x}{y}, \quad \frac{r}{x}, \quad \frac{r}{y}, \tag{1}$$

omitting those fractions for quadrantal angles where $x = 0$ or $y = 0$ in a denominator. On the terminal side of θ, select any second point $P_1:(x_1, y_1)$, not O, with radius vector r_1. Then, new ratios (1) formed with x_1, y_1, and r_1 are equal to the ratios formed with x, y, and r. For instance, since the directed distances OA and OA_1 have the same sign, by properties of the similar triangles OAP and OA_1P_1 we obtain

Fig. 35

$$\frac{x}{r} = \frac{OA}{OP} = \frac{OA_1}{OP_1} = \frac{x_1}{r_1}; \quad \frac{y}{x} = \frac{y_1}{x_1}; \text{ etc.}$$

Thus, the values of the ratios in (1) depend *only on the position of the terminal side of θ* and not on the particular point P used to find x, y, and r. Hence, *corresponding to each value of θ* (with certain exceptions for quadrantal angles to be noted later) *there exists a unique value for each of the six ratios in* (1). Thus, each ratio is a *single-valued function of the angle θ*, called a *trigonometric function* of θ. For any value of θ, the values of these functions are defined as follows, where x, y, and r are illustrated in Figure 36. We *name* and *read* the functions as at the left in (2) below, and *abbreviate* as at the right in (2).

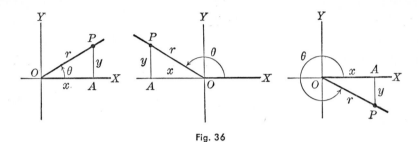

Fig. 36

DEFINITION I. *Place angle θ in standard position on a coordinate system. Choose any point P, not the origin, on the terminal side of θ; let the coordinates and radius vector of P be (x, y) and r, respectively. Then,*

$$sine\ \theta = \frac{ordinate\ of\ P}{radius\ vector\ of\ P}, \quad or \quad \sin \theta = \frac{y}{r};$$

$$cosine\ \theta = \frac{abscissa\ of\ P}{radius\ vector\ of\ P}, \quad or \quad \cos \theta = \frac{x}{r};$$

$$tangent\ \theta = \frac{ordinate\ of\ P}{abscissa\ of\ P}, \quad or \quad \tan \theta = \frac{y}{x};$$

$$cotangent\ \theta = \frac{abscissa\ of\ P}{ordinate\ of\ P}, \quad or \quad \cot \theta = \frac{x}{y}; \qquad (2)$$

$$secant\ \theta = \frac{radius\ vector\ of\ P}{abscissa\ of\ P}, \quad or \quad \sec \theta = \frac{r}{x};$$

$$cosecant\ \theta = \frac{radius\ vector\ of\ P}{ordinate\ of\ P}, \quad or \quad \csc \theta = \frac{r}{y}.$$

Since Definition I involves only the terminal side of θ, **if two angles are coterminal their trigonometric functions are equal.**

ILLUSTRATION 1. Since $30°$ and $390°$ are coterminal, $\cos 30° = \cos 390°$.

EXAMPLE 1. Find the *functions* * (meaning the *values of the functions*) of an angle θ if its terminal side in standard position passes through $P:(3, -4)$.

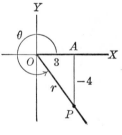

SOLUTION. A reference triangle for θ is shown in Figure 37. We select P with $x = 3$ and $y = -4$; then $r = \sqrt{3^2 + (-4)^2} = 5$. Hence, from (2),

$$\sin \theta = -\tfrac{4}{5}; \quad \cos \theta = \tfrac{3}{5}; \quad \tan \theta = -\tfrac{4}{3};$$

$$\csc \theta = -\tfrac{5}{4}; \quad \sec \theta = \tfrac{5}{3}; \quad \cot \theta = -\tfrac{3}{4}.$$

Fig. 37

* Until otherwise indicated, in any reference to a *function* or to a *trigonometric function* of an angle, we shall mean one of the fundamental functions of Definition I.

Note 1. In order to find r when x and y are given, we recall

$$r^2 = x^2 + y^2; \qquad r = \sqrt{x^2 + y^2}. \tag{3}$$

ILLUSTRATION 2. If the terminal side of an angle θ in its standard position passes through $P:(-\sqrt{3}, 1)$, then

$$r = \sqrt{(-\sqrt{3})^2 + 1} = 2 \text{ and}$$

$$\sec\theta = \frac{2}{-\sqrt{3}} = -\frac{2}{\sqrt{3}} \cdot \frac{\sqrt{3}}{\sqrt{3}} = -\frac{2}{3}\sqrt{3} = -1.155. \qquad \text{(Table I)}$$

On page 34, an *identity* was described as an equation which is true for all admissible values of the literal numbers which are involved. A trigonometric identity is one involving general values of trigonometric functions. From Definition I, we observe that each of the following identities, called the *reciprocal relations*, is satisfied for all * values of θ for which both functions are defined.

$$\left. \begin{array}{ll} \sin\theta = \dfrac{1}{\csc\theta}, & or \quad \csc\theta = \dfrac{1}{\sin\theta}; \\[2mm] \cos\theta = \dfrac{1}{\sec\theta}, & or \quad \sec\theta = \dfrac{1}{\cos\theta}; \\[2mm] \tan\theta = \dfrac{1}{\cot\theta}, & or \quad \cot\theta = \dfrac{1}{\tan\theta}. \end{array} \right\} \tag{4}$$

ILLUSTRATION 3. If $\sin\theta \neq 0$, $\quad \dfrac{1}{\sin\theta} = \dfrac{1}{\frac{y}{r}} = \dfrac{r}{y}, \quad or \quad \dfrac{1}{\sin\theta} = \csc\theta.$

ILLUSTRATION 4. If $\quad \tan\theta = \frac{5}{7}, \quad then \quad \cot\theta = \frac{7}{5}.$

In Figure 36 on page 140 for any angle θ, neither $|OA|$ nor $|AP|$ is greater than OP. Hence, the absolute value of x or of y *cannot exceed* r, and the absolute value of x/r or of y/r *cannot exceed* 1. Similarly, the absolute value of r/x or of r/y *cannot be smaller than* 1. That is, for all values of θ,

$\left\{ \begin{array}{l} \sin\theta \text{ and } \cos\theta \text{ are } \textbf{numerically less than or equal to 1}; \\ \sec\theta \text{ and } \csc\theta \text{ are } \textbf{numerically greater than or equal to 1}. \end{array} \right.$

Note 2. On page 71, the domain of any function was described as a set of *numbers*. In contrast, the domain of each of the trigonometric functions, as described on page 140, is a set of *geometrical objects called angles*. Thus, for each angle θ, we defined a number $\sin\theta$; the domain of the sine function, or the range for θ, is the set of *all angles*. With this viewpoint, the unit of angular measurement is of no present importance. In degree measure, θ is a number of degrees, but this denominate † number is considered merely

* In the case of $\tan\theta$, $\cot\theta$, $\sec\theta$, and $\csc\theta$, "*all values of* θ" always will mean "*all for which the function is defined.*"
† A **denominate number** is a *number of units of a certain variety.* Thus, 50° is a denominate number, where the number 50 occurs, and the unit is 1°.

as a *symbol for an angle*. If $1°$ is the angular unit, then $\theta = x°$, where x is a real number. Later, we shall think of the domain of the trigonometric functions as the set of *all real numbers* $\{x\}$; then, the angular unit will assume extreme importance.

We verify the signs of the trigonometric functions as indicated in Figure 38. In any quadrant, $\sin \theta$ and $\csc \theta$ have the same sign because $\sin \theta = 1/\csc \theta$; $\tan \theta$ and $\cot \theta$ have the same sign; $\cos \theta$ and $\sec \theta$ have the same sign. Thus, if we remember the signs of $\sin \theta$, $\cos \theta$, and $\tan \theta$ in any quadrant, the signs of the other functions can be specified immediately.

EXAMPLE 2. Determine the signs of the trigonometric functions for angles in quadrant II.

SOLUTION. If θ is in quadrant II, then $x < 0$, $y > 0$, and $r > 0$ in Definition I. Hence, regarding only signs,

$$\sin \theta = \frac{y}{r} = \frac{+}{+} = +;$$

$$\cos \theta = \frac{x}{r} = \frac{-}{+} = -;$$

$$\tan \theta = \frac{y}{x} = \frac{+}{-} = -.$$

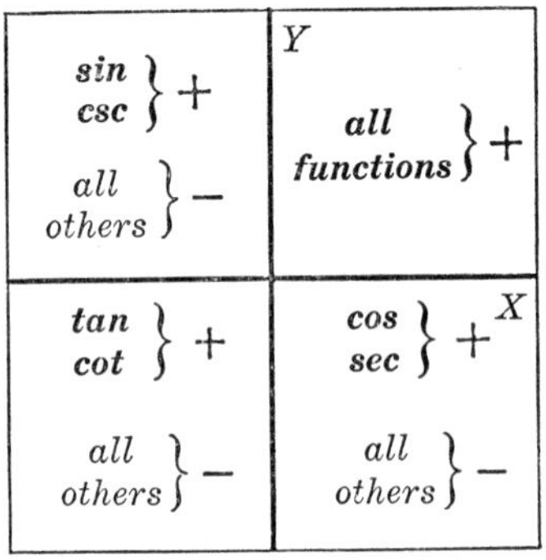

Fig. 38

EXAMPLE 3. If $\sin \theta > 0$ and $\cot \theta < 0$, in what quadrant does θ lie?

SOLUTION. Since $\sin \theta > 0$, θ is in quadrant I or quadrant II. Since $\cot \theta < 0$, θ is in quadrant II or quadrant IV. Hence, θ is in quadrant II.

EXERCISE 47

Find the trigonometric functions of the angle θ if the terminal side of θ, in its standard position, passes through the given point on a coordinate system. Draw a figure and find decimal values where radicals arise.

1. $(4, 3)$.   2. $(5, 12)$.   3. $(7, 24)$.   4. $(12, -5)$.
5. $(-3, -2)$.   6. $(-24, 7)$.   7. $(-15, 8)$.   8. $(-8, -15)$.
9. $(6, -8)$.   10. $(-1, 1)$.   11. $(1, -\sqrt{3})$. 12. $(\sqrt{3}, 1)$.
13. $(0, 4)$.   14. $(4, -5)$.   15. $(0, -2)$.   16. $(2, -3)$.
17. $(-1, -1)$.   18. $(5, 0)$.   19. $(-3, 5)$.   20. $(-2, 0)$.

21. Verify the signs in Figure 38 for quadrant I; quadrant III; quadrant IV.

Give the value of another function of the angle whose function is given.

22. $\tan \theta = \frac{3}{7}$.   23. $\cos \alpha = \frac{4}{9}$.   24. $\cot \beta = \frac{5}{2}$.   25. $\sec \gamma = \frac{7}{3}$.

Under the given condition, in which quadrants may θ lie?

26. $\sin \theta < 0$.   27. $\tan \theta < 0$.   28. $\sec \theta > 0$.   29. $\cot \theta > 0$.

30. What are the signs of the trigonometric functions of an obtuse angle?

Under the given conditions, in which quadrant must θ lie?

31. sin θ < 0 and tan θ > 0.   **32.** cos θ < 0 and sin θ > 0.

33. tan θ < 0 and sin θ < 0.   **34.** sec θ < 0 and tan θ > 0.

35. cos θ < 0 and cot θ < 0.   **36.** csc θ > 0 and cot θ < 0.

37. cos θ < 0 and tan θ > 0.   **38.** sin θ < 0 and cos θ < 0.

75. Quadrantal angles and other special angles

EXAMPLE 1. Find the functions of 180°.

SOLUTION. 1. Draw 180° in standard position, as in Figure 39. The ordinate of any point on the terminal side is zero.

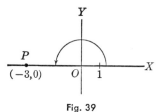

Fig. 39

2. Choose P as $(-3, 0)$. Then $r = OP = 3$. On substituting $x = -3$, $y = 0$, and $r = 3$ in (2) on page 140 we obtain

$$\tan 180° = \frac{0}{-3} = 0; \quad \sec 180° = \frac{3}{-3} = -1;$$

$$\sin 180° = \frac{0}{3} = 0; \quad \cos 180° = \frac{-3}{3} = -1.$$

Since $y = 0$, r/y and x/y are meaningless because *division by zero has no meaning.* Therefore, **180° has no cosecant and no cotangent.**

If θ is any quadrantal angle, so that its terminal side falls on a coordinate axis, either cot θ and csc θ, or tan θ and sec θ, are *undefined* for the reason just met in discussing cot 180° and csc 180°. From Example 1 and later problems, a complete list of the undefined functions of angles from 0° to 360°, inclusive, is as follows:

$$\left.\begin{array}{l} \text{UNDEFINED} \\ \text{FUNCTIONS} \end{array}\right\{ \begin{array}{lllll} \cot 0°; & \tan 90°; & \cot 180°; & \tan 270°; & \cot 360°; \\ \csc 0°; & \sec 90°; & \csc 180°; & \sec 270°; & \csc 360°. \end{array} \right\} \quad (1)$$

We reserve this matter of undefined functions for later discussion.

EXAMPLE 2. Find the functions of 45°.

SOLUTION. Figure 40 shows the angle 45° in its standard position. The reference triangle AOP is *isosceles* with $\overline{OA} = \overline{AP}$. Hence, we may choose P with $x = 1$ and $y = 1$; then $r = \sqrt{2}$ and, from page 140,

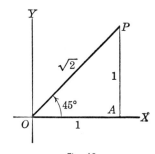

Fig. 40

$$\sin 45° = \frac{1}{\sqrt{2}} = \frac{1}{\sqrt{2}} \cdot \frac{\sqrt{2}}{\sqrt{2}} = \frac{1}{2}\sqrt{2};$$

$$\sec 45° = \frac{\sqrt{2}}{1} = \sqrt{2}; \ etc.$$

The student should memorize the convenient sides of △OAP.

Note 1. In the equilateral triangle ABD of Figure 41, drop a perpendicular BC to AD, obtaining two right triangles with the acute angles $30°$ and $60°$. If we let $AB = BD = AD = 2$, then $AC = 1$ and

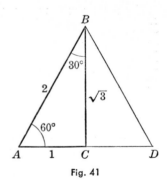

Fig. 41

$$\overline{BC}^2 + \overline{AC}^2 = \overline{AB}^2 \quad or$$
$$\overline{BC}^2 = \overline{AB}^2 - \overline{AC}^2 = 4 - 1 = 3.$$

Thus, $BC = \sqrt{3}$. Hence, as a *standard right triangle with the acute angles* $30°$ *and* $60°$, we may use triangle ABC with sides 1, 2, and $\sqrt{3}$.

ILLUSTRATION 1. To obtain the functions of $30°$, after placing the angle in its standard position in Figure 42, we choose P on the terminal side so that $OP = 2$. Then, the reference triangle OAP has the acute angles $30°$ and $60°$, and the standard sides 1, 2, and $\sqrt{3}$; we find

$$\sin 30° = \frac{1}{2}; \quad \tan 30° = \frac{1}{\sqrt{3}} = \frac{1}{\sqrt{3}} \cdot \frac{\sqrt{3}}{\sqrt{3}} = \frac{1}{3}\sqrt{3}; \quad etc.$$

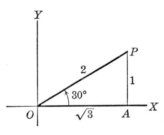

Fig. 42

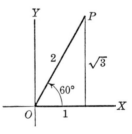

Fig. 43

To obtain the functions of $60°$ by use of Figure 43, we choose P so that $OP = 2$ and again the reference triangle has the acute angles $30°$ and $60°$, and sides 1, 2, and $\sqrt{3}$. The student should verify all entries in the following table.

ANGLE	SIN	COS	TAN	COT	SEC	CSC
$0°$	0	1	0	*none*	1	*none*
$30°$	$\dfrac{1}{2}$	$\dfrac{\sqrt{3}}{2}$	$\dfrac{1}{\sqrt{3}}$	$\sqrt{3}$	$\dfrac{2}{\sqrt{3}}$	2
$45°$	$\dfrac{1}{\sqrt{2}}$	$\dfrac{1}{\sqrt{2}}$	1	1	$\sqrt{2}$	$\sqrt{2}$
$60°$	$\dfrac{\sqrt{3}}{2}$	$\dfrac{1}{2}$	$\sqrt{3}$	$\dfrac{1}{\sqrt{3}}$	2	$\dfrac{2}{\sqrt{3}}$
$90°$	1	0	*none*	0	*none*	1

76. The reference angle for a given angle

It will be found later that the functions of an angle in any quadrant can be obtained if we have means available for finding the functions of acute angles. This convenience will result from use of a *reference angle*, described as follows.

DEFINITION II. *Let θ be any angle in any quadrant, and consider θ in standard position on a coordinate system. Then, the* **reference angle** *for θ is the acute angle α between the terminal side of θ and the horizontal coordinate axis.*

ILLUSTRATION 1. If $\theta = 120°$, as in Figure 44, then $\alpha = 60°$. If $\theta = -150°$, as in Figure 45, then $\alpha = 30°$. If $\theta = 225°$, as in Figure 46, then $\alpha = 45°$.

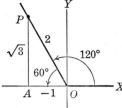

Fig. 44

If the reference angle for an angle θ is 30°, 45°, or 60°, any reference triangle for defining the functions of θ can be given the dimensions used in obtaining the functions of 30°, 45°, or 60°, respectively.

ILLUSTRATION 2. If $\theta = 225°$, the reference angle is 45°, in Figure 46, and triangle AOP has the sides 1, 1, and $\sqrt{2}$: P is $(-1, -1)$. Then,

$$\sin 225° = \frac{-1}{\sqrt{2}} = -\frac{1}{2}\sqrt{2}; \qquad \tan 225° = \frac{-1}{-1} = 1; \; etc.$$

For $\theta = 120°$ in Figure 44, and $\theta = -150°$ in Figure 45, $OP = 2$ and the reference triangles have the sides 1, 2, and $\sqrt{3}$; then

$$\tan 120° = \frac{\sqrt{3}}{-1} = -\sqrt{3}; \qquad \cos(-150°) = \frac{-\sqrt{3}}{2} = -\frac{1}{2}\sqrt{3}; \; etc.$$

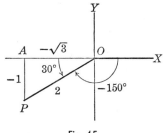

Fig. 45

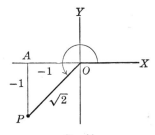

Fig. 46

On account of the similarity of the reference triangles for 45° and 225°, any function of 225° differs *at most in sign* from the same function of 45°. Likewise the functions of 120° and of $-150°$ *differ at most in signs* from the functions of their reference angles 60° and 30°, respectively.

In Illustration 2 we met special cases of the theorem that *any function of* *an angle θ differs at most in sign from the same function of the reference angle for θ.* We shall prove this theorem on page 153.

ILLUSTRATION 3. The angles between 90° and 360° with 30° as the reference angle, and hence with functions differing at most in signs from the functions of 30°, are 150°, 210°, 330°.

EXERCISE 48

Place the angle in its standard position on a coordinate system and find the trigonometric functions of the angle. Rationalize any radical denominator and compute by use of Table I, *if necessary.*

1. 0°.	**2.** 90°.	**3.** 30°.	**4.** 60°.	**5.** 135°.
6. 120°.	**7.** 150°.	**8.** 270°.	**9.** 360°.	**10.** 315°.
11. 330°.	**12.** 240°.	**13.** − 90°.	**14.** − 180°.	**15.** − 45°.
16. − 60°.	**17.** − 135°.	**18.** 225°.	**19.** 390°.	**20.** 405°.
21. 585°.	**22.** 495°.	**23.** 540°.	**24.** 480°.	**25.** − 495°.

26. Give all values of θ between − 360° and 360° such that the functions of θ are numerically equal to the corresponding functions of 45°; 30°; 60°.

27. Give all values of θ between − 720° and 720° for which (*a*) tan θ is not defined; (*b*) sec θ is not defined; (*c*) csc θ and cot θ are not defined.

77. The fundamental identities

By use of Definition I on page 140, we proved that the reciprocal relations (1) below are true for all angles θ for which no denominator is zero. Similarly, we shall prove the quotient relations (2) and the relations (3) involving squares.

$$\csc \theta = \frac{1}{\sin \theta}; \qquad \sec \theta = \frac{1}{\cos \theta}; \qquad \cot \theta = \frac{1}{\tan \theta}. \qquad (1)$$

$$\tan \theta = \frac{\sin \theta}{\cos \theta}; \qquad \cot \theta = \frac{\cos \theta}{\sin \theta}. \qquad (2)$$

$$\sin^2 \theta + \cos^2 \theta = 1; \quad \tan^2 \theta + 1 = \sec^2 \theta; \quad 1 + \cot^2 \theta = \csc^2 \theta. \quad (3)$$

Note 1. To indicate a power of a trigonometric function, we place the exponent between the function's name and the angle. An exception is made in case the exponent is − 1; thus, we write $(\sin \theta)^{-1}$, and not $\sin^{-1} \theta$, to mean $1/\sin \theta$.

Proof of (2). Let θ be any angle whose terminal side is not vertical when θ is placed in its standard position on a coordinate system. Then, in Definition I on page 140, $x \neq 0$ and hence cos $\theta \neq 0$, so that

$$\frac{\sin \theta}{\cos \theta} = \frac{\frac{y}{r}}{\frac{x}{r}} = \frac{y}{r} \cdot \frac{r}{x} = \frac{y}{x} = \tan \theta.$$

Similarly, the student will prove that cot θ = cos θ/sin θ if θ is any angle for which sin $\theta \neq 0$.

Proof of (3). From Note 1 on page 141, $\qquad x^2 + y^2 = r^2.$ $\qquad$ (4)

On dividing both sides of (4) by r^2, we obtain

$$\frac{y^2}{r^2} + \frac{x^2}{r^2} = 1, \quad or \quad \sin^2 \theta + \cos^2 \theta = 1.$$

Similarly, on dividing both sides of (4) in turn by x^2 when $x \neq 0$, and by y^2 when $y \neq 0$, we obtain the other relations in (3).

Identities (1), (2), and (3) should be memorized. Also, slight modifications of these identities should be recognized.

ILLUSTRATION 1. From (1), $\sin \theta = \dfrac{1}{\csc \theta}.$

From (2), $\qquad$ $\sin \theta = \cos \theta \tan \theta;$ $\qquad$ $\cos \theta = \sin \theta \cot \theta.$

From (3), $\qquad$ $\sin^2 \theta = 1 - \cos^2 \theta;$ $\qquad$ $\cos \theta = \pm \sqrt{1 - \sin^2 \theta}.$

From (1), $\qquad$ $\qquad$ $\qquad$ $\qquad$ $\tan \theta \cot \theta = 1.$

78. Functions of an angle for which one function is given

Suppose that only angles which are *not* quadrantal are involved for the moment. Then, we shall find that, if the value of one function of an unknown angle θ and its quadrant are given, there exists just *one location* for the terminal side of θ in standard position on a coordinate system. With the preceding type of data, we can construct θ and find all of its trigonometric functions. However, if merely *one function* of θ is given, there exist *two* corresponding locations for the terminal side of θ in standard position and thus two values for θ between 0° and 360°.

EXAMPLE 1. Construct θ in standard position if sin $\theta = \frac{3}{5}$ and θ is in quadrant II; find all functions of θ.

SOLUTION. 1. From page 140, since

$$\sin \theta = \frac{y}{r} = \frac{3}{5},$$

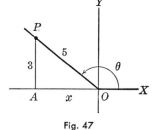

Fig. 47

the terminal side of θ in standard position passes through point P in quadrant II where $y = 3$ and $r = 5$. We sketch θ roughly to scale in Figure 47 and indicate any corresponding angle θ.

2. From $r^2 = x^2 + y^2$, $\qquad x^2 = r^2 - y^2 = 25 - 9 = 16;$ $x = \pm 4.$

Since P is in quadrant II, the abscissa of P is $x = -4$. Then, from Definition I on page 140 with $x = -4$, $y = 3$, and $r = 5$, we have cos $\theta = -\frac{4}{5}$, tan $\theta = -\frac{3}{4}$, etc.

Comment. An accurate figure was unnecessary. However, to construct OP as in Figure 48 accurately, draw a circle of radius 5 with center at O; construct the line $y = 3$, intersecting the circle at P in quadrant II and at Q in quadrant I. Then, $\sin \theta = \frac{3}{5}$ if θ has either OP or OQ as the terminal side. In Example 1, we use OP.

ILLUSTRATION 1. Without knowing the quadrant for θ, if we are given $\sin \theta = \frac{3}{5}$, then Figure 48 shows that there are two possible values for θ on the range $0° < \theta < 360°$, approximately $\theta_1 = 40°$ and $\theta_2 = 140°$. Similarly, with any given function for an angle θ which is not quadrantal, the student will verify that there are two corresponding values for θ on the range $0° < \theta < 360°$. Then, if the quadrant for θ is an added item of information, just one of the values for θ is determined.

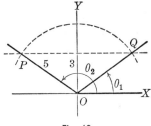

Fig. 48

ILLUSTRATION 2. If $\tan \theta = \frac{2}{3}$ and $\sin \theta < 0$, then θ lies in quadrant III. In the notation of page 140, we use $\frac{2}{3} = y/x$, and obtain $P: (x = -3, y = -2)$ as a corresponding point in quadrant III on the terminal side of θ. Then, we may construct this side, find $r = \sqrt{9+4} = \sqrt{13}$, and finally write all functions of θ by use of Definition I.

The fundamental identities of page 146 can be used to solve Example 1 without a figure. It is useful to carry out a few solutions by this method.

EXAMPLE 2. Solve Example 1 by use of the fundamental identities (1), (2), and (3) on page 146.

SOLUTION. With $\sin \theta = \frac{3}{5}$ and θ in quadrant II, first we obtain

$$\csc \theta = \frac{1}{\sin \theta} = \frac{5}{3}.$$

From $\sin^2 \theta + \cos^2 \theta = 1$,

$$\tfrac{9}{25} + \cos^2 \theta = 1; \quad \cos^2 \theta = \tfrac{16}{25}; \quad \cos \theta = \pm \tfrac{4}{5}.$$

Since θ is in quadrant II, we select $\cos \theta = -\frac{4}{5}$. Then, from (1) and (2) on page 146,

$$\sec \theta = \frac{1}{\cos \theta} = -\frac{5}{4}; \quad \tan \theta = \frac{\sin \theta}{\cos \theta} = \frac{\frac{3}{5}}{-\frac{4}{5}} = -\frac{3}{4}; \quad \cot \theta = \frac{1}{\tan \theta} = -\frac{4}{3}.$$

ILLUSTRATION 3. If $\tan \theta = \frac{2}{3}$ and θ is in quadrant III, we obtain

$$\sec^2 \theta = 1 + \tan^2 \theta = 1 + \frac{4}{9} = \frac{13}{9}; \quad hence \quad \sec \theta = \pm \frac{\sqrt{13}}{3};$$

we select $\sec \theta = -\sqrt{13}/3$ because θ is in quadrant III, etc.; all other functions of θ can be found by use of (1)–(3) on page 146.

EXERCISE 49

The Roman numeral specifies the quadrant for the angle θ. Construct a corresponding angle θ on the range $0° < \theta < 360°$ accurately in standard position on a coordinate system, and find the unknown functions of θ. Do not use the fundamental identities of page 146 in the first six problems. Thereafter, use the identities either partially or for the whole solution.

1. $\tan \theta = \frac{5}{12}$; θ in (I).   2. $\cot \theta = -\frac{4}{3}$; θ in (II).

3. $\sin \theta = \frac{4}{5}$; θ in (II).   4. $\cos \theta = \frac{5}{13}$; θ in (IV).

5. $\csc \theta = \frac{5}{3}$; θ in (I).   6. $\sec \theta = \frac{13}{12}$; θ in (I).

7. $\cot \theta = \frac{12}{5}$; θ in (III).   8. $\sin \theta = -\frac{15}{17}$; θ in (IV).

9. $\cos \theta = -\frac{15}{17}$; θ in (II).   10. $\tan \theta = -\frac{7}{24}$; θ in (II).

11. $\tan \theta = 1$; θ in (III).   12. $\sin \theta = \frac{2}{3}$; θ in (I).

13. $\sec \theta = \frac{4}{3}$; θ in (IV).   14. $\csc \theta = -\frac{5}{2}$; θ in (III).

15. θ is an acute angle and $\cos \theta = \frac{4}{5}$.

16. θ is an acute angle and $\sec \theta = \frac{25}{7}$.

17. θ is an obtuse angle and $\cot \theta = -\frac{8}{15}$.

18. θ is an obtuse angle and $\tan \theta = -\frac{24}{7}$.

Construct all angles θ between $0°$ and $360°$ in standard positions corresponding to the data. Estimate the values of θ with a protractor. Then, find all functions of each angle by use of fundamental identities.

19. $\tan \theta = \frac{2}{3}$.   20. $\sin \theta = \frac{2}{5}$.   21. $\cos \theta = -\frac{2}{3}$.   22. $\cot \theta = -\frac{5}{2}$.

By recalling a fundamental identity, write a proper right-hand member involving only one function or one number.

23. $\dfrac{1}{\cot \theta} = ?$ 24. $\dfrac{1}{\sec \theta} = ?$ 25. $\dfrac{1}{\csc \theta} = ?$

26. $\cos \theta \sec \theta = ?$ 27. $\tan \theta \cot \theta = ?$ 28. $\sin \theta \csc \theta = ?$

29. $1 - \sin^2 \theta = ?$ 30. $\sec^2 \theta - 1 = ?$ 31. $\csc^2 \theta - 1 = ?$

32. $1 - \cos^2 \theta = ?$ 33. $1 + \cot^2 \theta = ?$ 34. $\sec^2 \theta - \tan^2 \theta = ?$

35. Compute $3 \tan \theta \, (2 \cot \theta + 1 - \sec^2 \theta)$ if $\tan \theta = 2$.

36. Compute $3 \cot^2 \theta \, (\sin \theta + \csc \theta)$ if $\sin \theta = \frac{1}{4}$.

37. Compute $\tan \theta \, (\sin \theta - 1)$ if $\cos \theta = \frac{2}{3}$ and θ is in quadrant (IV).

Express each trigonometric function of the angle x in terms of the given function by use of fundamental identities.

38. $\tan x$.   39. $\sin x$.   40. $\cos x$.   41. $\sec x$.   42. $\csc x$.

HINT for Problem 38. $\cot x = 1/\tan x$; $\sec x = \pm \sqrt{1 + \tan^2 x}$;   etc.

79. Trigonometric functions of acute angles

Any acute angle α can be thought of as one of the angles of an associated right triangle. This fact permits us to prove special formulas for the functions of α involving the sides of the triangle.

Let triangle ABC in Figure 49 be a right triangle with the 90° angle at C, and with α and β as the acute angles at A and B, respectively. Let a, b, and c be the sides (or *lengths* of the sides) of triangle ABC opposite A, B, and C, respectively. Hereafter, in any typical right triangle, we shall assume that the preceding notation is in use. By the Pythagorean theorem,

$$c^2 = a^2 + b^2. \tag{1}$$

Let α be any acute angle, and let $\triangle ABC$ in Figure 49 be any right triangle having α as the angle at A. Then, to place α in standard position on a

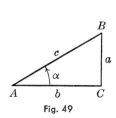

Fig. 49

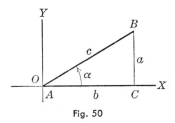

Fig. 50

coordinate system as in Figure 50, we locate $\triangle ABC$ with A at the origin, C on the positive half of the x-axis, and B above OX. In the terminology of page 139, $\triangle ABC$ becomes a *reference triangle* for α; B is a point on the terminal side of α with coordinates $(x = b, y = a)$ and radius vector $r = \overline{AB} = c$. We shall refer to a as the *side opposite* α, b as the *side adjacent* to α, and c as the *hypotenuse*. Then, with $x = b$, $y = a$, and $r = c$ in the definitions on page 140, we obtain

$$\left. \begin{array}{ll} \sin \alpha = \dfrac{a}{c} = \dfrac{\text{opposite side}}{\text{hypotenuse}}; & \csc \alpha = \dfrac{c}{a} = \dfrac{\text{hypotenuse}}{\text{opposite side}}; \\[2mm] \cos \alpha = \dfrac{b}{c} = \dfrac{\text{adjacent side}}{\text{hypotenuse}}; & \sec \alpha = \dfrac{c}{b} = \dfrac{\text{hypotenuse}}{\text{adjacent side}}; \\[2mm] \tan \alpha = \dfrac{a}{b} = \dfrac{\text{opposite side}}{\text{adjacent side}}; & \cot \alpha = \dfrac{b}{a} = \dfrac{\text{adjacent side}}{\text{opposite side}}. \end{array} \right\} \tag{2}$$

Thus, in (2), by use of the fundamental definitions on page 140, we have proved the following result, which emphatically applies *only to acute angles.*

$$\left. \begin{array}{l} \textit{If an acute angle } \alpha \textit{ is located as an angle in a right triangle,} \\ \textit{without using a coordinate system we can express the functions} \\ \textit{of } \alpha \textit{ as quotients of the lengths of sides of the triangle, as in (2).} \end{array} \right\} \tag{3}$$

ILLUSTRATION 1. From Figure 51,

$$\sin \alpha = \tfrac{3}{5}; \qquad \cos \alpha = \tfrac{4}{5}; \qquad \tan \alpha = \tfrac{3}{4};$$
$$\csc \alpha = \tfrac{5}{3}; \qquad \sec \alpha = \tfrac{5}{4}; \qquad \cot \alpha = \tfrac{4}{3};$$
$$\sin \beta = \tfrac{4}{5}; \qquad \cos \beta = \tfrac{3}{5}; \qquad \tan \beta = \tfrac{4}{3};$$
$$\csc \beta = \tfrac{5}{4}; \qquad \sec \beta = \tfrac{5}{3}; \qquad \cot \beta = \tfrac{3}{4}.$$

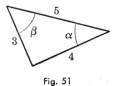

Fig. 51

EXAMPLE 1. Construct the acute angle α and find cos α and tan α, if $\sin \alpha = \frac{3}{4}$.

SOLUTION. In equations (2), $\sin \alpha = a/c$. The student should construct a right triangle with $a = 3$ and $c = 4$. Then, $b = \sqrt{7}$ and

$$\cos \alpha = \frac{\sqrt{7}}{4}; \quad \tan \alpha = \frac{3}{\sqrt{7}} = \frac{3}{7} \sqrt{7}.$$

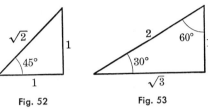

Fig. 52   Fig. 53

ILLUSTRATION 2. In Figures 52 and 53, we may read off the functions of 30°, 45°, and 60°.

If α and β are acute and $\alpha + \beta = 90°$, then α and β are said to be *complementary;* either is called the *complement* of the other angle.

ILLUSTRATION 3. The complement of 35° is (90° − 35°) or 55°.

If α and β are the acute angles of a right triangle ABC, then α and β are complementary, and $\beta = 90° − \alpha$. From Figure 54, side a is *opposite* α and *adjacent* to β. Hence, from (2) on page 150,

$$\sin \alpha = \frac{a}{c} = \cos \beta; \qquad \cos \alpha = \frac{b}{c} = \sin \beta;$$

$$\tan \alpha = \cot \beta; \qquad \cot \alpha = \tan \beta;$$

$$\sec \alpha = \csc \beta; \qquad \csc \alpha = \sec \beta.$$

Fig. 54

On using $\beta = 90° − \alpha$, the preceding results become

$$
\begin{aligned}
\sin \alpha &= \cos (90° − \alpha); & \sec \alpha &= \csc (90° − \alpha); \\
\cos \alpha &= \sin (90° − \alpha); & \csc \alpha &= \sec (90° − \alpha); \\
\tan \alpha &= \cot (90° − \alpha); & \cot \alpha &= \tan (90° − \alpha).
\end{aligned}
\qquad (4)
$$

The trigonometric functions may be grouped as follows: *sine* and **cosine**; *tangent* and **cotangent**; *secant* and **cosecant**. In each pair, either function may be referred to as the **cofunction** of the other one. Then, (4) states that *any function of an acute angle α is equal to the cofunction of the complement of α.* We call (4) the *cofunction relations.*

ILLUSTRATION 4. sin 33° = cos 57°. tan 29° = cot 61°. csc 15° = sec 75°.

Since   90° − 37° 38′ = 52° 22′,   tan 37° 38′ = cot 52° 22′.

Note 1. In the Middle Ages, it was customary at first to refer to the *cosine,* in Latin, as *complementi sinus,* meaning the sine of the complement. Eventually, *complementi sinus* was abbreviated to *cosinus.*

80. A three-place trigonometric table

In general, any value of a trigonometric function is an infinite decimal. By advanced methods, the functions of any angle can be computed to as many decimal places as desired. We shall learn later how the values of the trigonometric functions for any angle θ in any quadrant can be expressed in terms of the function values for an acute reference angle, α. Hence, if a table is available for finding the function values for angles from $0°$ to $90°$, the table will serve indirectly for corresponding angles of any size.

Table IV is a three-place table of the values of the trigonometric functions of angles from $0°$ to $90°$ inclusive at intervals of $1°$. For angles at most equal to $45°$, read angles at the left and titles of columns at the top in the table. For angles from $45°$ to $90°$ inclusive, read angles at the right and titles of columns at the bottom. At present we disregard the reference to radian measure in Table IV.

Each entry in the function columns of Table IV is a function of some angle and, also, is the cofunction of the complementary angle, on account of the identities (4) on page 151. Thus, those identities make each entry in Table IV serve a double purpose.

ILLUSTRATION 1. From Table IV, $\tan 57° = 1.540$. If α is acute and $\sin \alpha = .454$, from the column in Table IV headed sine at the top, we read that $.454 = \sin 27°$, and hence $\alpha = 27°$.

Note 1. By use of a process called *interpolation*, later we shall obtain from Table IV the values of functions of angles given to the nearest tenth of $1°$.

EXERCISE 50

Construct the acute angle α and find the values of its functions.

1. $\tan \alpha = \frac{3}{4}$. 2. $\sin \alpha = \frac{4}{5}$. 3. $\cos \alpha = \frac{7}{25}$. 4. $\sec \alpha = \frac{17}{8}$.
5. $\cos \alpha = \frac{15}{17}$. 6. $\cot \alpha = \frac{12}{5}$. 7. $\csc \alpha = \frac{3}{2}$. 8. $\cos \alpha = \frac{1}{3}$.
9. From Figures 52 and 53, page 151, find the functions of $30°$, $45°$, and $60°$.

Express each function value as a function value for the complementary angle. Also, obtain the function value from Table IV.

10. $\sin 20°$.   11. $\cos 15°$.   12. $\tan 49°$.   13. $\cot 38°$.
14. $\sec 41°$.   15. $\csc 12°$.   16. $\sec 81°$.   17. $\tan 39°$.
18. $\sec 85°$.   19. $\sin 67°$.   20. $\cot 67°$.   21. $\sin 82°$.

22. By use of a protractor, construct on cross-section paper a right triangle of generous dimensions with $35°$ as one acute angle. Then, by finding quotients of the measured lengths of the sides of the triangle, find the functions of $35°$ and $55°$ approximately to one decimal place.

23. In a standard right triangle ABC with sides a, b, and c and acute angles α and β, observe that $a < c$ and $b < c$. What facts does this recall about $\sin \alpha$, $\cos \alpha$, $\sec \alpha$, and $\csc \alpha$?

24. In the triangle ABC of Problem 23, what is true about sides a and b if (1) $\alpha = 45°$; (2) $\alpha < 45°$; (3) $\alpha > 45°$? In each case, also state corresponding facts about $\tan \alpha$ and $\cot \alpha$.

25. Prove that the equation $\sin 2\theta = 2 \sin \theta$ is **NOT** an identity.

81. Graphical reduction to acute angles

From page 145, we recall the notion of an acute *reference angle*, α, for an angle θ of any size in any quadrant. Various reference angles are exhibited in Figure 55. From other figures, the student may verify the following facts.

θ *between* $90°$ *and* $180°$; *reference angle is* $\alpha = 180° - \theta$.　　　(1)

θ *between* $180°$ *and* $270°$; *reference angle is* $\alpha = \theta - 180°$.　　　(2)

θ *between* $270°$ *and* $360°$; *reference angle is* $\alpha = 360° - \theta$.　　　(3)

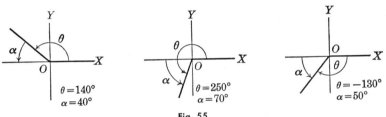

Fig. 55

THEOREM I. *The value of any trigonometric function of an angle θ in any quadrant is numerically equal to the value of the same-named function of the reference angle, α, for θ. That is,*

(any function of θ) = $\pm$ (same function of reference angle α),　　(4)

where "+" *or* "−" *applies according as the function of θ is positive or negative.*

ILLUSTRATION 1. To find $\tan 140°$, notice that $\alpha = 40°$ in Figure 55. Also, the tangent is negative in quadrant II. Hence, from (4) and Table IV,

$$\tan 140° = - \tan 40° = - .839.$$

ILLUSTRATION 2. The reference angle for $315°$ is $45°$ and $\tan 315°$ is negative, while $\cos 315°$ is positive. Hence, from (4),

$$\tan 315° = - \tan 45° = - 1; \quad \cos 315° = + \cos 45° = \tfrac{1}{2}\sqrt{2}.$$

Proof of Theorem I. 1. Place θ in its standard position on a coordinate system, as in Figure 56; the reference angle for θ is the acute angle α of the reference $\triangle AOP$.

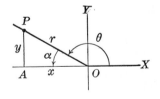

Fig. 56

2. Let the positive numbers $\overline{OA}$ and $\overline{AP}$ be the *lengths* of OA and AP. Then, $x = \pm \overline{OA}$ and $y = \pm \overline{AP}$, where the sign "+" or "−" in each case depends on the signs of x and y in the quadrant where P is located.

3. In $\triangle AOP$, $\overline{AP}$ and $\overline{OA}$ are the *lengths* of the sides opposite and adjacent to α, and $r = \overline{OP}$. Then, we obtain the functions of α by use of page 150, and the functions of θ from definitions on page 140:

$$\sin \alpha = \frac{\overline{AP}}{r}; \qquad \sin \theta = \frac{y}{r} = \pm \frac{\overline{AP}}{r} = \pm \sin \alpha.$$

$$\tan \alpha = \frac{\overline{AP}}{\overline{OA}}; \qquad \tan \theta = \frac{y}{x} = \frac{\pm \overline{AP}}{\pm \overline{OA}} = \pm \tan \alpha.$$

Similarly, each function of θ differs from the same function of α at most in sign. Since all functions of an acute angle are positive, the sign, $+$ or $-$, to use in (4) is the same as the sign of the function of θ which is involved.

EXAMPLE 1. Find $\tan 283°$ by use of Table IV.

SOLUTION. From a rough sketch, the student should verify that the reference angle is $(360° - 283°)$ or $77°$. Also, the tangent function is negative in quadrant IV. Hence,

$$\tan 283° = - \tan 77° = - 4.331.$$

ILLUSTRATION 3. Since $398° = 360° + 38°$, the angles $398°$ and $38°$ are coterminal and hence have the same values for their trigonometric functions. Also, we observe that $38°$ is the reference angle for $398°$. From either viewpoint, $\sin 398° = \sin 38°$.

Note 1. For a quadrantal angle θ, we may call $0°$ or $90°$ the reference angle for θ according as its terminal side, in standard position, falls on the *horizontal* or *vertical* coordinate axis. Then, (4) holds for quadrantal angles as well as all other angles. However, this fact is seldom used because it is easy to memorize the functions of quadrantal angles.

Note 2. Instead of (4), we can say that the *absolute value* of any trigonometric function of θ is equal to the same-named function of the acute reference angle for θ.

We can use Theorem I, without drawing a coordinate system, to find all functions of an angle θ if just *one function* of θ and its *quadrant* are given. We obtain the results by first finding the functions of the reference angle for θ from a right triangle.

EXAMPLE 2. Find $\sin \theta$ and $\tan \theta$ in case $\cos \theta = - \frac{2}{3}$ and θ is in quadrant III.

SOLUTION. 1. Let α be the reference angle for θ. Then, $\cos \alpha = \frac{2}{3}$. A right $\triangle ABC$ with α as one angle is shown roughly to scale in Figure 57; the value of a was computed: $a = \sqrt{9 - 4} = \sqrt{5}$.

2. From Figure 57, $\sin \alpha = \frac{1}{3}\sqrt{5}$ and $\tan \alpha = \frac{1}{2}\sqrt{5}$. We have $| \sin \theta | = \sin \alpha$ and $| \tan \theta | = \tan \alpha$; also, $\sin \theta < 0$ and $\tan \theta > 0$. Hence, $\sin \theta = - \frac{1}{3}\sqrt{5}$ and $\tan \theta = \frac{1}{2}\sqrt{5}$.

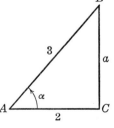

Fig. 57

EXERCISE 51

Sketch the angle in standard position and find the reference angle.

1. 121°. **2.** 203°. **3.** 267°. **4.** − 210°. **5.** 470°.

By use of a reference angle, find each function value. Give the result in exact form if the reference angle is 30°, 45°, or 60°, and otherwise use Table IV.

6. tan 115°. **7.** cot 142°. **8.** sin 208°. **9.** cos 225°.

10. sec 330°. **11.** csc 340°. **12.** sin 394°. **13.** cot 326°.

14. cos 117°. **15.** cot 153°. **16.** cot 210°. **17.** sin 120°.

18. sin (− 25°). **19.** tan (− 52°). **20.** cos (− 75°). **21.** sec (− 80°).

22. cot (− 130°). **23.** sec (− 120°). **24.** sin (− 210°). **25.** csc (− 230°).

26. sin 250°. **27.** sec 305°. **28.** tan 216°. **29.** cos 93°.

30. sin (− 200°). **31.** tan (− 302°). **32.** sec 420°. **33.** cos 495°.

34. sin 530°. **35.** cot 844°. **36.** sec (− 403°). **37.** cos 907°.

38. By placing each angle in standard position on a coordinate system as on page 138, obtain the values of all functions which exist for 0°, 90°, 180°, and 270°, to fill in a table with a row for each angle.

39. By reference to a coterminal angle in the table for Problem 38, read off the values of all trigonometric functions which exist for 360°; 540°; − 180°; − 270°; − 90°; − 720°; 450°; 630°.

40. Prove that each of the following equations is **NOT** an identity:

$$\cos (-\theta) = -\cos \theta; \quad \tan (-\theta) = \tan \theta; \quad \sin (\theta + \gamma) = \sin \theta + \sin \gamma.$$

By use of a right triangle corresponding to the reference angle, find the values of all functions of the angle θ satisfying the conditions.

41. $\tan \theta = -\frac{3}{5}$; θ in (II). **42.** $\sin \theta = -\frac{3}{4}$; θ in (IV).

43. $\cos \theta = -\frac{4}{7}$; θ in (II). **44.** $\cot \theta = \frac{5}{2}$; θ in (III).

82. Geometrical representation of sin θ and cos θ

Let θ be any angle, and suppose that it is placed in standard position on a coordinate system, as in Figure 58, where a circle of radius 1 is constructed with the origin as center. Let $P:(x, y)$ be the intersection of the terminal side of θ and the circle. Then,

$$r = OP = 1;$$

$$\sin \theta = \frac{y}{r} = \frac{y}{1} = y; \quad \cos \theta = \frac{x}{1} = x.$$

That is, for any angle θ, the *ordinate* of P is sin θ and the *abscissa* of P is cos θ.

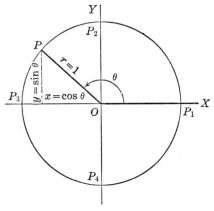

Fig. 58

If a variable angle θ changes continuously from $\theta = 0°$ to $\theta = 360°$, the corresponding variation in $\sin \theta$ or $\cos \theta$ can be learned by use of the geometrical interpretation of $\sin \theta$ and $\cos \theta$ in Figure 58. Thus, if θ increases from $0°$ to $90°$, point P of Figure 58 moves on the circle from P_1 to P_2, while $\sin \theta$ increases from 0 to 1. If θ increases from $90°$ to $270°$, then P moves from P_2 to P_4, and $\sin \theta$ decreases from $+1$ to -1. If θ increases from $270°$ to $360°$, then P moves from P_4 to P_1, and $\sin \theta$ increases from -1 to zero. Similarly, the student should discuss the variation of $\cos \theta$.

83. An auxiliary result

Let θ be any angle, positive, negative, or zero, with vertex O, initial side OB, and terminal side OC, where $OB = 1$ and $OC = 1$. Then, if triangle OBC is completed, as in Figure 59, we shall prove that

$$\overline{BC}^2 = 2 - 2 \cos \theta. \qquad (1)$$

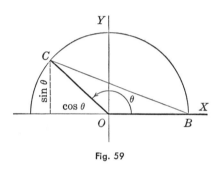

Fig. 59

Proof. 1. Place θ in standard position on a coordinate system, as in Figure 59, with B on the x-axis in the positive direction from O. Then, from Figure 58 on page 155, the coordinates of C are $(\cos \theta, \sin \theta)$, and the coordinates of B are $(1, 0)$, for any angle θ.

2. By the distance formula, page 61,

$$\overline{BC}^2 = (\cos \theta - 1)^2 + (\sin \theta - 0)^2 = \cos^2 \theta - 2 \cos \theta + 1 + \sin^2 \theta$$
$$= 1 + (\sin^2 \theta + \cos^2 \theta) - 2 \cos \theta = 2 - 2 \cos \theta.$$

84. Addition formulas for the sine and cosine

We shall prove that, for all angles α and β,

$$\sin (\alpha + \beta) = \sin \alpha \cos \beta + \cos \alpha \sin \beta; \qquad (1)$$

$$\sin (\alpha - \beta) = \sin \alpha \cos \beta - \cos \alpha \sin \beta; \qquad (2)$$

$$\cos (\alpha + \beta) = \cos \alpha \cos \beta - \sin \alpha \sin \beta; \qquad (3)$$

$$\cos (\alpha - \beta) = \cos \alpha \cos \beta + \sin \alpha \sin \beta. \qquad (4)$$

We refer to (1) and (3) as *addition formulas;* (2) and (4) are special cases of (1) and (3), respectively.

Proof of (4). 1. For any angles α and β, let $\phi = \alpha - \beta$. Then, $\alpha = \phi + \beta$. Place β in standard position on a coordinate system, as in Figure 60 on page 157, with initial side OM and terminal side OC, where $\overline{OM} = \overline{OC} = 1$. The semicircle in Figure 60 has radius 1 and center at O. Rotate OC through the angle ϕ to form $\alpha = \phi + \beta$, with OB as the terminal side of α and $OB = 1$. Then, α also is in standard position.

2. From Figure 58 on page 155, the coordinates of C are $(\cos \beta, \sin \beta)$, and of B are $(\cos \alpha, \sin \alpha)$. By use of the distance formula of page 61,

$$\overline{BC}^2 = (\cos \alpha - \cos \beta)^2 + (\sin \alpha - \sin \beta)^2$$
$$= (\cos^2 \alpha + \sin^2 \alpha) + (\cos^2 \beta + \sin^2 \beta) - 2(\cos \alpha \cos \beta + \sin \alpha \sin \beta). \quad (5)$$

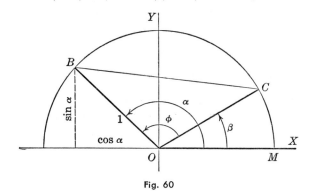

Fig. 60

From (1) of Section 83 on page 156, and (5), we then obtain (4):

$$2 - 2 \cos \phi = 2 - 2(\cos \alpha \cos \beta + \sin \alpha \sin \beta), \; or$$
$$\cos \phi = \cos (\alpha - \beta) = \cos \alpha \cos \beta + \sin \alpha \sin \beta.$$

By use of (4), we shall prove that, for all angles θ,

$$\sin (- \theta) = - \sin \theta; \quad \cos (- \theta) = \cos \theta. \quad (6)$$
$$\sin (90° - \theta) = \cos \theta; \quad \cos (90° - \theta) = \sin \theta. \quad (7)$$

Proof of **cos** $(- \theta) =$ **cos** θ. From (4) with $\alpha = 0°$ and $\beta = \theta$,

$$\cos (0° - \theta) = \cos (- \theta) = \cos 0° \cos \theta + \sin 0° \sin \theta = \cos \theta,$$

because $\cos 0° = 1$ and $\sin 0° = 0$.

Proof of **cos** $(90° - \theta) =$ **sin** θ. From (4) with $\alpha = 90°$ and $\beta = \theta$,

$$\cos (90° - \theta) = \cos 90° \cos \theta + \sin 90° \sin \theta = \sin \theta,$$

because $\cos 90° = 0$ and $\sin 90° = 1$.

Proof of **sin** $(90° - \theta) =$ **cos** θ. In $\cos (90° - \theta) = \sin \theta$, when θ is replaced by $(90° - \theta)$ on both sides, we obtain

$$\cos [90° - (90° - \theta)] = \sin (90° - \theta), \quad or \quad \cos \theta = \sin (90° - \theta).$$

Proof of **sin** $(- \theta) = -$ **sin** θ. From $\cos (90° - \theta) = \sin \theta$ with θ replaced by $- \theta$, we obtain

$$\sin (- \theta) = \cos [90° - (- \theta)] = \cos [\theta - (- 90°)]. \quad (8)$$

On using (4) with $\alpha = \theta$ and $\beta = - 90°$ in (8), we find

$$\sin (- \theta) = \cos \theta \cos (- 90°) + \sin \theta \sin (- 90°) = - \sin \theta,$$

since $\cos (- 90°) = 0$ and $\sin (- 90°) = - 1$. Thus, (6) and (7) are proved.

Proof of (1).   By use of sin θ = cos (90° − θ) with θ = $\alpha + \beta$, and then from (4) with α replaced by (90° − α), we obtain

$$\sin (\alpha + \beta) = \cos [90° - (\alpha + \beta)] = \cos [(90° - \alpha) - \beta]$$
$$= \cos (90° - \alpha) \cos \beta + \sin (90° - \alpha) \sin \beta$$
$$= \sin \alpha \cos \beta + \cos \alpha \sin \beta,$$

where we used (7) with θ = α.   Hence, (1) is true.

Proof of (2) *and* (3).   If we replace β by − β, and use (6), then (1) yields (2) and (4) becomes (3).   Thus, from (1) and then (6),

$$\sin [\alpha + (- \beta)] = \sin \alpha \cos (- \beta) + \cos \alpha \sin (- \beta)$$
$$= \sin \alpha \cos \beta - \cos \alpha \sin \beta.$$

EXAMPLE 1.   Find sin 135° and cos 135° by using 90° and 45°.

SOLUTION.   From (1) with α = 90° and β = 45°,

$$\sin 135° = \sin 90° \cos 45° + \cos 90° \sin 45° = \cos 45° = \tfrac{1}{2}\sqrt{2},$$

because sin 90° = 1 and cos 90° = 0.   Similarly, from (3), cos 135° = $- \tfrac{1}{2}\sqrt{2}$.

EXAMPLE 2.   Find sin $(\alpha + \beta)$ if sin α = $\tfrac{3}{5}$, cos β = $- \tfrac{5}{13}$, α is in quadrant I, and β is in quadrant II.

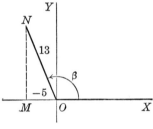

Fig. 61

SOLUTION.   Figure 61 shows a possible illustration of β, where the reference $\triangle OMN$ has $\overline{ON}$ = 13, $\overline{OM}$ = 5, and therefore $\overline{MN}$ = 12, by the Pythagorean theorem.   Then sin β = $\tfrac{12}{13}$. Similarly, from a reference triangle with sides 3, 4, and 5, cos α = $\tfrac{4}{5}$.   Hence, (1) gives

$$\sin (\alpha + \beta) = \tfrac{3}{5}(- \tfrac{5}{13}) + \tfrac{4}{5}(\tfrac{12}{13}) = \tfrac{33}{65}.$$

EXERCISE 52

Express the angle as a sum or difference and solve by use of (1)–(4) *on page* 156.

1. Find sin 225° and cos 225° by using functions of 180° and 45°.
2. Find sin 210° and cos 210° by using functions of 180° and 30°.
3. Find sin 315° and cos 315° by using functions of 360° and 45°.
4. Find sin 150° and cos 150° by using functions of 180° and 30°.
5. Find sin 180° and cos 180° by using functions of 240° and 60°.
6. Find sin 45° and cos 45° by using functions of 180° and 135°.
7. Find sin 75° and cos 75° by using functions of 135° and 60°.

Find the sine and cosine of the angle without using a table; the result may be left in radical form.   Solve by first expressing the angle as a sum or difference of convenient angles.

8. 105°.   9. 165°.   10. 195°.   11. 285°.   12. 255°.

Without use of tables, find the sine and cosine, and then the tangent and co-tangent of $(\alpha + \beta)$ and of $(\alpha - \beta)$.

13. $\sin \alpha = \frac{4}{5}$, α in quadrant I; $\cos \beta = -\frac{12}{13}$, β in quadrant II.

14. $\sin \alpha = \frac{24}{25}$, α in quadrant II; $\cos \beta = \frac{5}{13}$, β in quadrant IV.

15. $\sin \alpha = \frac{5}{13}$, α in quadrant II; $\cos \beta = -\frac{24}{25}$, β in quadrant III.

Expand by use of (1)–(4) on page 156 and insert known function values.

16. $\sin (30° + \theta)$. **17.** $\cos (45° - \alpha)$. **18.** $\sin (60° + \theta)$.

19. $\sin (90° + \theta)$. **20.** $\cos (90° + \theta)$. **21.** $\sin (\theta - 90°)$.

22. $\sin (270° - \theta)$. **23.** $\sin (180° + \theta)$. **24.** $\cos (\theta - 270°)$.

25. $\cos (\theta - 180°)$. **26.** $\sin (\theta - 450°)$. **27.** $\sin (- 90° - \theta)$. *stop*

*Prove that the equation is **NOT** an identity in the angles α and β.*

28. $\sin (\alpha - \beta) = \sin \alpha - \sin \beta$. **29.** $\cos (\alpha - \beta) = \cos \alpha - \cos \beta$.

85. Periodicity of the trigonometric functions

Let f be a function defined on a domain D, where x is to represent the general number of D. Suppose that p is a positive constant such that

$$f(x + p) = f(x) \text{ at all admissible values of } x. \tag{1}$$

Then, we say that f is **periodic** and has p as a **period**. This means that values of f repeat at intervals of length p in the values of x. We observe then that

$$f(x + 2p) = f[(x + p) + p] = f(x + p) = f(x),$$

so that $2p$ also is seen to be a period for f. Similarly, $3p$, $4p$, or in general np is a period for f, with n as any positive integer. If f is periodic, the *smallest number p* which is a period for f is called **THE period** for f. On replacing x in (1) by $(x - p)$, we obtain $f[(x - p) + p] = f(x - p)$, or

$$f(x) = f(x - p) \text{ at all values of } x. \tag{2}$$

ILLUSTRATION 1. Let the function $f(x)$ have the graph shown in Figure 62, where a semicircle of radius 2 is repeated above the x-axis endlessly to the left and the right. Then, from this graph of $y = f(x)$, we see that f is periodic with the period 4, because $f(x + 4) = f(x)$ at all values of x. For instance,

$$f(0) = 2 = f(\pm 4) = f(\pm 8) = etc.; \quad f(2) = 0 = f(- 2) = f(6) = etc.$$

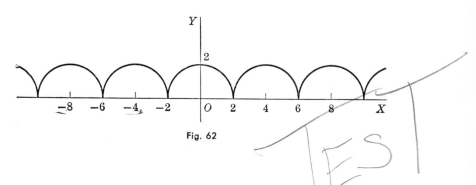

Fig. 62

THEOREM II. *Each trigonometric function of an angle θ is periodic and has 360°, or one complete rotation, as a period.* That is,* for all values of θ,

[any function of $(\theta + 360°)$] = (same function of θ);   (3)

[any function of $(\theta - 360°)$] = (same function of θ).   (4)

Proof. For every value of θ, the angles θ, $(\theta + 360°)$, and $(\theta - 360°)$ are coterminal. Since coterminal angles have identical trigonometric functions, identities (3) and (4) are true for all values of θ.

Note 1. In illustrative Example 1 on page 221, and Problem 33 on page 222, it is proved that the smallest period of the functions $\tan \theta$ and $\cot \theta$ is 180°, and of $\sin \theta$, $\cos \theta$, $\sec \theta$, and $\csc \theta$ is 360°.

Equation (3) abbreviates six identities,

$\sin (\theta + 360°) = \sin \theta$, $\cos (\theta + 360°) = \cos \theta$, $\cdots$, $\csc (\theta + 360°) = \csc \theta$.

ILLUSTRATION 2. From (3) and (4), the values of $\sin \theta$ repeat at intervals of 360° in the values of θ if we increase or decrease θ. Thus, $\sin \theta$ repeats the value $\sin 30° = \frac{1}{2}$ at intervals of 360°:

$$\tfrac{1}{2} = \sin 30° = \sin (30° \pm 360°) = \sin (30° \pm 720°) = etc.$$

Identities (3) and (4) are equivalent, although in different notation. Thus, either (3) or (4) states that, *if two angles differ by 360°, the values of corresponding functions of the two angles are equal.*

86. Reduction formulas

Simple relations exist between the values of the trigonometric functions of any two angles whose sum or whose difference is an integral multiple of 90°. In (1) below, the multiple of 90° is $0 \cdot 90°$; in (2), the multiple is $1 \cdot 90°$; in (3), the multiple is $\pm 2 \cdot 90°$. Identities of this variety are called *reduction formulas.* The periodicity identities of Section 85 are reduction formulas.

Any reduction formula involving the sine or cosine functions can be proved by use of (1)–(4) on page 156. The following reduction formulas are so useful that they deserve being memorized.

$\sin (- \theta) = - \sin \theta$; $\cos (- \theta) = \cos \theta$; $\tan (- \theta) = - \tan \theta$. (1)

[any trig. function of $(90° - \theta)$] = (cofunction of θ). (2)

$\tan (\theta \pm 180°) = \tan \theta$; $\cot (\theta \pm 180°) = \cot \theta$. (3)

$\sin (180° - \theta) = \sin \theta$; $\cos (180° - \theta) = - \cos \theta$. (4)

We call (2) the **cofunction relations.** Identities (3) state that the tangent and cotangent functions are periodic with the period 180°, as well as the larger period 360° which is common to all trigonometric functions.

* With the added proviso that, when the tangent, cotangent, secant, or cosecant is involved, the equation does not hold true for any quadrantal value of θ for which the function is not defined. This exception is understood in all future trigonometric identities.

ILLUSTRATION 1. In Section 84, we proved the identities for the sine and cosine in (1). Then, from the fundamental identities of page 146, we obtain

$$\tan (- \theta) = \frac{\sin (- \theta)}{\cos (- \theta)} = \frac{- \sin \theta}{\cos \theta} = - \tan \theta.$$

From (1), by taking reciprocals, we may write

$$\csc (- \theta) = \frac{1}{\sin (- \theta)} = \frac{1}{- \sin \theta} = - \frac{1}{\sin \theta} = - \csc \theta;$$

$$\sec (- \theta) = \sec \theta; \qquad \cot (- \theta) = - \cot \theta.$$

Similarly, for any set of reduction formulas, if we obtain those involving the sines and cosines, we can prove the corresponding formulas for the other functions by use of fundamental identities.

ILLUSTRATION 2. In Section 84, we proved (2) for $\sin (90° - \theta)$ and $\cos (90° - \theta)$ on the left. Hence, we obtain

$$\tan (90° - \theta) = \frac{\sin (90° - \theta)}{\cos (90° - \theta)} = \frac{\cos \theta}{\sin \theta} = \cot \theta.$$

Then, on taking reciprocals as in Illustration 1, we could show that (2) holds for $\cot (90° - \theta)$, $\sec (90° - \theta)$, and $\csc (90° - \theta)$.

ILLUSTRATION 3. By use of the addition formula for the sine, with $\sin 180° = 0$ and $\cos 180° = - 1$,

$$\sin (\theta + 180°) = \sin \theta \cos 180° + \cos \theta \sin 180° = - \sin \theta.$$

Similarly, $\cos (\theta + 180°) = - \cos \theta$. Hence,

$$\tan (\theta + 180°) = \frac{\sin (\theta + 180°)}{\cos (\theta + 180°)} = \frac{- \sin \theta}{- \cos \theta} = \tan \theta. \qquad (5)$$

Then, $\cot (\theta + 180°) = \cot \theta$. Identities (3) for $(\theta - 180°)$ can be proved first by use of (2) and (4) on page 156 for $\sin (\theta - 180°)$ and $\cos (\theta - 180°)$, and then by use of fundamental identities, as in (5).

ILLUSTRATION 4. If θ is an acute angle, the *supplement* of θ is $(180° - \theta)$. Thus, (4) gives the sine and cosine of the supplement of θ in terms of $\sin \theta$ and $\cos \theta$, respectively. The student should prove (4) for any angle θ by use of (2) and (4) on page 156.

All reduction formulas are special cases of the following general identity, which can be proved by use of the addition formulas for the sine and cosine and the fundamental identities, as in Illustration 3. In (6), n represents any integer, 0, positive, or negative.

$$\left\{ \begin{array}{l} \textbf{Any trigonometric} \\ \textbf{function of } (\pm \theta + n \cdot 90°) \end{array} \right\} = \left\{ \begin{array}{l} \pm \text{ (same function of } \theta\text{), } n \text{ even;} \\ \pm \text{ (cofunction of } \theta\text{), } n \text{ odd.} \end{array} \right\} \qquad (6)$$

In (6), for any specified function on the left-hand side, and any integer n, just one sign, + or −, applies on the right, with the *same sign involved for all values of θ*. Thus, we find that, for all values of $θ$,

$$\sin(270° + θ) = -\cos θ; \qquad \cos(270° + θ) = \sin θ. \qquad (7)$$

A general proof of (6) is suggested in the next exercise. For any particular angle $(± θ + n·90°)$, the formulas obtainable from (6) can be proved as in Illustration 3.

ILLUSTRATION 5. To prove (7), we use (1) and (3) of page 156 with $α = 270°$ and $β = θ$:

$$\sin(270° + θ) = \sin 270° \cos θ + \cos 270° \sin θ = -\cos θ,$$

because $\sin 270° = -1$ and $\cos 270° = 0$. Similarly, the student should obtain $\cos(270° + θ) = \sin θ$. Then, by use of the fundamental identities,

$$\tan(270° + θ) = \frac{\sin(270° + θ)}{\cos(270° + θ)} = \frac{-\cos θ}{\sin θ} = -\cot θ.$$

Hereafter, unless otherwise specified, we shall use (6) without proof in any special case.

EXAMPLE 1. Express $\cot(270° - θ)$ in terms of a function of $θ$.

SOLUTION. 1. From (6), since $270° = 3·90°$, we have

$$\cot(270° - θ) = ± \tan θ, \qquad (8)$$

where the sign $±$ is independent of the value of $θ$.

2. To determine the sign on the right in (8), let $θ$ be thought of as an acute angle. Then, $(270° - θ)$ is an angle in quadrant III, and $\cot(270° - θ) > 0$; since $\tan θ > 0$ when $θ$ is acute, we must use "+" on the right in (8) to make the right-hand side positive. Hence, when $θ$ is acute, and therefore for *all* admissible values of $θ$, we have $\cot(270° - θ) = \tan θ$.

SUMMARY. *To obtain any particular reduction formula, use (6) with an ambiguous sign. Then, determine the proper sign by checking signs on the two sides for the case where θ is acute.*

By use of the periodicity of the trigonometric functions and (1), any trigonometric function of an angle $θ$ of any magnitude, positive or negative, can be expressed as a function of a *nonnegative angle* less than 360°. Then, by use of an acute reference angle, the function of $θ$ can be expressed as a function of an acute angle, in two ways if (2) is used.

ILLUSTRATION 6. To find $\tan(-1257°)$, notice that $1257° = 1080° + 177°$. Then, by (1) and the periodicity of the tangent function,

$$\tan(-1257°) = -\tan 1257° = -\tan(3·360° + 177°) = -\tan 177°.$$

The acute reference angle for 177° is 3°; $\tan 177° = -\tan 3°$. Hence,

$$\tan(-1257°) = -(-\tan 3°) = \tan 3° = .052 \qquad \text{(Table IV)}$$

$$= \cot 87° = .052. \qquad \text{[Using (2)]}$$

EXERCISE 53

Prove the reduction formulas for the specified functions by use of the addition formulas for the sine and cosine.

1. $\sin(270° - \theta)$.
2. $\cos(\theta - 270°)$.
3. $\cos(\theta - 180°)$.
4. $\sin(\theta - 90°)$.
5. $\cos(\theta + 90°)$.
6. $\sin(450° + \theta)$.
7. $\sin(\theta - 180°)$.
8. $\cos(\theta + 540°)$.
9. $\sin(\theta - 270°)$.

By use of addition formulas, prove the reduction formulas for the sine and cosine of the specified angle, and then obtain the reduction formulas for all other functions of the angle by use of the fundamental identities.

10. $(\theta - 90°)$.
11. $(270° - \theta)$.
12. $(540° - \theta)$.
13. $(\theta + 90°)$.
14. $(\theta + 270°)$.
15. $(450° - \theta)$.
16. $(\theta + 450°)$.
17. $(630° - \theta)$.

Express the function value in terms of the value of a function of θ, by use of the general identity (6) on page 161, or by use of periodicity relations and identities (1) or (2) on page 160.

18. $\cot(180° + \theta)$.
19. $\sin(270° + \theta)$.
20. $\cos(270° - \theta)$.
21. $\tan(270° - \theta)$.
22. $\csc(180° + \theta)$.
23. $\tan(360° + \theta)$.
24. $\sin(\theta - 720°)$.
25. $\sec(270° + \theta)$.
26. $\csc(360° - \theta)$.
27. $\sec(-\theta)$.
28. $\cos(450° + \theta)$.
29. $\sin(-270° + \theta)$.
30. $\tan(270° - \theta)$.
31. $\cot(540° + \theta)$.
32. $\tan(\theta - 540°)$.
33. $\csc(\theta - 360°)$.
34. $\cot(-180° + \theta)$.
35. $\sec(90° + \theta)$.

Sketch the angle roughly in standard position on a coordinate system, and express the sine, cosine, and tangent of the angle in terms of a trigonometric function value for a positive angle at most equal to 45°. Use the cofunction relations.

36. $47°$.
37. $63°$.
38. $129°$.
39. $147°$.
40. $218°$.
41. $176°$.
42. $243°$.
43. $284°$.
44. $304°$.
45. $352°$.
46. $-37°$.
47. $-56°$.
48. $-124°$.
49. $-256°$.
50. $-310°$.
51. $305°$.
52. $487°$.
53. $-247°$.
54. $-849°$.
55. $-283°$.

★56. Prove the identity (6) on page 161 for the cases of the sine and cosine on the left, if n is an even integer. Then, prove (6) for the tangent on the left.

Hint. If n is an even integer, $\sin n \cdot 90° = 0$ and $\cos n \cdot 90° = \pm 1$, where the sign $\pm$ depends on n.

★57. Repeat Problem 56 for the case where n is odd.

87. Graphs of the sine and cosine, in degree measure

In Definition I on page 140, as emphasized in Note 2 on page 141, the domain of each of the trigonometric functions is specified as a set of *geometrical objects*, called *angles*. Sometimes, with this viewpoint, Definition I is said to describe the *geometric trigonometric functions*.

In the definition of the graph of a function on page 73, both the *domain* and the *range* of the function were sets of *abstract numbers*. We desire to obtain this situation for the trigonometric functions, in order to consider their graphs. Hence, we depart from the viewpoint of Definition I, and shall refer to each trigonometric function as having a domain consisting of *real numbers*, which are the *measures of angles*, at present *measured in degrees*.

ILLUSTRATION 1. Let f be a function whose domain is the set, D, of all real numbers and whose value at any point x of D is $f(x) = \sin x°$. Thus, $f(2) = \sin 2° = .035$, by Table IV; $f(90) = \sin 90° = 1$.

When we refer to the graphs of the trigonometric functions in degree measure, we shall be speaking of the graphs of the functions $\sin x°$, $\cos x°$, $\tan x°$, $\cot x°$, $\sec x°$, and $\csc x°$, where the independent variable is x, and the range for x is *all real numbers* * for which the functions are defined.

The graph of the function $\sin x°$ is the graph of the equation $y = \sin x°$. We make up the entries in the following table, with x ranging from 0 to 90, by use of Table IV or from memory about the convenient angles $0°$, $30°$, $45°$, $60°$, and $90°$. Then we choose other values of x so that the acute reference angles for $x°$ are those just used. Thus, corresponding to $75°$, we have

$$\sin 105° = \sin 75° = .97; \quad \sin (180° + 75°) = \sin 255° = -\sin 75° = -.97; \; etc.$$

x	0	30	45	60	75	90	105	120	135	150	180
$y = \sin x°$	0	.50	.71	.87	.97	1.00	.97	.87	.71	.50	0
x	180	210	225	240	255	270	285	300	315	330	360
$y = \sin x°$	0	-.50	-.71	-.87	-.97	-1.00	-.97	-.87	-.71	-.50	0

The points (x, y) from the table were used to obtain the graph in Figure 63. The complete graph consists of this wave and its endless repetitions on both sides, because $\sin x°$ is a periodic function with the period 360. That is,

$$\sin (x \pm 360)° = \sin (x° \pm 360°) = \sin x°.$$

Thus, to plot the point (x, y) on the graph where $x = -330$, we use the ordinate where $x = 30$, because $-330° + 360° = 30°$, and hence

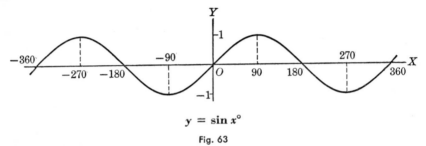

$$y = \sin x°$$

Fig. 63

* Sometimes, with this viewpoint, the functions are referred to as *analytic trigonometric functions*, or *trigonometric functions of numbers*.

sin $(- 330°) = \sin 30°$. The graph of $y = \cos x°$ can be obtained similarly.

The identity $\sin (x° + 90°) = \cos x°$ states that *the cosine of any angle is the same as the sine of an angle which is 90° greater*. Therefore, if we shift the graph of sin $x°$ to the left, through a distance equal to 90 on the horizontal scale, we obtain the graph of cos $x°$, as in Figure 64.

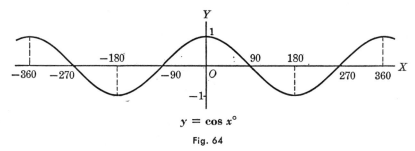

$y = \cos x°$

Fig. 64

ILLUSTRATION 2. In Figure 63 on page 164, if x varies from $x = 0$ to $x = 90$, the graph *rises*, or sin $x°$ *increases* from 0 to 1. If x varies from 90 to 270, the graph *falls*, or sin $x°$ *decreases* from 1 to $- 1$; etc.

ILLUSTRATION 3. It is clear that an equation such as sin $\theta = \frac{1}{2}$ is not an identity, because the sine function does not always have the value $\frac{1}{2}$. Hence, sin $\theta = \frac{1}{2}$ is a conditional equation, considered as requesting the unknown values of angle θ for which the equation is true. We call it a *trigonometric equation*. To solve sin $\theta = \frac{1}{2}$, we recall the sines of convenient angles and the signs of the sine function in the various quadrants. We see that θ must be in quadrant I or quadrant II. Hence, on the range $- 360° < \theta < 360°$, the solutions of sin $\theta = \frac{1}{2}$ are, first, 30° and 150°, and then the coterminal angles θ such that $- 360° < \theta < 0°$, or $- 210°$ and $- 330°$. Thus, we have four solutions 30°, 150°, $- 210°$, and $- 330°$. In Figure 63 on page 164, if the student draws the line $y = \frac{1}{2}$, it will intersect the graph of $y = \sin x°$ at four points, where x has the values $- 210$, $- 330$, 30, and 150, corresponding to the values of θ above. From the periodicity of sin θ, all solutions of sin $\theta = \frac{1}{2}$, with no limitation on the size of θ, are of the following forms where n may be any integer, positive, negative, or zero:

$$\theta = 30° + n(360°) \quad and \quad \theta = 150° + n(360°).$$

Let $T(\theta)$ represent any trigonometric function of an angle θ, and consider solving a trigonometric equation $T(\theta) = b$, where b is a known number. Let α be the acute reference angle for θ. Then, $T(\alpha) = |b|$. Hence, to solve $T(\theta) = b$, we first find the acute angle α, if any, satisfying $T(\alpha) = |b|$. Then, on any desired interval of values for θ, the solutions of $T(\theta) = b$ are the angles, in the proper quadrants, whose acute reference angle is α. Usually $T(\theta) = b$ will have two solutions on the interval $0° \leq \theta < 360°$, as seen geometrically in Illustration 1, page 148.

ILLUSTRATION 4.   To find all solutions of $\sin \theta = -\frac{1}{2}\sqrt{3}$ on the range $0° \leq \theta < 360°$, let α be the acute reference angle for θ.   Then, $\sin \alpha = |-\frac{1}{2}\sqrt{3}|$, or $\sin \alpha = \frac{1}{2}\sqrt{3}$; hence $\alpha = 60°$. Since θ is in quadrant III or quadrant IV because $\sin \theta < 0$, we obtain the solutions $\theta = 180° + 60°$ and $\theta = 360° - 60°$, or $240°$ and $300°$.

EXERCISE 54

Graph the functions in an xy-plane.   In arranging x and y scales, make the distance for 180 units on the x-axis about three times the unit distance on the y-axis.   Use periodicity in making up the tables of values.

1. The function $\sin x°$, for $-180 \leq x \leq 540$.

2. The function $\cos x°$, for $270 \leq x \leq 450$.

3. By inspection of a graph, describe the variation of each of the functions $\sin \theta$ and $\cos \theta$ as the angle θ changes continuously from $0°$ to $360°$.

Graph each of the equations on the range $0 \leq x \leq 360$, by use of just quadrantal angles x°.   Make gracefully rounded curves.

4. $y = 2 \sin x°$.   5. $y = -2 \sin x°$.   6. $y = 3 \cos x°$.

Find all solutions of the given equation for the unknown angle θ on the range $-360° \leq \theta \leq 360°$.

7. $\sin \theta = 1$.   8. $\cos \theta = -1$.   9. $\cos \theta = 0$.   10. $\cos \theta = \frac{1}{2}$.

11. $\sin \theta = 0$.   12. $\sin \theta = -1$.   13. $\cos \theta = -\frac{1}{2}$.

14. $\sin \theta = -\frac{1}{2}$.   15. $\cos \theta = \frac{1}{2}\sqrt{2}$.   16. $\sin \theta = \frac{1}{2}\sqrt{2}$.

17. $\sin \theta = \frac{1}{2}\sqrt{3}$.   18. $\cos \theta = \frac{1}{2}\sqrt{3}$.   19. $\sin \theta = -\frac{1}{2}\sqrt{2}$.

20. $\cos \theta = -\frac{1}{2}\sqrt{2}$.   21. $\cos \theta = -\frac{1}{2}\sqrt{3}$.   22. $\sin \theta = \frac{1}{2}$.

23. In the artillery service of the armed forces, angles frequently are measured in **mils,** where $(1600 \; mils) = 90°$. Let g be a function whose domain is the set D of all real numbers and whose value at any point x in D is $g(x) = \sin x^{(m)}$, where $x^{(m)}$ means x mils. Let $f(x) = \sin x°$. Find $g(800)$; $f(800)$; $f(320)$; $g(320)$. Are f and g the same function?

★24. Write expressions for all solutions in Problems 15 and 22.

88. Variation of the tan θ and sec θ

Suppose that $0° \leq \theta < 90°$, and that θ is placed in standard position on a coordinate system, as in Figure 65 on page 167, where $P:(x, y)$ is chosen on the terminal side of θ so that $x = 1$. Then, from page 140,

$$\tan \theta = \frac{y}{x} = \frac{y}{1} = y; \qquad \sec \theta = \frac{r}{x} = r. \tag{1}$$

Or, the ordinate of P is equal to $\tan \theta$ and $r = \sec \theta$.

If θ increases steadily from $0°$ and approaches $90°$ as a limit, then the corresponding point P in Figure 65 moves upward beyond all bounds; the ordinate $\tan \theta$ of P increases from 0 through all positive values. Hence, tan θ becomes greater than any specified number, however large, for all values of θ sufficiently near 90°. We summarize this by saying that **tan θ becomes positively infinite,** or **approaches + ∞** (read *plus infinity*) *as the acute angle θ approaches* 90° *as a limit.* Figure 65 does not apply when θ = 90°, and we recall that tan 90° does not exist because y/x is not defined if $x = 0$. Similar statements can be made about sec θ, or *r* in Figure 65, as θ → 90° (where "→" is read *approaches*). Thus, **sec θ becomes positively infinite** *as the acute angle* θ → 90°.

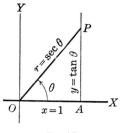

Fig. 65

In Figure 66 for θ > 90°, we choose $P:(x, y)$ so that $x = -1$. Then, from page 140,

$$\tan \theta = \frac{y}{x} = \frac{y}{-1} = -y, \quad or \quad y = -\tan \theta;$$

$$\sec \theta = \frac{r}{-1} = -r, \quad or \quad r = -\sec \theta.$$

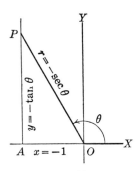

Fig. 66

If θ decreases steadily from 180° and approaches 90° as a limit, then the absolute value of tan θ, and of sec θ, or the lengths of *AP* and *OP*, become positively infinite. That is, tan θ and sec θ become *negatively infinite* as the obtuse angle θ → 90°. All of the facts we have just mentioned about tan θ and sec θ are implied as the meanings of the statements

tan 90° is infinite;   sec 90° is infinite. (2)

In summary, (2) abbreviates the following information:

1. *There is no tangent (and no secant) for* 90°.

2. *The absolute value of tan θ (and of sec θ) becomes greater than any number, however large, for all values of θ sufficiently near* 90°, *or*

$$\underset{\theta \to 90°}{\text{limit}} |\tan \theta| = \infty; \quad \underset{\theta \to 90°}{\text{limit}} |\sec \theta| = \infty. \tag{3}$$

In (3), we read "*the limit of* | tan θ | *is infinite as* θ → 90°," etc. Similarly, we find that

$$\left\{ \begin{array}{l} \tan \theta \text{ and sec } \theta \text{ are infinite if } \theta \text{ is any angle whose} \\ \textit{terminal side in standard position is } \textbf{vertical.} \end{array} \right\} \tag{4}$$

ILLUSTRATION 1. From (4), tan 270° and sec 270° are infinite. By use of trigonometric tables not in this text, we find

tan 89° = 57:   tan 89° 59′ = 3438;   tan 89° 59′ 59″ = 206,265.

89. Variation of cot θ and csc θ

From Definition I on page 140, we recall that cot θ and csc θ do not exist when $y = 0$, which occurs when the terminal side of θ is *horizontal* on page 140. For other values of θ, from (1) and (2) on page 146,

$$\cot \theta = \frac{\cos \theta}{\sin \theta} \quad and \quad \csc \theta = \frac{1}{\sin \theta}. \tag{1}$$

If $\theta \to 0°$, or $\theta \to 180°$, etc., then $|\sin \theta| \to 0$ and $|\cos \theta| \to 1$. Hence, the absolute value of each fraction in (1) grows large without bound, or $|\cot \theta| \to \infty$ and $|\csc \theta| \to \infty$ as $\theta \to 0°$, or as $\theta \to 180°$, etc. In particular, we arrive at the following conclusions:

cot 0° is infinite, *and* **csc 0° is infinite,** *or* (2)

$$\underset{\theta \to 0°}{\text{limit}} \; |\cot \theta| = \infty; \qquad \underset{\theta \to 0°}{\text{limit}} \; |\csc \theta| = \infty. \tag{3}$$

Our general reasoning justifies the statement that

$$\left\{ \begin{array}{l} cot \; \theta \; and \; csc \; \theta \; are \; infinite \; if \; \theta \; is \; any \; angle \; whose \\ terminal \; side \; in \; standard \; position \; is \; \textbf{horizontal.} \end{array} \right\} \tag{4}$$

Note 1. Recall that $\cos \theta = 0$ if the terminal side of θ is *vertical* when θ is in standard position on a coordinate system. Then, we could use reasoning such as above to replace the geometrical reasoning about tan θ and sec θ in Section 88. That is, since

$$\sec \theta = \frac{1}{\cos \theta} \quad and \quad \tan \theta = \frac{\sin \theta}{\cos \theta},$$

both $|\sec \theta|$ and $|\tan \theta|$ become infinite if θ approaches a value for which the cosine is zero.

90. Graphs of the tangent and cotangent, in degree measure

Let x be a variable with the range D consisting of *all real numbers.* Then the *analytic* trigonometric functions tan $x°$, cot $x°$, sec $x°$, and csc $x°$ are defined for all x in the domain D, except for certain values of x for each function, where $x°$ is quadrantal. To graph the functions tan $x°$ and cot $x°$ in an xy-plane, we graph the equations $y = \tan x°$ and $y = \cot x°$, respectively. Each of these functions is periodic with the period 180, because

$$\tan (x + 180)° = \tan (x° + 180°) = \tan x°; \tag{1}$$

$$\cot (x + 180)° = \cot (x° + 180°) = \cot x°. \tag{2}$$

Hence, the complete graph of $y = \tan x°$ consists of the piece shown from $x = 90$ to $x = 270$ in Figure 67 on page 169, and endless repetitions of this piece to the left and the right. Similarly, the graph of $y = \cot x°$ consists of the piece for the range $0 < x < 180$ and endless repetitions of this piece to the left and the right in Figure 68 on page 169.

ILLUSTRATION 1. The graph of $y = \tan x°$ was constructed by use of the following table. First, points were plotted from the table. Then, points on

x	0	15	30	45	60	75	78	90
$y = \tan x°$	0	.3	.6	1.0	1.7	3.7	4.7	∞
x	180	165	150	135	120	105	102	90
$y = \tan x°$	0	− .3	− .6	− 1.0	− 1.7	− 3.7	− 4.7	∞

the range $180 \leqq x < 360$ were plotted by use of the periodicity identity in (1). Thus, since $(x = 30, y = .6)$ is a point from the table, we find $(x = 30 + 180, y = .6)$ as a point on the graph. In Figure 67, the vertical broken lines are called **asymptotes,** and have the equations $x = 90$ and $x = 270$, respectively. The graph does not meet the line $x = 90$ because the angle 90° has no tangent. If $x \to 90$, from either side, the corresponding point $P:(x, y)$ on the graph recedes from the x-axis beyond all bounds because the absolute value of y grows large without bound, or

$$\lim_{x \to 90} \left| \tan x° \right| = \infty. \tag{3}$$

We can approach as closely as we desire to the asymptote $x = 90$, but never reach it, by receding sufficiently far from the x-axis on the graph. To construct Figure 67, the asymptotes were drawn first as guide lines. Then, the branches of the graph were drawn with the objective of making the curves approach the asymptotes smoothly. The entry ∞ for $x = 90$ in the table is just an abbreviated reminder of (3).

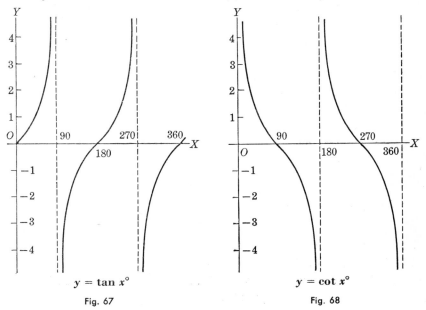

$y = \tan x°$

Fig. 67

$y = \cot x°$

Fig. 68

91. Graphs of the secant and cosecant, in degree measure

Graphs of the functions sec $x°$ and csc $x°$ are shown in Figures 69–70. Each graph has a vertical asymptote corresponding to each value of x for which the function is undefined. Thus, the graph of $y = \csc x°$ has the vertical lines $x = 0$, $x = 180$, and $x = 360$ as asymptotes because each of csc 0°, csc 180°, and csc 360° is infinite.

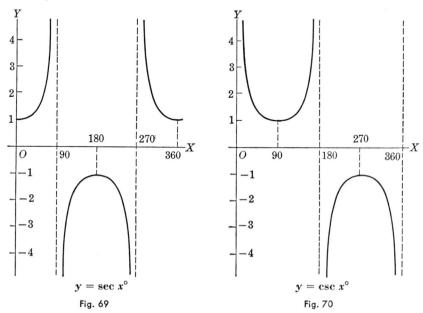

$$y = \sec x°$$

Fig. 69

$$y = \csc x°$$

Fig. 70

EXAMPLE 1. Describe the variation of sec $x°$ on the range $0 \leq x \leq 360$.

SOLUTION. From Figure 69, if x increases continuously from 0 to 90, the graph rises, or sec $x°$ increases from 1 to plus infinity $(+ \infty)$; as x increases from 90 to 180, the graph rises, or sec $x°$ increases from $- \infty$ to $- 1$; as x increases from 180 to 270, sec $x°$ decreases from $- 1$ to $- \infty$; as x increases from 270 to 360, sec $x°$ decreases from $+ \infty$ to 1.

ILLUSTRATION 1. The only solution of the equation tan $\theta = 1$ on the range 0° to 90° is $\theta = 45°$. Therefore, since tan θ has 180° as a period, the solutions of tan $\theta = 1$ on the range 0° to 360° are $\theta = 45°$ and $\theta = 225°$, where we were aided by Figure 67 on page 169 in our decision.

EXAMPLE 2. Find all values of θ on the range $- 360°$ to $+ 360°$ for which

$$\sec \theta \text{ is infinite.} \tag{1}$$

SOLUTION. From Figure 64 on page 165, cos $\theta = 0$ when $\theta = - 270°$, $- 90°$, 90°, and 270°. Since sec $\theta = 1/\cos \theta$, we have (1) when θ is $- 270°$, $- 90°$, 90°, and 270°, where we verify that $x = 90$ and $x = 270$ are the equations of the asymptotes in Figure 69.

EXERCISE 55

Graph the function in an xy-plane, with units on the axes chosen as in Exercise 54. Use periodicity in making up the table of values. Draw any asymptotes possessed by the graph.

1. $\tan x°$, for $-90 < x < 450$.
2. $\cot x°$, for $-180 < x < 360$.
3. $\sec x°$, for $-90 < x < 450$.
4. $\csc x°$, for $-180 < x < 540$.

5. On one coordinate system, graph $y = \sin x°$ and $y = \csc x°$, by use of computed points only for values of x where $x°$ is quadrantal, and by use of the known general shapes of the curves, for $-180 \le x \le 360$.
6. Repeat Problem 5 for $y = \cos x°$ and $y = \sec x°$ on the range $0 < x < 540$.

Find all angles θ which satisfy the equation or statement for the unknown angle θ on the interval $-360° < \theta < 360°$.

7. $\tan \theta = 0$.
8. $\cot \theta = 1$.
9. $\cot \theta = 0$.
10. $\tan \theta = -1$.
11. $\cot \theta = -1$.
12. $\sec \theta = 2$.
13. $\csc \theta = 1$.
14. $\csc \theta = -1$.
15. $\sec \theta = -1$.
16. $\tan \theta = \sqrt{3}$.
17. $\tan \theta = -\frac{1}{3}\sqrt{3}$.
18. $\cot \theta = -\sqrt{3}$.
19. $\cot \theta = \frac{1}{3}\sqrt{3}$.
20. $\sec \theta = \sqrt{2}$.
21. $\csc \theta = \frac{2}{3}\sqrt{3}$.
22. $\csc \theta = -\sqrt{2}$.
23. $\cot \theta$ is infinite.
24. $\tan \theta$ is infinite.
25. $\csc \theta$ is infinite.

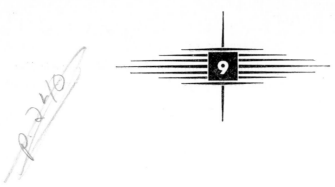

Logarithms and Computation

92. Significant digits

Suppose that the word *number* means a *real number* until otherwise specified. At present, assume that any number is written in decimal notation, where we visualize an *endless sequence of decimal places* in the number. A *terminating decimal* is one with an endless sequence of zeros to the right of a certain decimal place. An *endless decimal* is one which does not terminate.

ILLUSTRATION 1. 35.673, or 35.673000 · · ·, is a terminating decimal. The constant $\pi = 3.141593 \cdot \cdot \cdot$ is an endless, nonrepeating decimal.

In any number N, let us read its digits from left to right. Then, by definition, the **significant digits** or **figures** of N are its digits, in sequence, starting with the first one not zero and ending with the last one definitely specified. Notice that this definition does not involve any reference to the position of the decimal point in N. Usually we do not mention *final zeros* at the right in referring to the significant digits of N, except when it is the approximate value of some item of data.

ILLUSTRATION 2. The significant digits of 410.58 or of .0041058 are (4, 1, 0, 5, 8).

If T is the *true value*, and A is an *approximate value* of a quantity, we agree to call $|A - T|$ the **error** * of A.

ILLUSTRATION 3. If $T = 35.62$, and if $A = 35.60$ is an approximation to T, then the error of A is $|35.60 - 35.62|$ or .02.

The significant digits in an approximate value A should indicate the maximum possible error of A. This error is understood to be *at most one half of a unit in the last significant place in A* or, which is the same, *not more than 5 units in the next place to the right.*

---

* Sometimes, the error is defined as $(A - T)$, which thus is positive, negative, or zero. Then, a positive error means that $A > T$. Also, the error sometimes is defined as $(T - A)$, which reverses the preceding inequality. This lack of uniformity, and the frequent use of $|A - T|$ as the error, causes us to adopt this meaning.

ILLUSTRATION 4. If a surveyor measures a distance as 256.8 yards, he should mean that the error is at most .05 yard and that the true result lies between 256.75 and 256.85, inclusive, since the error might be .05.

In referring to the significant digits of an *approximate* value A, *it is essential to mention all final zeros designated in* A.

ILLUSTRATION 5. To state that a measured weight is 35.60 pounds should mean that the true weight differs from 35.60 pounds by at most .005 pound. To state that the weight is 35.6 pounds should mean that the true weight differs from this by at most .05 pound.

For abbreviation, or to indicate how many digits in a large number are significant, we may write a number N in the following form, sometimes called the **scientific notation** for a number:

Express the number N as the product of an integral power of 10 and a number equal to or greater than 1 but less than 10, with as many significant digits as are justified by the data.

ILLUSTRATION 6. $\qquad 385{,}720 = 3.8572(100{,}000) = 3.8572(10^5)$.

$$.000'000'368 = 3.68(.000'000'1) = 3.68(10^{-7}).$$

ILLUSTRATION 7. If 5,630,000 is an approximate value, its appearance fails to show how many zeros are significant. If five digits are significant, we write $5.6300(10^6)$, and if just three are significant, $5.63(10^6)$.

93. Accuracy of computation

In referring to a *place* in a number, we shall mean any place where a significant digit stands. In referring to a *decimal place*, the word *decimal* will be used explicitly.

To round off N to k figures, or to write a k-place approximation for N, means to write an approximate value with k significant digits so that the error of this value is not more than one half of a unit in the kth place, or 5 units in the first neglected place. This condition on the approximate value of N leads us to the following routine.

SUMMARY. **To round off a number N to k places,** *drop off the part of N beyond the kth place (filling in zeros if necessary to the left of the decimal point) and then proceed as follows.*

1. *Leave the digit of N in the kth place* **unchanged** *or* **increase it by 1,** *according as the omitted part of N is* **less than** *or* **greater than 5 units** *in the $(k + 1)$th place.*

2. *If the omitted part is exactly 5 units in the $(k + 1)$th place,* **increase the digit** *in the kth place by 1 or* **leave the digit unchanged,** *with the object of making* **the final choice an even digit.**[*]

---

[*] This agreement could be replaced by various similar and equally justified rules.

ILLUSTRATION 1. The seven-place approximation to π is 3.141593. On rounding off to five places, we obtain $\pi = 3.1416$; the four-place approximation is $\pi = 3.142$. In rounding off 315.475 to five places, with equal justification we could specify 315.47 or 315.48; in accordance with (2) in the Summary we choose 315.48.

By illustrations, we can verify that the following rules do not *underestimate* the accuracy of computation. On the other hand, we admit that the rules sometimes *overestimate* the accuracy. However, we shall assume that a result obtained by these rules will have a negligible error in the last significant place which is specified.

I. *In adding approximate values, round off the result in the first place where the last significant digit of any given value is found.*

II. *In multiplying or dividing approximate values, round off the result to the smallest number of significant figures found in any given value.*

ILLUSTRATION 2. Let $a = 35.64$, $b = 342.72$, and $c = .03147$ be approximate values. Then, $a + b + c$ is not reliable beyond the *second* decimal place because a and b are subject to an unknown error which may be as large as 5 units in the third decimal place. Hence, we write

$$a + b + c = 378.39147 = 378.39, \text{ } approximately.$$

ILLUSTRATION 3. If $x = 31.27$ and $y = .021$ are approximate values, by Rule II we take $xy = .66$, because y has only two significant digits:

$$xy = 31.27(.021) = .65667 = .66, \text{ } approximately.$$

To avoid unnecessary work in multiplying, it is sensible to retain only two places beyond those to which the result will be rounded off by Rule II.

ILLUSTRATION 4. If a surveyor measures a rectangular field as 385.6' by 432.4', it would be unjustified to write that the area is $(385.6)(432.4) = 166,733.44$ square feet. For, an error of .05 foot in either dimension would cause an error of about 20 square feet in the area. By Rule II, a justified result would be that the area is 166,700 square feet, to the nearest 100 square feet, or $1.667(10^5)$ square feet.

In problems where approximate values enter, or where approximate results are obtained from exact data, the results should be rounded off so as to avoid giving a false appearance of accuracy. No hard and fast rules for such rounding off should be adopted, and the final decision as to the accuracy of a result should be made only after a careful examination of the details of the solution. Until otherwise stated in this text, we shall assume that the data in any problem are *exact*, and we shall compute our results as accurately as is justified by the means at our disposal. Later, we shall introduce agreements about approximate data.

EXERCISE 56

Express as a power of 10.

1. 10,000,000. **2.** 100,000. **3.** .0001. **4.** .01. **5.** 1.

Round off, first to five and then to three significant digits.

6. 13.24683. **7.** .2123589. **8.** 215.634. **9.** .00215388.

10. 6.312162. **11.** .0493576. **12.** 1,593,485. **13.** 612,915.

Write the number in ordinary decimal form.

14. $2.63(10^3)$. **15.** $1.598(10^7)$. **16.** $3.4153(10^{-3})$. **17.** $8.195(10^{-6})$.

Write as the product of a power of 10 *and a number between* 1 *and* 10.

18. 2,567,000. **19.** 89,315,000. **20.** .0000578. **21.** .00000364.

If the measured length of a rod is given as the specified number of inches, tell between what two values, inclusive, the true length lies.

22. 238. **23.** 238.3. **24.** 238.0. **25.** 42.16. **26.** 21.60.

Assume that the numbers are approximate data. Find their sum and their product, and express the results without false accuracy.

27. 21.65 and .0324. **28.** .024512 and 2.15. **29.** 2.8 and .3167.

30. The measured dimensions of a field are 238.7 feet and 58.4 feet. Find the perimeter and the area of the field.

Write the number as the product of an integral power of ten and a number between 1 *and* 10 *under the assumption, first, that there are just five significant digits and, second, that there are just three significant digits.*

31. 8,426,000. **32.** 290,000. **33.** 42,700,000. **34.** 629,000,000.

94. Irrational exponents

A logical foundation for the use of irrational exponents is beyond the scope of this text. Hence, without discussion, we shall assume the fact that irrational powers have meaning, and that the laws of exponents hold if the exponents involved are real numbers, either *rational* or *irrational*, provided that the base is *positive*.*

ILLUSTRATION 1. The student may use his intuition safely in connection with the symbol $10^{\sqrt{2}} = 10^{1.414\cdots}$, where the exponent is irrational. Closer and closer approximations to $10^{\sqrt{2}}$ are obtained if the successive decimal approximations to $\sqrt{2}$ are used as exponents. That is, $10^{\sqrt{2}}$ can be approximated as closely as we please if we proceed far enough out in the sequence

$$10^1,\ 10^{1.4},\ 10^{1.41},\ 10^{1.414},\ \cdots,$$

where all exponents are rational numbers. Thus,

$$1.41 = \frac{141}{100};\quad 1.414 = \frac{1414}{1000}.$$

---

* A foundation for the use of irrational exponents involves a logical basis for the real number system, and a mature appreciation of the limit concept.

95. Logarithms

Logarithms are auxiliary numbers which are *exponents*, and permit us to simplify the operations of multiplication, division, raising to powers, and extraction of roots, with explicit numbers. In the following definition, a represents any *positive number, not* 1, and N is any *positive number*.

DEFINITION I. *The **logarithm** of a number N to the **base** a is the exponent of the power to which the base a must be raised to obtain N.*

In other words, to say that x *is the logarithm of N to the base a* means that $N = a^x$. To abbreviate "*the logarithm of N to the base a*," we write "$\log_a N$." Then, by Definition I, the following equations state the same fact:

$$N = a^x \quad and \quad x = \log_a N. \tag{1}$$

ILLUSTRATION 1. If $N = 4^5$, then 5 is the logarithm of N to the base 4.

ILLUSTRATION 2. "$\log_2 64$" is read "*the logarithm of 64 to the base 2*":

$$since \quad 64 = 2^6, \quad \log_2 64 = 6.$$

ILLUSTRATION 3. Since $\qquad \sqrt[3]{5} = 5^{\frac{1}{3}}, \qquad \log_5 \sqrt[3]{5} = \frac{1}{3} = .333 \cdots.$

ILLUSTRATION 4. Since $\qquad \dfrac{1}{8} = \dfrac{1}{2^3} = 2^{-3}, \qquad \log_2 \dfrac{1}{8} = -3.$

ILLUSTRATION 5. If $\log_b 16 = 4$, then $b^4 = 16$; $b = \sqrt[4]{16} = 2$.

ILLUSTRATION 6. If $\log_a 2 = -\frac{1}{3}$, then $a^{-\frac{1}{3}} = 2$. Hence,

$$\frac{1}{a^{\frac{1}{3}}} = 2; \quad a^{\frac{1}{3}} = \frac{1}{2}; \quad a = \left(\frac{1}{2}\right)^3 = \frac{1}{8}.$$

ILLUSTRATION 7. If $\log_{10} N = -4$, then $N = 10^{-4} = .0001$.

For any base a, we have $a^0 = 1$ and $a^1 = a$. Hence,

$$\log_a 1 = 0; \qquad \log_a a = 1. \tag{2}$$

In advanced mathematics, it is proved that, if $N > 0$ and $a > 0$, there exists just one real number x such that $N = a^x$. That is, *every positive number N has just one real logarithm to the base a.*

Note 1. We do not use $a = 1$ as a base for logarithms because every power of 1 is 1, and hence no number except 1 could have a logarithm to the base 1.

Note 2. We shall not define or use logarithms of *negative* numbers. If $N < 0$, or if $a < 0$, $\log_a N$ can be defined as a complex number.

EXERCISE 57

Write a logarithmic equation equivalent to the exponential form.

1. $N = 2^6$.   **2.** $N = 10^4$.   **3.** $N = 5^{-2}$.   **4.** $N = 10^{-\frac{1}{2}}$.

5. $H = 4^{\frac{1}{3}}$.   **6.** $K = 10^{\frac{5}{3}}$.   **7.** $N = 10^{.35}$.   **8.** $32 = 2^5$.

9. $625 = 5^4$.   **10.** $\frac{1}{49} = 7^{-2}$.   **11.** $\frac{1}{27} = 3^{-3}$.   **12.** $.0001 = 10^{-4}$.

Find the number whose logarithm is given.

13. $\log_6 N = 2.$ **14.** $\log_2 N = 3.$ **15.** $\log_{10} N = 4.$

16. $\log_7 M = 2.$ **17.** $\log_5 M = 3.$ **18.** $\log_{10} K = 0.$

19. $\log_{15} K = 1.$ **20.** $\log_{10} N = 1.$ **21.** $\log_5 N = -1.$

22. $\log_{10} M = -2.$ **23.** $\log_b M = 1.$ **24.** $\log_{11} N = -2.$

25. $\log_9 N = \frac{1}{2}.$ **26.** $\log_{64} N = \frac{1}{3}.$ **27.** $\log_{216} N = -\frac{1}{3}.$

28. $\log_4 N = \frac{3}{2}.$ **29.** $\log_{27} N = \frac{2}{3}.$ **30.** $\log_8 N = \frac{5}{3}.$

Find the following logarithms.

31. $\log_9 81.$ **32.** $\log_5 25.$ **33.** $\log_3 81.$ **34.** $\log_9 3.$

35. $\log_{10} 100.$ **36.** $\log_{10} 1000.$ **37.** $\log_3 243.$ **38.** $\log_{11} 121.$

39. $\log_{16} 4.$ **40.** $\log_{100} 10.$ **41.** $\log_7 \frac{1}{7}.$ **42.** $\log_4 \frac{1}{4}.$

43. $\log_3 \frac{1}{27}.$ **44.** $\log_2 \frac{1}{16}.$ **45.** $\log_{10} .001.$ **46.** $\log_{10} .0001.$

Find a, N, or x, whichever is not given.

47. $\log_a 8 = 2.$ **48.** $\log_a 64 = 3.$ **49.** $\log_a 10,000 = 4.$

50. $\log_a 10,000 = 2.$ **51.** $\log_a 5 = \frac{1}{2}.$ **52.** $\log_a 4 = \frac{1}{3}.$

53. $\log_6 N = 3.$ **54.** $\log_{10} N = -3.$ **55.** $\log_{49} N = \frac{3}{2}.$

56. $\log_{16} N = \frac{3}{4}.$ **57.** $\log_{27} N = -\frac{4}{3}.$ **58.** $\log_a 4 = -\frac{2}{3}.$

59. $\log_{256} 16 = x.$ **60.** $\log_5 625 = x.$ **61.** $\log_{10} x = -\frac{1}{2}.$

96. Some properties of logarithms

PROPERTY I.   *The logarithm of a product is equal to the sum of the logarithms of the factors, for instance,*

$$\log_a MN = \log_a M + \log_a N. \tag{1}$$

ILLUSTRATION 1. $\log_{10} 897(596) = \log_{10} 897 + \log_{10} 596.$

Proof of (1). Let $x = \log_a M$ and $y = \log_a N.$ Then,

$$M = a^x \quad and \quad N = a^y. \qquad \text{(Definition of a logarithm)}$$

$$MN = a^x a^y = a^{x+y}. \qquad \text{(A law of exponents)}$$

Therefore, by the definition of a logarithm, we obtain (1):

$$\log_a MN = x + y = \log_a M + \log_a N.$$

Note 1. By use of (1) we can prove Property I for a product of any number of factors. Thus, since $MNP = (MN)(P),$

$$\log_a MNP = \log_a MN + \log_a P = \log_a M + \log_a N + \log_a P.$$

PROPERTY II.   *The logarithm of a quotient is equal to the logarithm of the dividend minus the logarithm of the divisor:*

$$\log_a \frac{M}{N} = \log_a M - \log_a N. \tag{2}$$

ILLUSTRATION 2. $\log_{10} \frac{89}{57} = \log_{10} 89 - \log_{10} 57.$

Proof of (2). Let $\log_a M = x$ and $\log_a N = y$. Then,

$$\frac{M}{N} = \frac{a^x}{a^y} = a^{x-y}. \qquad \text{(A law of exponents)}$$

Hence, by the definition of a logarithm, we obtain (2):

$$\log_a \frac{M}{N} = x - y = \log_a M - \log_a N.$$

ILLUSTRATION 3. By use of (1) and (2),

$$\log_a \frac{MK}{N} = \log_a MK - \log_a N = \log_a M + \log_a K - \log_a N.$$

PROPERTY III. *The logarithm of the kth power of a number N is equal to k times the logarithm of N:*

$$\log_a N^k = k \log_a N. \qquad (3)$$

ILLUSTRATION 4. $\log_a 7^5 = 5 \log_a 7$. $\log_a \sqrt[4]{3} = \log_a 3^{\frac{1}{4}} = \frac{1}{4} \log_a 3$.

Proof of (3). Let $x = \log_a N$. Then, $N = a^x$ and

$$N^k = (a^x)^k = a^{kx}. \qquad \text{(A law of exponents)}$$

Hence, by the definition of a logarithm, we obtain (3):

$$\log_a N^k = kx = k \log_a N.$$

Since $\sqrt[h]{N} = N^{\frac{1}{h}}$, by use of (3) with $k = 1/h$ we obtain

$$\log_a \sqrt[h]{N} = \frac{1}{h} \log_a N. \qquad (4)$$

ILLUSTRATION 5. $\log_a \sqrt{N} = \frac{1}{2} \log_a N$; $\log_a \sqrt[3]{25} = \frac{1}{3} \log_a 25$.

Logarithms to the base 10 are called **common logarithms** and are the most useful variety for computational purposes. Hereafter, unless otherwise stated, when we mention a *logarithm* we shall mean a *common* logarithm. For abbreviation, we shall write merely log N, instead of $\log_{10} N$, for the common logarithm of N. The following common logarithms will be useful later; the student should obtain them by use of Definition I.

$N =$	.0001	.001	.01	.1	1	10	100	1000	10,000	100,000
$\log N =$	-4	-3	-2	-1	0	1	2	3	4	5

ILLUSTRATION 6. If we are given log 3 = .4771, then by use of Properties I, II, and III we obtain the following results:

$$\log 300 = \log 3(100) = \log 3 + \log 100 = .4771 + 2 = 2.4771;$$

$$\log .003 = \log \frac{3}{1000} = \log 3 - \log 1000 = .4771 - 3 = -2.5229;$$

$$\log \sqrt[4]{3} = \log 3^{\frac{1}{4}} = \frac{1}{4} \log 3 = \frac{1}{4}(.4771) = .1193.$$

EXERCISE 58

Find the common logarithm of each number by use of properties of logarithms and the following common logarithms.

log 2 = .3010;   log 3 = .4771;   log 7 = .8451;   log 17 = 1.2304.

1. 14.	**2.** 51.	**3.** 30.	**4.** 170.	**5.** 21.	**6.** 42.
7. $\frac{7}{2}$.	**8.** $\frac{17}{3}$.	**9.** $\frac{3}{7}$.	**10.** $\frac{10}{3}$.	**11.** $\frac{17}{14}$.	**12.** .7.
13. 200.	**14.** $\frac{34}{3}$.	**15.** $\frac{2}{21}$.	**16.** $\frac{100}{17}$.	**17.** $\frac{100}{21}$.	**18.** 49.
19. 32.	**20.** 81.	**21.** $\sqrt{3}$.	**22.** $\sqrt{14}$.	**23.** $\sqrt{\frac{7}{3}}$.	**24.** $\sqrt[3]{\frac{2}{17}}$.

97. Characteristic and mantissa

Every number, and hence *every logarithm*, can be written as the sum of *an integer and a decimal fraction* which is *positive or zero* and *less than* 1. When log N is written in this way, we call the integer the *characteristic* and the fraction the *mantissa* of log N.

log N = (an integer) + (a fraction, $\geq$ 0, < 1);

log N = characteristic + mantissa.   (1)

ILLUSTRATION 1. If log N = 4.6832 = 4 + .6832, then .6832 is the mantissa and 4 is the characteristic of log N.

ILLUSTRATION 2. The following logarithms were obtained by later methods. The student should verify the three columns at the right.

	LOGARITHM	CHARACTERISTIC	MANTISSA
log 300 = 2.4771	= 2 + .4771	2	.4771
log 50 = 1.6990	= 1 + .6990	1	.6990
log .001 = − 3	= − 3 + .0000	− 3	.0000
log 6.5 = 0.8129	= 0 + .8129	0	.8129
log .0385 = − 1.4145	= − 2 + .5855	− 2	.5855
log .005 = − 2.3010	= − 3 + .6990	− 3	.6990

ILLUSTRATION 3. All numbers whose logarithms are given below have the same significant digits (3, 8, 0, 4). To obtain the logarithms, log 3.804 was found from a table to be discussed later; the other logarithms were obtained then by the use of Properties I and II.

$$\log 380.4 \quad = \log 100(3.804) \quad = \log 100 + \log 3.804 \quad = \quad 2 + .5802;$$

$$\log 38.04 \quad = \log 10(3.804) \quad = \log 10 + \log 3.804 \quad = \quad 1 + .5802;$$

$$\log 3.804 \quad = .5802 \qquad\qquad\qquad\qquad\qquad = \quad 0 + .5802;$$

$$\log .3804 \quad = \log \frac{3.804}{10} \quad\quad = \log 3.804 - \log 10 \quad = -1 + .5802;$$

$$\log .03804 \quad = \log \frac{3.804}{100} \quad\quad = \log 3.804 - \log 100 \quad = -2 + .5802.$$

Similarly, if N is *any* number whose significant digits are (3, 8, 0, 4), then N is equal to 3.804 multiplied, or else divided, by a positive integral power of 10; hence, it follows as before that .5802 is the mantissa of log N.

We notice that the *characteristic* of log N is *negative* if and only if log N *itself is negative.*

ILLUSTRATION 4. If log $N = -3.75$, then log N lies between -4 and -3. Hence, log $N = -4 + (a \; fraction)$. To find the fraction, subtract: $4 - 3.75 = .25$. Hence, log $N = -3.75 = -4 + .25$.

Let $x = $ log M and $y = $ log N; then $M = 10^x$ and $N = 10^y$. For integral values of x and y we observe that, if $x < y$, then $10^x < 10^y$, and conversely. This relation extends to the case where x and y are not necessarily integers; that is,

$$\text{log } M < \text{log } N \quad \textit{if and only if} \quad M < N. \tag{2}$$

In Illustration 3, the characteristic of log 380.4 is 2, of log 38.04 is 1, etc. These facts could have been learned as follows.

ILLUSTRATION 5. To find the characteristic of log 380.4, notice the two successive integral powers of 10 between which 380.4 lies:

$$100 < 380.4 < 1000.$$

Hence,   log $100 < $ log $380.4 < $ log 1000;   *or* $2 < $ log $380.4 < 3$.

Therefore, log $380.4 = 2 + $ (a fraction, > 0, < 1); or, by definition, the characteristic of log 380.4 is 2.

In Illustration 3 we met special cases of the following theorems.

THEOREM I. *The mantissa of* log N *depends only on the sequence of significant digits in* N. *That is,* **if two numbers differ only in the position of the decimal point, their logarithms have the same mantissa.**

THEOREM II. **When** $N > 1$, *the characteristic of* log N *is an integer, positive or zero, which is* **one less than the number of digits in** N **to the left of the decimal point.**

THEOREM III. **If** $N < 1$, *the characteristic of* log N *is a negative integer;* **if the first significant digit of** N **is in the** k**th decimal place, then** $-k$ **is the characteristic of log** N.

ILLUSTRATION 6. By use of Theorems II and III, we find the characteristic of log N by merely inspecting N. Thus, by Theorem III, the characteristic of log .00039 is -4 because "3" is in the 4th decimal place. By Theorem II, the characteristic of log 1578.6 is 3.

For convenience in computation, **if the characteristic of log** N **is negative,** $-k$**, change it to the equivalent value**

$$[(10 - k) - 10], \quad or \quad [(20 - k) - 20], \text{ etc.}$$

ILLUSTRATION 7. Given that log .000843 = − 4 + .9258, we write

$$\log .000843 = -4 + .9258 = (6 - 10) + .9258 = 6.9258 - 10.$$

The characteristics of the following logarithms are obtained by use of Theorem III; the mantissas are identical, by Theorem I.

1st Signif. Digit in	Illustration	Log N	Standard Form
1st *decimal place*	$N = .843$	$-1 + .9258 = 9.9258 - 10$	
2d *decimal place*	$N = .0843$	$-2 + .9258 = 8.9258 - 10$	
6th *decimal place*	$N = .00000843$	$-6 + .9258 = 4.9258 - 10$	

98. Tables of logarithms

Mantissas can be computed by advanced methods and, usually, are endless decimal fractions. Computed mantissas are found in tables of logarithms, also called *tables of mantissas*.

Table V gives the mantissa of log N correct to four decimal places, if N has at most three significant digits aside from additional zeros at the right. A decimal point is understood at the left of each mantissa in the table. If N lies between 1 and 10, the characteristic of log N is *zero*, so that log N is *the same as its mantissa*. Hence, a four-place table of mantissas also is a table of *the actual four-place logarithms of all numbers with at most three significant digits from* $N = 1.00$ *to* $N = 9.99$. If $N \geqq 10$ or $N < 1$, we supply the characteristic of log N by use of Theorems II and III of Section 97.

EXAMPLE 1. Find log .0316 from Table V.

SOLUTION. 1. *To obtain the mantissa:* find "31" in the column headed N in the table; in the row for "31," read the entry in the column headed "6." The mantissa is .4997.

2. By Theorem III, the characteristic of log .0316 is − 2, or (8 − 10):

$$\log .0316 = -2 + .4997 = 8.4997 - 10.$$

ILLUSTRATION 1. From Table V and Theorem II, log 31,600 = 4.4997.

EXAMPLE 2. Find N if log N = 7.6064 − 10.

SOLUTION. 1. *To find the significant digits of* N: the mantissa of log N is .6064; this is found in Table V as the mantissa for the digits "404."

2. *To locate the decimal point in* N: the characteristic of log N is (7 − 10), or − 3; hence, by Theorem III, $N = .00404$.

ILLUSTRATION 2. If log N = 3.6064, the characteristic is 3 and, by Theorem II, N has 4 figures to the left of the decimal point: the mantissa is the same as in Example 2. Hence, $N = 4040$.

DEFINITION II. *To say that N is the antilogarithm of L means that log $N = L$, or $N = 10^L$, and we write $N =$ antilog L.*

ILLUSTRATION 3. Since log 1000 = 3, then 1000 = antilog 3.

ILLUSTRATION 4. In Example 2 we found *antilog* $(7.6064 - 10) = .00404$.

EXERCISE 59

The given number is the logarithm of some number N. State the characteristic and the mantissa of log *N.*

1. 3.5217.   2. 25.3189.   3. $- 2.450$.   4. $6.3159 - 10$.

5. $- 3.1582$.   6. $- .6354$.   7. $5.2891 - 10$.   8. $9.1346 - 10$.

Write the following negative logarithms in standard form.

9. $- 2 + .1356$.   10. $.2341 - 3$.   11. $.5268 - 4$.   12. $- 5.3214$.

State the characteristic of the logarithm of each number.

13. 41,356.   14. 249.   15. .000047.   16. .0036.   17. .000007.

Use Table V to find the four-place logarithm of the number.

18. 35.6.   19. 124.   20. 8950.   21. .261.   22. .495.

23. .0562.   24. .00008.   25. 20,900.   26. .000419.   27. .909.

28. .0861.   29. 15,200.   30. .000643.   31. .0000219.   32. 256,000.

Find the antilogarithm of the given logarithm by use of Table V.

33. 2.1335.   34. 3.5263.   35. $9.7185 - 10$.   36. $7.4183 - 10$.

37. 1.7459.   38. 0.2148.   39. $8.5752 - 10$.   40. $4.2945 - 10$.

41. 0.5198.   42. 6.3096.   43. $7.4669 - 10$.   44. $9.3201 - 10$.

45. 7.5172.   46. 1.2304.   47. $6.6325 - 10$.   48. $2.4955 - 10$.

49. Find N if (a) log $N = - 3.6021$; (b) log $N = 7.6021 - 10$.

50. Find N if (a) log $N = 3 - 2.3979$; (b) log $N = 8.3979 - 10$.

99. Interpolation in a table of logarithms

Interpolation in a table of mantissas is based on the assumption that, *for small changes in N, the corresponding changes in* log *N are proportional to the changes in N.* This **principle of proportional parts** is merely a useful approximation to the truth.

We agree that, when a mantissa is found by interpolation from a table, we shall express the result *only to the number of decimal places given in table entries.* Also, in finding N by interpolation in a table of mantissas when log N is given, we agree to specify just **four** or just **five** significant digits according as we are using a **four-place** or a **five-place** table. No greater accuracy is justified.

In using a four-place table of logarithms, it is convenient to act as if each number N whose logarithm is mentioned has *just four significant digits,* perhaps including one or more zeros at the right. Thus, we attach one or more final zeros to the significant part of N if it has *less* than four significant digits. Or, we *round off* N to four significant digits if N initially has more than four-place accuracy. We then think of each entry in Table V as the mantissa for the logarithm of a number N with *four* significant digits, obtained by attaching a final zero to the part arising in the table.

EXAMPLE 1. Find log 13.86 by interpolation in Table V.

SOLUTION. Since 13.86 has four significant digits, with the 4th not zero, the mantissa for log 13.86 cannot be read directly from the table. In the following table, log 13.80 and log 13.90 are obtained from Table V. The equation for x is a consequence of the principle of proportional parts.

$$.10\left[.06\left[\begin{matrix}\log 13.80 = 1.1399 \\ \log 13.86 = \quad? \\ \log 13.90 = 1.1430\end{matrix}\right]x\right]31 \qquad \begin{matrix}\textbf{Tabular difference } is \text{ .0031.} \\ \dfrac{x}{31} = \dfrac{.06}{.10}; \quad x = \dfrac{6}{10}\,(31).\end{matrix}$$

$$x = .6(.0031) = .00186 = .0019, \; approximately;$$

$$\textbf{log 13.86} = \textbf{1.1399} + \textbf{.0019} = \textbf{1.1418.}$$

Comment. We found $.6(31) = 18.6$ by use of the table headed 31 under the column of *proportional parts* in Table V.

Note 1. When interpolating in a table of mantissas, if there is equal reason for choosing either of two successive digits, for uniformity we agree to make that choice which gives an **even digit** in the last significant place of the **final result** of the interpolation.

ILLUSTRATION 1. To find log .002913 from Table V:

$$10\left[3\left[\begin{matrix}2910: \; mantissa \; is \; .4639 \\ 2913: \; mantissa \; is \quad ? \\ 2920: \; mantissa \; is \; .4654\end{matrix}\right]x\right]15 \qquad \begin{matrix}\textbf{Tabular difference } is \\ .4654 - .4639 = .0015. \\ x = .3(15) = 4.5, \text{ or } 5.\end{matrix}$$

$$Hence, \; the \; mantissa \; for \; 2913 \; is \; \textbf{.4639} + \textbf{.0005} = \textbf{.4644.}$$

By Theorem III, $\qquad \log .002913 = -3 + .4644 = 7.4644 - 10.$

We used $.3(15)$ as 5, instead of 4, in agreement with Note 1.

EXAMPLE 2. Find N from Table V if log $N = 1.6187$.

SOLUTION. 1. The mantissa .6187 is not in Table V but lies between the consecutive entries .6180 and .6191, the mantissas for 415 and 416.

2. Since .6187 is $\frac{7}{11}$ of the way from .6180 to .6191, we assume that N is $\frac{7}{11}$ of the way from 41.50 to 41.60. Thus, in the following table,

$$\frac{x}{.10} = \frac{7}{11}, \quad or \quad x = \frac{7}{11}\,(.10).$$

$$11\left[7\left[\begin{matrix}1.6180 = \log 41.50 \\ 1.6187 = \log N \\ 1.6191 = \log 41.60\end{matrix}\right]x\right].10 \qquad \begin{matrix}41.60 - 41.50 = .10. \\ x = \tfrac{7}{11}(.10) = .064, \; or \\ approximately \; .06.\end{matrix}$$

$$N = 41.50 + \tfrac{7}{11}(.10) = 41.50 + .06 = 41.56.$$

ILLUSTRATION 2. To find N if $\log N = 6.1053 - 10$:

$$
34\left\downarrow 15\left\downarrow \begin{array}{l} .1038, \textit{mantissa for } 1270 \\ .1053, \textit{mantissa for } \quad ? \\ .1072, \textit{mantissa for } 1280 \end{array}\right\downarrow x \right\downarrow 10 \qquad \begin{array}{l} \frac{15}{34} = .4. \quad \textit{Hence,} \\ x = .4(10) = 4. \\ 1270 + 4 = 1274. \end{array}
$$

Hence, .1053 is the mantissa for 1274 and **N = .0001274.**

Comment. We obtain $\frac{15}{34} = .4$ by inspection of the tenths of 34 in the columns of proportional parts. We read

$$
13.6 = .4(34) \quad or \quad \frac{13.6}{34} = .4, \quad and \quad \frac{17}{34} = .5.
$$

Since 15 is nearer to 13.6 than to 17, then $\frac{15}{34}$ is nearer to .4 than to .5.

Suppose that a number N is written in the scientific notation $N = P(10^k)$, where k is an integer and $1 \leqq P < 10$. Then

$$
\log N = \log P + \log 10^k = k + \log P,
$$

where $0 \leqq \log P < 1$ because $1 \leqq P < 10$. Thus, with N written in the scientific notation, k is the *characteristic* and $\log P$ is the *mantissa* for $\log N$.

ILLUSTRATION 3. If $\log N = 9.7419$, and if we seek to use the form $N = P(10^k)$, we have $k = 9$ and $\log P = 0.7419$. Hence,

$$
P = 5.520; \quad N = 5.520(10^9). \qquad \textit{(Four digits significant.)}
$$

EXERCISE 60

Find the four-place logarithm of the number from Table V.

1. 1923.	**2.** 2725.	**3.** 5815.	**4.** 12.76.
5. 9.436.	**6.** .1787.	**7.** .7094.	**8.** .003196.
9. .005135.	**10.** .0001245.	**11.** .0002007.	**12.** 2.456(10⁵).
13. 80,090.	**14.** 204,600.	**15.** 3.126.	**16.** 1.573.
17. 25,780.	**18.** 2.643(10⁶).	**19.** 6.214(10⁻³).	**20.** 5.439(10⁻⁵).

Find the antilogarithm of the four-place logarithm, from Table V.

21. 1.6553.	**22.** 2.3468.	**23.** 9.0226 − 10.	**24.** 8.1691 − 10.
25. 0.5510.	**26.** 1.3754.	**27.** 8.6432 − 10.	**28.** 0.5309.
29. 2.0360.	**30.** 7.4483 − 10.	**31.** 6.0211 − 10.	**32.** 2.0493.
33. 5.9367 − 10.	**34.** 6.3194.	**35.** 7.0364.	**36.** 0.2779.
37. 3.3614.	**38.** 2.8547.	**39.** 9.9546 − 10.	**40.** 9.9990 − 10.
41. 0.9871.	**42.** 6.2338 − 10.	**43.** 1.5648.	**44.** 3.1542 − 10.

100. Computation of products and quotients

Unless otherwise specified, we shall assume that the data of any given problem are *exact*. Under this assumption, the accuracy of a product, quotient, or power computed by use of logarithms depends on the number of places in the table being used. The result frequently is subject to an unavoidable error which usually is at most a few units in the last significant place given by interpolation. Hence, as a rule, we should compute with at least *five-place* logarithms to obtain *four-place accuracy*, and with at least *four-place* logarithms to obtain *three-place accuracy*. Usually, in any result, we shall give *all digits obtainable by interpolation* in the specified table.

EXAMPLE 1. Compute .0631(7.208)(.5127) by use of Table V.

SOLUTION. Let P represent the product. By Property I, we obtain log P by adding the logarithms of the factors. We find the logarithms of the factors from Table V, add to obtain log P, and then finally obtain P from Table V. The computing form, given in blackface type, was made up completely as *the first step in the solution.*

log .0631 =	**8.8000 − 10**	(Table V)
log 7.208 =	**0.8578**	(Table V)
log .5127 =	**9.7099 − 10**	(Table V)

(add) **log P = 19.3677 − 20 = 9.3677 − 10.**

Hence, P = .2332.   [= antilog (9.3677 − 10), Table V]

EXAMPLE 2. Compute $q = \dfrac{431.91}{15.6873}$ by use of Table V.

SOLUTION. 1. By Property II, log q is equal to *the logarithm of the numerator minus the logarithm of the denominator*, or

$$\log q = \log 431.91 - \log 15.6873.$$

2. Before computing, we *round off* each given number to *four* significant digits because we are using a four-place table.

log 431.9 = 2.6354	(Table V)
(−) log 15.69 = 1.1956	(Table V)
log q = 1.4398. **Hence, q = 27.53.**	(Table V)

EXAMPLE 3. Compute $q = \dfrac{257}{8956}$ by use of Table V.

SOLUTION.   **log 257 = 2.4099 = 12.4099 − 10**
          (−) log 8956 = 3.9521 =   3.9521
                    log q =   ?   =   8.4578 − 10; q = .02869.

Comment. We saw that log q would be *negative* because log 8956 is *greater* than log 257. In order that log q should appear immediately in the *standard form for a negative logarithm*, we changed log 257 by adding 10 and then subtracting 10 to compensate for the first change. Actually,

$$\log q = 2.4099 - 3.9521 = -1.5422 = 8.4578 - 10.$$

Whenever it is necessary to subtract a logarithm from a smaller one in computing a quotient, add 10 to the characteristic of the smaller logarithm and then subtract 10 to compensate for the change.

EXAMPLE 4.   Compute $q = \dfrac{(4.803)(269.9)(1.636)}{(7880)(253.6)}.$

INCOMPLETE SOLUTION.   We make a **computing form,** to subtract the logarithm of the denominator from the logarithm of the numerator.

$$(+) \begin{cases} \textbf{log 4.803} = \\ \textbf{log 269.9} = \\ \textbf{log 1.636} = \end{cases}$$
$$\overline{\textbf{log numer.}} =$$
$$(-) \textbf{ log denom.} =$$
$$\overline{\textbf{log } q =}$$

$$(+) \begin{cases} \textbf{log 7880} = \\ \textbf{log 253.6} = \end{cases}$$
$$\overline{\textbf{log denom.}} =$$

Hence, $q =$

EXAMPLE 5.   Compute the reciprocal of 189 by use of Table V.

SOLUTION.   Let $R = 1/189$.

$$\begin{aligned} \textbf{log 1} &= 0.0000 = 10.0000 - 10 \\ (-) \textbf{ log 189} &= 2.2765 = 2.2765 \\ \hline \textbf{log } R &= ? = 7.7235 - 10. \end{aligned}$$

Hence, $R = .005290$.

Comment.   In writing any approximate value, indicate all final zeros which are significant.   In $R = .005290$ in Example 5, the final zero was essential.

Note 1.   It is essential to become familiar with rounding off data, if necessary, to that number of significant digits which should be used with a *given table of logarithms.*   Retention of more than these digits causes unnecessary labor and does not increase accuracy.   Recall that we round off data to *four figures* if *four-place* logarithms are in use, and to *five figures* if *five-place logarithms* are to be employed.

★101. Cologarithms

The logarithm of the *reciprocal* of N, that is, the logarithm of $\dfrac{1}{N}$, is called the *cologarithm* of N and is written **colog N.**   Since log 1 = 0,

$$\textbf{colog } N = \textbf{log } \frac{1}{N} = 0 - \textbf{log } N. \tag{1}$$

ILLUSTRATION 1.   Colog $.031 = \log \dfrac{1}{.031}$:

$$\begin{aligned} \textbf{log 1} &= 10.0000 - 10 \\ (-) \textbf{ log .031} &= 8.4914 - 10 \\ \hline \textbf{colog .031} &= 1.5086. \end{aligned}$$

The positive part of colog N can be obtained quickly by inspection of log N: *subtract each digit (except the last) in the positive part of* log N *from 9, and subtract the last digit from* $\overset{\backprime}{1}\overset{\backprime}{0}$.

EXAMPLE 1. Compute $q = \dfrac{16.083 \times 256}{47 \times .0158}$ by use of cologarithms.

SOLUTION. To *divide* by N is the same as to *multiply* by $1/N$. Hence, instead of *subtracting the logarithm* of each factor of the denominator, we *add the cologarithm* of the factor:

$$q = \frac{16.083 \times 256}{47 \times .0158} = (16.083 \times 256)\left(\frac{1}{47}\right)\left(\frac{1}{.0158}\right).$$

log 16.08 = 1.2063
log 256 = 2.4082

log 47 = 1.6721; hence,
colog 47 = 8.3279 − 10

log .0158 = 8.1987 − 10; hence,
colog .0158 = 1.8013

$\overline{(add) \text{ log } q = 13.7437 - 10}$

= 3.7437.

$q = 5542.$

Note 1. Use cologarithms only as directed by the instructor.

EXERCISE 61

Compute by use of four-place logarithms.

1. 32.51×71.63.
2. $.8328 \times .0843$.
3. $913.421 \times .00314$.
4. $83.47 \times .156$.
5. $.0381 \times .25672$.
6. $3.14586 \times .00314$.
7. $(-31.92)(.0059)(.23646)$.
8. $(23.6)(153.867)(-.00076)$.

HINT. Only positive numbers have real logarithms. First compute as if all factors were positive; then attach the proper final sign.

9. $\dfrac{483}{13.49}$.
10. $\dfrac{658.432}{748}$.
11. $\dfrac{.0359}{.7288}$.
12. $\dfrac{1}{4159.38}$.

13. $\dfrac{593.6}{25.89}$.
14. $\dfrac{634.157}{8349.6}$.
15. $\dfrac{1}{.00847}$.
16. $\dfrac{.0358}{.42849}$.

17. $\dfrac{26.037(198)}{54(.1475)}$.
18. $\dfrac{18.6(487)}{.721543(.582)}$.
19. $\dfrac{1}{628(.09372)}$.

20. $\dfrac{.4835(.846)}{.264536(.137)}$.
21. $\dfrac{6.39(.14758)}{23.1349(28.7)}$.
22. $\dfrac{1}{.0036(.2542)}$.

23. $\dfrac{-37(.045)(-.0026)}{(-2003.56)(4.53)}$.
24. $\dfrac{6.7(-39.42)(.8531)}{(-264)(-3.54293)}$.

Compute the reciprocal of the number.

25. 53847.
26. 16.2983.
27. $.03489$.
28. $.026(5.7426)$.

Compute by use of four-place logarithms.

29. $10^{-2.1567}$.
30. $2.314(10^{1.5872})$.
31. $4.738(10^{1.2678})$.
32. $1.57(10^{-1.6894})$.

HINT. $\log 10^{-2.1567} = -2.1567 = -3 + (\ \cdots\ )$.

33. Compute (a) $498(765)$; (b) compute $(\log 498)(\log 765)$.
34. Compute (a) $.483/.269$; (b) compute $(\log .483) \div (\log .269)$.

102. Computation of powers and roots

We recall the following results, where k may be any real number and h is a positive integer:

$$\log N^k = k \log N; \tag{1}$$

since $\sqrt[h]{N} = N^{\frac{1}{h}}$, $\log \sqrt[h]{N} = \dfrac{\log N}{h}. \tag{2}$

EXAMPLE 1.   Compute $(.3156)^4$.

SOLUTION. $\log (.3156)^4 = 4 \log (.3156) = 4(9.4991 - 10)$.

$\log (.3156)^4 = 37.9964 - 40 = 7.9964 - 10$.

Therefore, $(.3156)^4 = .009918$.

EXAMPLE 2.   Compute $\sqrt[6]{.08351}$.

SOLUTION.   By (2), $\log \sqrt[6]{N} = \frac{1}{6} \log N$.

$$\log \sqrt[6]{.08351} = \frac{\log .08351}{6} = \frac{8.9218 - 10}{6};$$

$$\log \sqrt[6]{.08351} = \frac{58.9218 - 60}{6} = 9.8203 - 10. \tag{3}$$

Therefore, $\sqrt[6]{.08351} = .6611$.

Comment.   Before dividing a negative logarithm by a positive integer, usually it is best to write the logarithm in such a way that *the negative part after division will be* -10.   Thus, in (3), we altered $(8.9218 - 10)$ by *subtracting* 50 from -10 to make it -60, and by *adding* 50 to 8.9218 to compensate for the subtraction;   the result after division by 6 is in the standard form for a negative logarithm.

EXAMPLE 3.   Compute $q = \left(\dfrac{(.5831)^3}{65.3\sqrt{146}} \right)^{\frac{2}{5}}$.

SOLUTION.   1. Let F represent the fraction.   Then $\log q = \frac{2}{5} \log F$.

2. Notice that $\log (.5831)^3 = 3 \log .5831$; $\log \sqrt{146} = \frac{1}{2} \log 146$.

$\log .5831 = 9.7658 - 10$ $(+) \begin{cases} \log 65.3 = 1.8149 \\ \frac{1}{2} \log 146 = 1.0822 \end{cases}$
$\log 146 = 2.1644$
$3 \log .5831 = 9.2974 - 10$ $\Big\}$ $\overline{\quad \log \text{denom.} = 2.8971. \quad}$
$(-) \log \text{denom.} = 2.8971$

$\log F = 6.4003 - 10;$ $2 \log F = 2.8006 - 10 = 42.8006 - 50.$

$\log q = \dfrac{2 \log F}{5} = \dfrac{42.8006 - 50}{5} = 8.5601 - 10;$ $q = .03632.$

Note 1.   Logarithms were invented by a Scotchman, JOHN NAPIER, Laird of Merchiston (1550–1617).   His logarithms were not defined as exponents of powers of a base.   Common logarithms were invented by an Englishman, HENRY BRIGGS (1556–1631), who was aided by Napier.

EXERCISE 62

Compute by use of four-place logarithms.

1. $(18.7)^3$.
2. $(4.1734)^4$.
3. $(.924)^5$.
4. $(.0327)^3$.

5. $\sqrt{35.6}$.
6. $\sqrt[3]{132.473}$.
7. $\sqrt[5]{.936}$.
8. $\sqrt[3]{.08572}$.

9. $\sqrt[4]{.00314787}$.
10. $(2.35)^6$.
11. $\sqrt[4]{10,000}$.
12. $(.31426)^{\frac{1}{6}}$.

13. $(173.215)^{\frac{1}{2}}$.
14. $(21.498)^{\frac{1}{4}}$.
15. $\sqrt[3]{.0001}$.
16. $(-38.9)^{\frac{1}{3}}$.

17. $(-248,742)^{\frac{1}{5}}$.
18. $(269)^{\frac{2}{3}}$.
19. $(-.00317)^3$.
20. $(-126.8)^3$.

21. $(.721317)^{\frac{3}{4}}$.
22. $(5.738)^{-4}$.
23. $(.13172)^{-2}$.
24. $(.2163)^{\frac{2}{3}}$.

Hint for Problem 22. Recall $(5.738)^{-4} = 1 \div (5.738)^4$.

25. $(757.2)^{\frac{3}{5}}$.
26. $(.63)^{-3}$.
27. $(1.03)^7$.
28. $(1.02)^{-3}$.

29. $(2.675)^{-4}$.
30. $(.0789268)^{-5}$.
31. $10^{3.56}(28)^4$.
32. $\sqrt[3]{258(64)}$.

33. (a) Compute $(1.04)^{100}$. (b) Given the seven-place log $1.04 = 0.0170333$, compute $(1.04)^{100}$ by starting with this logarithm, and finishing with the four-place table.

34. $675(8.39)^2$.
35. $.253\sqrt{.628}$.
36. $(3.41)^3\sqrt[3]{.849}$.

37. $10^{2.78}\sqrt{9.34}$.
38. $10^{1.56}(.631)^3$.
39. $10^{-3.24}(.163)^2$.

40. $\dfrac{.139(24.61)^3}{126.48}$.
41. $\dfrac{356.2(298)^2}{675\sqrt{4.1327}}$.
42. $\dfrac{.037(149)^3}{(2.16217)^2}$.

43. $\sqrt{\dfrac{653.2}{217(.0834)}}$.
44. $\sqrt[3]{\dfrac{25.682}{173(.0298)}}$.
45. $\dfrac{10^{.56}\sqrt{.38}}{(.813946)^2}$.

46. $\dfrac{\sqrt[3]{-264.137}}{\sqrt{14.2193}}$.
47. $\left(\dfrac{2139.27}{427.31\sqrt{.242}}\right)^{\frac{2}{3}}$.
48. $\left(\dfrac{621.9}{10^{1.48}\sqrt{69}}\right)^{\frac{1}{2}}$.

49. $(1.35)^{2.75}$.
50. $(21.98)^{.863}$.
51. $(69.3)^{-.26}$.
52. $(.03294)^{-.468}$.

Hint for Problem 51.

$$\log (69.3)^{-.26} = -.26(1.8407) = -.4786 = 9.5214 - 10.$$

Note 1. Observe that no property of logarithms is available to simplify the computation of a *sum*. Use logarithms below wherever possible.

53. $\dfrac{(26.8)^2 + 49.316}{\sqrt{69} + 1.589}$.
54. $\dfrac{\sqrt[3]{67} - 268.42}{(.7531)^3 + 89.2}$.
55. $\dfrac{\sqrt{29} - \sqrt{156}}{253(.210317)}$.

56. $\dfrac{(1.02)^4 + 1}{\sqrt{1.02} + 3}$.
57. $\dfrac{\log 65}{\log 89.3}$.
58. $\dfrac{26 + \log 298}{\log .846}$.

59. Compute (a) $(\text{antilog } 2.4731)^2$; (b) $[\text{antilog } (-1.2687)]^3$.

*The **geometric mean** of n numbers is defined as the nth root of the product of the numbers. Find the geometric mean of the given numbers.*

60. 267; 349; 242; 1563; 214.
61. .0314; .268; .00143; .763.

If a, b, and c are the lengths of the sides of a triangle, it is proved on page 387 that A, the area of the triangle, is given by

$$A = \sqrt{S(S-a)(S-b)(S-c)}, \quad where \quad S = \tfrac{1}{2}(a+b+c).$$

Find the area if the sides have the given lengths, in inches.

62. 268.39; 154.32; 264.93.   **63.** 1.3584; .9863; 1.321.

64. The period of oscillation, t, in seconds for a simple pendulum, whose length is l centimeters, is given by $t = 2\pi\sqrt{\dfrac{l}{g}}$, where $g = 980$ and $\pi = 3.1416$.   (*a*) Find t if $l = 13.8$ centimeters.   (*b*) Find l if $t = 4.63$.

65. The force F in foot-pounds due to wind blowing on a certain sail is $F = Av^2/400$, where A is the sail area in square feet and v is the wind velocity in miles per hour.   Find F if $A = 206$ and $v = 25.7$.

66. If a volume v_1 cubic feet of a certain gas at a pressure of p_1 pounds per square inch is compressed to a volume v_2 cubic feet at a pressure of p_2 pounds per square inch, without losing any of the heat generated by the compression, then $p_2 = p_1(v_1/v_2)^{1.41}$.   Under this condition, find the pressure to compress 143 cubic feet of the gas at a pressure of 30.5 pounds per square inch to 45.6 cubic feet.

★103. Exponential and logarithmic equations

A *logarithmic equation* is one in which there appears the logarithm of some expression involving the unknown quantity.

EXAMPLE 1.   Solve for x: $\log x + \log \dfrac{2x}{5} = 6$.

SOLUTION.   By use of Properties I and II of logarithms,

$$\log x + \log 2 + \log x - \log 5 = 6.$$
$$2 \log x = 6 + \log 5 - \log 2 = 6.3980. \qquad \text{(Table V)}$$
$$\log x = 3.1990; \quad x = \text{antilog } 3.1990 = 1581. \qquad \text{(Table V)}$$

An equation where the unknown quantity appears in an exponent is called an *exponential equation*.   Sometimes, an exponential equation can be solved by equating the logarithms of the members of the equation.

EXAMPLE 2.   Solve $16^x = 74$.

SOLUTION.   Equate the logarithms of the two sides: $x \log 16 = \log 74$;

$$x = \frac{\log 74}{\log 16} = \frac{1.8692}{1.2041}.$$

$$\begin{aligned}\log 1.869 &= 0.2716\\ (-) \log 1.204 &= 0.0806\\ \hline \log x &= 0.1910; \quad hence \quad x = 1.552.\end{aligned}$$

★104. Logarithms to various bases

The base 10 is convenient for logarithms when they are being used to simplify computation.   The only other base which is used appreciably is a certain irrational number $e = 2.71828\cdots$.   Logarithms to the base e are called **natural logarithms**, and are indispensable, for noncomputational purposes, in calculus and other parts of advanced mathematics.

Recall that the equations $N = a^z$ and $x = \log_a N$ are equivalent. Hence, if N and a are given, we can find $\log_a N$ by solving the exponential equation $N = a^z$ by use of *common* logarithms. In particular, the natural logarithm of N can be found by solving $N = e^z$ for x. For future use, notice that

$$\textbf{log}_{10}\ e = \textbf{0.4343}; \qquad \textbf{log}_{10}\ \textbf{.4343} = \textbf{9.6378} - \textbf{10.} \qquad (1)$$

EXAMPLE 1. Find $\log_e 35$.

SOLUTION. Let $x = \log_e 35$; then, $35 = e^z$. On taking the common logarithms of both sides we obtain $x \log_{10} e = \log_{10} 35$.

$$x = \frac{\log_{10} 35}{\log_{10} e} = \frac{1.5441}{0.4343};$$

$$x = 3.555 = \log_e 35.$$

$$\begin{aligned} \log 1.544 &= 10.1886 - 10 \\ (-) \log .4343 &= \ \ 9.6378 - 10 \\ \hline \log x &= \ \ 0.5508. \end{aligned}$$

THEOREM IV. *If a and b are any two bases, then*

$$\textbf{log}_a\ N = (\textbf{log}_a\ b)(\textbf{log}_b\ N). \qquad (2)$$

Proof. Let $y = \log_b N$; then $\qquad\qquad N = b^y.$ $\qquad\qquad (3)$

Hence, $\qquad\qquad \log_a N = \log_a b^y = y \log_a b = (\log_a b)(\log_b N).$

The number $\textbf{log}_a\ b$ is called the **modulus** of the system of base a with respect to the system of base b. Given a table of logarithms to the base b, we could form a table of logarithms to the base a by multiplying each entry of the given table by $\log_a b$.

★EXERCISE 63

Solve for x, or for n, or compute the specified logarithm.

1. $15^x = 32$.
2. $28^x = 478$.
3. $6^{2x} = 30(3^x)$.
4. $12^{3x} = 98(3^x)$.
5. $.87^x = 12$.
6. $.075^x = 15$.
7. $16^{x^2} = 85$.
8. $6.58^{-x} = .0893$.
9. $5^{x^2+x} = 23$.
10. $(1.04)^n = 1.562$.
11. $(1.02)^{-n} = .721$.
12. $\log x^3 - \log \frac{2}{5}x = 7.42$.
13. $\log 6x^2 + \log (3/x) = 6.789$.
14. $\log_e 85$.
15. $\log_e 1250$.
16. $\log_e 125$.
17. $\log_e 10$.
18. $\log_e 100$.
19. $\log_{12} 500$.
20. $\log_6 1.08$.
21. $\log_7 24.6$.
22. Find the natural logarithm of (a) 529.7; (b) 5.297. Notice that the results do not differ by an integer, as in the case of common logarithms.
23. Find the modulus of each system with respect to the other: the Briggs system and the natural system of logarithms.
24. Prove that $\log_a b = 1/\log_b a$.

★105. Graphs of logarithmic and exponential functions

We recall that, with $a > 0$, $y = \log_a x$ and $x = a^y$ are equivalent relations. We refer to the functions $\log_a x$ and a^y as **inverse functions**; each is called the **inverse** of the other function. We call $\log_a x$ a *logarithmic function* of x and a^y an *exponential function* of y.

ILLUSTRATION 1. In Figure 71, we have the graph of $y = \log_e x$. For any base $a > 1$, the graph of $\log_a x$ would be similar. This graph assists us in remembering the following facts.

I. *If x is negative, $\log_a x$ is not defined.*

II. *If $0 < x < 1$, $\log_a x$ is negative, and $\log_a 1 = 0$.*

III. *If x increases without limit, $\log_a x$ increases without limit; if x approaches zero, $\log_a x$ decreases without limit.*

Since $y = \log_a x$ is equivalent to $x = a^y$, *these equations have the same graph.* Thus, in Figure 71 we have a graph of $x = e^y$.

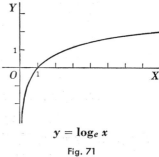

$y = \log_e x$

Fig. 71

ILLUSTRATION 2. To graph $y = \log_2 x$, we could work more easily with $x = 2^y$; on assigning suitable values to y we could compute the corresponding values of x and then form the graph.

ILLUSTRATION 3. To graph $y = 10^{-\frac{x^2}{4}}$, we would assign values to x and compute y. Thus, if $x = 3$, then $y = 10^{-\frac{9}{4}} = 10^{-2.25}$; hence,

$$\log_{10} y = -2.25 = 7.7500 - 10; \quad \textit{from Table} \text{ V,} \quad y = .0056.$$

★EXERCISE 64

1. Graph $y = \log_{10} x$ for $0 < x \leq 20$. From the graph, read $10^{1.2}$; $10^{-.7}$; $10^{.3}$; $\log_{10} 7$; $\log_{10} 1.6$.

2. Graph $y = 2^x$ from $x = -5$ to $x = 5$. From the graph, read $\log_2 10$; $\log_2 5$; $\log_2 .8$; $2^{3.7}$; $2^{-2.5}$. The units on the axes need not be equal.

Graph the equation from $x = -4$ to $x = 4$, or over some similarly symmetrical range, using several values of x near $x = 0$ in the table of values. Use four-place logarithms, where necessary, to compute y.

3. $y = 10^{-x}$.   4. $y = 10^x$.   5. $y = 10^{-x^2}$.   6. $y = 2^{-x}$.

7. $y = 3^{-x^2}$.   8. $y = 10^{-\frac{1}{2}x^2}$.   9. $y = e^{\frac{1}{2}x^2}$.   10. $y = .5^{-x}$.

11. Draw a graph of $y = \log_{.5} x$ by graphing $x = .5^y$.

Applications of Right Triangles

106. A four-place trigonometric table

Unless otherwise stated, any angle to which we refer in this chapter will be acute. Table VII is a four-place table of the trigonometric functions of acute angles at intervals of 10'. Each entry in Table VII has been rounded off in the last significant place, leaving four significant digits except in a few entries. For angles at most equal to 45°, read angles at the left and titles of columns at the top in the main part of each page of the table. For angles greater than 45°, read titles at the bottom and angles at the right.

ILLUSTRATION 1. To find cot 5° 30', look in the left-hand angle columns for 5° 30': cot 5° 30' = 10.39. To find sin 77° 20', look for 77° 20' in the right-hand angle columns: sin 77° 20' = .9757.

Each entry in the function columns of Table VII is a function value for some angle and, also, is the value of the *cofunction* for the *complementary angle*, on account of the cofunction identities on page 151.

ILLUSTRATION 2. We read in Table VII that
$$.9757 = \sin 77° 20' = \cos 12° 40'.$$

EXAMPLE 1. From Table VII, find α if $\cos \alpha = .4173$.

SOLUTION. We look for .4173 in the cosine columns in Table VII. We find .4173 on page 15 in the column with cosine at the bottom; hence we read that
$$.4173 = \cos 65° 20', \quad or \quad \alpha = 65° 20'.$$

107. Interpolation in a four-place table

By means of interpolation, we shall use Table VII for angles not tabulated there. By the principle of proportional parts, we shall assume that, *for small changes in an angle α, the corresponding changes in the value of any trigonometric function of α are proportional to the changes in α.* This assumption leads to results sufficiently accurate for practical purposes.

EXAMPLE 1. By use of Table VII, find sin 27° 43'.

SOLUTION. 1. We see that 27° 43' is bracketed by 27° 40' and 27° 50', whose functions are in the table.

2. By the principle of proportional parts, an increase of 3' in the angle 27° 40' should cause 3/10 as much change in the sine as is caused by an increase of 10'. Or, in the following table, with d expressed in units in the 4th decimal place, to the nearest unit $d = 8$. Hence,

$$\text{sin } 27° 43' = .4643 + .0008 = .4651. \tag{1}$$

$$10 \begin{bmatrix} 3 \begin{bmatrix} \textit{From table:} & \text{sin } 27° 40' = .4643 \\ & \text{sin } 27° 43' = \quad ? \\ \textit{From table:} & \text{sin } 27° 50' = .4669 \end{bmatrix} d \end{bmatrix} 26 \qquad \frac{d}{26} = \frac{3}{10}; \\ d = .3(26) = 7.8.$$

EXAMPLE 2. Find csc 19° 27' from Table VII.

SOLUTION. 1. 19° 27' is 7/10 of the way from 19° 20' to 19° 27'.

$$10 \begin{bmatrix} 7 \begin{bmatrix} \textit{From table:} & \text{csc } 19° 20' = 3.021 \\ & \text{csc } 19° 27' = \quad ? \\ \textit{From table:} & \text{csc } 19° 30' = 2.996 \end{bmatrix} d \end{bmatrix} 25 \qquad \frac{d}{25} = \frac{7}{10}; \\ d = .7(25) = 17.5.$$

2. We can find .7(25) = 17.5 in the auxiliary column of tenths of 25 on page 431 in Table VII. Since there is a *decrease* of .025 in passing from 3.021 to 2.996, we *subtract* d from 3.021. We could choose $d = 17$ or $d = 18$. In interpolation, whenever such ambiguity is met, we have agreed to make that choice which gives **an even last digit in the final result.** Hence, we use $d = 17$:

$$\text{csc } 19° 27' = 3.021 - .017 = 3.004.$$

EXAMPLE 3. Find α if sin $\alpha = .9254$.

SOLUTION. In the sine column of Table VII, we search for the entries which bracket .9254; we find .9250 = sin 67° 40' and .9261 = sin 67° 50'. Hence, α lies between 67° 40' and 67° 50'. In the following table, x is the unknown difference in minutes between α and 67° 40'. By the *principle of proportional parts*, $(x/10) = (4/11)$.

$$11 \begin{bmatrix} 4 \begin{bmatrix} .9250 = \text{sin } 67° 40' \\ .9254 = \text{sin } \alpha \\ .9261 = \text{sin } 67° 50' \end{bmatrix} x \end{bmatrix} 10 \qquad \frac{x}{10} = \frac{4}{11}; \quad x = \frac{4}{11} (10); \\ \tfrac{4}{11} = .36 = .4, \textit{ to nearest tenth;} \\ \alpha = 67° 40' + .4(10') = 67° 44'.$$

Comment. When using Table VII to find an unknown angle, we agree to state the result to the *nearest minute*, because such accuracy but no greater refinement is justified. Hence, in Example 3, we computed 4/11 to the *nearest tenth* because we were to multiply by 10'.

EXAMPLE 4. Find α if cot $\alpha = 1.387$.

SOLUTION. Since cot $\alpha > 1$, we have $\alpha < 45°$. Hence, we look in the columns of Table VII labeled *cotangent* at the *top*, and find the entries 1.393 and 1.385 which *bracket* 1.387. Since 1.387 is 6/8 of the way from 1.393 to 1.385, we assume that α is 6/8 of the way from 35° 40′ to 35° 50′.

$$8\begin{bmatrix} 6\begin{bmatrix} 1.393 = \cot 35°\ 40' \\ 1.387 = \cot \alpha \\ 1.385 = \cot 35°\ 50' \end{bmatrix}x \end{bmatrix}10 \qquad \begin{array}{c} \tfrac{6}{8} = .75 = .8 \ approximately, \\ x = .8(10) = 8. \\ \alpha = 35°\ 40' + .8(10') = 35°\ 48'. \end{array}$$

EXERCISE 65

Find each function value by use of Table VII.

1. sin 12°. **2.** tan 33°. **3.** cot 58°. **4.** sec 64°.

5. cot 85° 20′. **6.** cos 9° 20′. **7.** sin 13° 30′. **8.** tan 53° 40′.

Find angle α by inspection of Table VII.

9. tan $\alpha = .4074$. **10.** sin $\alpha = .1016$. **11.** sec $\alpha = 1.167$.

12. csc $\alpha = 1.033$. **13.** tan $\alpha = 1.437$. **14.** cos $\alpha = .3035$.

15. cot $\alpha = .4841$. **16.** cos $\alpha = .6180$. **17.** sin $\alpha = .3502$.

Find each function value by interpolation in Table VII.

18. sin 80° 17′. **19.** sin 28° 5′. **20.** csc 65° 39′. **21.** sec 53° 13′.

22. cot 27° 4′. **23.** tan 4° 43′. **24.** cos 24° 44′. **25.** cot 32° 38′.

26. cot 77° 16′. **27.** cos 28° 19′. **28.** sin 1° 11′. **29.** tan 6° 23′.

30. csc 76° 44′. **31.** tan 81° 53′. **32.** cot 67° 32′. **33.** sin 14° 24′.

Find angle α by interpolation in Table VII.

34. tan $\alpha = .0831$. **35.** sin $\alpha = .4955$. **36.** cos $\alpha = .9381$.

37. cot $\alpha = 1.558$. **38.** sec $\alpha = 1.506$. **39.** cos $\alpha = .7037$.

40. tan $\alpha = 1.322$. **41.** csc $\alpha = 1.265$. **42.** cot $\alpha = .6720$.

43. tan $\alpha = 1.026$. **44.** sin $\alpha = .7967$. **45.** cos $\alpha = .9987$.

Find α, without interpolation, to the nearest 10′ by use of Table VII.

46. sin $\alpha = .2231$. **47.** tan $\alpha = 7.703$. **48.** cot $\alpha = 4.671$.

49. cos $\alpha = .3437$. **50.** sin $\alpha = .6773$. **51.** csc $\alpha = 1.230$.

108. Solution of a right triangle

A right triangle has six parts, consisting of *three sides* and *three angles*, one of which is 90°. In the standard right triangle ABC, as in Figure 72, we let α and β be the acute angles (or their measures). We let a and b be the *lengths* of the sides opposite α and β, respectively, and let c be the *length* of the hypotenuse. Also, for abbreviation, we shall use a, b, and c as symbols for the sides

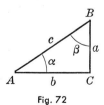

Fig. 72

themselves.   By means of trigonometry, if *two sides*, or *an acute angle and a side*, of $\triangle ABC$ are given,* we can compute the unknown parts.   This computation is called the *solution of the triangle*.   First, we shall consider the solution of right triangles without use of logarithms.   Recall the following formulas from page 150 for $\triangle ABC$ in Figure 72 on page 195.

$$a^2 + b^2 = c^2. \qquad (1) \qquad\qquad \alpha + \beta = 90°. \qquad (2)$$

$$\sin \alpha = \frac{a}{c} = \cos \beta. \qquad (3) \qquad\qquad \cos \alpha = \frac{b}{c} = \sin \beta. \qquad (4)$$

$$\tan \alpha = \frac{a}{b} = \cot \beta. \qquad (5) \qquad\qquad \cot \alpha = \frac{b}{a} = \tan \beta. \qquad (6)$$

$$\sec \alpha = \frac{c}{b} = \csc \beta. \qquad (7) \qquad\qquad \csc \alpha = \frac{c}{a} = \sec \beta. \qquad (8)$$

From (3) and (4) we obtain the following useful formulas:

$$a = c \sin \alpha; \qquad b = c \cos \alpha; \qquad\qquad (9)$$

or, *the leg opposite α is equal to the hypotenuse times* sin α, *and the leg adjacent to α is equal to the hypotenuse times* cos α.   We shall avoid (1) until we use logarithms.   As an aid to accuracy, we usually employ (3) or (4) in preference to (7) or (8) in finding angles.   Formulas (7) and (8) are useful in avoiding division when finding c.

To solve a right triangle with given data, first sketch the triangle roughly to scale.   Then, outline the formulas to be used; for any unknown part, if possible, choose a formula involving it *but no other unknown part*.   Also, if convenient, use a formula *avoiding division*.   To check the results roughly, compare them with the preliminary sketch.   For a more refined check, substitute *from the results and the data in any one of* (3) *to* (8) *not used in the solution*, and compute both sides of the formula for comparison.   In results, round off lengths, quotients, and products to four significant digits and angles to minutes if four-place tables are used.

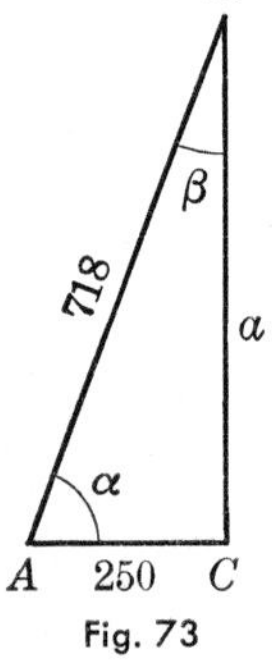

EXAMPLE 1.   Solve right $\triangle ABC$ if $b = 250$ and $c = 718$.

SOLUTION.   1. *Outline of formulas:* See Figure 73.

To obtain β, $\qquad\qquad\qquad \sin \beta = \frac{b}{c}.$ $\qquad\qquad (10)$

From $\alpha + \beta = 90°,$ $\qquad\qquad \alpha = 90° - \beta.$ $\qquad\qquad (11)$

From $\cot \beta = \frac{a}{b},$ $\qquad\qquad a = b \cot \beta.$ $\qquad\qquad (12)$

Check formula: $\qquad\qquad\qquad a = c \sin \alpha.$ $\qquad\qquad (13)$

2. *Computation.* $\qquad\qquad \sin \beta = \frac{250}{718} = .3482.$

Fig. 73

* Recall that then it is possible to construct the triangle by plane geometry.

By interpolation in Table VII, $\beta = 20° 23'$.

Hence, $\alpha = 90° - 20° 23' = 69° 37'$.

From (12) and Table VII,

$$a = 250 \cot 20° 23' = 250(2.692) = 673.0.$$

3. *Check.* $c \sin \alpha = 718 \sin 69° 37' = 718(.9374) = 673.1$. Since $a = 673.0$, the check is satisfactory; the difference between 673.1 and 673.0 could be due to errors introduced by rounding off in computation.

EXAMPLE 2. Solve right $\triangle ABC$ if $a = 30.5$ and $\beta = 32° 10'$.

OUTLINE OF SOLUTION. Since $\alpha + \beta = 90°$, $\qquad \boldsymbol{\alpha = 90° - \beta.}$

From $\dfrac{b}{a} = \tan \beta$, $\qquad\qquad\qquad\qquad \boldsymbol{b = a \tan \beta.}$

From $\dfrac{c}{a} = \sec \beta$, $\qquad\qquad\qquad\qquad \boldsymbol{c = a \sec \beta.}$

Check formula: $\qquad\qquad\qquad\qquad\qquad \boldsymbol{b = c \cos \alpha.}$

109. Applications of right triangles

In either diagram in Figure 74, O is a point from which we sight an object at C, and OH is a horizontal line in the same vertical plane as C. Then,

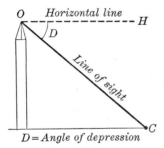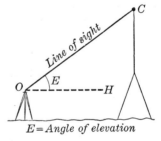

Fig. 74

the acute angle COH between the line of sight to C and the horizontal line is called the *angle of elevation* of C or the *angle of depression* of C, as seen from O, according as C is *above* O or *below* O.

EXAMPLE 1. From a cliff, 700 feet above a plane, the angle of depression of a church is $38° 27'$. Find the distance from the cliff to the church.

OUTLINE OF SOLUTION. 1. In Figure 75, C represents the church. The angle of depression is $\angle CAH$, or θ. We desire to find $x = KC$.

2. In right $\triangle AKC$, $y = 700$ and $\theta = 38° 27'$.

3. From $\cot \theta = x/y$, $\qquad x = y \cot \theta.$

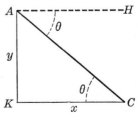

Fig. 75

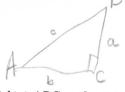

EXERCISE 66

Solve right △ABC or the stated problem by use of Table VII.

1. $\alpha = 23° 30'$; $a = 50$.   2. $b = 75$; $\alpha = 68° 40'$.

3. $c = 125$; $\beta = 13° 20'$.   4. $c = 15$; $\alpha = 56° 30'$.

5. $a = 400$; $b = 446$.   6. $c = 7.5$; $b = 5.083$.

7. $a = 85.22$; $b = 65$.   8. $c = 1.4$; $\alpha = 16° 13'$.

9. $a = .518$; $c = 1.16$.   10. $b = .48$; $c = .97$.

11. $a = 2.3$; $b = 1.25$.   12. $a = .262$; $c = .43$.

13. $b = .425$; $c = .73$.   14. $a = 25.4$; $b = 89.6$.

15. $b = .013$; $\alpha = 52° 11'$.   16. $b = .38$; $\beta = 48° 1'$.

17. $c = 1.6$; $\alpha = 80° 12'$.   18. $a = 1625$; $b = 2950$.

19. $b = 4500$; $c = 8600$.   20. $b = .135$; $\beta = 79° 28'$.

21. Find the length of the horizontal shadow of a man 6 feet tall when the angle of elevation of the sun is 75° 36'.

22. How tall is a chimney whose horizontal shadow is 90 feet long when the angle of elevation of the sun is 67° 42'?

23. A guy wire 35 feet long is stretched from level ground to the top of a pole 25 feet high. Find the angle between the pole and the wire.

24. From a mountaintop 4000 feet above a fort, its angle of depression is 16° 45'. Find the air-line distance from the mountaintop to the fort.

25. How high does an airplane rise in flying 4000 feet upward along a straight path inclined 28° 47' from the horizontal?

26. From an airplane, flying 7000 feet above the ground, the angle of depression of a landing field is 19° 32'. Find the air-line distance from the plane to the field.

27. Find the height of the Empire State Building in New York City if the angle of elevation of its top is 61° 37' when seen from a point on the street level 675.4 feet from the building.

28. An inclined ramp into a garage is 260 feet long and rises 76 feet. Find the inclination of the ramp from the horizontal.

29. The largest tree in California is the General Sherman tree in the Sequoia National Park. At a point 185 feet from the tree, at the same elevation as its foot, the angle of elevation of the top of the tree is 55° 49'. How tall is the tree?

30. In flying upward for 1260 yards along a straight inclined path, an airplane rises 156 yards. Find the climbing angle.

31. Find the length of the shortest ladder to reach a window 40 feet above the ground and not incline more than 78° from the horizontal.

32. On a 3% railroad grade, at what angle are the rails inclined to the horizontal, and how far does one rise in traveling upward 9000 feet along the rails? (The tracks rise 3 feet for each 100 feet of horizontal distance.)

110. Logarithms of trigonometric functions

Frequently, in computation involving products or quotients of trigonometric functions, Table VI makes it unnecessary to use Table VII.

EXAMPLE 1. Compute 156 sin 21° 10′ by four-place logarithms.

SOLUTION. In Table VI we find **log sin** 21° 10′, *the logarithm of* sin 21° 10′. We read "log sin 21° 10′" briefly *as it is written:* "*log, sine,* 21° 10′."

$$\begin{array}{lr}
\log 156 = 2.1931 & \text{(Table V)} \\
(+) \log \sin 21° \ 10′ = 9.5576 - 10 & \text{(Table VI)} \\
\hline
\log 156 \sin 21° \ 10′ = 1.7507. &
\end{array}$$

Hence, 156 sin 21° 10′ = 56.32, where we found antilog 1.7507 from Table V.

The sine or cosine of any angle between 0° and 90°, or the tangent of any angle between 0° and 45°, or the cotangent of any angle between 45° and 90° is *not zero* and is *less than* 1. Therefore the logarithms of these functions have *negative* characteristics. For abbreviation, Table VI omits "− 10" belonging with each of these logarithms which are tabulated. Hence, **in using the columns labeled log sin, log cos, and log tan for 0° to 45°, we subtract 10 from each given entry.** To abbreviate the tables, we omit the logarithms of secants and cosecants. Hence, before computing a trigonometric expression by use of logarithms, if the *secant* or *cosecant* of an angle occurs as a factor, we change this function value to the *reciprocal* of the *cosine* or *sine*, respectively, of the angle.

Sometimes the values of trigonometric functions are referred to as **natural functions,** to emphasize the distinction between them and *their logarithms.* Thus, we call Table VII a table of the *natural trigonometric functions.*

EXAMPLE 2. Find log tan 29° 27′ by use of Table VI.

SOLUTION. We see that 29° 27′ is 7/10 of the way from 29° 20′ to 29° 30′. Hence, by the principle of proportional parts, we assume that the desired logarithm is 7/10 of the way from the entry for 29° 20′ to that for 29° 30′. The entries are on page 10 of the tables. We omit "− 10" until the end of the solution. The tabular difference is 29. With *d* as the unknown increment in the following table,

$$\frac{d}{29} = \frac{7}{10} \quad or \quad d = .7(29) = 20.$$

We add *d* below because the table entries increase. We found .7(29) = 20.3 in the auxiliary column of tenths of 29. The solution is summarized below.

log tan 29° 20′ → 9.7497 ⎤ *d* ⎤ 29 log tan 29° 27′ → ? ⎟ ⎟ log tan 29° 30′ → 9.7526 ⎦	$d = .7(29) = 20.$ $9.7497 + .0020 = 9.7517.$ **log tan 29° 27′ = 9.7517 − 10.**

Note 1. Recall that $\tan \alpha = \dfrac{1}{\cot \alpha}$ and hence

$$\log \tan \alpha = \log 1 - \log \cot \alpha = 0 - \log \cot \alpha = -\log \cot \alpha.$$

Therefore, any change in log tan α corresponds to a change of *equal numerical value, but opposite sign,* in log cot α. Hence, in Table VI, the single column headed "*c d*" gives the *common differences* for the columns headed *log tan* and *log cot.*

EXAMPLE 3.   Find the acute angle α if log sin $\alpha = 8.7808 - 10$, by use of Table VI.

SOLUTION.   Since the characteristic is $(8 - 10)$ or -2, sin α is a small decimal with its first significant digit in the 2d decimal place. Hence, α is near $0°$, and we begin looking for 8.7808 on page 422 in Table VI. The bracketing entries are 8.7645 and 8.7857 in the column headed "L Sin" at the top, where the tabular difference is 212, in the 4th decimal place. Since the partial difference, as in the table below, is

$$7808 - 7645 = 163 \quad and \quad \frac{163}{212} = .8, \; approximately,$$

angle α is taken .8 of the way from $3° 20'$ to $3° 30'$. The auxiliary column of tenths of 212 was used to obtain $\frac{163}{212} = .8$, approximately.

$$212 \left[163 \left[\begin{array}{l} 8.7645 \rightarrow 3° 20' \\ 8.7808 \rightarrow \quad \alpha \\ 8.7857 \rightarrow 3° 30' \end{array} \right] x \right] 10 \qquad \begin{array}{c} \frac{163}{212} = .8 \; to \; nearest \; tenth. \\ x = .8(10) = 8. \\ \alpha = 3° 20' + 8' = 3° 28'. \end{array}$$

In using Table VI, we round off any given angle to the nearest minute. In case an unknown angle is found by use of Table VI, we agree to state the resulting value to the nearest minute, as obtained by interpolation. No greater accuracy is justified.

EXERCISE 67

1. (a) Find sin $12° 20'$ from Table VII.   (b) Find the logarithm of the result of Part (a) from Table V.   (c) Find log sin $12° 20'$ from Table VI.

Find the four-place logarithm of the function value from Table VI.

2. cot $55° 40'$.   3. sin $78° 37'$.   4. cos $45° 18'$.   5. sin $53° 24'$.

6. tan $23° 26'$.   7. cos $63° 13'$.   8. sin $26° 42'$.   9. tan $32° 57'$.

10. sin $16° 18'$.   11. cot $23° 51'$.   12. cos $15° 19'$.   13. cot $79° 16'$.

Find the angle α by use of Table VI.

14. log cot $\alpha = 9.9595 - 10$.   15. log tan $\alpha = 0.3141$.

16. log cos $\alpha = 9.4113 - 10$.   17. log sin $\alpha = 9.5470 - 10$.

18. log sin $\alpha = 9.9349 - 10$.   19. log tan $\alpha = 9.4201 - 10$.

20. log cos $\alpha = 8.9850 - 10$.   21. log cot $\alpha = 9.2931 - 10$.

111. Logarithmic solution of right triangles

When we employ logarithms, we discard use of the secant and cosecant, because they can be replaced by the reciprocals of the cosine and sine, respectively. For $\triangle ABC$ of Figure 76, we have formulas (1)–(6) of page 196. In place of $a^2 + b^2 = c^2$, with logarithms it may be convenient to write $a^2 = c^2 - b^2$, or $b^2 = c^2 - a^2$. Then

$$a = \sqrt{(c - b)(c + b)} \quad and \quad b = \sqrt{(c - a)(c + a)}. \tag{1}$$

Sometimes it is desirable to use (1) to find an unknown side, with the square root computed by use of logarithms. However, (1) probably is most useful as a check formula. Different methods of solution for a right triangle may yield slightly different results, because of unavoidable errors due to rounding off numbers in the use of tables. This possibility should be remembered in referring to the answer book.

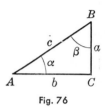

Fig. 76

EXAMPLE 1. By use of four-place logarithms, solve right $\triangle ABC$ if $a = 135.1$ and $c = 367.2$.

SOLUTION. We arrange the computing form, which is given in heavy type, *before looking up any logarithms.*

Formulas	Computation
	Data: $a = 135.1$, $c = 367.2$.
$\sin \alpha = \dfrac{a}{c}$.	$\log a = 2.1306$ (Table V) $(-) \log c = 2.5649$ (Table V) $\log \sin \alpha = 9.5657 - 10$ $\alpha = 21° \ 35'.$ (Table VI)
$\cos \alpha = \dfrac{b}{c}$, *or* $b = c \cos \alpha.$	$\log c = 2.5649$ (Above) $(+) \log \cos \alpha = 9.9684 - 10$ (Table VI) $\log b = 2.5333; \ \ b = 341.4.$ (Table V)
$\beta = 90° - \alpha.$	$\beta = 90° - 21° \ 35' = 68° \ 25'.$
Summary:	$\alpha = 21° \ 35',$ $\beta = 68° \ 25',$ $b = 341.4.$

Check. $a = \sqrt{(c - b)(c + b)}$,   or $\log a = \frac{1}{2} \log [(c - b)(c + b)].$
$c - b = 25.8$ $\log (c - b) = 1.4116$
$c + b = 708.6$ $(+) \log (c + b) = 2.8504$
                                 $\log [(c - b)(c + b)] = 4.2620.$
$\log a = 2.1306 \longrightarrow \longleftarrow \frac{1}{2} \log [(c - b)(c + b)] = 2.1310.$

Comment. The check is satisfactory. The difference $(2.1310 - 2.1306)$, or $.0004$, could result from an error of less than one unit in the *fourth* significant digit of b, because this would affect the *third* digit of $(c - b)$.

EXAMPLE 2. Solve right $\triangle ABC$ if $a = .8421$ and $\alpha = 27° 39.7'$.

SOLUTION. The student should check the following solution by use of (1).

Formulas	Computation
	Data: $a = .8421;$ $\alpha = 27° 40'.$
$\beta = 90° - \alpha.$	$\beta = 90° - 27° 40' = 62° 20'.$
$\dfrac{b}{a} = \cot \alpha,$ or $b = a \cot \alpha.$	$\log a = 9.9254 - 10$ (Table V) $(+) \log \cot \alpha = 0.2804$ (Table VI) $\overline{\quad\log b = 0.2058;\quad b = 1.606.}$
$\dfrac{a}{c} = \sin \alpha,$ or $c = \dfrac{a}{\sin \alpha}.$	$\log a = 9.9254 - 10$ $(-) \log \sin \alpha = 9.6668 - 10$ $\overline{\quad\log c = 0.2586;\quad c = 1.814.}$
Summary:	$\beta = 62° 20',$ $b = 1.606,$ $c = 1.814.$

EXERCISE 68

Solve by use of four-place logarithms in this exercise.

Solve right $\triangle ABC$ with the given data.   Check the solution.

1. $a = 15.7$; $\alpha = 36° 20'.$

2. $c = .943$; $\beta = 62° 40'.$

3. $a = .3590$; $b = .6611.$

4. $a = 23.18$; $\beta = 47° 17'.$

5. $c = .685$; $\alpha = 29° 43'.$

6. $c = .3675$; $a = .1943.$

7. $a = .5731$; $b = .6298.$

8. $\alpha = 25° 8'$; $c = 37.857.$

9. $\alpha = 31° 24.7'$; $a = 1.6315.$

10. $a = 2.1523$; $b = 4.1392.$

11. $c = 915.62$; $b = 411.37.$

12. $\alpha = 68° 39' 14''$; $c = 1000.3.$

13. $\beta = 43° 17' 34''$; $a = 42.930.$

14. $\alpha = 53° 22.6'$; $b = 93.142.$

★*An isosceles $\triangle ABK$ has its equal angles at A and B, and angle γ at K. Find the unknown sides or angles of the triangle under the given conditions. (Divide the triangle into two right triangles by dropping a perpendicular to AB from K, as in Figure 77.)*

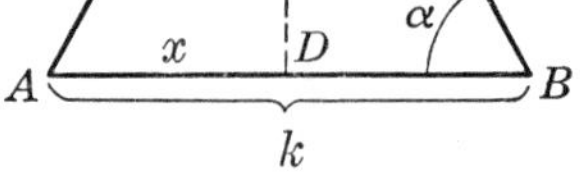

15. $\gamma = 68° 20'$; $\overline{AK} = 456.$

16. $\overline{AB} = .63284$; $\overline{AK} = .83172.$

Fig. 77

Note 1. In any $\triangle ABC$, as in Figure 78, page 203, let α, β, and γ be the angles at A, B, and C, and let a, b, and c be the lengths of the sides opposite A, B, and C, respectively. If we are given *two sides and one angle* or *two angles and one side* of the triangle, we can find its unknown parts by solving two right triangles. To obtain them, we drop a perpendicular from an end point of a known side to the opposite side.

★Solve $\triangle ABC$ with the given data. That is, find any unknown sides and angles of the triangle.

17. $\begin{cases} b = 275, \\ \alpha = 46° 26', \\ \gamma = 103° 54'. \end{cases}$ 18. $\begin{cases} c = .9438, \\ \alpha = 43° 18', \\ \gamma = 61° 44'. \end{cases}$

19. $\begin{cases} c = 68.452, \\ b = 31.267, \\ \alpha = 28° 15.6'. \end{cases}$ 20. $\begin{cases} a = 14.56, \\ b = 19.37, \\ \beta = 110° 50'. \end{cases}$

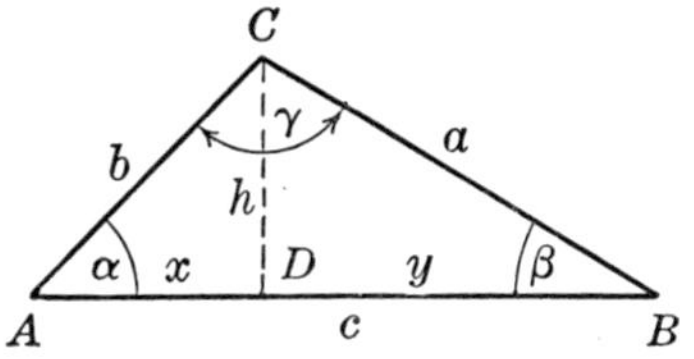

Fig. 78

112. Problems with approximate data

In computation in this book up to the present time, the emphasis has been placed on computing with *all the accuracy obtainable from our tables,* under the assumption that *the data are exact.* Now we consider computation where the given numbers are only *approximate values* of corresponding quantities. Then, we ask the following questions: (a) *With what refinement should computation be performed when the data are known to have only a specified degree of accuracy?* (b) *To what stage of accuracy should the final results be specified?* No hard and fast rules should be followed in answering (a) and (b) in any problem. However, the following agreements are satisfactory for problems of the types which the student is likely to meet.

1. *In data concerning triangles, it is roughly true that three-place, four-place, and five-place accuracy in the lengths of sides correspond to accuracy to the nearest 10', 1', and .1', respectively, in the angles.*

2. *In computing, use four-place or five-place* * *tables according as the data are accurate to three or to four places.*

3. *Round off final results to the same number of places as were specified in the data.*

In stating that certain data have *four-place accuracy,* for instance, we shall mean that the angular data are accurate to the nearest *minute,* and the lengths to *four significant digits.* Rule 2 is a suggestion to carry *at least one protective place* beyond the stage to which final results will be rounded off.

Hereafter in this book, assume that the data in any applied problem *stated in words* are *not exact* but are the result of measurement, with accuracy limited to the significant places in the given numbers. Answers to exercises will be listed as they appear after being rounded off to a number of places which appear reasonably justified by the data. It is admitted that, at times, different and equally valid decisions might be made about the number of significant places in the answers.

* See *Logarithmic and Trigonometric Tables* by WILLIAM L. HART, D. C. Heath and Company, publishers. In this text, due to the absence of five-place tables, compute with four-place tables in any problem where the data are given with either three-place or four-place accuracy.

113. Projections

In a given plane, let OL be a given line and let CD be any line segment. Then, if A and B are the feet of the perpendiculars from C and D to OL, we call AB the *projection* of CD on OL. If OL and CD (possibly extended) form an acute angle α, as in Figure 79, we construct ECH parallel to OL

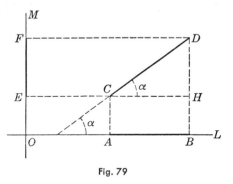

Fig. 79

and obtain triangle CHD. Then, $CH = AB$ and

$$\frac{CH}{CD} = \frac{AB}{CD} = \cos \alpha, \text{ or}$$

$$AB = CD \cdot \cos \alpha. \qquad (1)$$

If OM is perpendicular to OL in Figure 79, the projection of CD on OM is EF. Then, in triangle CHD, $HD = EF$ and

$$EF = CD \cdot \sin \alpha. \qquad (2)$$

Thus, *the projection of CD on OL is equal to CD·cos α, and the projection of CD on a line perpendicular to OL is equal to CD·sin α*, where α is the acute angle formed by OL and CD.

ILLUSTRATION 1. If a train travels 3000 feet along a straight grade inclined $2° 37'$ from the horizontal, the horizontal and vertical projections of the path of the train are $3000 \cos 2° 37'$ and $3000 \sin 2° 37'$, respectively.

114. Bearing angle and azimuth

In a horizontal plane, let any direction be represented by a directed line segment or arrow radiating from some fixed point O, as in Figure 80. Frequently, a direction is called a **bearing,** and it may be described by stating the acute angle made by it with the *north* or *south* direction. This angle will be called the **acute bearing angle** for the given direction.

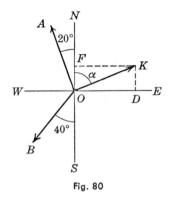

Fig. 80

ILLUSTRATION 1. In Figure 80, the bearing of OA is $20°$ west of north, abbreviated $N 20° W$. The bearing of OB is $S 40° W$. To describe the bearing of a line, we first write the letter N (or S), then the acute angle between the given line and ON (or OS), and finally write E or W to show on which side the given direction falls.

EXAMPLE 1. Find the bearing and distance of K as seen from O, if K is 30.6 miles north and 78.3 miles east of O.

SOLUTION. 1. In Figure 80, $FK \perp ON$; $OF = 30.6$; $FK = 78.3$.

2. In $\triangle OFK$, $\tan \alpha = \dfrac{78.3}{30.6}$; $\dfrac{OF}{OK} = \cos \alpha$ or $OK = \dfrac{OF}{\cos \alpha}$.

By use of four-place logarithms, $\alpha = 68° 39'$ and $OK = 84.0$. Hence, K is 84.0 miles from O in the direction $N\ 68° 39'\ E$. OD and OF are, respectively, the *east* and *north projections*, or *components*, of OK.

In the navigation of an airplane or a ship, in astronomy, and in the artillery service, the direction from a point G to a point B in the horizontal plane frequently is described by telling the angle through which a line GN pointing *north* must be *rotated* (clockwise) *toward the east* in order to coincide with GB. This angle is called the **azimuth** of B from G, or the azimuth of GB, and is an angle α such that $0° \leqq \alpha < 360°$. Frequently, to find the azimuth of a specified direction, we shall first find its acute bearing angle.

ILLUSTRATION 2. In Figure 81, the azimuth of GB is $220°$. The bearing of GB is $S\ 40°\ W$.

Fig. 81

In any problem which refers to the flight of an airplane or the sailing of a ship, we shall assume that the motion is in a *horizontal plane*, unless otherwise specified. Essentially, then, we shall be dealing with a navigation problem in *plane sailing*. Other examples of a similar nature will be in the field of *plane surveying*, where the surveyor is assumed to work in a horizontal plane, except as points may be elevated above or below it.

EXERCISE 69

Solve by use of logarithms except as directed by the instructor, or the statement of the problem.

1. From the top row in a football stadium, 85 feet above the ground, the angle of depression of the center of the field is $32° 10'$. Find the air-line distance from the top row to the center of the field.

2. Find the area of a parallelogram whose sides are 150.6 feet and 235.3 feet long, if one angle is $127° 46'$.

Find the horizontal and vertical projections of line segment AB with the given length and inclination from the horizontal.

3. 137.5 ft.; inclination $17° 18'$.   4. .1638 ft.; inclination $49° 7'$.

5. An airplane makes a straight ascent from A to B. Find the inclination of the path AB from the horizontal if its horizontal and vertical projections are 1780 ft. and 2360 ft., respectively.

Find the azimuth of a direction having the given bearing.

6. $S\ 20°\ E.$ 7. $N\ 39°\ W.$ 8. $N\ 53°\ E.$ 9. $S\ 72° 13'\ W.$

10. In planning a straight railroad grade to rise 75 feet, it is decided to incline the tracks 4° 32′ from the horizontal. Find the horizontal projection of the grade, and its length.

11. How far north or south, and how far east or west is M from P if M is 385 miles from P in the direction N 43° 20′ W?

Find the distance MP, and the bearing and azimuth of MP.

12. M is 58.9 miles north and 32.7 miles east of P.

13. P is 138 miles north and 289 miles east of M.

14. A battery of artillery emplaced at B is ordered to fire at a target T which is 6480 yards west and 5720 yards north of B. Find the range, bearing, and azimuth of T from B.

15. The *pitch* of a gable roof is defined as the *height* of its peak above the eaves *divided by* the roof's *width*. Find the pitch of a roof 45.7 feet wide whose peak is 17.6 feet above the lowest point (the eaves). Also, find the angle at which a side of the gable is inclined from the horizontal.

16. A porch, whose roof is 10.6 feet above the ground, projects 15.3 feet from the wall of a house. Find the length of the shortest ladder which would reach over the porch to a window 55.6 feet above the ground.

17. A regular octagon is inscribed in a circle whose radius is 36.8 feet. Find the length of a side of the octagon and the radius of its inscribed circle.

Hint. The radii to the ends of any side create an isosceles triangle.

18. Each side of a regular hexagon (six sides) is 50.8 inches long. Find the radii of its inscribed and circumscribed circles.

19. A tower stands on a cliff 653 feet above a horizontal plane. From a point A in the plane, the angles of elevation of the top and the bottom of the tower are 47° 28′ and 43° 36′. How high is the tower?

An airplane flies or a ship sails from A to B and the navigator then heads for C. Find the distance and azimuth of C from B for the given data.

★**20.** $AB = 120$ mi., N 27° 16′ E; C is 257 mi. east and 55 mi. north of A.

★**21.** $AB = 250$ mi., S 57° 40′ W; C is 350 mi. west and 30 mi. north of A.

★**22.** From two points 835.7 yards apart on a horizontal road running due east from a mountain, the angles of elevation of its top are, respectively, 43° 27′ and 30° 18′. How high above the road is the mountaintop?

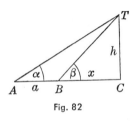

Fig. 82

Hint. 1. In Figure 82, we desire h; a, α, and β are given.

2. From $\triangle BCT$,
$$x = h \cot \beta. \tag{1}$$

3. From $\triangle ACT$, $\cot \alpha = AC/h$, or
$$a + x = h \cot \alpha. \tag{2}$$

4. Solve (1) and (2) for h. The equations involve two unknowns, x and h, but the value of x is not needed.

115. Vectors

A directed line segment or arrow, such as $\overrightarrow{OR}$ in Figure 83, may be called a **stroke.** The measure of the length of $\overrightarrow{OR}$ in some linear unit is called the *magnitude* of $\overrightarrow{OR}$ and is denoted sometimes by $|\overrightarrow{OR}|$. Thus, a stroke $\overrightarrow{OR}$ has a *direction*, a *magnitude*, an *initial point O*, and a *terminal point R*. Now, consider a given set of strokes, all in a certain plane, or perhaps in space of three dimensions. Then, the strokes are called **vectors** if they combine in accordance with certain agreements, where the rules essential for our purposes are met in the following discussion. At present, any vectors which we consider simultaneously will be in the same plane (*coplanar* vectors).

Two vectors are said to be *equal* if they have the same direction and magnitude, regardless of their locations. Thus, *if a vector is moved without altering its direction and magnitude, the vector is considered unaltered.* The *zero vector* is defined as one having the magnitude zero and any direction.

Let two vectors $\overrightarrow{OF}$ and $\overrightarrow{OP}$ be given, and let them be drawn with a common initial point O, as in Figure 83. Then, we define the *sum*,* or the **resultant,** of $\overrightarrow{OP}$ and $\overrightarrow{OF}$ as a vector $\overrightarrow{OR}$ where R is located as follows: *place the initial point, O, of $\overrightarrow{OF}$ on the terminal point, P, of $\overrightarrow{OP}$, giving PR.* When OP and OF do not have the same or opposite directions, the preceding construction is equivalent to the following description: *The resultant of $\overrightarrow{OP}$ and $\overrightarrow{OF}$ is the vector $\overrightarrow{OR}$ which is the diagonal of the parallelogram having $\overrightarrow{OP}$ and $\overrightarrow{OF}$ as adjacent sides.* This definition is referred to as the *parallelogram law for the addition of vectors.* We call $\overrightarrow{OP}$ and $\overrightarrow{OF}$ the *components of $\overrightarrow{OR}$* along the lines of the corresponding sides of the parallelogram. The sum of two vectors of the same magnitude but opposite directions is seen to be the zero vector.

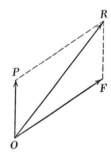

Fig. 83

ILLUSTRATION 1. Any force, velocity, or acceleration, as defined in physics, possesses a direction and a magnitude, and hence can be represented geometrically by a properly directed stroke, with the measure of its length in some linear unit equal to the measure of the physical quantity in some physical unit. In Figure 83, let $\overrightarrow{OF}$ and $\overrightarrow{OP}$ represent any two forces pulling (or *acting*) simultaneously on an object at O. Then, in physics it is found that the combined effect of forces $\overrightarrow{OF}$ and $\overrightarrow{OP}$ is the same as the effect of the single **resultant force** represented by the *resultant vector* $\overrightarrow{OR}$. This fact is referred to as the *parallelogram law for the composition of forces.* If $\overrightarrow{OF}$ and $\overrightarrow{OP}$ repre-

---

* In vector analysis, the operation of subtraction, and various notions of products are defined for vectors.

sent velocities simultaneously imposed on an object at O, the resultant velocity is represented by $\overrightarrow{OR}$. Thus, velocities and, similarly, accelerations also obey the parallelogram law in composition. Hence, we are justified in representing sets of forces, or velocities, or accelerations as vectors.

Any physical quantity with the property just mentioned for forces, velocities, and accelerations is referred to as a **vector quantity.** In contrast, if a symbol or quantity merely has a *value* (with no direction characteristic), we sometimes call it a **scalar.**

The components of a vector $\overrightarrow{OR}$ along two perpendicular lines ON and OE are the vectors obtained by projecting $\overrightarrow{OR}$ on ON and OE. In Figure 84, the magnitudes of the components are seen to be

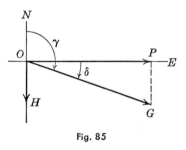

$$\overline{OB} = \overline{OR} \cos \beta; \quad \overline{OD} = \overline{OR} \sin \beta.$$

The given vector $\overrightarrow{OR}$ is the resultant of its components $\overrightarrow{OB}$ and $\overrightarrow{OD}$. In finding $\overrightarrow{OB}$ and $\overrightarrow{OD}$ in Figure 84, we say that we have *resolved* the given vector into *components*.

ILLUSTRATION 2. In Figure 84, let $\overrightarrow{OR}$ represent a force of 150 pounds acting in the direction $N\ 31°\ E$; the acute bearing angle is $\beta = 31°$.

Fig. 84

$$OB = 150 \cos 31° = 129; \quad OD = 150 \sin 31° = 77.$$

The north component is 129 pounds; the east component is 77 pounds.

Note 1. If the *weight* of an object is w pounds, the attraction of gravity on it is a vertical *force* of w pounds acting at the object's center of gravity.

Note 2. The direction in which the nose of an airplane or the prow of a ship is pointed in its motion is called the *heading.* The direction of the motion relative to the ground is called the *course* of the airplane or ship.

EXAMPLE 1. An airplane is headed east with an airspeed of 240 miles per hour. A north wind is blowing with a speed of 40 miles per hour. Find the airplane's ground-speed per hour and course.

Fig. 85

SOLUTION. 1. In Figure 85, $\overrightarrow{OH}$ represents the wind velocity, with which the air moves. The airplane's velocity *in the moving air* is represented by $\overrightarrow{OP}$, called the *airspeed vector*, whose magnitude * is the *airspeed.* The airplane's

* The *magnitude* of any *velocity* is called *speed.*

ground velocity (relative to the ground) is represented by $\overrightarrow{OG}$, the resultant of $\overrightarrow{OH}$ and $\overrightarrow{OP}$. We call $\overrightarrow{OG}$ the *groundspeed vector;* its magnitude is the groundspeed; the *azimuth* of $\overrightarrow{OG}$ is called the *course* of the airplane.

2. In $\triangle OPG$, we have $OP = 240$ and $PG = 40$; on solving, we find $\delta = 9°\ 28'$ and $OG = 243$. The groundspeed is 243 miles and the course is azimuth $99°\ 28'$.

Comment. The smallest angle between the *heading* and *course* of an airplane is called the *drift angle.* It is $9°\ 28'$ in Example 2; the wind blows the airplane $9°\ 28'$ *off its heading.*

EXAMPLE 2. Find the force which is just sufficient to keep a 1000-pound weight from sliding down a plane inclined $47°$ to the horizontal, under the assumption that there is no friction.

SOLUTION. 1. The attraction of gravity on the weight A, in Figure 86, is a vertical force $\overrightarrow{AW}$, of 1000 pounds. We resolve $\overrightarrow{AW}$ into two perpendicular components, $\overrightarrow{AK}$ acting along the plane and $\overrightarrow{AH}$ perpendicular to the plane. Force $\overrightarrow{AH}$ creates pressure on the plane and is counteracted by its supports. Force $\overrightarrow{AK}$ acts to move the weight A downward. Hence, we must apply force $\overrightarrow{AF}$ equal in magnitude to $\overrightarrow{AK}$ and opposite in direction.

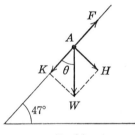

Fig. 86

2. In $\triangle KAW$, $\theta = 43°$ and $AW = 1000$. Thus we obtain

$$AK = 1000 \cos 43° = 731.4.$$

Hence, a force of 731.4 lb. would hold the weight steady. Any greater force would move the weight upward. The favorable difference between 1000 and 731.4 shows the advantage of the inclined ramp. A force slightly greater than 1000 lb. is necessary to raise the weight vertically.

EXERCISE 70

Find the horizontal and vertical components of the force.

1. 153.8 lb. acting downward at inclination of $56°\ 34'$ from horizontal.
2. 2183 lb. acting downward at inclination of $36°\ 33'$ from horizontal.

Find the north or south and east or west components of the given force, or given ground velocity of an airplane.

3. 42.65 lb. force acting $S\ 31°\ 10'\ W$. 4. 1329 lb. force acting $N\ 31°\ 37'\ W$.
5. Groundspeed of 300 miles per hour with azimuth $160°$.
6. Groundspeed of 150 miles per hour with azimuth $250°$.

A body is acted upon by the given forces simultaneously. Find the magnitude of the resultant force and its direction.

7. 162 lb. north; 53.7 lb. east.   8. 638 lb. south; 217 lb. west.

For the given wind velocity, find the groundspeed, course, and drift angle for the airplane. All speeds are "per hour."

9. Wind blowing 30 miles from west; airspeed 200 miles north.

10. Wind blowing 25 miles from east; airspeed 220 miles south.

11. A ship is headed east at 18 miles per hour relative to the water. An ocean current is carrying the water south at 3 miles per hour. Find the course of the ship and its speed with respect to the ocean floor.

12. A 150-pound shell for a battery of artillery is dragged up a runway inclined 42° to the horizontal. Find the pressure of the shell against the runway and the force required to drag the shell.

13. A truck weighing 6875 pounds moves up a bridge inclined 7° 32' from the horizontal. Find the pressure of the truck against the bridge.

14. An automobile weighing 2600 pounds stands on a hill inclined 25° 36' from the horizontal. How large a force must be counteracted by the brakes of the automobile to prevent it from rolling downhill?

15. A guy wire 78 feet long runs from the top of a telegraph pole 56 feet high to the ground and pulls on the pole with a force of 290 pounds. (*a*) What is the horizontal pull of the wire on the top of the pole? (*b*) What vertical force does the wire exert as an addition to the pressure of the pole against the ground?

16. What force must be exerted to drag a 150-pound weight up a slope which inclines 25° from the horizontal?

17. Find the largest weight which a man can drag up a slope inclined 35° from the horizontal, if he is able to pull with a force of 125 pounds.

18. At what speed with respect to the water should a ship head south in order to sail in the direction with azimuth 168° 26', if the ship is in a current flowing east at the rate of 5 miles per hour?

★*Find the magnitude and direction of the resultant of the given forces acting simultaneously on an object.*

19. 50 lb. acting $N\ 21°\ 16'\ E$; 150 lb. acting $N\ 49°\ 28'\ W$.

20. 57.3 lb. acting $N\ 21°\ 10'\ E$; 158 lb. acting $N\ 49°\ 20'\ E$.

Trigonometric Functions of Numbers

116. Radian measure for angles

On page 137, to define 1° as an angular unit for measuring rotation, we considered a central angle in a circle. We shall define a new unit of angular measurement, called a *radian*, in a similar fashion.

DEFINITION I. *One* **radian** *is the measure of a positive angle for which, if its vertex is at the center of a circle, rotation of the initial side to the terminal side will sweep out on the circumference an arc whose length is the radius of the circle.*

Thus, a central angle of one radian in a circle *intercepts* on the circumference an arc whose length is the radius of the circle.

ILLUSTRATION 1. In Figure 87, the measure of angle BOC is one radian, and the length of the intercepted arc BC is r.

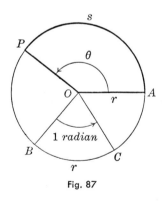

Fig. 87

Let K be the measure in radians of the angle generated by revolving OB of Figure 87 about O through a complete revolution, counterclockwise. We recall that the measures of central angles in a circle are proportional to the lengths of the arcs intercepted by the angles on the circumference. The angle K intercepts the whole circumference, of length $2\pi r$, and 1 radian intercepts BC, of length r. Hence,

$$\frac{K}{1} = \frac{2\pi r}{r}, \quad or \quad K = 2\pi. \tag{1}$$

That is, the measure of the complete (counterclockwise) angle about a point is 2π radians. Since this angle also has the measure 360°,

$$360° = (2\pi \text{ radians}), \, or \tag{2}$$

$$180° = (\pi \text{ radians}). \tag{3}$$

Notice that (2) and (3), and similar statements of equality below, are *not equations* in the usual sense of expressing the equality of *two numbers*. Thus, (2) is just a convenient abbreviation for "*an angle of* 360° *also has the measure* 2π *radians.*" On dividing both sides of (3) first by 180, and second by π, we obtain

$$1° = \left(\frac{\pi}{180} \text{ radians}\right) = .0174533 \text{ radian, } \textit{approximately;} \qquad (4)$$

$$(1 \text{ radian}) = \frac{180°}{\pi} = 57.2958°, \textit{approximately.} \qquad (5)$$

From (4) and (5), respectively, we arrive at the following rules:

$$\left\{ \begin{array}{l} \textit{To change degree measure to radian measure,} \\ \textit{multiply the number of degrees by } \boldsymbol{\pi/180.} \end{array} \right\} \qquad (6)$$

$$\left\{ \begin{array}{l} \textit{To change radian measure to degree measure,} \\ \textit{multiply the number of radians by } \boldsymbol{180/\pi.} \end{array} \right\} \qquad (7)$$

Instead of (6), frequently it is useful to recall (3), and notice that *any multiple of* 180° *is the same multiple of* π *radians.*

ILLUSTRATION 2. $\qquad 30° = \frac{1}{6}(180°) = (\frac{1}{6}\pi \textit{ radians});$

$$45° = \frac{1}{4}(180°) = (\tfrac{1}{4}\pi \textit{ radians}); \qquad 60° = (\tfrac{1}{3}\pi \textit{ radians});$$

$$90° = \tfrac{1}{2}(180°) = (\tfrac{1}{2}\pi \textit{ radians}) = (1.5708 \textit{ radians}).$$

From (7), $(3.2 \textit{ radians}) = 3.2 \dfrac{180°}{\pi} = \dfrac{(3.2)(180°)}{3.1416} = 183.35°, \textit{ by logarithms.}$

ILLUSTRATION 3. To change 143° 27′ to radians, first express 27′ as a decimal part of 1° and multiply by $\pi/180$ with the aid of logarithms. Thus,

$$27' = \tfrac{27}{60}(1°) = .45°;$$

$$143.45° = \left[\frac{(143.45)(\pi)}{180} \textit{ rad.}\right] = \left[\frac{(143.45)(3.1416)}{180} \textit{ rad.}\right] = [2.5037 \textit{ rad.}].$$

117. Relation between arc, angle, and radius

In a circle of radius r, in Figure 87 on page 211, let s represent the length of the arc intercepted on the circumference by a central angle of θ radians. Since 1 radian at the center intercepts an arc whose length is r, then θ radians intercept an arc whose length is $\theta \cdot r$. That is,

$$s = r\theta; \qquad (1)$$

$$\text{arc} = (\text{radius}) \times (\text{angle, in radians}). \qquad (2)$$

ILLUSTRATION 1. If $r = 25$ feet and $s = 75$ feet, then, from (1),

$$\theta = \frac{s}{r} = \frac{75}{25} = 3 \textit{ radians.}$$

EXAMPLE 1. Find the length of the arc intercepted by a central angle of 35° in a circle whose radius is 20 feet.

SOLUTION. 1. Let θ be the radian measure of $35°$:

$$\theta = 35 \cdot \frac{\pi}{180} = \frac{7\pi}{36} \; radian.$$

2. Since $r = 20$, $\quad s = r\theta = 20 \cdot \frac{7\pi}{36} = \frac{35\pi}{9},\quad or \quad s = 12.2 \text{ ft.}$

Note 1. Example 1 can also be solved by use of a simple proportion, without use of radian measure. Thus, $s : 2\pi r = 35° : 360°$.

118. Linear and angular speed

Consider an object P which is moving with uniform speed on the circumference of a circle with center O and radius r. Let v represent the length of arc traversed by P in one unit of time. Then v is the **linear speed** of P. In Figure 88, let ω be the measure (positive) of the angle through which the line OP turns about O in one unit of time. Then, we call ω the **angular speed** of P with respect to O. If ω is expressed in radian measure, from (1) of Section 117 we obtain

$$v = r\omega. \tag{1}$$

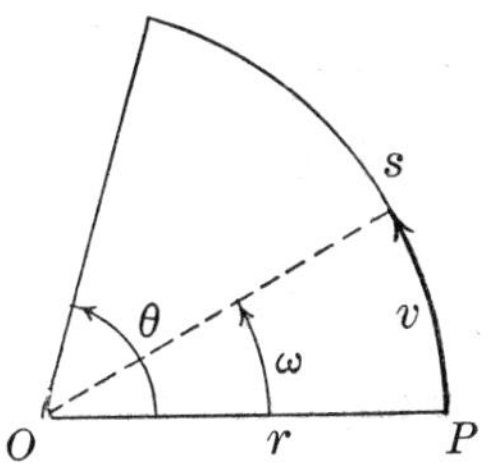

If, in t units of time, P moves over an arc of length s and OP revolves through an angle θ, then

$$s = vt; \qquad \theta = \omega t. \tag{2}$$

Any circular motion which we shall consider will be at uniform speed.

Fig. 88

EXAMPLE 1. A belt passes over the rim of a flywheel 30 inches in diameter. Find the speed of the belt if it drives the wheel at the rate of 5 revolutions per second.

SOLUTION. 1. The belt moves with the same speed as a point on the rim.
2. One revolution is 2π radians; hence, $\omega = (5 \times 2\pi) = (10\pi \; rad. \; per \; sec.)$.
3. From (1), $v = 15(10\pi) = 150\pi = 471.2$ in. per sec., the belt speed.

EXERCISE 71

Express the angle as a multiple of π radians.

1. $30°$. 2. $45°$. 3. $60°$. 4. $36°$. 5. $120°$.
6. $135°$. 7. $150°$. 8. $720°$. 9. $-90°$. 10. $-180°$.
11. $240°$. 12. $270°$. 13. $300°$. 14. $-315°$. 15. $450°$.

Given the radian measure of an angle, change to degree measure.

16. $\frac{\pi}{6}$. 17. $\frac{\pi}{3}$. 18. $\frac{3\pi}{4}$. 19. $\frac{\pi}{9}$. 20. $\frac{5\pi}{6}$.
21. $\frac{7\pi}{6}$. 22. $\frac{7\pi}{4}$. 23. $\frac{4\pi}{3}$. 24. $\frac{5\pi}{12}$. 25. $\frac{7\pi}{15}$.
26. 3π. 27. 2. 28. 4. 29. 2.5. 30. 3.6.

Construct the angle approximately to scale.

31. 3 rad.   **32.** 2 rad.   **33.** .1 rad.   **34.** 1.5 rad.

35. In a triangle, one angle is 36° and another is $\frac{2}{3}\pi$ radians. Find the third angle in radians.

36. Through how many radians does the hour hand of a clock revolve in 40 minutes?

37. Through how many radians does the minute hand of a clock revolve in 25 minutes?

Express in radians, using Table V in the computation.

38. 38° 21′.   **39.** 123° 50′.   **40.** 273° 45′.   **41.** 183° 18′.

Obtain each result in the following problems to three significant digits.

By use of $s = r\theta$, find whichever of (r, s, θ) is not given, where θ is the measure of an angle in radians, at the center of a circle of radius r, and s is the arc on the circumference intercepted by the angle θ. In any problem, α represents the degree measure corresponding to θ radians.

42. $r = 10$ ft.; $\theta = 2.3$.   **43.** $r = 450$ ft.; $\theta = 5.7$.

44. $\theta = \frac{7}{6}\pi$; $s = 125$ in.   **45.** $\theta = 6.8$; $s = 50.6$ in.

46. $\alpha = 120°$; $s = 375$ in.   **47.** $\alpha = 340°$; $r = 50$ ft.

48. $s = 175$ in.; $r = 4$ ft.   **49.** $s = 2500$ ft.; $r = .75$ mi.

50. On a circle, if an arc 30 feet long is intercepted by an angle of 2 radians at the center, find the radius of the circle.

51. In a circle 16 inches in diameter, how long an arc is intercepted on the circumference by an angle of 2.4 radians at the center?

52. A railroad curve, in the form of an arc of a circle, is 850 yards long. If the radius of the circle is 950 yards, find the angle in degrees through which a train turns in going around the curve.

53. In going around a circular curve which is 645 yards long, a railroad train turns through an angle of 57° 35′. Find the radius of the curve.

54. If a flywheel is 4 feet in diameter, find the speed of a belt which drives the wheel at 400 revolutions per minute.

55. If a flywheel is 3 feet in diameter and if a belt over the wheel is traveling at the rate of 3000 feet per minute, find the number of revolutions of the wheel per minute.

56. Find the radius of a flywheel if it is turned at 1250 revolutions per minute by a belt over the rim with a speed of 60 feet per second.

57. A flywheel, 48 inches in diameter, is driven by a belt moving over the rim with a speed of 3600 feet per minute. Find the angular speed of the wheel (*a*) in radians per minute; (*b*) in revolutions per minute.

58. Assume that the earth is a sphere with a radius of 4000 miles which revolves on its axis once in 24 hours. Disregarding the other motions of the earth, find the linear speed per second of a point on the equator.

119. Trigonometric functions of angles, with radian measure

Hereafter, when no unit is indicated in giving the measure of an angle, **we agree that the unit of measurement is a radian.** Frequently, then, we shall let the value of an angle in radians be used as a symbol for the angle. Thus, we may refer to *the angle x*, meaning an angle whose measure is x radians.

ILLUSTRATION 1. The "*cosine of π radians*" is denoted by cos π. Since (π *radians*) = 180°, cos π = -1. From Table VIII, sin 1.18 = .92461. From Table IV, 33° has the measure .576 radian; hence tan .576 = .649.

All of the trigonometric identities in Chapter 8, where θ, α, β, or some other letter represented an angle involved, now may be interpreted as identities where the symbol for the angle is understood to be its value in radian measure. Any statement of a property of the trigonometric functions involving remarks about a multiple of 90° implies a corresponding statement involving a multiple of $\frac{1}{2}\pi$ radians. In particular, if x represents an angle with measure x radians, the reduction formulas of page 160, in radian measure, are as follows:

$$[\text{any trig. function of } (x \pm 2\pi)] = (\text{same function of } x); \qquad (1)$$

$$\tan (x \pm \pi) = \tan x; \qquad \cot (x \pm \pi) = \cot x; \qquad (2)$$

$$[\text{any trig. function of } (\tfrac{1}{2}\pi - x)] = (\text{cofunction of } x); \qquad (3)$$

$$\sin (-x) = -\sin x; \quad \cos (-x) = \cos x; \quad \tan (-x) = -\tan x; \quad (4)$$

$$\sin (\pi - x) = \sin x; \qquad \cos (\pi - x) = -\cos x; \qquad (5)$$

$$\left[\text{any trig. func. of } \left(n \cdot \frac{\pi}{2} \pm x\right)\right] = \begin{cases} \pm (\text{same func. of } x), \ n \text{ even;} \\ \pm (\text{cofunc. of } x), \ n \text{ odd.} \end{cases} \quad (6)$$

ILLUSTRATION 2. By (1) each trigonometric function has the period 2π and, by (2), tan x and cot x have the smaller period π. Thus, by (1), sin $(x \pm 2\pi)$ = sin x.

EXAMPLE 1. Express sin $(\pi - \theta)$ and tan $(\frac{3}{2}\pi + \theta)$ in terms of functions of θ, by use of (6).

SOLUTION. 1. Since $\pi = 2(\frac{1}{2}\pi)$, from (6) for n *even* we obtain the following result, where we must still choose the proper sign:

$$\sin (\pi - \theta) = \pm \sin \theta. \qquad (7)$$

If θ is acute, then $(\pi - \theta)$ is an angle in quadrant II, where the sine is positive. Hence, to make the right-hand side positive in (7) we need the plus sign: sin $(\pi - \theta) = +\sin \theta$.

2. From (6) for n odd, tan $(\frac{3}{2}\pi + \theta) = \pm \cot \theta$. If θ is acute, $(\frac{3}{2}\pi + \theta)$ is an angle in quadrant IV where the tangent is negative. Hence, we obtain tan $(\frac{3}{2}\pi + \theta) = -\cot \theta$.

ILLUSTRATION 3. Since Table VIII extends only through an angle of 1.60 radians, for larger angles we must use reduction formulas or acute reference angles before referring to Table VIII. To obtain cos 3.59, we recall $\pi = 3.14$, and $3.59 - 3.14 = .45$:

$$\cos 3.59 = \cos (\pi + .45) = - \cos .45 = - .90045. \qquad \text{(Table VIII)}$$

Thus, we recognized .45 radian as the *reference angle* for 3.59 radians. Or, we used the *reduction formula* $\cos (\pi + x) = - \cos x$ with $x = .45$.

With the numbers x and y representing angles whose measures are x and y radians, respectively, the addition formulas for the sine and cosine on page 156 become

$$\sin (x + y) = \sin x \cos y + \cos x \sin y; \qquad (8)$$

$$\cos (x + y) = \cos x \cos y - \sin x \sin y; \qquad (9)$$

$$\sin (x - y) = \sin x \cos y - \cos x \sin y; \qquad (10)$$

$$\cos (x - y) = \cos x \cos y + \sin x \sin y. \qquad (11)$$

ILLUSTRATION 4. From (8), $\sin (\frac{3}{2}\pi + x) = \sin \frac{3}{2}\pi \cos x + \cos \frac{3}{2}\pi \sin x$, or

$$\sin (\tfrac{3}{2}\pi + x) = (- 1) \cos x + (0) \sin x = - \cos x.$$

In calculus, for convenience in various important classes of operations where trigonometric functions are met, it becomes imperative that any angle involved should be measured in *radians*. Hence, since this text is designed for students who are preparing for calculus, **we shall use radian measure for angles exclusively hereafter,** except where occasional use of degree measure clarifies the content, and except when we solve triangles.

EXERCISE 72

1. Without using a trigonometric table, make up a table showing the exact values of all trigonometric functions (which exist) for the angles $0, \frac{1}{6}\pi, \frac{1}{4}\pi, \frac{1}{3}\pi, \frac{1}{2}\pi, \frac{2}{3}\pi, \frac{3}{4}\pi, \frac{5}{6}\pi, \pi, \frac{7}{6}\pi, \frac{5}{4}\pi, \frac{4}{3}\pi, \frac{3}{2}\pi, \frac{5}{3}\pi, \frac{7}{4}\pi, \frac{11}{6}\pi$, and 2π.

By use of Table IV, *find the value of the angle in radian measure.*

2. 37°.   **3.** 77°.   **4.** 53°.   **5.** 98°.   **6.** 238°.   **7.** 329°.

HINT for Problem 5. $98° = 90° + 8°$. Add $\frac{1}{2}\pi$ or 1.571 to the table value for 8°.

Find the function value by use of Table VIII.

8. sin 1.35.   **9.** cos .84.   **10.** tan 1.02.   **11.** sin 1.47.

12. cot 4.29.   **13.** sin 2.64.   **14.** cos 5.23.   **15.** tan 3.79.

Apply the addition formulas (8)–(11) *above to obtain the reduction formula for the given function.*

16. $\sin (\pi + x)$.   **17.** $\cos (\pi - x)$.   **18.** $\sin (x - \frac{3}{2}\pi)$.

19. $\cos (x - \frac{3}{2}\pi)$.   **20.** $\sin (x - \frac{1}{2}\pi)$.   **21.** $\cos (x - \frac{1}{2}\pi)$.

22. $\sin (x + \frac{5}{2}\pi)$.   **23.** $\cos (x + \frac{5}{2}\pi)$.   **24.** $\sin (x - \frac{5}{2}\pi)$.

Express each function value in terms of the value of a trigonometric function of x, by use of (1)–(6) on page 215.

25. tan $(2\pi - x)$.	26. sin $(x - 2\pi)$.	27. cot $(x - \pi)$.
28. tan $(\frac{1}{2}\pi - x)$.	29. cos $(\frac{1}{2}\pi - x)$.	30. sec $(\frac{1}{2}\pi - x)$.
31. sec $(- x)$.	32. csc $(- x)$.	33. cot $(- x)$.
34. tan $(\pi + x)$.	35. sin $(\pi + x)$.	36. tan $(3\pi + x)$.
37. sin $(x - 4\pi)$.	38. cos $(x + 3\pi)$.	39. tan $(\frac{3}{2}\pi - x)$.
40. tan $(\frac{5}{2}\pi + x)$.	41. sec $(\frac{1}{2}\pi + x)$.	42. sin $(\frac{1}{2}\pi + x)$.
43. cos $(x - \frac{5}{2}\pi)$.	44. cot $(x - \frac{5}{2}\pi)$.	45. sin $(x - \frac{3}{2}\pi)$.

120. The standard trigonometric functions of numbers

On the basis of Definition I on page 140, we refer to sin x as the (*geometrical*) sine of *the angle x radians,* and "x" in sin x is a symbol for this *angle.* With an altered viewpoint, let us say that, *for every number x, a corresponding number* "sin x" *has been defined.* Thus, we have pairs of numbers, $(x, \sin x)$. *These pairs form a function,* to be called the **standard (analytic) sine function,** whose domain is the set, D, of all real numbers x, and whose general value sin x is *the sine of x radians.* Similarly, we have the other standard trigonometric functions cos x, tan x, cot x, sec x, and csc x, each having the domain * D.

Hereafter *in this text and in the whole of calculus,* except when otherwise specified, a *trigonometric function* means one of the *standard functions.* The *value* of any one of these for any number x in D is the value of the *same-named geometric function of the angle x radians.* Hence, any property or identity known for the geometric functions translates into a property for the standard functions. Whenever useful, we may alter our viewpoint about the meaning of the independent variable x and, for instance, reinterpret the symbol for the standard function sin x as the geometric sine of the angle x radians. However, in dealing with a standard function such as sin x, usually there will be no necessity for thinking of any angle x; only the *values* of sin x, *for all real numbers x,* will be of importance.

ILLUSTRATION 1. From (1) on page 215, the standard trigonometric functions are periodic with the period 2π; tan x and cot x have the smaller period π. Thus, sin $(x + 2\pi) = \sin x$; tan $(x + \pi) = \tan x$.

In connection with the standard trigonometric functions, we shall say that the independent variable x *lies on an interval in quadrant* I, II, III, or IV if *the angle x radians is in that quadrant.*

ILLUSTRATION 2. If x is on an interval in quadrant III, then tan $x > 0$ and sin $x < 0$. For instance, sin $\frac{5}{4}\pi < 0$.

* With the usual omissions when x radians is a quadrantal angle, in the case of tan x, cot x, sec x, and csc x.

Note 1. The standard trigonometric functions sometimes are called **trigonometric functions of numbers** because the domain of the functions consists of *real numbers, x,* and *not of angles* as on page 140. We introduced other trigonometric functions of numbers, based on degree measure, on page 164.*

In dealing with the values of the standard trigonometric functions at a particular value of the independent variable x, we define the **reference number** for x to be that number w such that w radians is the reference angle for x radians.

ILLUSTRATION 3. With $x = \frac{3}{4}\pi$, the reference number for x is $\frac{1}{4}\pi$. Thus, each trigonometric function of $\frac{3}{4}\pi$ is numerically equal to the corresponding function of $\frac{1}{4}\pi$.

121. Graphs of the standard trigonometric functions

In calculus and related fields, the graphs of the trigonometric functions usually are made subject to the following agreements, which we adopt: †

I. *To graph a trigonometric function means to graph one of the* **standard functions** *of Section* 120.

II. *A single unit is used for measuring all distances in the coordinate plane; in particular, then, the unit distance is the same on the two axes.*

EXAMPLE 1. Graph the function sin x on the range $0 \leq x \leq \pi$.

SOLUTION. We graph the equation $y = \sin x$. We use Table IV, with x interpreted as the measure of an angle in *radians.* On the interval $0 \leq x \leq \frac{1}{2}\pi = 1.57$, we take the convenient multiples of π, and just one other value (equivalent to 75°); then we obtain sin x from Table IV or from memory. By use of the identity sin $(\pi - x) = \sin x$, or from memory of convenient values, we find values of sin x for x on the interval $\frac{1}{2}\pi \leq x \leq \pi$. The decimal values of x for the multiples of π can be computed by use of $\pi = 3.142$, or can be read from Table IV. In the table below, γ is the degree measure of x radians. Points (x, y) from the table were the basis for Figure 89.

γ	0°	30°	45°	60°	75°	90°	105°	120°	135°	150°	180°
$x =$	0	$\frac{1}{6}\pi$	$\frac{1}{4}\pi$	$\frac{1}{3}\pi$	$\frac{5}{12}\pi$	$\frac{1}{2}\pi$	$\frac{7}{12}\pi$	$\frac{2}{3}\pi$	$\frac{3}{4}\pi$	$\frac{5}{6}\pi$	π
$x =$	0	.52	.79	1.05	1.31	1.57	1.83	2.09	2.36	2.62	3.14
$y = \sin x$	0	.50	.71	.87	.97	1.00	.97	.87	.71	.50	0

* In this text, we first introduced the trigonometric functions of *angles* (see Note 2, page 141). Then, in the present section we have made the transition to the trigonometric functions of *numbers.* This sequence of ideas can be reversed. That is, we could first introduce trigonometric functions of *numbers, without mentioning or thinking about associated angles,* and later make a transition to the familiar functions of *angles.* This attitude is adopted in Note 1 of the Appendix.
† The student must not infer that graphs based on degree measure are of no importance. However, they are ruled out frequently in calculus.

Comment 1. To graph $y = \sin x$ quickly, memory of $\sin \frac{1}{6}\pi = \sin \frac{5}{6}\pi = \frac{1}{2}$, $\sin 0 = \sin \pi = 0$, and $\sin \frac{1}{2}\pi = 1$, and recollection of the rounded appearance of the graph near $x = \frac{1}{2}\pi$ should give a near duplicate of Figure 89. Then, we recall the reduction formula

$$\sin (\pi + x) = - \sin x. \tag{1}$$

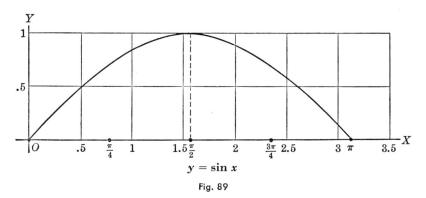

$y = \sin x$

Fig. 89

This result shows that the graph of $y = \sin x$ on the interval $\pi \leq x \leq 2\pi$ is obtainable by translating the curve of Figure 89 to the *right* for a distance of π units and then **reflecting** * *the curve in the x-axis.* Or the student might prefer to prepare a table of values for $y = \sin x$ by listing $\sin x$ for x having the values $0, \frac{1}{6}\pi, \frac{1}{2}\pi, \frac{5}{6}\pi, \pi, \frac{7}{6}\pi, \frac{3}{2}\pi, \frac{11}{6}\pi$, and 2π. Since the function $\sin x$ is periodic with the period 2π, or $\sin (x + 2\pi) = \sin x$, the graph of $y = \sin x$ consists of the wave for $0 \leq x \leq 2\pi$ repeated endlessly to the left and the right, as shown for $-2\pi \leq x \leq 2\pi$ in Figure 90.

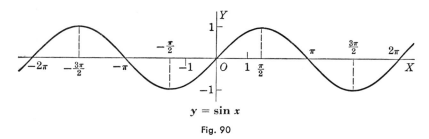

$y = \sin x$

Fig. 90

ILLUSTRATION 1. To graph the function $\cos x$, or the equation $y = \cos x$, recall the identity $\cos x = \sin (x + \frac{1}{2}\pi)$. Hence, for any value of x, $\cos x$ is equal to the value of the sine function at the point $(x + \frac{1}{2}\pi)$, which is $\frac{1}{2}\pi$ units to the *right.* That is, *if the graph of* $\sin x$ *is shifted* $\frac{1}{2}\pi$ *units to the left*, we obtain the graph of $\cos x$, as shown in Figure 91 on page 220. Or,

* The **reflection** of a curve *in the x-axis* is obtained on replacing each point (x, y) on the curve by the point $(x, - y)$, symmetrical to (x, y) with respect to the x-axis. The reflection can be thought of as if the given curve were *reflected downward in water* where the water level is at the x-axis.

the student may prefer to list the few values of cos x in the following table, as a basis for drawing the graph.

x	0	$\frac{1}{2}\pi$	π	$\frac{3}{2}\pi$	2π
$y = \cos x$	1	0	-1	0	1

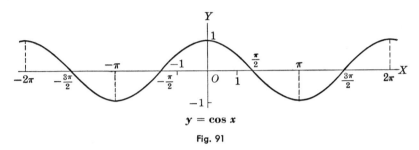

$$y = \cos x$$

Fig. 91

ILLUSTRATION 2. To graph the equation $y = \tan x$, we recall that tan x is infinite when x is $-\frac{1}{2}\pi$, $\frac{1}{2}\pi$, $\frac{3}{2}\pi$, etc., and tan $x = 0$ when $x = 0$, π, 2π, etc. Also, tan x is a *periodic* function with the *period* π. The following values of tan x, and its asymptotes $x = -\frac{1}{2}\pi$ and $x = \frac{1}{2}\pi$, were the basis for the typical piece of the graph in Figure 92. Similarly, we obtain one section of

x	$-\frac{1}{2}\pi$	$-\frac{1}{4}\pi$	0	$\frac{1}{4}\pi$	$\frac{1}{2}\pi$
$y = \tan x$	∞	-1	0	1	∞

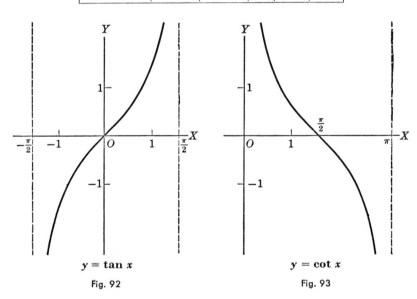

$$y = \tan x \qquad\qquad y = \cot x$$

Fig. 92   Fig. 93

the graph of the function cot x in Figure 93 from a brief table, periodicity of the function, and asymptotes. A graph of the function sec x would be produced by use of the following table of values, periodicity, and the asymptotes, which are the lines $x = -\frac{1}{2}\pi$ and $x = \frac{1}{2}\pi$. Similar remarks apply to csc x.

x	$-\frac{1}{2}\pi$	$-\frac{1}{3}\pi$	0	$\frac{1}{3}\pi$	$\frac{1}{2}\pi$
$y = \sec x$	∞	2	1	2	∞

The graphs of the trigonometric functions are useful in solving simple trigonometric equations.

ILLUSTRATION 3. To solve the equation $\sin x = 0$, recall Figure 90 on page 219. The values of x on the interval $-2\pi \leq x \leq 2\pi$ for which $\sin x = 0$, or the *solutions* of this equation on the specified interval, are the x-intercepts of the graph in Figure 90, or -2π, $-\pi$, 0, π, and 2π.

ILLUSTRATION 4. To solve $\cos x = -\frac{1}{2}\sqrt{3}$, for all values of x on the interval $-2\pi \leq x \leq 2\pi$, we recall that $\cos \frac{1}{6}\pi = \frac{1}{2}\sqrt{3}$, and $\cos x$ is *negative* if x is on an interval in quadrant II or quadrant III. Hence, with $\frac{1}{6}\pi$ as the *reference number* for x, the solutions of $\cos x = -\frac{1}{2}\sqrt{3}$ are $(\pi - \frac{1}{6}\pi)$ or $\frac{5}{6}\pi$, $\frac{7}{6}\pi$, $-\frac{5}{6}\pi$, and $-\frac{7}{6}\pi$. These are the values of x at the points where the horizontal line $y = -\frac{1}{2}\sqrt{3}$ would intersect the graph of $y = \cos x$ in Figure 91 on page 220. The student should sketch the line $y = -\frac{1}{2}\sqrt{3}$ lightly with a pencil in Figure 91 to check the preceding statements. The remarks preceding Illustration 1 on page 148 should be reviewed at this time.

EXAMPLE 1. Prove that 2π is the smallest period (understood to be *positive*) of the function $f(x) = \sin x$, and similarly for the functions $\cos x$, csc x, and $\sec x$.

SOLUTION. 1. If the function $f(x)$ is periodic with p as a period, then $f(x \pm p) = f(x)$ at all values of x.

2. Let p be any period of $f(x)$. Then,

$$f(x - p) = f(x), \quad or \quad \sin (x - p) = \sin x. \tag{2}$$

In (2), let $x = \frac{1}{2}\pi$. Then, we obtain

$$\sin (\tfrac{1}{2}\pi - p) = \sin \tfrac{1}{2}\pi = 1. \tag{3}$$

But, by the cofunction identities, $\sin (\frac{1}{2}\pi - p) = \cos p$. Hence, from (3), $\cos p = 1$. The smallest positive solution of this equation for p is $p = 2\pi$, and this fact proves our desired result.

EXERCISE 73

Draw graphs for the standard trigonometric functions as indicated. Use relatively few plotted points but obtain smooth graphs and draw any asymptotes which exist.

1. $y = \sin x$; $x = -2\pi$ to $x = 2\pi$. 2. $y = \cos x$; $x = -\frac{3}{2}\pi$ to $x = \frac{5}{2}\pi$.

3. $y = \tan x$; $x = -\frac{1}{2}\pi$ to $x = \frac{5}{2}\pi$. 4. $y = \cot x$; $x = -\pi$ to $x = 2\pi$.

5. $y = \sec x$; $x = -\frac{1}{2}\pi$ to $x = \frac{5}{2}\pi$. 6. $y = \csc x$; $x = -\pi$ to $x = 2\pi$.

Write the equation of each asymptote possessed by the graph of the equation on the interval $-\pi \leqq x \leqq 3\pi$.

7. $y = \tan x$.   8. $y = \cot x$.   9. $y = \sec x$.   10. $y = \csc x$.

Find all solutions of the equation on the interval $-2\pi \leqq x \leqq 2\pi$.

11. $\sin x = 0$.   12. $\cos x = 0$.   13. $\tan x = 0$.   14. $\cot x = 0$.

15. $\sec x = 0$.   16. $\csc x = 0$.   17. $\sin x = -1$.   18. $\cos x = -1$.

19. $\tan x = 1$.   20. $\cot x = -1$.   21. $\sec x = 1$.   22. $\csc x = -1$.

23. $\sin x = -\frac{1}{2}$.   24. $\cos x = \frac{1}{2}\sqrt{3}$.   25. $\tan x = -\sqrt{3}$.

26. $\csc x = 2$.   27. $\cos x = -\frac{1}{2}$.   28. $\sin x = -\frac{1}{2}\sqrt{3}$.

29. $\sin x = \frac{1}{2}\sqrt{2}$.   30. $\cos x = \frac{1}{2}\sqrt{2}$.   31. $\tan x = \frac{1}{3}\sqrt{3}$.

32. For what values of x on the interval $-\pi \leqq x \leqq 3\pi$ is the statement true? (*a*) $\tan x$ is infinite. (*b*) $\cot x$ is infinite. (*c*) $\sec x$ is infinite.

★33. Prove that π is the smallest period of the functions $\tan x$ and $\cot x$.

122. Graphs of composite trigonometric functions

An expression like $\sin x$ is a special case of the common functional notation, such as $f(x)$, with "sin" playing the role of f. Then, in $\sin x$, on replacing x by any function of x, such as $g(x)$, we obtain $\sin g(x)$ as a new function of x; $\sin g(x)$ is the standard sine function *of the function* $g(x)$. We may call $\sin g(x)$ a *composite* trigonometric function, but the name is not important at this point.

EXAMPLE 1.   Graph the function $\sin 3x$ from $x = 0$ to $x = 2\pi$.

SOLUTION.   1. We desire the graph of $y = \sin 3x$. If x increases from 0 to 2π, then $3x$ increases from 0 to 6π, and thus $\sin 3x$ passes through all values taken on by $\sin \alpha$ if α ranges from 0 to 6π. Thus, on the interval from $x = 0$ to $x = 2\pi$, the graph of $y = \sin 3x$ will consist of *three* sine waves, whereas the graph of $\sin x$ would consist of just *one* wave. The *amplitude* (maximum ordinate) of the wave for $\sin 3x$ is the same as for $\sin x$.

2. The x-intercepts of the graph are the values of x which satisfy the equation $\sin 3x = 0$; its solutions for $3x$ on the range 0 to 6π are

$$3x = 0, \pi, 2\pi, 3\pi, 4\pi, 5\pi, \text{ and } 6\pi; \text{ hence,}$$

$$x = 0, \tfrac{1}{3}\pi, \tfrac{2}{3}\pi, \pi, \tfrac{4}{3}\pi, \tfrac{5}{3}\pi, \text{ and } 2\pi. \tag{1}$$

The values in (1) are the x-intercepts of the graph in Figure 94 on page 223.

3. The *maximum* value of y occurs when $\sin 3x = 1$; the solutions of this equation for $3x$ on the range 0 to 6π are

$$3x = \tfrac{1}{2}\pi, (2\pi + \tfrac{1}{2}\pi) \text{ or } \tfrac{5}{2}\pi, \text{ and } \tfrac{9}{2}\pi; \text{ or } x = \tfrac{1}{6}\pi, \tfrac{5}{6}\pi, \text{ and } \tfrac{3}{2}\pi. \tag{2}$$

Similarly, $y = -1$ when $\sin 3x = -1$, or when $x = \tfrac{1}{2}\pi, \tfrac{7}{6}\pi$, and $\tfrac{11}{6}\pi$.

4. The points (x, y) corresponding to the values of x found in Steps 2 and 3 were the basis for the graph of $y = \sin 3x$ in Figure 94.

Comment. Since sin θ has the period 2π,

$$\sin 3x = \sin (3x + 2\pi) = \sin 3(x + \tfrac{2}{3}\pi).$$

Or sin $3x$ is a periodic function with the period $2\pi/3$. This corresponds to the fact that there are three complete waves in Figure 94. Similarly, if n is any positive number, the functions sin nx, cos nx, sec nx, and csc nx are periodic with the period $2\pi/n$. The functions tan nx and cot nx are periodic with the period π/n because tan θ and cot θ have the period π.

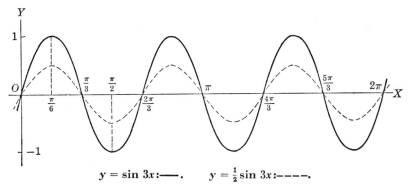

$y = \sin 3x$:———. $y = \tfrac{1}{2}\sin 3x$:—————.

Fig. 94

ILLUSTRATION 1. The graph of $y = \tfrac{1}{2}\sin 3x$ is the broken-line curve in Figure 94 where each wave has one half of the amplitude of the wave for $y = \sin 3x$.

123. Addition of ordinates

Let g, h, and F be functions with the same domain, D, and suppose that $F(x) = h(x) + g(x)$ for all numbers x in D. In some cases it may be desirable to graph F by first graphing h and g separately on one coordinate system. Then, to obtain the point on the graph of F, for any value of x, we may *add geometrically* (by use of dividers or a ruler) *the ordinates of the graphs of f and*

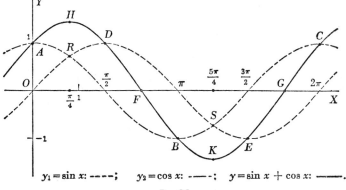

$y_1 = \sin x$: ————; $y_2 = \cos x$: —— · ——; $y = \sin x + \cos x$: ———.

Fig. 95

g *at this value of* x. When this is done, we say that the graph of F is obtained by *addition* (or *composition*) of ordinates.

EXAMPLE 1. Graph the function $(\sin x + \cos x)$.

SOLUTION. 1. We wish the graph of $y = \sin x + \cos x$. Let $y_1 = \sin x$ and $y_2 = \cos x$; the graphs of these equations are shown in Figure 95 on page 223.

2. At any value of x, we have $y = y_1 + y_2$. Hence, at any value of x, we may add the corresponding ordinates y_1 and y_2 to obtain y.

3. If $y_1 = 0$, then $y = y_2$; this gives A, B, C on the desired graph; D and E are obtained where $y_2 = 0$. If $y_1 = -y_2$, then $y = 0$; this gives F and G. Other ordinates were added. The graph is the full-line curve in Figure 95.

★124. General sine waves

EXAMPLE 1. Express the function $f(x) = \sin x + \cos x$ of Example 1 above in the form $f(x) = H \sin (x + \alpha)$ where $H > 0$ and $|\alpha| < \pi$.

SOLUTION. 1. We desire H and α so that

$$\sin x + \cos x = H \sin (x + \alpha) = (H \cos \alpha) \sin x + (H \sin \alpha) \cos x, \quad (1)$$

where we used the addition formula (8) of page 216. From (1),

$$H \cos \alpha = 1 \quad and \quad H \sin \alpha = 1. \quad (2)$$

From (2), $\qquad\qquad H^2 \sin^2 \alpha + H^2 \cos^2 \alpha = 2, \quad or \quad H^2 = 2.$

Thus, we take $H = \sqrt{2}$.

2. From (2), $\sin \alpha = \frac{1}{2}\sqrt{2}$ and $\cos \alpha = \frac{1}{2}\sqrt{2}$. Hence, we take $\alpha = \frac{1}{4}\pi$ and $H = \sqrt{2}$ to satisfy (1). Hence we obtain $f(x) = \sqrt{2} \sin (x + \frac{1}{4}\pi)$.

Comment. Also, we could have obtained the form $f(x) = \sqrt{2} \cos (x - \frac{1}{4}\pi)$.

From Example 1, we note that the graph of the function in Figure 95 on page 223 is the graph of $y = \sqrt{2} \sin (x + \frac{1}{4}\pi)$, which is a sine wave with amplitude (maximum ordinate) $\sqrt{2}$ and period 2π, with an x-intercept at $x = -\frac{1}{4}\pi$. The graph could be obtained by shifting (translating) the graph of $y = \sqrt{2} \sin x$ through the horizontal distance $\frac{1}{4}\pi$ to the *left*, because $\sin (x + \frac{1}{4}\pi)$ at any value of x is the value of $\sin \theta$ at the point $\theta = x + \frac{1}{4}\pi$, which is $\frac{1}{4}\pi$ units to the *right*.

Now, consider any function $f(x) = H \sin (ax + k)$, where we arrange to have $H > 0$ and $a > 0$. With $\alpha = k/a$, we obtain $f(x) = H \sin a(x + \alpha)$. We call the graph of $f(x)$ a *sine wave* with amplitude H. Since $a\alpha = k$, and

$$f\left(x + \frac{2\pi}{a}\right) = H \sin a\left(x + \frac{2\pi}{a} + \alpha\right) = H \sin [a(x + \alpha) + 2\pi], \; or$$

$$f\left(x + \frac{2\pi}{a}\right) = H \sin a(x + \alpha), \quad we \; have \quad f\left(x + \frac{2\pi}{a}\right) = f(x),$$

at all values of x. Hence, $f(x)$ has the *period* $2\pi/a$. The graph of the equation $y = f(x)$ can be thought of as the graph of the *simple sine wave* $H \sin ax$, shifted α units to the *left* in the xy-plane. Hence, we refer to k as the **phase constant** for $f(x)$. In Example 1, we found a phase constant $\frac{1}{4}\pi$. By the method of Example 1, any function of the form $f(x) = b \sin ax + c \cos ax$ with * $a > 0$ and $b^2 + c^2 \neq 0$ can be expressed in the form $f(x) = H \sin a(x + \alpha)$ or $H \cos a(x + \alpha)$, as we please, with $H > 0$ and $|a\alpha| \le \pi$. Hence, the graph of $f(x)$ is a sine wave.

EXERCISE 74

Find Period

Graph each equation on the interval $0 \le x \le 2\pi$.

1. $y = 3 \sin x$.   2. $y = -2 \cos x$.   3. $y = \sin 2x$.   4. $y = \cos 3x$.

5. $y = \cot 3x$.   6. $y = \tan 2x$.   7. $y = \sec 2x$.   8. $y = \csc 3x$.

9. $y = -3 \sin x$.   10. $y = -\sin 3x$.   11. $y = \sin \frac{1}{2}x$.

12. $y = \cos \frac{1}{3}x$.   13. $y = \cos x + \sin 2x$. *GRAPH*   14. $y = \sin x - \cos x$.

15. $y = \cos 2x + \sin x$.   16. $y = \sin 2x + \cos 2x$.   17. $y = \cot x + \cos x$.

18. $y = x + \sin x$.   19. $y = x + \cos x$.   20. $y = 2x - \sin x$.

★ *For the function f whose value for any real number x is given by the indicated expression, write $f(x)$ in the form $H \sin a(x + \alpha)$ and then draw the graph of the function f by use of the new form, without adding ordinates. Also, tell the period of f.*

21. $2 \sin x + 2\sqrt{3} \cos x$.   22. $5 \sin 2x - 5 \cos 2x$.

23. $3 \sin \frac{1}{2}x - 3\sqrt{3} \cos \frac{1}{2}x$.   24. $-4 \sin 3x - 4 \cos 3x$.

* If $a < 0$, we use $\sin(-\theta) = -\sin \theta$ and $\cos(-\theta) = \cos \theta$ to obtain a new form with $a > 0$.

Trigonometric Identities and Equations

125. Review of the fundamental identities

From page 146, we have the following fundamental identities, where the functions may be thought of either as the standard trigonometric functions of numbers or as the geometric trigonometric functions of angles.

$$\csc\theta = \frac{1}{\sin\theta}; \qquad \sec\theta = \frac{1}{\cos\theta}; \qquad \cot\theta = \frac{1}{\tan\theta}. \tag{1}$$

$$\tan\theta = \frac{\sin\theta}{\cos\theta}; \qquad \cot\theta = \frac{\cos\theta}{\sin\theta}. \tag{2}$$

$$\sin^2\theta + \cos^2\theta = 1; \quad \tan^2\theta + 1 = \sec^2\theta; \quad 1 + \cot^2\theta = \csc^2\theta. \tag{3}$$

From (1) and (2), all trigonometric functions of θ are expressible in terms of $\sin\theta$ and $\cos\theta$ without introducing radicals.

ILLUSTRATION 1. On using (1) and (2), we obtain *

$$\frac{\tan\theta + \cot\theta}{\tan\theta - \cot\theta} = \frac{\dfrac{\sin\theta}{\cos\theta} + \dfrac{\cos\theta}{\sin\theta}}{\dfrac{\sin\theta}{\cos\theta} - \dfrac{\cos\theta}{\sin\theta}} = \frac{\dfrac{\sin^2\theta + \cos^2\theta}{\sin\theta\cos\theta}}{\dfrac{\sin^2\theta - \cos^2\theta}{\sin\theta\cos\theta}}$$

$$= \frac{1}{\sin\theta\cos\theta} \cdot \frac{\sin\theta\cos\theta}{\sin^2\theta - \cos^2\theta} = \frac{1}{\sin^2\theta - \cos^2\theta}.$$

126. Proofs of identities

In applications of trigonometry in later mathematics, it is sometimes necessary to prove that one trigonometric expression is equal to another for all values involved for the independent variables. That is, it frequently is necessary to prove *trigonometric identities*. On account of the nature of the applications, Method I of the following Summary will be emphasized. Also, a method not in this Summary will be met later.

* It will be assumed hereafter (usually without remarks) that the independent variables are restricted to values for which *no denominator is zero*, and for which *all function values exist*, in any equation or identity which is considered.

226

SUMMARY. *Methods for use in proving identities.*

I. *Leave one side* **unaltered,** *and change the appearance of the other side to the same form as the first side.*

II. *Alter the appearance of* **both sides independently** *until they are exhibited in identical form.*

EXAMPLE 1. Prove the identity:

$$\tan \theta + 2 \cot \theta = \frac{\sin^2 \theta + 2 \cos^2 \theta}{\sin \theta \cos \theta}. \tag{1}$$

SOLUTION. We decide to leave the right-hand side unaltered. Since it involves only $\sin \theta$ and $\cos \theta$, we express the left-hand side in terms of $\sin \theta$ and $\cos \theta$, by use of (2) in Section 125.

$$\tan \theta + 2 \cot \theta = \frac{\sin \theta}{\cos \theta} + \frac{2 \cos \theta}{\sin \theta} = \frac{\sin^2 \theta + 2 \cos^2 \theta}{\sin \theta \cos \theta}.$$

Hence, (1) is true for all values of θ for which $\sin \theta \cos \theta \neq 0$. Notice that the solution used Method I of the Summary.

EXAMPLE 2. Prove the identity: $\quad \tan x + \cot x = \dfrac{\csc x}{\cos x}. \tag{2}$

SOLUTION *by Method* II. We shall operate on both sides of (2), to change them to the same form. In the details below, a double line is drawn separating the two sides and thus emphasizing that their equality is not being assumed while we are trying to prove it.

$$
\begin{array}{c|c}
\tan x + \cot x = \dfrac{\sin x}{\cos x} + \dfrac{\cos x}{\sin x} & \dfrac{\csc x}{\cos x} = \csc x \cdot \dfrac{1}{\cos x} \\[2ex]
= \dfrac{\sin^2 x + \cos^2 x}{\sin x \cos x} = \dfrac{1}{\sin x \cos x}. & = \dfrac{1}{\sin x} \cdot \dfrac{1}{\cos x} = \dfrac{1}{\sin x \cos x}.
\end{array}
$$

Hence, each side of (2) is equal to $1/(\sin x \cos x)$, and the two sides of (2) have the same value for every value of x where $\sin x \cos x \neq 0$.

EXAMPLE 3. Prove the identity: $\quad \dfrac{1 + \cos x}{\sin x} = \dfrac{\sin x}{1 - \cos x}. \tag{3}$

SOLUTION. 1. We wish to prove (3) in case $\sin x \neq 0$ and $1 - \cos x \neq 0$.

2. **IF** (3) **is true,** we may multiply both sides by $(\sin x)(1 - \cos x)$:

$$1 - \cos^2 x = \sin^2 x. \tag{4}$$

We know that (4) **IS TRUE** because $\sin^2 x + \cos^2 x = 1$.

3. To prove that (3) is true, we now start with (4). Since (4) is true, on dividing both sides of (4) by $(1 - \cos x)$ and by $\sin x$, which are not zero in either case, we know that *the resulting equation is true.* This division gives

$$\frac{1 + \cos x}{\sin x} = \frac{\sin x}{1 - \cos x}; \text{ hence, (3) is true.}$$

Comment. In the preceding solution, we illustrated a third method, as follows, for proving an identity.

1. Assume that the conjectured identity is true *and manipulate it until an obvious identity is obtained.*

2. Start anew with the obvious identity *and prove that, from it, the conjectured identity can be obtained by* **reversal of the previous steps.**

We emphasize that *Part 1 of the method by itself does not constitute a proof.*

Example 4. Prove the identity:

$$\sqrt{\frac{\sec x - \tan x}{\sec x + \tan x}} = \frac{1}{\sec x + \tan x}. \tag{5}$$

Solution. We leave the right-hand side unaltered, and rationalize the denominator on the left by multiplying both numerator and denominator by $\sec x + \tan x$ under the radical:

$$\sqrt{\frac{\sec x - \tan x}{\sec x + \tan x}} = \sqrt{\frac{\sec x - \tan x}{\sec x + \tan x} \cdot \frac{\sec x + \tan x}{\sec x + \tan x}} = \sqrt{\frac{\sec^2 x - \tan^2 x}{(\sec x + \tan x)^2}}$$

[using (3) on page 226] $= \dfrac{1}{\sec x + \tan x}.$

Comment. As a rule, in any identity involving a radical, as in Example 4, we shall assume that the values of the variables are restricted to a range where any factor removed from under the radical is *positive.** This will avoid the ambiguous sign $\pm$ on many occasions. Thus, in Example 4, we restrict x so that $\sec x + \tan x > 0$. If $\sec x + \tan x < 0$, a minus sign should precede the right-hand side in (5).

The following suggestions are useful in proving identities.

a. *If possible, avoid using formulas involving radicals.*

b. *Perhaps express all functions in terms of sines and cosines.*

c. *If one side of the identity involves just one function, perhaps express everything on the other side in terms of this function.*

EXERCISE 75

Prove the identity by use of the fundamental identities.

1. $\cos \alpha \csc \alpha = \cot \alpha.$

2. $\sin \theta \sec \theta = \tan \theta.$

3. $\cos^2 \theta - \sin^2 \theta = 2\cos^2 \theta - 1.$

4. $\cos^2 \theta - \sin^2 \theta = 1 - 2\sin^2 \theta.$

5. $\cot x + \tan x = \sec x \csc x.$

6. $\csc^2 x \tan^2 x = \tan^2 x + 1.$

7. $(\sin \theta + \cos \theta)^2 = 1 + 2\sin \theta \cos \theta.$

8. $(\cot x + 1)^2 = \csc^2 x + 2 \cot x.$

9. $\tan \theta = \dfrac{\sec \theta}{\csc \theta}.$

10. $\sin \theta = \dfrac{\cos \theta}{\cot \theta}.$

11. $\dfrac{1 - \sin^2 x}{\sin x} = \dfrac{\cos x}{\tan x}.$

* If $H > 0$, recall that $\sqrt{H}$ represents the *positive* square root of H. If $a > 0$, then $\sqrt{a^2} = a$. If $a < 0$, then $\sqrt{a^2} = -a$.

12. $\dfrac{1 - \cos^2 \beta}{\cos \beta} = \sin \beta \tan \beta.$

13. $\dfrac{\cos^2 \theta}{1 - \sin \theta} = 1 + \sin \theta.$

14. $\dfrac{\tan^2 \beta}{\sec^2 \beta} + \dfrac{\cot^2 \beta}{\csc^2 \beta} = 1.$

15. $\dfrac{1 - \tan^2 x}{1 + \tan^2 x} = 1 - 2 \sin^2 x.$

16. $\dfrac{\tan^2 \theta + 1}{\cot^2 \theta + 1} = \tan^2 \theta.$

17. $\dfrac{1 + \csc x}{\sec x} = \cos x + \cot x.$

18. $\dfrac{\tan \theta - 1}{\tan \theta + 1} = \dfrac{1 - \cot \theta}{1 + \cot \theta}.$

19. $\dfrac{\sin y - \cos y}{\sin y + \cos y} = \dfrac{\tan y - 1}{\tan y + 1}.$

20. $\dfrac{\sin x - \cos y}{\sin x + \cos y} = \dfrac{\sec y - \csc x}{\sec y + \csc x}.$

21. $\dfrac{\sec x}{\cot x + \tan x} = \sin x.$

22. $\sec x + \tan x = \dfrac{\sin^2 x + \sin x + \cos^2 x}{\cos x}.$

23. $\dfrac{\tan x - \cos x \cot x}{\csc x} = \dfrac{\sin x}{\cot x} - \dfrac{\cos x}{\sec x}.$

24. $\cot x - \tan x = 2 \cos x \csc x - \sec x \csc x.$

25. $\dfrac{\tan x - \tan y}{1 + \tan x \tan y} = \dfrac{\cot y - \cot x}{\cot x \cot y + 1}.$

26. $\dfrac{\sec^2 x}{\sec^2 x - 1} = \csc^2 x.$

27. $\dfrac{\sin x - \cos x}{\tan x \csc x - \sec x \cot x} = \sin x \cos x.$

28. $\dfrac{\sec^2 x + 2 \tan x}{1 + \tan x} = 1 + \tan x.$

29. $1 + \sin x = \dfrac{\cos x}{\sec x - \tan x}.$

30. $(\csc x + \sec x)^2 = \dfrac{\sec^2 x + 2 \tan x}{\sin^2 x}.$

31. $\dfrac{1}{\csc x - \cot x} - \dfrac{1}{\csc x + \cot x} = \dfrac{2}{\tan x}.$

32. $\cos^4 x - \sin^4 x = 1 - 2 \sin^2 x.$

33. $\sec^4 x - \tan^4 x = \dfrac{1 + \sin^2 x}{\cos^2 x}.$

34. $\dfrac{\cos x \cos y - \sin x \sin y}{\cos x \sin y + \sin x \cos y} = \dfrac{\cot x \cot y - 1}{\cot x + \cot y}.$

35. $\dfrac{\sin x \cos y + \cos x \sin y}{\cos x \cos y - \sin x \sin y} = \dfrac{\tan x + \tan y}{1 - \tan x \tan y}.$

Prove the identity without altering the right-hand side.

36. $\dfrac{1 + \sin x}{\cos x} = \dfrac{\cos x}{1 - \sin x}.$

37. $\sqrt{\dfrac{1 - \sin x}{1 + \sin x}} = \sec x - \tan x.$

38. $\dfrac{1}{\sec x + \tan x} = \dfrac{1 - \sin x}{\cos x}.$

39. $\sqrt{\dfrac{\csc x - \cot x}{\csc x + \cot x}} = \dfrac{1 - \cos x}{\sin x}.$

40. $\sqrt{\dfrac{\sec x - 1}{\sec x + 1}} = \dfrac{\sin x}{1 + \cos x}.$

41. $\sqrt{\dfrac{\sec x - \tan x}{\sec x + \tan x}} = \dfrac{\cos x}{1 + \sin x}.$

127. Elementary trigonometric equations in one unknown

The most simple type of trigonometric equation is one which is linear in the value of one trigonometric function of one number θ, and thus gives this function value immediately. Then, there are usually two corresponding values of θ on the interval $0 \leq \theta < 2\pi$, as we observed geometrically (with θ interpreted as an angle) in Illustration 1 on page 148. On account of the periodicity of the trigonometric functions, usually a trigonometric equation will be found to possess infinitely many solutions, with unbounded absolute values. In this book, unless otherwise stated, *to solve* a trigonometric equation in θ will mean to obtain only those solutions on the interval $0 \leq \theta < 2\pi$ or, if θ is interpreted as an angle in degree measure, on the interval $0° \leq \theta < 360°$.

EXAMPLE 1. Solve: $2 \cos \theta + 1 = 0$.

SOLUTION. 1. We find $2 \cos \theta = -1$ or $\cos \theta = -\frac{1}{2}$.

2. Let α be on the interval $0 \leq \alpha \leq \frac{1}{2}\pi$, with $\cos \alpha = \frac{1}{2}$. Then, $\alpha = \frac{1}{3}\pi$. Hence, α is the reference number for θ, and θ is on an interval in quadrant II or quadrant III, where the cosine function is negative. Thus, $\theta = \pi - \frac{1}{3}\pi$ or $\theta = \pi + \frac{1}{3}\pi$, or the solutions are $\frac{2}{3}\pi$ and $\frac{4}{3}\pi$.

Comment. Since $\cos \theta$ is periodic with the period 2π, the set of all solutions of $2 \cos \theta + 1 = 0$ consists of all numbers θ of the form

$$\theta = \tfrac{2}{3}\pi + 2n\pi \quad or \quad \theta = \tfrac{4}{3}\pi + 2n\pi,$$

where n takes on all integral values, positive, negative, or zero.

In Example 1, we illustrated the following method, which was employed earlier in Illustration 4 on page 221.

SUMMARY. *To find θ on the interval $0 \leq \theta < 2\pi$ when the value of one trigonometric function, T, is known at the point θ; or, with $T(\theta) = b$, to find θ when b is known.*

1. From a trigonometric table or from memory of the trigonometric functions of $0, \frac{1}{6}\pi, \frac{1}{4}\pi, \frac{1}{3}\pi, and \frac{1}{2}\pi, find α on the range $0 \leq \alpha \leq \frac{1}{2}\pi$ so that $T(\alpha) = |b|$.

2. From knowledge of the signs of the trigonometric functions for the various quadrant intervals, locate the numbers θ on the interval $0 \leq \theta < 2\pi$ having α as the corresponding reference number.

EXAMPLE 2. Find all angles θ, in degree measure, if $\sin \theta = -.9872$.

SOLUTION. 1. Let α be the acute reference angle for θ. Then, $\sin \alpha = .9872$. From Table VII, $\alpha = 80° 50'$.

2. The sine function is negative in quadrants III and IV. Hence, the solutions for θ are $\theta = 180° + 80° 50'$ and $\theta = 360° - 80° 50'$, which the student should verify from a figure. Thus, the values of θ are found to be $260° 50'$ and $279° 10'$.

128. Solution of trigonometric equations by factoring

A trigonometric equation in one unknown number x, which is in the *quadratic form* in the value of one trigonometric function of x, can be solved by use of methods met with quadratic equations in algebra. In particular, solution by factoring may apply.

EXAMPLE 1. Solve: $2 \sin^2 x - 1 = 0$.

SOLUTION.   1. $2 \sin^2 x = 1$; $\sin^2 x = \frac{1}{2}$.   Hence,

$$\sin x = \pm \sqrt{\tfrac{1}{2}}; \quad or \quad \sin x = \tfrac{1}{2}\sqrt{2} \quad or \quad \sin x = -\tfrac{1}{2}\sqrt{2}.$$

2. From $\sin x = \frac{1}{2}\sqrt{2}$, the solutions are $x = \frac{1}{4}\pi$ and $x = \frac{3}{4}\pi$. The solutions of $\sin x = -\frac{1}{2}\sqrt{2}$ are $x = \frac{5}{4}\pi$ and $x = \frac{7}{4}\pi$. Thus, the given equation has the four solutions $\frac{1}{4}\pi$, $\frac{3}{4}\pi$, $\frac{5}{4}\pi$, and $\frac{7}{4}\pi$.

EXAMPLE 2. Solve: $2 \sin^2 x - \sin x - 1 = 0$.

SOLUTION.   1. We say that this equation is in the quadratic form in $\sin x$ because, if we should let $v = \sin x$ (which is unnecessary) the equation would become $2v^2 - v - 1 = 0$. To solve the given equation we first factor:

$$(2 \sin x + 1)(\sin x - 1) = 0. \tag{1}$$

2. The equation is satisfied if:

$2 \sin x + 1 = 0$;   *then* $\sin x = -\frac{1}{2}$,   *and* $x = \frac{7}{6}\pi$ *or* $x = \frac{11}{6}\pi$.

$\sin x - 1 = 0$;   *then* $\sin x = 1$,   *and* $x = \frac{1}{2}\pi$.

To solve an equation by use of factoring, recall that the equation must first be written with *one member zero*.

EXAMPLE 3. Solve: $\sin x \cos x = \cos x$.   (2)

SOLUTION.   1. Subtract $\cos x$ from both sides; then factor:

$$\sin x \cos x - \cos x = 0; \quad \cos x(\sin x - 1) = 0.$$

2. If $\cos x = 0$, then $x = \frac{1}{2}\pi$ or $\frac{3}{2}\pi$. If $\sin x - 1 = 0$, then $x = \frac{1}{2}\pi$. Thus, (2) has the solutions $\frac{1}{2}\pi$ and $\frac{3}{2}\pi$.

INCORRECT SOLUTION.   Divide both sides by $\cos x$: $\sin x = 1$; $x = \frac{1}{2}\pi$.

Comment. If both sides of an equation are divided by an expression **involving the unknowns, remember that solutions may be lost.** Thus, the division by $\cos x$ caused the loss of the solution $\frac{3}{2}\pi$ for which $\cos x = 0$.

EXERCISE 76

Find all numbers x on the interval $0 \leq x < 2\pi$ which satisfy the equation, or which correspond to the given statement about an infinite limit. In a few problems, also write expressions for all solutions of the equation.

1. $\tan x = 1$.   **2.** $\cos x = \frac{1}{2}$.   **3.** $\sec x = -1$.   **4.** $\cos x = 0$.

5. $\sin x = \frac{1}{2}\sqrt{2}$.   **6.** $\sec x = \frac{1}{3}$.   **7.** $\sin x = 2$.   **8.** $\cot x = -1$.

9. $\tan x$ is *infinite*.   10. $\sec x$ is *infinite*.   11. $\csc x$ is *infinite*.

12. $2 \sin x - 1 = 0$.   13. $2 \cos x + \sqrt{2} = 0$.   14. $\tan x - \sqrt{3} = 0$.

15. $3 \cot x + \sqrt{3} = 0$.   16. $\cos x + 2 = 0$.   17. $2 \sin x + \sqrt{3} = 0$.

18. $\sin^2 x = 1$.   19. $\tan^2 x = 1$.   20. $2 \cos^2 x - 1 = 0$.

21. $4 \sin^2 x - 3 = 0$.   22. $\sec^2 x = 2$.   23. $4 \cos^2 x - 3 = 0$.

24. $3 \tan^2 x - 1 = 0$.   25. $(\sin x + 1)(2 \sin x - 1) = 0$.

26. $\cos x(2 \cos x - 1) = 0$.   27. $(\tan x - \sqrt{3})(\tan x + 1) = 0$.

28. $2 \cos^2 x - \cos x - 1 = 0$.   29. $\sin^2 x - 2 \sin x + 1 = 0$.

30. $\csc^2 x - 4 \csc x + 4 = 0$.   31. $2 \cos^2 x + 3 \cos x + 1 = 0$.

32. $4 \cos^2 x - 1 = 0$.   33. $\sin^2 x = \sin x$.   34. $2 \cos^2 x = - \cos x$.

35. $\sec^2 x - 3 \sec x + 2 = 0$.   36. $\csc^2 x - \csc x - 2 = 0$.

37. $2 \sin^2 x + \sqrt{2} \sin x = 0$.   38. $3 \tan^2 x - \sqrt{3} \tan x = 0$.

39. $\sin x \sec^2 x - 2 \sin x = 0$.   40. $\cos x \cot^2 x - 3 \cos x = 0$.

Find all angles in degree measure on the range $0° \leqq \theta < 360°$ *which satisfy the equation. Use Table VII.*

41. $\cos \theta = .9224$.   42. $\sin \theta = .4318$.   43. $\tan \theta = 1.621$.

44. $\tan \theta = 4.449$.   45. $\cot \theta = - 7.770$.   46. $\cos \theta = - .8225$.

★*Solve by factoring, for* x *on the interval* $0 \leqq x < 2\pi$.

47. $2 \sin^4 x - 3 \sin^2 x + 1 = 0$.   48. $3 \tan^3 x - \tan x = 0$.

49. $3 \cot^4 x + 2 \cot^2 x - 1 = 0$.   50. $\sin^2 x - 8 \sin x + 15 = 0$.

129. Trigonometric equations solved with the aid of identities

In solving a trigonometric equation, we aim to find one or more equations, each involving the value of just one trigonometric function of one unknown number, which are *equivalent* to the given equation. To accomplish this aim, it may be useful to modify given expressions by use of known identities. The following actions should be thought of as possibilities.

I. *Express the value of each trigonometric function of the unknown,* x, *in terms of one function of* x.

II. *Express the value of each trigonometric function of* x *in terms of the sine and cosine.*

EXAMPLE 1. Solve: $\sin x - \cos x = 0$.   (1)

SOLUTION. 1. If $\cos x \neq 0$, then (1) is equivalent to the new equation obtained on dividing both sides of (1) by $\cos x$, which gives

$$\frac{\sin x}{\cos x} - 1 = 0, \quad or \quad \tan x = 1. \tag{2}$$

We see that $x = \frac{1}{4}\pi$ and $x = \frac{5}{4}\pi$ are solutions of (2).

2. Notice that $\cos \frac{1}{4}\pi \neq 0$ and $\cos \frac{5}{4}\pi \neq 0$; hence (2) is equivalent to (1) at the values found for x. Thus, (1) has the solutions $\frac{1}{4}\pi$ and $\frac{5}{4}\pi$.

EXAMPLE 2. Solve: $\tan^2 x + 3 \sec x + 3 = 0$.

SOLUTION. 1. Use $\tan^2 x = \sec^2 x - 1$: $\sec^2 x + 3 \sec x + 2 = 0$.

2. Factor: $(\sec x + 2)(\sec x + 1) = 0$.

3. If $\sec x + 2 = 0$, then $\sec x = -2$; $x = \frac{2}{3}\pi$ or $x = \frac{4}{3}\pi$.

4. If $\sec x + 1 = 0$, then $\sec x = -1$; $x = \pi$.

5. The solutions are $\frac{2}{3}\pi$, π, and $\frac{4}{3}\pi$.

130. Extraneous solutions

In solving an equation, we sometimes employ one or both of the following operations, as discussed on pages 38 and 95.

I. *Square both sides, or raise both sides to any specified power.*

II. *Multiply both sides by an expression involving the unknown.*

We recall that (I) and (II) may lead to equations not equivalent to the given equation. Or, in other words, (I) and (II) may introduce *extraneous roots.* Hence, whenever (I) or (II) is used in the process of solution, it is essential to test all values obtained for the unknown, to reject extraneous roots, if any.

EXAMPLE 1. Solve: $\cos x + 1 = \sin x$.   (1)

SOLUTION. 1. From $\sin^2 x = 1 - \cos^2 x$, $\sin x = \pm \sqrt{1 - \cos^2 x}$. (2)

Hence, with no knowledge of the sign, $\pm$, which applies, we write

$$\cos x + 1 = \pm \sqrt{1 - \cos^2 x}.$$

2. Square both sides: $(1 + \cos x)^2 = 1 - \cos^2 x$;

$$1 + 2 \cos x + \cos^2 x = 1 - \cos^2 x; \quad 2 \cos x + 2 \cos^2 x = 0;$$

$$2 \cos x(1 + \cos x) = 0. \tag{3}$$

From (3), $\cos x = 0$ *or* $\cos x = -1$.

Hence, (3) has the solutions $x = \frac{1}{2}\pi$, $x = \frac{3}{2}\pi$, and $x = \pi$. **If (1) has any solutions, they are found among these values of x.**

3. **Test of values.** Substitute $x = \frac{3}{2}\pi$ in (1):

Does $\cos \frac{3}{2}\pi + 1 = \sin \frac{3}{2}\pi$? *Or does* $0 + 1 = -1$? **NO.**

Hence, $x = \frac{3}{2}\pi$ is not a solution of (1). Similarly, we find that $x = \frac{1}{2}\pi$ and $x = \pi$ satisfy (1), and thus are the desired solutions.

EXAMPLE 2. Solve: $\sec x - 2 \cos x - \tan x = 0$.   (4)

SOLUTION. 1. Express each function value in terms of $\sin x$ and $\cos x$:

$$\frac{1}{\cos x} - 2 \cos x - \frac{\sin x}{\cos x} = 0. \tag{5}$$

2. If $\cos x \neq 0$, then (5) is equivalent to the equation obtained on multiplying both sides by $\cos x$, which gives

$$1 - 2 \cos^2 x - \sin x = 0. \tag{6}$$

Use $\cos^2 x = 1 - \sin^2 x$ in (6):

$$1 - 2(1 - \sin^2 x) - \sin x = 0, \; or$$

$$2 \sin^2 x - \sin x - 1 = 0; \; or$$

$$(2 \sin x + 1)(\sin x - 1) = 0. \tag{7}$$

3. From (7), $\sin x = 1$ or $\sin x = -\frac{1}{2}$, which gives the solutions $x = \frac{1}{2}\pi$, $x = \frac{7}{6}\pi$, and $x = \frac{11}{6}\pi$.

4. **Test of values.** If $x = \frac{1}{2}\pi$, then $\cos x = 0$ and hence (6) is not equivalent to (5) or (4). In fact, (4) has no meaning when $x = \frac{1}{2}\pi$, because then $\tan x$ and $\sec x$ are infinite. Hence, we reject $\frac{1}{2}\pi$ as a solution of (4). At $x = \frac{7}{6}\pi$ and $x = \frac{11}{6}\pi$, we have $\cos x \neq 0$ so that (6) or (7) is equivalent to (5); since these values satisfy (7), they also satisfy (5), as could be verified * by substitution. Hence, the only solutions of (4) are $x = \frac{7}{6}\pi$ and $x = \frac{11}{6}\pi$.

EXERCISE 77

Find all solutions of the equation on the interval $0 \leq x < 2\pi$.

1. $2 \cos^2 x + \sin x - 1 = 0.$

2. $3 + 3 \cos x = 2 \sin^2 x.$

3. $\cos^2 x + \sin x + 1 = 0.$

4. $3 \sin^2 x - \cos^2 x - 1 = 0.$

5. $2 \sin^2 x - 2 \cos^2 x = 3.$

6. $\sqrt{3} \cot x + 1 = \csc^2 x.$

7. $\sec^2 x - 1 = \tan x.$

8. $2 \sec x + 3 = 2 \cos x.$

9. $3 \csc x + 2 = \sin x.$

10. $\csc^2 x - \cot x - 1 = 0.$

11. $\tan^2 x + \sec^2 x = 7.$

12. $\cot^2 x + \csc^2 x = 3.$

13. $\tan x = 3 \cot x.$

14. $\cos x = \sin x.$

15. $3 \sin x = \sqrt{3} \cos x.$

16. $3 \tan x - \cot x = 0.$

17. $\tan^2 x - \sec x = 1.$

18. $3 \cos x = -\sqrt{3} \sin x.$

19. $\cot^2 x + 3 \csc x + 3 = 0.$

20. $\csc x - 2 \sin x = \cot x.$

21. $\sec x = \cos x - \tan x.$

22. $3 \sec x + 3 \tan x = 2 \cos x.$

23. $\csc x + \cot x = 2 \sin x.$

24. $\csc x = \sin x - \cot x.$

25. $\sin x + 1 = \cos x.$

26. $\sin x = 1 + \cos x.$

27. $\cos x = 1 - \sin x.$

28. $\cot x + 1 = \csc x.$

29. $\tan x = \sec x + 1.$

30. $\sec x + \tan x = 1.$

31. $\sin^2 x \sec x + 2 \sec x - \cos x = 3 \tan x.$

32. $3 \cot x - \cos^2 x \csc x - 2 \csc x + \sin x = 0.$

33. $9 \csc^2 x = 4 \tan^2 x.$

34. $2 \cot^2 x = \sec^2 x.$

35. $\sec^2 x - 1 = \cot^2 x.$

36. $\sec^2 x + 3 \cot^2 x = 5.$

37. $3 \csc^2 x - \tan^2 x = 1.$

Find all angles θ in degree measure which satisfy the equation.

38. $\tan^2 \theta + \sec^2 \theta = 9.$

39. $\cot^2 \theta + \csc^2 \theta = 19.$

40. $\sec \theta + 3 = \tan \theta.$

41. $\cot \theta = \csc \theta + 2.$

* The verification is *not necessary* because (7) is equivalent to (5) at $\frac{7}{6}\pi$ and $\frac{11}{6}\pi$.

131. Addition formulas for the analytic sine, cosine, and tangent

In the remainder of this chapter, we shall number consecutively with Roman numerals those identities to which we shall refer frequently. The following addition formulas (I) and (III), and their special cases (II) and (IV), respectively, were proved on page 156 for the sine and cosine when the domain of these functions was thought of as all angles. We now interpret x and y in (I)–(IV) as variables whose range is all *real numbers*, and the identities are available for the analytic trigonometric functions of numbers as introduced on page 217. However, whenever convenient, we may return to the interpretation of (I)–(IV) as identities for the geometric trigonometric functions of angles, with x and y as symbols for angles whose measures are x and y in terms of any angular unit.

$$\sin (x + y) = \sin x \cos y + \cos x \sin y. \tag{I}$$

$$\sin (x - y) = \sin x \cos y - \cos x \sin y. \tag{II}$$

$$\cos (x + y) = \cos x \cos y - \sin x \sin y. \tag{III}$$

$$\cos (x - y) = \cos x \cos y + \sin x \sin y. \tag{IV}$$

ILLUSTRATION 1. In (II), if $y = \frac{3}{2}\pi$, we obtain the following reduction formula, because $\sin \frac{3}{2}\pi = -1$ and $\cos \frac{3}{2}\pi = 0$.

$$\sin (x - \tfrac{3}{2}\pi) = -\cos x \sin \tfrac{3}{2}\pi = \cos x.$$

By use of (I) and (III), we shall prove the addition formula (V) for the tangent function, and then obtain the special case (VI), of (V), by applying (4) of page 215.

$$\tan (x + y) = \frac{\tan x + \tan y}{1 - \tan x \tan y}. \tag{V}$$

$$\tan (x - y) = \frac{\tan x - \tan y}{1 + \tan x \tan y}. \tag{VI}$$

Proof of (V). 1. From (I) and (III), when $\cos (x + y) \neq 0$,

$$\tan (x + y) = \frac{\sin (x + y)}{\cos (x + y)} = \frac{\sin x \cos y + \cos x \sin y}{\cos x \cos y - \sin x \sin y}. \tag{1}$$

2. In (1), divide numerator and denominator on the right by $\cos x \cos y$, with the assumption that $\cos x \neq 0$ and $\cos y \neq 0$:

$$\tan (x + y) = \frac{\dfrac{\sin x \cos y}{\cos x \cos y} + \dfrac{\cos x \sin y}{\cos x \cos y}}{\dfrac{\cos x \cos y}{\cos x \cos y} - \dfrac{\sin x \sin y}{\cos x \cos y}} = \frac{\dfrac{\sin x}{\cos x} + \dfrac{\sin y}{\cos y}}{1 - \dfrac{\sin x}{\cos x} \cdot \dfrac{\sin y}{\cos y}},$$

which is identical with the fraction at the right in (V). Hence, (V) is true at all values of x and y for which the two sides of (V) have meaning.

Proof of (VI). In (V), replace y by $-y$, and recall from page 215 that $\tan (-\theta) = \tan \theta$. Then, (V) becomes (VI).

Example 1. Find tan 75° by use of tan 45° and tan 30°.

Solution. In (V), we interpret x and y as angles, and use x as 45° and y as 30°. Then,

$$\tan 75° = \tan (45° + 30°)$$

$$= \frac{\tan 45° + \tan 30°}{1 - \tan 45° \tan 30°};$$

$$\tan 75° = \frac{1 + \frac{1}{3}\sqrt{3}}{1 - \frac{1}{3}\sqrt{3}} = \frac{3 + \sqrt{3}}{3 - \sqrt{3}}, \tag{2}$$

where we multiplied both numerator and denominator by 3. In (2), on the right we multiply numerator and denominator by $(3 + \sqrt{3})$ to rationalize the denominator, and obtain

$$\tan 75° = \frac{(3 + \sqrt{3})^2}{9 - 3} = 2 + \sqrt{3}.$$

EXERCISE 78

By use of (I)–(VI), find the function values for the specified number by expressing it as a sum or difference of the suggested numbers.

1. Find $\cos \frac{3}{4}\pi$ and $\sin \frac{3}{4}\pi$ by using function values at $\frac{1}{2}\pi$ and $\frac{1}{4}\pi$.
2. Find $\sin \frac{5}{4}\pi$ and $\tan \frac{5}{4}\pi$ by using function values at π and $\frac{1}{4}\pi$.
3. Find $\tan \frac{7}{6}\pi$ and $\cos \frac{7}{6}\pi$ by using function values at π and $\frac{1}{6}\pi$.
4. Find $\cos \frac{11}{6}\pi$ by using function values at $\frac{3}{2}\pi$ and $\frac{1}{3}\pi$.
5. Find $\cos \frac{7}{4}\pi$ and $\tan \frac{7}{4}\pi$ by using function values at 2π and $\frac{1}{4}\pi$.
6. Find $\cos \frac{5}{6}\pi$ and $\tan \frac{5}{6}\pi$ by using function values at π and at $\frac{1}{6}\pi$.
7. Find $\sin \pi$ and $\cos \pi$ by using function values at $\frac{4}{3}\pi$ and $\frac{1}{3}\pi$.
8. Since $45° = 180° - 135°$, obtain $\cos 45°$ and $\tan 45°$ by use of 180° and 135°.

Find the tangent and cotangent of the angle without using tables; the result may be left in radical form. Solve by first expressing the angle as a sum or difference of convenient angles.

9. 75°.   10. 105°.   11. 165°.   12. 195°.   13. 285°.   14. 255°.

Expand by use of (I)–(VI) and insert known function values.

15. $\cos (\frac{1}{4}\pi - x)$.
16. $\tan (x + \frac{1}{4}\pi)$.
17. $\tan (\frac{1}{4}\pi - x)$.
18. $\cos (x - \frac{1}{4}\pi)$.
19. $\sin (x + \frac{1}{3}\pi)$.
20. $\sin (x - \frac{1}{6}\pi)$.
21. $\tan (x - \frac{3}{4}\pi)$.
22. $\sin (\frac{2}{3}\pi - x)$.
23. $\cos (\frac{5}{3}\pi - x)$.
24. $\tan (x + \frac{5}{4}\pi)$.
25. $\sin (\frac{7}{6}\pi + x)$.
26. $\cos (\frac{7}{4}\pi + x)$.

27. By use of (I) and (III), prove the following addition formula for the cotangent function. Then, obtain $\cot (x - y)$ by use of $\cot (- y) = - \cot y$.

$$\cot (x + y) = \frac{\cot x \cot y - 1}{\cot x + \cot y}; \qquad \cot (x - y) = \frac{\cot x \cot y + 1}{\cot y - \cot x}.$$

Prove the identity.

28. $\sin\left(\frac{1}{4}\pi + x\right) - \sin\left(\frac{1}{4}\pi - x\right) = \sqrt{2}\sin x$.

29. $\cos\left(\frac{1}{6}\pi + x\right)\cos\left(\frac{1}{6}\pi - x\right) - \sin\left(\frac{1}{6}\pi + x\right)\sin\left(\frac{1}{6}\pi - x\right) = \frac{1}{2}$.

30. $\cos\left(\pi + x\right)\cos\left(\pi - x\right) + \sin\left(\pi + x\right)\sin\left(\pi - x\right) = \cos 2x$.

31. $\cot\left(\frac{1}{4}\pi + x\right) = \dfrac{1 - \tan x}{1 + \tan x}$.   **32.** $\tan\left(\frac{1}{4}\pi - x\right) = \dfrac{\cot x - 1}{\cot x + 1}$.

132. Double-angle formulas

On substituting $y = x$ in (I) and (III), we find

$$\sin (x + x) = \sin 2x = \sin x \cos x + \cos x \sin x = 2 \sin x \cos x;$$

$$\cos (x + x) = \cos 2x = \cos x \cos x - \sin x \sin x = \cos^2 x - \sin^2 x.$$

Thus, we obtain (VII) and (VIII$_a$) below. We substitute $\sin^2 x = 1 - \cos^2 x$ in (VIII$_a$) to prove (VIII$_b$). To obtain (VIII$_c$), we substitute $\cos^2 x = 1 - \sin^2 x$ in (VIII$_a$). To derive (IX), let $y = x$ in (V).

$$\sin 2x = 2 \sin x \cos x. \tag{VII}$$

$$\cos 2x = \cos^2 x - \sin^2 x. \tag{VIII$_a$}$$

$$\cos 2x = 2 \cos^2 x - 1. \tag{VIII$_b$}$$

$$\cos 2x = 1 - 2 \sin^2 x. \tag{VIII$_c$}$$

$$\tan 2x = \frac{2 \tan x}{1 - \tan^2 x}. \tag{IX}$$

These results are called *double-angle formulas.* They express trigonometric functions of $2x$ in terms of trigonometric functions of x. From (VIII$_b$) and (VIII$_c$) we obtain

$$1 + \cos 2x = 2 \cos^2 x; \qquad 1 - \cos 2x = 2 \sin^2 x. \tag{X}$$

ILLUSTRATION 1. From (VIII$_b$) with $x = \frac{1}{3}\pi$,

$$\cos \tfrac{2}{3}\pi = \cos 2(\tfrac{1}{3}\pi) = 2 \cos^2 \tfrac{1}{3}\pi - 1 = 2\left(\frac{1}{2}\right)^2 - 1 = -\frac{1}{2}.$$

133. Half-angle formulas

To exhibit (X) in different notation, we replace x by $\frac{1}{2}x$ on both sides of each equation in (X), to obtain

$$2 \cos^2 \frac{x}{2} = 1 + \cos x; \qquad 2 \sin^2 \frac{x}{2} = 1 - \cos x. \tag{XI}$$

From (XI), we derive

$$\cos^2 \frac{x}{2} = \frac{1 + \cos x}{2}; \qquad \sin^2 \frac{x}{2} = \frac{1 - \cos x}{2}; \tag{1}$$

$$\tan^2 \frac{x}{2} = \frac{\sin^2 \frac{1}{2}x}{\cos^2 \frac{1}{2}x} = \frac{1 - \cos x}{1 + \cos x}; \tag{2}$$

$$\sin\frac{x}{2} = \pm\sqrt{\frac{1-\cos x}{2}}; \qquad \cos\frac{x}{2} = \pm\sqrt{\frac{1+\cos x}{2}}; \qquad \text{(XII)}$$

$$\tan\frac{x}{2} = \pm\sqrt{\frac{1-\cos x}{1+\cos x}}. \qquad \frac{1-\cos x}{\sin x} \qquad \text{(XIII)}$$

In (XII) and (XIII), the sign to use on the right depends on the quadrant interval where $\frac{1}{2}x$ lies. The student is advised to concentrate on memorizing (XI), instead of (XII) and (XIII), which can be derived from (XI). We call (XI)–(XIII) the *half-angle formulas* because they express trigonometric functions of $\frac{1}{2}x$ in terms of functions of x.

ILLUSTRATION 1. By use of (XIII) with $x = \frac{2}{3}\pi$,

$$\tan\tfrac{1}{3}\pi = \sqrt{\frac{1-\cos\frac{2}{3}\pi}{1+\cos\frac{2}{3}\pi}} = \sqrt{\frac{1-(-\frac{1}{2})}{1-\frac{1}{2}}} = \sqrt{\frac{\frac{3}{2}}{\frac{1}{2}}} = \sqrt{3},$$

where the "+" sign was used on the right in (XIII) because $\frac{1}{3}\pi$ is on an interval in quadrant I.

EXAMPLE 1. Prove that the following identity is true at all values of x where cot x exists, with cot $x \neq -1$ and $\cos 2x \neq 0$:

$$\frac{\cot x - 1}{\cot x + 1} = \frac{1 - \sin 2x}{\cos 2x}. \qquad (3)$$

SOLUTION. $\qquad \dfrac{1-\sin 2x}{\cos 2x} = \dfrac{1 - 2\sin x \cos x}{\cos^2 x - \sin^2 x} \qquad$ (VII) *and* (VIII$_a$)

$$= \frac{\sin^2 x + \cos^2 x - 2\sin x \cos x}{\cos^2 x - \sin^2 x} \qquad (1 = \sin^2 x + \cos^2 x)$$

$$= \frac{(\cos x - \sin x)^2}{(\cos x - \sin x)(\cos x + \sin x)} = \frac{\cos x - \sin x}{\cos x + \sin x} \qquad (4)$$

$$= \frac{\dfrac{\cos x}{\sin x} - \dfrac{\sin x}{\sin x}}{\dfrac{\cos x}{\sin x} + \dfrac{\sin x}{\sin x}} = \frac{\cot x - 1}{\cot x + 1}, \qquad (5)$$

where we divided both numerator and denominator on the right in (4) by $\sin x$ to obtain (5), which proves (3) when $\sin x \neq 0$. (We know that $\sin x \neq 0$ when cot x exists, which we assumed.)

EXAMPLE 2. Express $\sin 3x$ in terms of trigonometric functions (a) of $6x$; (b) of $\frac{3}{2}x$. Or, with $3x$ thought of as an angle, express $\sin 3x$ in terms of functions of *twice the angle*, and functions of *half of the angle* $3x$.

SOLUTION. 1. Since $3x = \frac{1}{2}(6x)$, we use (XII) with x replaced by $6x$:

$$\sin 3x = \pm\sqrt{\frac{1-\cos 6x}{2}}, \quad or \quad 2\sin^2 3x = 1 - \cos 6x.$$

2. From (VII) with x replaced by $\frac{3}{2}x$, $\qquad \sin 3x = 2\sin\frac{3}{2}x \cos\frac{3}{2}x.$

EXERCISE 79

From (VII)–(XIII), *find the sine, cosine, and tangent of the first angle, in radian measure or degree measure, by use of the second angle.*

1. $60°$ by use of $30°$.

2. $60°$ by use of $120°$.

3. $\frac{2}{3}\pi$ by use of $\frac{4}{3}\pi$.

4. $\frac{2}{3}\pi$ by use of $\frac{1}{3}\pi$.

5. $\frac{1}{6}\pi$ by use of $\frac{1}{3}\pi$.

6. $\frac{5}{3}\pi$ by use of $\frac{5}{6}\pi$.

7. $\frac{1}{2}\pi$, where possible, by use of $\frac{1}{4}\pi$.

8. $\frac{1}{2}\pi$, where possible, by use of π.

9. $-\frac{3}{4}\pi$ by use of $-\frac{3}{2}\pi$.

10. $-\frac{3}{2}\pi$ by use of $-\frac{3}{4}\pi$.

Prove the identity.

11. $\tan x = \dfrac{\sin 2x}{1 + \cos 2x}$.

12. $\cot x = \dfrac{1 + \cos 2x}{\sin 2x}$.

13. $\sec 2x = \dfrac{1}{1 - 2\sin^2 x}$.

14. $\sec^2 x = \dfrac{2}{1 + \cos 2x}$.

15. $\csc^2 x = \dfrac{2}{1 - \cos 2x}$.

16. $\cot 2\theta = \dfrac{\csc \theta - 2\sin \theta}{2\cos \theta}$.

17. $(\sin \alpha + \cos \alpha)^2 = 1 + \sin 2\alpha$.

18. $\sec^2 \theta \cos 2\theta = \sec^2 \theta - 2\tan^2 \theta$.

19. $2\cos \theta - \cos 2\theta \sec \theta = \sec \theta$.

20. $\dfrac{\sec^2 x}{4\sin^2 x} = \dfrac{1}{\sin^2 2x}$.

21. $\sec 2\alpha = \dfrac{\sec^2 \alpha}{1 - \tan^2 \alpha}$.

22. $\sec^2 2\alpha = \dfrac{\csc^2 \alpha}{\cot^2 \alpha - 1}$.

23. $\dfrac{\tan 2\alpha}{2\tan \alpha} = \dfrac{\cot^2 \alpha}{\cot^2 \alpha - 1}$.

24. $\dfrac{1 - \tan x}{1 + \tan x} = \dfrac{1 - \sin 2x}{\cos 2x}$.

25. $\tan 2x = \dfrac{2}{\cot x - \tan x}$.

Express the sine, cosine, and tangent of the first number in terms of trigonometric functions of the second number.

26. 4α, in terms of 2α.

27. $2A$, in terms of $4A$.

28. $4x$, in terms of $8x$.

29. $8x$, in terms of $4x$.

30. $\frac{1}{2}x$, in terms of $\frac{1}{4}x$.

31. α, in terms of $\frac{1}{2}\alpha$.

32. 3θ, in terms of $\frac{3}{2}\theta$.

33. $\frac{3}{2}x$, in terms of $3x$.

Express the first function value in terms of the second.

34. $\sin 3x$, in terms of $\sin x$.

35. $\cos 3x$, in terms of $\cos x$.

36. $\sin 4x$, in terms of $\sin x$.

37. $\tan 3x$, in terms of $\tan x$.

134. Product formulas

We recall the following identities:

$$\sin (\alpha + \beta) = \sin \alpha \cos \beta + \cos \alpha \sin \beta; \tag{1}$$

$$\sin (\alpha - \beta) = \sin \alpha \cos \beta - \cos \alpha \sin \beta; \tag{2}$$

$$\cos (\alpha + \beta) = \cos \alpha \cos \beta - \sin \alpha \sin \beta; \tag{3}$$

$$\cos (\alpha - \beta) = \cos \alpha \cos \beta + \sin \alpha \sin \beta. \tag{4}$$

On adding corresponding sides in (1) and (2), we obtain the following formula (XIV). On adding in (3) and (4) we obtain (XV). On subtracting in the order (3) from (4) we obtain (XVI). On subtracting sides in the order (2) from (1) we obtain (XVII).

$$2 \sin \alpha \cos \beta = \sin (\alpha + \beta) + \sin (\alpha - \beta). \tag{XIV}$$

$$2 \cos \alpha \cos \beta = \cos (\alpha + \beta) + \cos (\alpha - \beta). \tag{XV}$$

$$2 \sin \alpha \sin \beta = \cos (\alpha - \beta) - \cos (\alpha + \beta). \tag{XVI}$$

$$2 \cos \alpha \sin \beta = \sin (\alpha + \beta) - \sin (\alpha - \beta). \tag{XVII}$$

Although (XIV)–(XVII) occasionally are useful in applications, their main importance in this text is that they give a means for proving formulas in the next section. Hence, the student is not advised to memorize (XIV)–(XVII) but should have the power to derive them, as above.

ILLUSTRATION 1. From (XIV),

$$2 \sin 150° \cos 30° = \sin (150° + 30°) + \sin (150° - 30°)$$
$$= \sin 180° + \sin 120° = 0 + \tfrac{1}{2}\sqrt{3} = \tfrac{1}{2}\sqrt{3}.$$

Note 1. Since $\sin (\alpha - \beta) = \sin [- (\beta - \alpha)] = - \sin (\beta - \alpha)$, we observe that (XVII) is the same as (XIV) with a mere interchange of α and β.

135. Sums and differences of sines or cosines

In (XIV)–(XVII), let

$$x = \alpha + \beta; \qquad y = \alpha - \beta. \tag{1}$$

Then, $x + y = 2\alpha; \qquad x - y = 2\beta.$

Hence, $\alpha = \tfrac{1}{2}(x + y); \qquad \beta = \tfrac{1}{2}(x - y). \tag{2}$

On using (1) and (2) in (XIV), (XVII), (XV), and (XVI), respectively, we obtain

$$\sin x + \sin y = 2 \sin \frac{x + y}{2} \cos \frac{x - y}{2}; \tag{XVIII}$$

$$\sin x - \sin y = 2 \cos \frac{x + y}{2} \sin \frac{x - y}{2}; \tag{XIX}$$

$$\cos x + \cos y = 2 \cos \frac{x + y}{2} \cos \frac{x - y}{2}; \tag{XX}$$

$$\cos x - \cos y = - 2 \sin \frac{x + y}{2} \sin \frac{x - y}{2}. \tag{XXI}$$

ILLUSTRATION 1. By use of (XVIII),

$$\sin 50° + \sin 10° = 2 \sin \tfrac{1}{2}(60°) \cos \tfrac{1}{2}(40°) = 2 \sin 30° \cos 20°;$$
$$\sin 20° + \sin 80° = 2 \sin \tfrac{1}{2}(100°) \cos \tfrac{1}{2}(- 60°) = 2 \sin 50° \cos (- 30°)$$
$$[\text{Since } \cos (- \theta) = \cos \theta] \qquad\qquad\qquad = 2 \sin 50° \cos 30°.$$

2Cos6θSin30θ = θ + 2

4. 2Sin3θCos5θ = Sin8θ + Sin2θ

5. 2Sin2θCos5θ = Sin7θ - Sen3θ

6. 2Sin3θCos3θ = Sin7θ + Sin2θ

7. 2Sin3θSin5θ = Cos2θ - Cos8θ

8. 2Cos3θCos5θ = Cos8θ + Cos2θ

9. 2Sin3θSin7θ = Cos4θ + Sin2θ

10. 2Sin3θSin7θ = Cos8θ - Cos10θ = -(Cos8θ + Cos8θ)

11. 2Cos4θSin2θ = -Cos10θ = -(Cos8θ + Cos10θ)

12. Cos40°Cos8θ = 2Sin7θCoSin2θ

13. Cos4x - Cos4x = 2Sin3x·2Sin3x

14. Sin7y + Sin7y = 2Sin8yCosy

15. Cos3x - Cosx = 2SinxCos3x

Charles Aldridge
10-308 Dec 30

1. $2 \sin 60 \cos 30 = 1 + \frac{1}{2} = \frac{3}{2}$ ✓ ✓

2. $2 \cos 60 \cos 30 = 0 + \frac{\sqrt{3}}{2}$

2. $2 \sin 60 \sin 30 = \frac{\sqrt{3}}{2} - 0$

2. $2 \cos 60 \sin 30 = 1 - \frac{1}{2} = \frac{1}{2}$

2. $2 \sin 30 \cos 60 = 1 - \frac{1}{2} = \frac{1}{2}$

2. $2 \cos 30 \cos 60 = 0 + \frac{\sqrt{3}}{2} = \frac{\sqrt{3}}{2}$

2. $2 \sin 30 \sin 60 = \frac{\sqrt{3}}{2} - 0 = \frac{\sqrt{3}}{2}$

2. $2 \cos 30 \sin 60 = 1 + \frac{1}{2} = \frac{3}{2}$

3. $2 \sin 60 \cos 300 = 0 + \frac{1}{2} = \frac{1}{2}$

2. $2 \cos 60 \cos 300 = 1 + \frac{\sqrt{3}}{2} = \sqrt{3}$

$2 \sin 60 \cos 300 = 1 - 1 = 3$

16. $\sin x - \sin 3x = -2$

17. $\cos 3y - \cos 6y = 2 \cos \frac{y}{2} \cos \frac{5}{2}y$

Comment. By use of the identities for $\sin(-\theta)$ and $\cos(-\theta)$, whenever the negative of a number appears as the argument of a sine or cosine, we may change to a form where the negative sign is removed, as in Illustration 1.

ILLUSTRATION 2. By use of (XX), with $x = 4A$ and $y = 2A$,

$$\cos 4A + \cos 2A = 2 \cos \tfrac{1}{2}(6A) \cos \tfrac{1}{2}(2A) = 2 \cos 3A \cos A.$$

EXAMPLE 1. Prove the identity: $\dfrac{\cos 5\alpha + \cos 3\alpha}{\sin 5\alpha - \sin 3\alpha} = \cot \alpha.$

SOLUTION. Apply (XX) in the numerator and (XIX) in the denominator:

$$\frac{\cos 5\alpha + \cos 3\alpha}{\sin 5\alpha - \sin 3\alpha} = \frac{2 \cos 4\alpha \cos \alpha}{2 \cos 4\alpha \sin \alpha} = \frac{\cos \alpha}{\sin \alpha} = \cot \alpha.$$

EXERCISE 80

Check (XIV)–(XVII) *for the given angles.*

1. $\alpha = 60°, \beta = 30°.$ **2.** $\alpha = 30°, \beta = 60°.$ **3.** $\alpha = 60°, \beta = 300°.$

Express as a sum or difference of functions of multiples of θ.

4. $2 \sin 3\theta \cos 5\theta.$ **5.** $2 \sin 2\theta \cos 5\theta.$ **6.** $2 \sin 3\theta \cos \theta.$

7. $2 \sin 3\theta \sin 5\theta.$ **8.** $2 \cos 3\theta \cos 5\theta.$ **9.** $2 \sin \theta \sin 9\theta.$

Express each sum or difference as a product.

10. $\sin 60° - \sin 20°.$ **11.** $\cos 40° - \cos 80°.$

12. $\sin 4x - \sin 2x.$ **13.** $\cos 2x - \cos 4x.$ **14.** $\sin 7y + \sin 9y.$

15. $\cos 3x - \cos x.$ **16.** $\sin x - \sin 3x.$ **17.** $\cos 3y + \cos 8y.$

Prove each identity.

18. $\dfrac{\sin 5x + \sin 3x}{\sin 5x - \sin 3x} = \dfrac{\tan 4x}{\tan x}.$ **19.** $\dfrac{\cos x + \cos 9x}{\sin x + \sin 9x} = \cot 5x.$

20. $\dfrac{\cos 4x - \cos 2x}{\cos 4x + \cos 2x} = -\dfrac{\tan 3x}{\cot x}.$ **21.** $\dfrac{\cos 2x - \cos 6x}{\sin 6x - \sin 2x} = \tan 4x.$

22. $\dfrac{\sin 5x + \sin 3x}{\cos 5x - \cos 3x} = -\cot x.$ **23.** $\dfrac{\sin 2x - \sin x}{\cos 2x + \cos x} = \tan \dfrac{x}{2}.$

24. $\dfrac{\cos 5x + \cos 2x}{\sin 5x + \sin 2x} = \cot \dfrac{7x}{2}.$ **25.** $\dfrac{\sin 4x - \sin 2x}{\cos 4x + \cos 2x} = \tan x.$

136. Miscellaneous trigonometric identities

We give renewed emphasis to the following suggestions for proving trigonometric identities or solving trigonometric equations.

I. *If possible, avoid introducing radicals.*

II. *Usually, it is best to express any cotangent, secant, or cosecant of a complicated number in terms of the tangent, cosine, or sine, because of the nature of the formulas we have derived.*

III. *It may be convenient to express all function values in terms of function values for a single number.*

EXAMPLE 1. Prove the identity: $\cos 3x = \cos x - 4 \sin^2 x \cos x$.

SOLUTION. By use of (III),

$$\cos 3x = \cos (x + 2x) = \cos x \cos 2x - \sin x \sin 2x$$
$$= \cos x(1 - 2 \sin^2 x) - \sin x(2 \sin x \cos x)$$
$$= \cos x - 4 \sin^2 x \cos x.$$

EXAMPLE 2. Prove the identity: $\dfrac{\cos x}{\sec 3x} + \dfrac{\sin x}{\csc 3x} = \cos 2x$.

SOLUTION. Since $\sec 3x = \dfrac{1}{\cos 3x}$ and $\csc 3x = \dfrac{1}{\sin 3x}$,

$$\frac{\cos x}{\sec 3x} + \frac{\sin x}{\csc 3x} = \cos x \cos 3x + \sin x \sin 3x = \cos (3x - x) = \cos 2x.$$

EXAMPLE 3. Prove the identity:

$$\sin 3\theta - \sin \theta = 2 \cos^2 \theta \sin \theta - 2 \sin^3 \theta.$$

SOLUTION. By use of (XIX) and (VIII$_a$),

$$\sin 3\theta - \sin \theta = 2 \cos 2\theta \sin \theta$$
$$= 2 (\cos^2 \theta - \sin^2 \theta) \sin \theta = 2 \cos^2 \theta \sin \theta - 2 \sin^3 \theta.$$

EXAMPLE 4. Prove the identity: $\cot \dfrac{\theta}{2} = \dfrac{\sin \theta}{1 - \cos \theta}$.

SOLUTION. By use of (VII) with $x = \tfrac{1}{2}\theta$, and (XI),

$$\frac{\sin \theta}{1 - \cos \theta} = \frac{2 \sin \dfrac{\theta}{2} \cos \dfrac{\theta}{2}}{2 \sin^2 \dfrac{\theta}{2}} = \frac{\cos \dfrac{\theta}{2}}{\sin \dfrac{\theta}{2}} = \cot \frac{\theta}{2}.$$

Comment. A more complicated solution would result from use of (XIII). A trigonometric function of any number is more conveniently expressible in terms of functions of *half of the number* rather than *twice the number*.

EXERCISE 81

Prove the identity.

1. $\tan \alpha \sin 2\alpha = 2 \sin^2 \alpha$.

2. $2 \cos \alpha = \csc \alpha \sin 2\alpha$.

3. $\cot \alpha \sin 2\alpha = 1 + \cos 2\alpha$.

4. $(\sin x + \cos x)^2 = 1 + \sin 2x$.

5. $\cos 3x + \cos x = 4 \cos^3 x - 2 \cos x$.

6. $\sin 3x = 3 \cos^2 x \sin x - \sin^3 x$.

7. $\sin 4x = 4 \sin x \cos x \cos 2x$.

8. $\cos (x + \tfrac{1}{6}\pi) \cos (x - \tfrac{1}{6}\pi) + \sin (x + \tfrac{1}{6}\pi) \sin (x - \tfrac{1}{6}\pi) = \tfrac{1}{2}$.

9. $\dfrac{\sin x}{\sec 2x} + \dfrac{\cos x}{\csc 2x} = \sin 3x$.

10. $\csc 2\alpha = \dfrac{\tan \alpha}{2 \sin^2 \alpha}$.

11. $\dfrac{\cos 2x}{\sec x} - \dfrac{\sin x}{\csc 2x} = \cos 3x$.

12. $\dfrac{2 \tan \alpha}{\tan 2\alpha} = 1 - \tan^2 \alpha$.

13. $\cot 3\alpha = \dfrac{1 - 3 \tan^2 \alpha}{3 \tan \alpha - \tan^3 \alpha}.$

14. $\sec 2\alpha = \dfrac{\sec \alpha}{2 \cos \alpha - \sec \alpha}.$

15. $\sec 2\alpha = \dfrac{\sec \alpha}{\cos \alpha - \sin \alpha \tan \alpha}.$

16. $2 \tan \alpha = \dfrac{1 - \tan^2 \alpha}{\cot 2\alpha}.$

17. $\tan^2 \theta + \cos 2\theta = 1 - \cos 2\theta \tan^2 \theta.$

18. $\dfrac{\cos 3x}{\sec x} - \dfrac{\sin x}{\csc 3x} = \cos^2 2x - \sin^2 2x.$

19. $\cot 2\alpha = \dfrac{\cos \alpha - \sin \alpha \tan \alpha}{2 \sin \alpha}.$

20. $\dfrac{1 + \cot x}{\cot x - 1} = \dfrac{1 + \sin 2x}{\cos 2x}.$

21. $\cos (\alpha + \beta) \cos (\alpha - \beta) = \cos^2 \beta - \sin^2 \alpha.$

22. $\sin 3x \cot x + \cos 3x = \sin 4x \csc x.$

23. $\sec 3x \sin 6x = 2 \tan 3x \cos 3x.$

24. $\sin 6\alpha \tan 3\alpha = 2 \sin^2 3\alpha.$

25. $\dfrac{\sin x}{1 + \cos x} = \tan \dfrac{x}{2}.$

26. $\dfrac{1 + \cos 6x}{1 - \cos 6x} = \csc^2 3x - 1.$

27. $\dfrac{\cos^3 x + \sin^3 x}{2 - \sin 2x} = \dfrac{\sin x + \cos x}{2}.$

28. $2 \cot x = \cot \dfrac{x}{2} - \tan \dfrac{x}{2}.$

29. $\dfrac{\cos x}{1 + \sin x} = \dfrac{\cot \frac{1}{2}x - 1}{\cot \frac{1}{2}x + 1}.$

30. $\sec 2x = \dfrac{1}{\cos^4 x - \sin^4 x}.$

31. $4 \cos 6x \sin 2x \cos 4x = \sin 4x - \sin 8x + \sin 12x.$

32. $4 \sin^3 \theta = 3 \sin \theta - \sin 3\theta.$

33. $4 \cos^3 \theta = 3 \cos \theta + \cos 3\theta.$

137. Miscellaneous equations

An equation in x which states the value of one trigonometric function of some constant multiple of an unknown number x should be solved without alteration, by inspection or perhaps with the aid of a trigonometric table.

EXAMPLE 1. Find all solutions of $\sin 3x = \frac{1}{2}$ on the interval $0 \leqq x < 2\pi$.

SOLUTION. Recall that $\sin \frac{1}{6}\pi = \frac{1}{2} = \sin \frac{5}{6}\pi$. Hence, $\frac{1}{6}\pi$ or $\frac{5}{6}\pi$, or either of these plus any integral multiple of 2π is a value of $3x$ which satisfies the given equation. To obtain all solutions for x on the interval $0 \leqq x < 2\pi$, we first list all values of $3x$ on the interval $0 \leqq 3x < 6\pi$, which gives,

for $3x$: $\qquad \frac{1}{6}\pi, \frac{5}{6}\pi, (2\pi + \frac{1}{6}\pi), (2\pi + \frac{5}{6}\pi), (4\pi + \frac{1}{6}\pi), (4\pi + \frac{5}{6}\pi).$

To find the values of x which are solutions, we divide each of the preceding numbers by 3, which gives

solutions for x: $\qquad \frac{1}{18}\pi, \frac{5}{18}\pi, \frac{13}{18}\pi, \frac{17}{18}\pi, \frac{25}{18}\pi, \frac{29}{18}\pi.$

To solve a trigonometric equation in an unknown number x, we aim to find one or more equations, each involving only *one* trigonometric function of *one* constant multiple of x, whose solutions include all solutions of the given equation. If the operations in our work are of types which produce equations equivalent to our given equation, no test of the final results is necessary. However, if we employ operations which might introduce extraneous roots, final results must be tested in the original equation.

EXAMPLE 2. Solve: $\cos 2x - \cos x = 0.$

SOLUTION. 1. Use (VIII$_b$) so that only values of trigonometric functions of the number x will remain:

$$2 \cos^2 x - 1 - \cos x = 0, \quad or \quad (2 \cos x + 1)(\cos x - 1) = 0.$$

2. We solve $2 \cos x + 1 = 0$ and $\cos x - 1 = 0$ and obtain

$$x = 0, \quad x = \tfrac{2}{3}\pi, \quad and \quad x = \tfrac{4}{3}\pi.$$

EXAMPLE 3. Solve: $\sin 5x - \sin x = \cos 3x.$

SOLUTION. 1. Use (XIX): $2 \cos 3x \sin 2x = \cos 3x.$

$$2 \cos 3x \sin 2x - \cos 3x = 0; \quad \cos 3x (2 \sin 2x - 1) = 0.$$

2. Hence, $\cos 3x = 0 \quad or \quad 2 \sin 2x - 1 = 0.$

The student should complete the solution of these equations as in Example 1.

EXERCISE 82

Solve for all values of x on the interval $0 \leq x < 2\pi$. If no solutions exist on this interval, find just one positive solution if there is any.

1. $\sin 2x = 0.$

2. $\cos 2x = \tfrac{1}{2}\sqrt{3}.$

3. $\sin^2 3x = \tfrac{1}{4}.$

4. $\tan 3x = -1.$

5. $\sec 3x = -\sqrt{2}.$

6. $\csc 4x = -2.$

7. $\sin \tfrac{1}{2}x = \tfrac{1}{2}\sqrt{2}.$

8. $\tan^2 \tfrac{1}{4}x = 3.$

9. $\cot 2x = \tfrac{1}{3}\sqrt{3}.$

10. $\cos \tfrac{1}{2}x = -1.$

11. $\tan \tfrac{1}{3}x = 1.$

12. $\cos \tfrac{1}{3}x = -\tfrac{1}{2}\sqrt{2}.$

13. $\tan 2x$ is infinite.

14. $\sec 3x$ is infinite.

15. $\cos x = \sin 2x.$

16. $\cos 2x = \sin x.$

17. $\cos 2x = -\cos x.$

18. $\sin 2x = -\sin x.$

19. $\tan 2x = \tan x.$

20. $\cos 2x = \cos^2 x.$

21. $\sin x + \cos 2x = 1.$

22. $\cos 2x + 1 = \cos x.$

23. $\cos 2x = 2 \sin^2 x - 2.$

24. $4 \cos^2 3x - 3 = 0.$

25. $3 = \tan^2 2x.$

26. $\cos 4x = \cos 2x.$

27. $\cos 4x = \cos^2 2x.$

28. $\sin \tfrac{1}{2}x = \sin x.$

29. $\sin x = 2 \cos \tfrac{1}{2}x.$

30. $\cos x = \sin \tfrac{1}{2}x.$

31. $\cos 3x \cos x - \sin x \sin 3x = \tfrac{1}{2}.$

32. $\sin 3x + \sin x = 0.$

HINT for Problem 32. Change to a product.

33. $6 \sec^2 3x + \sec 3x = 2.$

34. $\cos 2x + \cos 3x = 0.$

35. $\cos 2x = \cos 6x.$

36. $\tan 3x = \tan x.$

37. $\cot \tfrac{1}{2}x$ is infinite.

By use of Table VII if necessary, find in degree measure all angles on the range $0° \leq \theta < 360°$ which are solutions of the equation.

38. $\sin 3\theta = -\tfrac{1}{2}\sqrt{3}.$

39. $\sin 2\theta = .2136.$

40. $\tan 2\theta = .1883.$

41. $6 \sin^2 2\theta + 5 \sin 2\theta = 6.$

42. $\cos \tfrac{1}{2}\theta = -.1564.$

EXERCISE 83
Review of Chapters 10–12

1. By use of Definition I on page 140, prove that $\cos \theta = \cot \theta / \csc \theta$.

2. (a) By use of the fundamental identities, without a figure, find all trigonometric functions of θ if θ is on an interval in quadrant II and $\cos \theta = -\frac{7}{25}$. (b) With θ interpreted as the measure of an angle in radians, construct θ in standard position on a coordinate system and obtain the functions of θ from the figure.

3. Express $\cot x$ in terms of $\sin x$; $\sin x$ in terms of $\cot x$.

4. Find all angles θ in degree measure on the interval $0° \leqq \theta < 360°$ for which $\cos \theta = -.9580$. Use Table VII.

5. Find the sine, cosine, and tangent of the given angle by the specified method, without use of a table: (a) 75°, by use of a sum of two angles; (b) 105°, by use of the difference of two angles.

6. Find the values of the trigonometric functions of $\frac{1}{3}\pi$ by use of trigonometric function values (a) for $\frac{2}{3}\pi$; (b) for $\frac{1}{6}\pi$.

7. If x is on an interval in quadrant II, and $0 \leqq y \leqq \frac{1}{2}\pi$, with $\sin x = \frac{3}{5}$ and $\cos y = \frac{8}{17}$, find the sine, cosine, and tangent (a) of $(x+y)$; (b) of $2x$; (c) of $\frac{1}{2}x$.

8. By use of Table VII, find all angles θ on the interval $0° \leqq \theta < 360°$ in degree measure if (a) $\tan \theta = .7173$; (b) $\sin \theta = -.5110$.

9. By interpolation in Table IV, find all angles θ in radian measure on the interval $0 \leqq \theta < 2\pi$ if (a) $\sin \theta = .875$; (b) $\cos \theta = -.407$; (c) $\tan \theta = .675$.

10. By use of relatively few points, draw graphs on the range $-3\pi \leqq x \leqq \pi$ for the standard trigonometric functions $\cos x$, $\sec x$, and $\cot x$. Draw each asymptote, if any. Repeat the problem, with $-4\pi \leqq x \leqq 2\pi$, for the functions $\sin x$, $\csc x$, and $\tan x$.

11. Graph the functions $3 \sin 2x$ and $4 \sin x$ on the interval $0 \leqq x \leqq 3\pi$.

12. Express as a product: $\sin 4x + \sin 5x$; $\cos 3x - \cos 2x$.

Prove the identity.

13. $\dfrac{\sin x}{\sin x + \cos x} = \dfrac{\sec x}{\sec x + \csc x}$.

14. $\dfrac{\cos x}{\cos x - \sin x} = \dfrac{1}{1 - \tan x}$.

15. $\dfrac{\tan x - \csc x}{\tan x + \csc x} = \dfrac{\sin^2 x - \cos x}{\sin^2 x + \cos x}$.

16. $\dfrac{\sin x - \cos 2x}{1 + \sin x} = 2 \sin x - 1$.

17. $\sec^4 \theta + \tan^4 \theta = 1 + 2 \sec^2 \theta \tan^2 \theta$.

18. $\dfrac{\sin (\alpha + \beta)}{\cos (\alpha + \beta)} = \dfrac{\tan \alpha \cot \beta + 1}{\cot \beta - \tan \alpha}$.

19. $\sec x = \dfrac{\sec \frac{1}{2}x}{2 \cos \frac{1}{2}x - \sec \frac{1}{2}x}$.

20. $\dfrac{\cos x - \cos 3x}{\cos 3x + \cos x} = \dfrac{\tan x}{\cot 2x}$.

21. $\dfrac{\cos 2x + \sin 2x}{\cos 2x - \sin 2x} = \dfrac{1 + \cot 2x}{\cot 2x - 1}$.

22. $\cot \dfrac{x}{2} = \dfrac{1 + \cos x}{\sin x}$.

Find all values of x on the interval $0 \leqq x < 2\pi$ satisfying the equation or statement.

23. $\sin 2x = -\frac{1}{2}\sqrt{3}$.   **24.** $\tan^2 3x = 3$.   **25.** $\cos^2 \frac{1}{2}x = \frac{1}{2}$.

26. $\tan 2x$ is infinite.   **27.** $\sec 3x$ is infinite.

28. $2 \cos x = \cos^2 x$.   **29.** $\cot^2 x = \cot x$.   **30.** $2 \sin x = 5$.

31. $2 \cot x \sin x - \cot x = 0$.   **32.** $1 + \sin x - 2 \sin^2 x = 0$.

33. $\sec^2 x + 4 \sec x + 4 = 0$.   **34.** $\sin^2 x + \cos x + 1 = 0$.

35. $\cos x + 2 \cos^2 \frac{1}{2}x = 2$.   **36.** $\tan^2 2x + \sec^2 2x = 3$.

37. $\sin 2x = 1 - \cos 2x$.   **38.** $\cos 3x = 1 - \sin 3x$.

Proceed as if you are trying to prove that the equality is an identity, operating simultaneously on both sides of the equality. Prove that it is an identity or find all of its solutions on the interval $0 \leqq x < 2\pi$.

39. $(\sin x - \cos x)^2 = 1 - 2 \cot x \sin^2 x$.

40. $3 - \cos^2 x \csc x - 3 \sin^2 x = 2 \cos^2 x$.

41. $\sin x \tan x - 2 \sin^2 x \cos x + \tan x = 2 \tan x \cos^2 x$.

42. Express $\sin (x + y - z)$ in terms of function values for the sine or cosine of x, y, and z.

Solve right $\triangle ABC$ without logarithms; use Table VII.

43. $c = 17.5$; $a = 10.5$.   **44.** $\alpha = 42° 36'$; $b = .45$.   **45.** $c = 63$; $\alpha = 6° 35'$.

46–48. Solve Problems 43–45, respectively, by use of four-place logarithms and check the solutions.

49. Find the length of arc intercepted on a circle of radius 10 inches by a central angle of 3.7 radians.

50. Find the measure in radians of a central angle in a circle with radius 15 inches, if the angle intercepts an arc 45 inches long.

51. Change to radian measure: (*a*) 325°; (*b*) 160° 35'.

52. Change to degree measure: (*a*) 1.5 radians; (*b*) $\frac{11}{6}\pi$ radians.

Inequalities

138. Absolute and conditional inequalities

Let a and b be any real numbers. Then, to say that b *is less than a*, or *a is greater than b*, means that $(a - b)$ is *positive:*

$$b < a \quad means\ that \quad (a - b)\ is\ \textbf{positive}. \tag{1}$$

Let $a - b = h$ or $a = b + h$, and suppose that a and b are plotted on the scale in Figure 96. Then, (1) means that $a = b + h$, where $h > 0$, or a is obtained by *adding h units to b;* that is, *a is h units to the right of b.* Thus, as on page 10, $b < a$ means geometrically that *b is to the left of a* on the scale in Figure 96. Any relation stated by use of $<$ or $>$ is called an *inequality.*

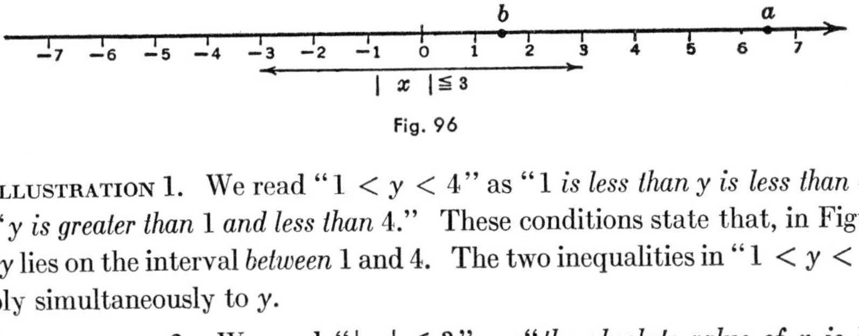

$$| x | \leq 3$$

Fig. 96

ILLUSTRATION 1. We read "$1 < y < 4$" as "1 *is less than y is less than* 4," or "*y is greater than* 1 *and less than* 4." These conditions state that, in Figure 96, y lies on the interval *between* 1 and 4. The two inequalities in "$1 < y < 4$" apply simultaneously to y.

ILLUSTRATION 2. We read "$| x | \leq 3$" as "*the absolute value of x is less than or equal to* 3." Then, x lies between $- 3$ and 3, inclusive, as in Figure 96:

$$| x | \leq 3 \quad means\ that \quad - 3 \leq x \leq 3. \tag{2}$$

If an inequality does not involve literal numbers, or if it is true for all permissible values of the letters involved, we call it an **absolute inequality**. **A conditional inequality** is one which is true only for certain values of the letters involved. **To solve an inequality** involving certain variables means to obtain a simple description of the values of the variables for which the inequality is true.

ILLUSTRATION 3. $8 > 3$ is an absolute inequality. $x - 3 < 0$ is a conditional inequality which is true only if $x < 3$. $d^2 \geqq 0$ is an absolute inequality because, for all real values of d, d^2 is positive or zero.

Note 1. The inequality relationship is defined only for *real* numbers a and b. In this chapter, only real numbers should be introduced.

139. Properties of inequalities

Two inequalities have the *same sense* if their inequality signs point in the *same direction*. Thus, $A < B$ and $C < D$ have the same sense.

THEOREM I. *If $A < B$ and if h is any number, then* * $A + h < B + h$.

Proof. Let $B - A = p$, which is positive because $A < B$. Hence,

$$(B + h) - (A + h) = B - A = p. \tag{1}$$

Therefore, by (1) on page 247, $A + h < B + h$, because the difference on the left in (1) above is equal to p, which is **positive.**

THEOREM II. *If $A < B$ and if $h > 0$, then $hA < hB$; if $h < 0$, then $hB < hA$.*

Proof. 1. Let $B - A = p$, which is *positive* because $A < B$. Hence, if $h > 0$, we have

$$hB - hA = h(B - A) = hp, \text{ which is } \textbf{positive.}$$

Therefore, by (1) on page 247, $hA < hB$ when $h > 0$.

2. If $h < 0$, then $hA - hB = h(A - B) = - hp$. Recall that $p > 0$ and $h < 0$; thus, $hp < 0$ and $- hp > 0$. Hence, by (1) on page 247, $hB < hA$.

We summarize Theorems I and II as follows:

1. *The sense of an inequality is* **not altered** *if any number is* **added to** *both sides, or if both sides are* **multiplied by a positive number.**

2. *The sense of an inequality is* **reversed** *if both sides are* **multiplied by a negative number;** *that is, if $h < 0$ and $A < B$, then $hA > hB$.*

ILLUSTRATION 1. We know that $- 2 < 5$. On multiplying both sides by $- 1$, we reverse the inequality, which gives $2 > - 5$, which is true.

THEOREM III. *If $A < B$ and $B < C$, then $A < C$.*

Proof. Let $p = B - A$ and $q = C - B$, where $p > 0$ and $q > 0$ because $A < B$ and $B < C$. Then,

$$C - A = (C - B) + (B - A) = p + q > 0.$$

Hence, by (1) on page 247, $A < C$.

Suppose that A and B are number expressions, perhaps involving one or more variables. Then, an inequality $A < B$ is said to be **equivalent to**

---

* *Subtraction* of a number k is equivalent to *adding h* where $h = - k$. Hence, Theorem I refers as well to *subtraction of the same number from both sides* of the inequality.

another inequality $C < D$ in case *the set of values of the variables satisfying $A < B$ is the same as the set satisfying $C < D$.*

THEOREM IV. *Let $A < B$ represent any inequality, perhaps involving certain variables.*

α. *If h is any number expression,* $A < B$ is equivalent to $A + h < B + h$.*
β. *If k is any positive-valued number expression,* $A < B$ is equivalent to $kA < kB$.*
γ. *If k is any negative-valued number expression,* $A < B$ is equivalent to $kA > kB$, where the inequality sign has been* **reversed.**

Proof of (β). For concreteness, suppose that A and B involve just one variable, x. Then, if a value $x = c$ satisfies $A < B$, it follows from Theorem II that $x = c$ also satisfies $kA < kB$. *Conversely,* since $1/k$ is *positive,* Theorem II states that, if $kA < kB$ is satisfied by a value $x = d$, then we have

$$\frac{1}{k}(kA) < \frac{1}{k}(kB), \quad or \quad A < B \text{ when } x = d.$$

Hence, the set of values of x satisfying $A < B$ is the *same set* as satisfies $kA < kB$, or these inequalities are *equivalent.* [Proofs of (α) and (γ) are left as exercises for the student.]

140. Linear inequalities

An inequality $A < B$ is said to be *linear* in a variable x in case A is of the form $(mx + c)$ and B is of the form $(nx + d)$, with $m \neq n$. In this case, because of Theorem IV, the inequality can be altered to an *equivalent inequality* $q < x$, or $x < q$, through *addition* of number expressions to both sides, or *multiplication* of both sides by constants.

EXAMPLE 1. Solve: $\qquad\qquad \dfrac{7x}{3} - 1 < 17 - \dfrac{2x}{3}. \qquad\qquad$ (1)

SOLUTION. 1. Multiply both sides by 3:

$$7x - 3 < 51 - 2x. \qquad\qquad (2)$$

2. Add $(3 + 2x)$ to both sides: $\qquad\qquad\qquad 9x < 54.$ $\qquad\qquad$ (3)

3. Divide by 9: $\qquad\qquad\qquad\qquad\qquad\qquad x < 6.$ $\qquad\qquad$ (4)

By Theorem IV, (4) is equivalent to (1). Thus, the range of values of x satisfying (1) is described by (4). We refer to (4) as the *solution* of (1).

Note 1. By multiplication of both sides by -1, an inequality such as $-x < a$, where the coefficient of x is *negative,* can be replaced by the equivalent inequality $x > -a$, where the coefficient of x is *positive.* This should be done in stating final results for solution of an inequality.

---

* Defined for all values of the literal numbers which satisfy $A < B$.

EXERCISE 84

Consider the value of x plotted on a scale, as in Figure 96 *on page* 247. *Express the given fact by use of inequalities without an absolute value symbol.*

1. x lies to the right of 4.   **2.** x lies to the right of -2.

3. x lies to the left of -3.   **4.** x lies to the left of 6.

5. x lies between 3 and 8.   **6.** x lies between -4 and 1.

7. x lies between -5 and 5.   **8.** x lies between 3 and -3.

9. $|x| < 3$.   **10.** $|x| < 4$.   **11.** $|x| \geqq 5$.   **12.** $|x| \geqq 6$.

Sketch where the values of x may lie on a number scale, in case the inequalities are true. Also, by use of $|x|$, state a single inequality equivalent to the given conditions.

13. $-7 < x < 7$.   **14.** $-8 \leqq x \leqq 8$.   **15.** $x < -4$ or $4 < x$.

16. $x < -3$ or $3 < x$.   **17.** $-a \leqq x \leqq a$, where $a > 0$.

18. $x < -a$ or $a < x$, where $a > 0$.

By algebraic methods, solve the inequality for x. That is, describe all values of x which satisfy the inequality. Also, represent these values on a number scale; the resulting set of points on the scale is called the **graph** *(one-dimensional) of the inequality.*

19. $3x - 15 < 0$.   **20.** $2x + 7 > 15$.   **21.** $\frac{2}{3}x - 7 < 4$.

22. $13 - 5x < 0$.   **23.** $7 - 2x > 3x$.   **24.** $\frac{1}{4}x - 3 < 2x$.

25. $2x - 3 < 5x + 7$.   **26.** $3x - \frac{2}{3} > \frac{5}{2}x - 4$.

27. $3x - \frac{2}{3} > \frac{2}{5}x + 1$.   **28.** $3x - a < b + 2x$.

141. Graphical solution of an inequality

Any inequality in a single variable, x, can be placed in the form $f(x) < 0$ or $f(x) > 0$ as we please, by transposing terms. To solve an inequality $f(x) > 0$ graphically, we graph the function $y = f(x)$ and find the values of x for which the graph is above the x-axis, or $y > 0$. We solve $f(x) < 0$ similarly.

EXAMPLE 1. Solve graphically: $7x + 4 - 2x^2 < 0$.   (1)

SOLUTION. 1. Transpose terms, to give x^2 a positive coefficient:

$$0 < 2x^2 - 7x - 4. \tag{2}$$

Let $f(x) = 2x^2 - 7x - 4$. Then, (2) becomes $0 < f(x)$.

2. Solve $f(x) = 0$ to find the x-intercepts of the graph of $y = f(x)$:

$$2x^2 - 7x - 4 = 0; \quad (2x + 1)(x - 4) = 0; \tag{3}$$
$$x = -\tfrac{1}{2} \quad and \quad x = 4.$$

3. The graph of $y = f(x)$ in Figure 97 on page 251 was drawn by use of $x = -\tfrac{1}{2}$, $x = 4$, and other values. The graph is above the x-axis, or $f(x) > 0$

$$if \quad x > 4 \quad or \quad x < -\tfrac{1}{2}. \tag{4}$$

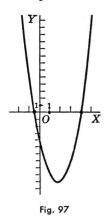

Fig. 97

The values of x satisfying (4) form the solution of (1). The corresponding points on an x-axis form the graph of (1).

Comment 1. Similarly, the solution of $f(x) < 0$ is the set of values of x between $-\frac{1}{2}$ and 4, or the set where $-\frac{1}{2} < x < 4$.

Comment 2. To obtain (4) accurately, all we needed was the x-intercepts $x = 4$ and $x = -\frac{1}{2}$, and our knowledge that the graph in Figure 97 is a parabola which is concave *upward.*

★*Note 1.* Notice that, for any real number a, we have

$$x - a < 0 \quad when \quad x < a; \tag{5}$$

$$x - a > 0 \quad when \quad x > a. \tag{6}$$

★EXAMPLE 2. Solve (1) without graphing.

SOLUTION. 1. From (2) and (3), we find that (1) is equivalent to

$$0 < 2(x + \tfrac{1}{2})(x - 4) \quad or \quad 0 < [x - (-\tfrac{1}{2})](x - 4). \tag{7}$$

2. The points $x = -\frac{1}{2}$ and $x = 4$ divide the x-axis in Figure 97 into three parts. Inequality (7) is satisfied in each part where both factors on the right have the *same sign.* If $x < -\frac{1}{2}$, from (5) we find that both factors are negative, so that (7) is true. If $-\frac{1}{2} < x < 4$, then $x - 4 < 0$ but $x - (-\frac{1}{2}) > 0$ so that (7) is *not* true. If $x > 4$, both factors on the right in (7) are positive so that (7) is true. Thus, the values of x satisfying (7) are those where $x < -\frac{1}{2}$ and those where $x > 4$, as stated otherwise in (4).

EXERCISE 85

Solve the inequality graphically or by general reasoning.

1. $5x - 7 < 0.$ **2.** $9 - 2x > 0.$ **3.** $x^2 - 4 > 0.$

4. $25 - x^2 < 0.$ **5.** $x^2 + 6 < 5x.$ **6.** $6x < 8 + x^2.$

7. $x^2 + 7 < 3x.$ **8.** $3x < 2x^2 + 2.$ **9.** $3 < 2x^2 + 5x.$

10. $x^2 + 6 < 0.$ **11.** $5x - 3x^2 < 0.$ **12.** $2x^2 + 7x < 0.$

13. $x^2 + 2 \leqq 4x.$ **14.** $2x^2 + 11 \geqq 10x.$ **15.** $3x^2 + 5 < x.$

Solve by inspection, without graphing.

16. $x^2 < 49.$ **17.** $4x^2 \geqq 25.$ **18.** $4x^2 < a^2$, if $a > 0.$

For what values of x is the radical real?

19. $\sqrt{x^2 - 9}.$ **20.** $\sqrt{16 - x^2}.$ **21.** $\sqrt{x^2 - 5x + 4}.$

★142. Analytical proofs of inequalities

To prove a specified inequality about variables, for all values on their ranges, it is sometimes convenient to proceed as follows.

1. **Suggestive analysis.** *Assume that the inequality is true and, from it, proceed to a simpler inequality which can be verified.*

2. **Demonstration.** *Start with the simpler inequality, and, from it, derive the given inequality by reversing the steps of the suggestive analysis, where each reversal must be justified, by Theorems* I, II, *and* III.

EXAMPLE 1. Prove that, if $x \neq 1$ and $x > 0$, $\qquad \dfrac{1}{x} + x > 2$.

SOLUTION. 1. *Suggestive part.* **IF** the inequality is true, then

(multiply by x) $\qquad\qquad\qquad\qquad 1 + x^2 > 2x;$

(subtract $2x$) $\qquad\qquad\qquad\quad 1 - 2x + x^2 > 0, \quad or \quad (1 - x)^2 > 0.$

2. *Proof.* Since x is real and $\neq 1$, then $1 - x \neq 0$ and

$$(1 - x)^2 > 0, \quad or \quad 1 - 2x + x^2 > 0;$$

(add $2x$) $\qquad\qquad\qquad\qquad 1 + x^2 > 2x.$

Since $x > 0$, by Theorem II we may divide both sides above by x without altering the inequality and thus obtain $\dfrac{1}{x} + x > 2$.

★EXERCISE 86

1. If $0 < A < B$ and $0 < C < D$, prove that $AC < BD$.

2. If $x + y > 0$ and $x \neq y$, prove that $\dfrac{x + y}{2} > \dfrac{2xy}{x + y}$.

3. If $A > 0$ and $B > 0$, prove that $A > B$ is equivalent to $A^2 > B^2$.

If $x > 0$, $y > 0$, and $x \neq y$, prove the inequality.

4. $\dfrac{x + y}{2} > \sqrt{xy}$. $\qquad$ 5. $\dfrac{x}{y} + \dfrac{y}{x} > 2$. $\qquad$ 6. $\dfrac{2xy}{x + y} < \sqrt{xy}$.

Note 1. From Problems 4 and 6, it follows that, if A, G, and H are, respectively, the arithmetic, geometric, and harmonic means of x and y, then $H < G < A$.

If $x > 0$, $y > 0$, and $x > y$, prove the inequality.

7. $x^3 - y^3 > (x - y)^3$. $\qquad$ 8. $x^3 - y^3 > xy(y - x)$. $\qquad$ 9. $x^3 > y^3$.

10. If $x > 1$, prove that $x < x^2$, without graphing.

11. If $0 < x < 1$, prove that $x > x^3$, without graphing.

12. Prove that $a^2 + b^2 \geqq 2ab$, for all values of a and b.

★143. Graph of an inequality in one or in two variables

If f and g are functions of a single independent variable, x, the one-dimensional graph of $f(x) < g(x)$ was described on page 250 as the set of all points on an x-axis representing the values of x which satisfy the inequality.

Let f and g be functions of two independent variables, (x, y). Then, the **graph of the inequality** $f(x, y) < g(x, y)$ is defined as the set of all points in an xy-plane whose coordinates satisfy the inequality.

ILLUSTRATION 1. Suppose that the units for distance are the same on the two axes of an xy-plane. Then, the graph of the equation $x^2 + y^2 = 4$ is the circle of radius 2 with the origin as center in Figure 98. The graph of $x^2 + y^2 > 4$ is the set of all points exterior to this circle. The graph of $x^2 + y^2 < 4$ is the set of points interior to the circle. Let $f(x, y) = x^2 + y^2 - 4$. It is instructive to realize that the graph of $f(x, y) = 0$ is the *boundary* between the points where $f(x, y) < 0$ and those where $f(x, y) > 0$.

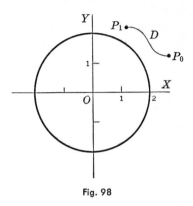

Fig. 98

If f is a function of a single variable, x, we may think of f as a special case of a function of two variables, x and y, having the same value for all values of y if x is assigned any value. Then, we may ask for the *two-dimensional* graph, for instance, of the inequality $f(x) < 0$ in an xy-plane. Thus for the inequality $x - 4 < 0$ or $x < 4$, the graph in an xy-plane consists of all points in the plane to the left of the vertical line $x = 4$.

A situation similar to that in Illustration 1 arises with the graph of any equation $f(x, y) = 0$ and the graphs of the two related inequalities $f(x, y) < 0$ and $f(x, y) > 0$. Let us assume that f is a *continuous* * function at all values of x and y which we consider. Then, $f(x, y) = 0$ on the curve C which is the graph of the equation. Let $P_0 : (x_0, y_0)$ be any point in the xy-plane where $f(x_0, y_0)$ is positive. Then, suppose that a point $P_1 : (x_1, y_1)$ can be joined to P_0 by a continuous curve D, as in Figure 98, not crossing the locus C where $f(x, y) = 0$. If a point $Q : (x, y)$ moves continuously from P_0 to P_1 on D, then *the value $f(x, y)$ changes continuously from $f(x_0, y_0)$*, which is *positive*, to $f(x_1, y_1)$ at P_1, and $f(x, y)$ *does not assume the value 0 because D does not meet C.* Hence, $f(x_1, y_1)$ *also is positive*, because $f(x, y)$ could not change from the *positive* value $f(x_0, y_0)$ to a *negative* value without becoming *zero* at some intermediate location. Reasoning of this nature will justify the following procedure in all usual problems.

SUMMARY. *To graph the inequalities $f(x, y) < 0$ and $f(x, y) > 0$ in an xy-plane, first draw the graph, C, of the equation $f(x, y) = 0$. Select a point in each of the regions † into which C divides the plane. Then, the value of $f(x, y)$ at the chosen point in any region determines the nature, positive or negative, of $f(x, y)$ at all points in the region.*

* We shall use "*continuity*" as an intuitionally clear concept; the value of $f(x, y)$ changes *continuously*, without jumps, if the values of x and y *change continuously*.
† We assume that there are such regions.

ILLUSTRATION 2.   Consider $y - 3x - 2 < 0$.   Let $f(x, y) = y - 3x - 2$. The graph of $f(x, y) = 0$ is the line AB in Figure 99.   At $(x = 0, y = 0)$, we have $f(0, 0) = -2$.   Hence, $f(x, y) < 0$ at all points in the plane *below* AB, or the graph of the inequality is the region which is *not* dotted in Figure 99. Similarly the graph of $y - 3x - 2 > 0$ is the region *above* AB.

ILLUSTRATION 3.   Consider the inequality $x^2 + y^2 - 4 > 0$, where we shall let
$$f(x, y) = x^2 + y^2 - 4.$$
We verify that the graph of $f(x, y) = 0$ is the circle in Figure 98, page 253.   At $(x = 0, y = 0)$, we have $f(0, 0) = -4 < 0$; $f(5, 0) > 0$.   Hence, $f(x, y) < 0$ *inside* the circle and $f(x, y) > 0$ outside the circle.   Thus, the graph of $f(x, y) > 0$ consists of all points outside the circle in Figure 98.

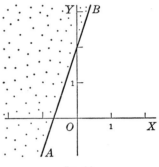

Fig. 99

Note 1.   The graph of a system of two (or more) inequalities in two variables (x, y), such as
$$f(x, y) < 0 \quad and \quad g(x, y) < 0, \tag{1}$$
in an xy-system of coordinates is defined as the set of all points (x, y) whose coordinates satisfy *all inequalities of the system.*

★EXERCISE 87 ★

Graph the inequality or system of inequalities in an xy-plane.   That is, crosshatch the set of points, or otherwise indicate the set forming the graph.

1. $y - x - 2 < 0$.   2. $2x - 3y - 6 > 0$.   3. $x - 3 < 0$.
4. $y - 2 > 0$.   5. $4x + 3y < -12$.   6. $2x + y > 4$.
7. $x^2 + y^2 < 9$, on an xy-system with equal units on the axes.
8. $x^2 + 4y^2 > 16$.   9. $x^2 - y^2 < 25$.   10. $x^2 - 9y^2 < 36$.
11. $y > x^2$.   12. $y < x^3$.   13. $y < x$.
14. $|x| > |y|$.   15. $y < x^2 - 4x + 6$.   16. $y > x^2 + 2x + 3$.
17. $x + 2 > 0$.   18. $2x - 3 < 0$.   19. $x^2 - 2x - 3 < 0$.

20. $\begin{cases} y - x - 1 < 0, \\ x + y - 3 > 0. \end{cases}$ 21. $\begin{cases} 2y - x - 6 < 0, \\ y - 2x - 1 > 0. \end{cases}$

22. $\begin{cases} 4x^2 + 9y^2 - 36 > 0, \\ y^2 - 4x > 0. \end{cases}$ 23. $\begin{cases} x^2 - 4y^2 - 16 < 0, \\ x^2 + y^2 - 4 > 0. \end{cases}$

★ Also see Note 1, page 306.

Complex Numbers

144. Complex numbers

In order to produce square roots for negative numbers, on page 45 we introduced the imaginary unit i with the property that $i^2 = -1$. We shall start at this point again in expanding the number system.

Let us join i to the system of real numbers. If b is any real number, the product of b and i is defined as a *new number*, written bi or $+ bi$, with the agreement that $0 \cdot i = 0$ and $1 \cdot i = i$. If a and b are real, the sum of a and bi is defined as a *new number*, to be written $(a + bi)$, and called a **complex number**. We agree to use $(0 + bi)$ and $(a + 0i)$ as optional symbols for bi and a, respectively. In $(a + bi)$, we call a the *real part*, bi the *imaginary part*, and b its *coefficient*. We introduce the following terminology in regard to the preceding varieties of numbers.

1. $(a + bi)$ *is called an* **imaginary number** *if* $b \neq 0$.

2. *If* $a = 0$ *and* $b \neq 0$, $(a + bi)$ *is called a* **pure imaginary number**.

3. *If* $b = 0$, *then* $(a + bi)$ *is called a* **real number**.

The number system now consists of *all complex numbers*, including real numbers as special cases. We call $(a + bi)$ the *standard form* for a complex number. Unless otherwise stated, any literal number except i will represent a real number.

ILLUSTRATION 1. $(5 + 7i)$ is an imaginary number. $4i$, or $(0 + 4i)$, is a pure imaginary number. The real number 6 can be written $(6 + 0i)$.

We agree to use the same system of notation for sums and products of complex numbers as in the case of real numbers. Then, we *define* addition and multiplication by specifying that *any sum or product of complex numbers shall have that value which is obtained on the following basis.*

FUNDAMENTAL AGREEMENT. *In addition and multiplication, i acts as if it were a real literal number, obeying Laws I–V of page 5, and satisfying the condition $i^2 = -1$.*

ILLUSTRATION 2. By the preceding agreement,
$$(- i)^2 = [(- 1)i]^2 = 1 \cdot i^2 = - 1.$$
Hence, $- i$ as well as i is a square root of $- 1$. If $P > 0$,
$$(i\sqrt{P})^2 = i^2P = - P; \quad (- i\sqrt{P})^2 = i^2P = - P. \tag{1}$$
Thus, $- P$ **has the two square roots** $\pm \sqrt{- P} = \pm i\sqrt{P}$. By definition,
$$(a + bi) + (c + di) = a + c + (b + d)i.$$
$$(a + bi)(c + di) = ac + (bc + ad)i + bdi^2, \; or$$
$$(a + bi)(c + di) = (ac - bd) + (bc + ad)i.$$

ILLUSTRATION 3. From $i^2 = - 1$, we have $i^4 = 1$. $i^9 = i^8i = (i^4)^2i = i$.

For complex numbers, we accept the definition of subtraction on page 7. Then, to subtract a complex number N, we add its negative, $- N$. Division for complex numbers will be met later.

DEFINITION I. *To say that two complex numbers $a + bi$ and $c + di$ are equal means that $a = c$ and $b = d$.*

From Definition I, since $0 = 0 + 0i$,
$$a + bi = 0 \quad means \; that \quad a = 0 \; and \; b = 0. \tag{2}$$

EXAMPLE 1. Find the real numbers x and y such that
$$2ix - 3iy + x + 2y - i - 4 = 0. \tag{3}$$

SOLUTION. 1. Write the left-hand side in the standard form $A + Bi$:
$$(x + 2y - 4) + i(2x - 3y - 1) = 0. \tag{4}$$
2. From (2) and (4), $\quad x + 2y - 4 = 0 \quad and \quad 2x - 3y - 1 = 0.$ (5)
On solving system (5), we obtain $(x = 2, y = 1)$.

The **conjugate complex number** for any complex number $(a + bi)$ is defined as $(a - bi)$. Thus, the conjugate of $(a - bi)$ is $[a - (- bi)]$ or $(a + bi)$. Hence, we call $(a + bi)$ and $(a - bi)$ *conjugate complex numbers;* each is *the conjugate of the other.*

ILLUSTRATION 4. The conjugate of $(3 + 2i)$ is $(3 - 2i)$. The conjugate of $(4 - 5i)$ is $(4 + 5i)$.

ILLUSTRATION 5. If $c + di \neq 0$, then c and d are not both zero, and
$$(c + di)(c - di) = c^2 - d^2i^2 = c^2 + d^2 \neq 0.$$

ILLUSTRATION 6. We verify that the *difference* of two conjugate numbers is a *pure imaginary number;* the *sum* and *product* of the conjugate numbers are *real numbers:*
$$(a + bi) - (a - bi) = 2bi;$$
$$(a + bi) + (a - bi) = 2a;$$
$$(a + bi)(a - bi) = a^2 - b^2i^2 = a^2 + b^2.$$

145. Division for complex numbers

We define division for complex numbers by specifying that, if $c + di \neq 0$, the quotient $(a + bi)/(c + di)$ is the complex number obtained by the following method:

$$\left\{ \begin{array}{c} \textit{Multiply both numerator and denominator} \\ \textit{by the conjugate of the denominator.} \end{array} \right\} \tag{1}$$

That is, by definition,

$$\frac{a + bi}{c + di} = \frac{(a + bi)(c - di)}{(c + di)(c - di)} = \frac{(a + bi)(c - di)}{c^2 + d^2}, \tag{2}$$

where $c^2 + d^2 \neq 0$ since $c + di \neq 0$. By use of (2), we may express any quotient $(a + bi)/(c + di)$ in the standard form $A + Bi$. We agree that $(a + bi)^{-n}$, where n is a positive integer, means $1/(a + bi)^n$.

ILLUSTRATION 1.
$$\frac{5 + 2i}{3 - 4i} = \frac{5 + 2i}{3 - 4i} \cdot \frac{3 + 4i}{3 + 4i} = \frac{15 + 26i + 8i^2}{9 - 16i^2}$$

$$= \frac{15 + 26i - 8}{9 + 16} = \frac{7}{25} + \frac{26}{25} i.$$

If we think of $3 - 4i = 3 - 4\sqrt{-1}$, then the preceding operation, where the numerator and denominator were multiplied by $3 + 4\sqrt{-1}$, is analogous to the procedure used in rationalizing denominators on page 52.

EXERCISE 88

Express in terms of i and simplify. Assume that $a > 0$ and $b > 0$.

1. $\sqrt{-121}$. **2.** $\sqrt{-75}$. **3.** $\sqrt{-81a^2}$. **4.** $\sqrt{-48b^3}$. **5.** $\sqrt{-\frac{25}{9}}$.

6. State the two square roots of -64; -45; $-25a^2$; $-\frac{4}{49}b^2$.

7. Specify the conjugate of $(5 - 7i)$; $-5i$; $6i$; 8; $(2 - 3\sqrt{-5})$.

Perform the indicated operation and simplify to the form $a + bi$.

8. i^9. **9.** i^{10}. **10.** i^5. **11.** i^{39}. **12.** $3i(8i^4)$.

13. $(2 + 3i) - (5 - 7i)$. **14.** $(8 + \sqrt{-4}) - (3 - \sqrt{-25})$.

15. $2i^4(3i^3)$. **16.** $(2i)^5$. **17.** $(3i^3)^2$. **18.** $(5i)^4$.

19. $\sqrt{-5}\sqrt{-20}$. **20.** $\sqrt{-2}\sqrt{-18}$. **21.** $\sqrt{-3}\sqrt{-15}$.

22. $(3 + 4i)(2 - 7i)$. **23.** $(4 - i)(3 + 5i)$. **24.** $(2 - 7i)(2 + 7i)$.

25. $(\sqrt{-5} + 2)(\sqrt{-5} - 2)$. **26.** $(3 - 4\sqrt{-2})(3 + 4\sqrt{-2})$.

27. $\dfrac{2 + 3i}{5 + 4i}$. **28.** $\dfrac{5 + i}{2 - i}$. **29.** $\dfrac{3 + 2i}{4 - 3i}$. **30.** $\dfrac{5}{3 + 2i}$.

31. $\dfrac{3 + \sqrt{-25}}{1 + \sqrt{-4}}$. **32.** $\dfrac{7}{4 - \sqrt{-9}}$. **33.** $\dfrac{36 + 5i}{3i}$. **34.** $\dfrac{6 - 5i}{4i}$.

35. $\dfrac{6}{5i}$. **36.** $\dfrac{-3}{2i}$. **37.** $\dfrac{-5}{4i}$. **38.** $\dfrac{1}{i}$. **39.** $\dfrac{3}{i^3}$. **40.** $\dfrac{-4}{3i^5}$.

41. $(2\sqrt{-5})^3$. **42.** $(3i - 5)^2$. **43.** $2i^{-5}$. **44.** $3i^{-7}$.

45. $(2 + i)^3$.   **46.** $(3 - 2i)^3$.   **47.** $(2 + \sqrt{-3})^3$.   **48.** $(3 + 2i)^{-1}$.

49. Find the reciprocal of $(-4 + \sqrt{-50})$ in the form $(a + bi)$.

Find the real numbers x and y to satisfy the equation.

50. $x - 3 + iy = 6i$.   **51.** $3x - y + ix + 2iy = 4 - i$.

52. If $c^2 + d^2 = 1$, find $(c + di)^{-1}$ in the standard form.

★53. Suppose that $c + di \neq 0$. Let $(a + bi)/(c + di)$ be defined (analogously to division on page 6) as *the number $(x + yi)$, if it exists, such that*

$$a + bi = (c + di)(x + yi). \tag{1}$$

Prove that the number on the right in (2) on page 257 satisfies (1); thus the present definition is equivalent to (2) on page 257. Also, multiply both sides of (1) by $(c - di)/(c^2 + d^2)$, to prove that only one number $(x + yi)$ satisfies (1).

146. The complex plane

Let $(x + yi)$ be any complex number. Then, we shall represent it geometrically in a coordinate plane by the *point P* whose abscissa is x and ordinate is y. Or, we may think of $(x + yi)$ as represented by the **vector** OP from the origin to the point $P:(x, y)$. This form of representation is illustrated in Figure 100.

ILLUSTRATION 1. In Figure 100, $(3 + 4i)$ is represented by $D:(3, 4)$ or by the vector OD, as we choose. The real number 3, or $(3 + 0i)$, is represented by A. The pure imaginary number $-4i$, or $(0 - 4i)$, is represented by B. Point C represents the number $(-4 + 2i)$.

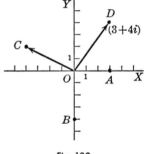

Fig. 100

In Figure 100, all real numbers are represented by the points on the horizontal axis OX, and all pure imaginary numbers by the points on OY. When we use a coordinate plane in this way, we call the horizontal axis *the axis of real numbers*, the vertical axis *the axis of pure imaginary numbers*, and the whole plane *the complex plane*.

The vector representation of a complex number is important as well as interesting because of the following result, which states that, as vectors, complex numbers obey the parallelogram law for vector addition.

THEOREM I. *If z_1 and z_2 are complex numbers, and $z = z_1 + z_2$, the vector OP representing z is obtained by drawing the vectors for z_1 and z_2 from the origin, completing the parallelogram with these vectors as sides, and drawing the diagonal OP of this parallelogram.*

Proof. 1. Let $z_1 = a + bi$; $z_2 = c + di$. Then $z = (a + c) + (b + d)i$. Vectors OM and ON represent z_1 and z_2, respectively, in Figure 101, page 259.

2. In Figure 101, P has the coordinates $x = OR$ and $y = RP$. By considering congruent triangles, it can be verified that, for all positions of M and N,

$$OR = OS + SR = OS + OK = a + c; \qquad (1)$$

$$RP = RH + HP = SM + KN = b + d. \qquad (2)$$

Hence, from (1) and (2), OP represents z.

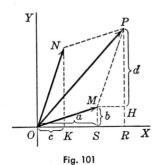

Fig. 101   Fig. 102

ILLUSTRATION 2. In Figure 102, we find

$$z = (5 + 3i) + (- 3 + 2i) = 2 + 5i$$

by adding the vectors for $(5 + 3i)$ and $(- 3 + 2i)$.

Note 1. To *subtract* $(c + di)$ from $(a + bi)$ geometrically, we geometrically *add* $(- c - di)$ to $(a + bi)$.

Note 2. Imaginary numbers were introduced in the 16th century by CARDANO but were not thoroughly appreciated until 100 years later. The words *real* and *imaginary*, as now employed in references to numbers, were introduced by DESCARTES (1637), and the symbol i for $\sqrt{-1}$ by EULER (1748). A Norwegian surveyor, WESSEL (1797), was the first to employ the geometrical representation of complex numbers on a plane.

EXERCISE 89

Represent the complex number as a point, and also as a vector.

1. $3 + 4i$.   **2.** $6i - 3$.   **3.** $- 4 - 5i$.   **4.** $8i$.   **5.** $- 3i$.

6. $2 - i\sqrt{2}$.   **7.** $3 - \sqrt{-9}$.   **8.** $\sqrt{-24}$.   **9.** $\sqrt{-25}$.   **10.** $- 7$.

On one plane, plot the number, its conjugate, and its negative.

11. $4 - 5i$.   **12.** $- 3 - 2i$.   **13.** 6.   **14.** $- 5i$.   **15.** $2 - \sqrt{-49}$.

Separately plot each number in parentheses, or its negative, and find the sum or difference geometrically. Read the sum from the figure.

16. $(2 + 2i) + (4 + i)$.   **17.** $(2 + i) + (- 3 + 5i)$.

18. $(- 2 + i) + (- 6 - 3i)$.   **19.** $(- 3 - 4i) + (7 - 2i)$.

20. $(5 + 0i) + (0 + 4i)$.   **21.** $(- 3 + 0i) + (0 - 6i)$.

22. $(1 + 3i) + (5 - 4i)$.   **23.** $(- 2 + 3i) - (4 + 2i)$.

24. $(-2i) + (4)$.   **25.** $(3i) + (-5)$.

26. $(2i) + (-4i)$.   **27.** $(-2-i) - (3+6i)$.

28. $(5+2i) - (3-4i)$.   **29.** $(5-2i) + (3+2i) + (-4+3i)$.

30. Let z be a complex number. State and demonstrate a construction for locating the point representing $-z$; the conjugate of z.

147. Trigonometric form

In our future discussion in this chapter, in any representation of complex numbers in an xy-plane, we shall assume that the units for distance on the two axes are equal. Also, in use of trigonometric functions, we shall consider them as functions of *angles*, with the attitude of Defini- 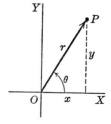 tion I on page 140. As a rule, on account of our principal objectives, we shall use degree measure for angles.

In Figure 103, let OP represent $x + yi$, let r be the length of OP, and let $\theta = \angle XOP$. Then, θ is in its stand-ard position on the coordinate system, and thus the fol-lowing equations are a consequence of Definition I on page 140.

Fig. 103

$$r = \sqrt{x^2 + y^2}; \qquad \tan \theta = \frac{y}{x}; \tag{1}$$

$$x = r \cos \theta; \qquad y = r \sin \theta; \tag{2}$$

$$x + yi = r(\cos \theta + i \sin \theta). \tag{3}$$

We call $r(\cos \theta + i \sin \theta)$ the **trigonometric** (or **polar**) form, θ the **amplitude** (or **argument**), and the positive length r the **absolute value** (or **modulus**) of $x + yi$. The amplitude may be taken as any angle with initial side OX and terminal side OP, because the values of the trigonometric functions are the same for all such coterminal angles. Hence, if θ is one amplitude, the other permissible amplitudes are $(\theta + k \cdot 360°)$, where k is any integer. Usually, we select the amplitude as an angle which is positive or $0°$ and less than $360°$. Two complex numbers are *equal* if and only if *their ab-solute values are equal* and *their amplitudes differ at most by an integral mul-tiple of $360°$.*

To plot $r(\cos \theta + i \sin \theta)$, *construct* $\angle XOP = \theta$, *with* $OP = r$; *then P represents the given complex number.*

ILLUSTRATION 1. In Figure 104, the vector OM represents

$$6(\cos 60° + i \sin 60°).$$

Instead of $60°$, we could use $420°$, or $-300°$, etc., as the amplitude.

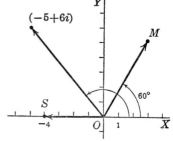

Fig. 104

ILLUSTRATION 2. We may write

$$0 = 0 \cdot (\cos \theta + i \sin \theta),$$

where θ has any value. That is, the absolute value of zero is 0, and the amplitude is *any* angle whatever.

To change a complex number *from the trigonometric form to the form* $(x + yi)$, obtain $\cos \theta$ and $\sin \theta$ from a trigonometric table, or from memory if θ is $0°$, $30°$, $45°$, $60°$, $90°$, or some corresponding angle greater than $90°$.

ILLUSTRATION 3. $3(\cos 45° + i \sin 45°) = \frac{3}{2}\sqrt{2} + \frac{3}{2}i\sqrt{2}.$

$$6(\cos 35° + i \sin 35°) = 6(.819 + .574i) \qquad \text{(Table IV)}$$

$$= 4.914 + 3.444i.$$

The absolute value of a real number a, or $(a + 0i)$, as defined for a complex number, is $\sqrt{a^2 + 0^2}$ or $\sqrt{a^2}$, which is $+ a$ if $a \geq 0$ and is $- a$ if $a < 0$; this is identical with $| a |$ as defined on page 6. Hence, *the two uses of the absolute value terminology are consistent.* Thus, it is consistent to use the symbol $| x + yi |$ to represent *the absolute value of* $(x + yi)$, that is, to represent r in the trigonometric form of $(x + yi)$:

$$| x + yi | = \sqrt{x^2 + y^2}. \qquad (4)$$

ILLUSTRATION 4. $| -4 + 0i | = | -4 | = 4.$ $| 3 + 4i | = \sqrt{25} = 5.$

SUMMARY. *To change from the form* $(x + yi)$ *to* $r(\cos \theta + i \sin \theta)$.

1. *Plot* $(x + yi)$ *as a vector OP, and indicate* θ *by an arrow.*

2. *If* $(x + yi)$ *is real or pure imaginary, read* $r = \overline{OP}$ *from the figure, observe the value of* θ*, and write the polar form.*

3. *If* θ *is not quadrantal, obtain* $r = \sqrt{x^2 + y^2}$*; find* θ *by noticing its quadrant, and also using one of the following functions of* θ:

$$\tan \theta = \frac{y}{x}; \qquad \sin \theta = \frac{y}{r}; \qquad \cos \theta = \frac{x}{r}. \qquad (5)$$

ILLUSTRATION 5. To express the real number -4 in polar form, we plot $(-4 + 0i)$, as vector OS in Figure 104 on page 260. The amplitude is $\theta = 180°$. The absolute value is $r = \overline{OS} = 4$. Hence,

$$-4 = -4 + 0i = 4(\cos 180° + i \sin 180°),$$

which can be checked by using $\cos 180° = -1$ and $\sin 180° = 0$.

EXAMPLE 1. Find the trigonometric form of $(-5 + 6i)$.

SOLUTION. 1. $r = \sqrt{61}$ and θ is in quadrant II (Figure 104 on page 260)

2. $\tan \theta = -\frac{6}{5} = -1.200$. In Table IV, we seek an acute angle α such that $\tan \alpha = 1.200$; we obtain $\alpha = 50.2°$. Hence,

$$\theta = 180° - 50.2° = 129.8°;$$

$$-5 + 6i = \sqrt{61}(\cos 129.8° + i \sin 129.8°).$$

EXERCISE 90

Plot the number. Then, express it in the form $x + yi$.

1. $3(\cos 30° + i \sin 30°)$.
2. $4(\cos 210° + i \sin 210°)$.
3. $2(\cos 360° + i \sin 360°)$.
4. $5(\cos 90° + i \sin 90°)$.
5. $3(\cos 300° + i \sin 300°)$.
6. $7(\cos 135° + i \sin 135°)$.
7. $4(\cos 225° + i \sin 225°)$.
8. $3(\cos 60° + i \sin 60°)$.
9. $5(\cos 270° + i \sin 270°)$.
10. $6(\cos 180° + i \sin 180°)$.
11. $4(\cos 123° + i \sin 123°)$.
12. $10(\cos 328° + i \sin 328°)$.
13. $\cos (-135°) + i \sin (-135°)$.
14. $2[\cos (-45°) + i \sin (-45°)]$.

HINT. Recall $\cos (-\theta) = \cos \theta$; $\sin (-\theta) = -\sin \theta$.

Change the given number to its polar form.

15. $3i$.   16. $-2i$.   17. -8.   18. 6.   19. $2 + 2i$.
20. $3 - 3i$.   21. $-8 + 8i$.   22. $\sqrt{3} + i$.   23. $i - \sqrt{3}$.
24. $-2 - 2i\sqrt{3}$.   25. $-4 + 4i\sqrt{3}$.   26. $3\sqrt{3} - 3i$.   27. $-5 - 5i$.
28. $3 + 4i$.   29. $-12 + 5i$.   30. $5 - 12i$.   31. $4 + 3i$.
32. $\cos 60° - i \sin 60°$.   33. $5(\cos 120° - i \sin 120°)$.

34. Change the number and its conjugate to polar form: $(1 + i)$.
35. Find the conjugate of $r(\cos \theta + i \sin \theta)$ in polar form.
36. Find the reciprocal of $r(\cos \theta + i \sin \theta)$ in polar form.
37. Compute $|5 - 12i|$; $|7 + 24i|$; $|h - ki|$.

148. Products and quotients in polar form

THEOREM II. *An amplitude for a product of complex numbers is the sum of their amplitudes, and the absolute value of the product is the product of the absolute values of the factors.*

Proof. Consider a product of just two complex numbers:

$r_1(\cos \theta_1 + i \sin \theta_1) \cdot r_2(\cos \theta_2 + i \sin \theta_2)$

$$= r_1r_2(\cos \theta_1 \cos \theta_2 + i \sin \theta_1 \cos \theta_2 + i \cos \theta_1 \sin \theta_2 + i^2 \sin \theta_1 \sin \theta_2)$$

$$= r_1r_2[(\cos \theta_1 \cos \theta_2 - \sin \theta_1 \sin \theta_2) + i(\sin \theta_1 \cos \theta_2 + \cos \theta_1 \sin \theta_2)].$$

Hence, from the addition formulas of page 235,

$$r_1(\cos \theta_1 + i \sin \theta_1) \cdot r_2(\cos \theta_2 + i \sin \theta_2)$$
$$= r_1r_2[\cos (\theta_1 + \theta_2) + i \sin (\theta_1 + \theta_2)]. \tag{1}$$

Note 1. We extend (1) to a product of any number of factors by successive applications of (1). Thus, we use (1) twice below:

$$r_1(\cos \theta_1 + i \sin \theta_1) \cdot r_2(\cos \theta_2 + i \sin \theta_2) \cdot r_3(\cos \theta_3 + i \sin \theta_3)$$
$$= r_1r_2[\cos (\theta_1 + \theta_2) + i \sin (\theta_1 + \theta_2)] \cdot r_3(\cos \theta_3 + i \sin \theta_3)$$
$$= r_1r_2r_3[\cos (\theta_1 + \theta_2 + \theta_3) + i \sin (\theta_1 + \theta_2 + \theta_3)]. \tag{2}$$

ILLUSTRATION 1. $\qquad$ $3(\cos 40° + i \sin 40°) \cdot 5(\cos 170° + i \sin 170°)$

$$= 15(\cos 210° + i \sin 210°).$$

COROLLARY 1. *A product of complex numbers is equal to zero if and only if at least one factor is zero.*

Proof. The product is zero if and only if its absolute value is zero. This absolute value is the product of the absolute values of all factors. The product of these real numbers is zero if and only if *at least one factor is zero*, which means that at least one of the original complex numbers has *zero as its absolute value*, which proves the corollary.

A complex number is zero if and only if its absolute value is zero. Thus, in considering a fraction with the denominator $s(\cos \beta + i \sin \beta)$, an assumption that it is *not zero* is equivalent to the condition $s \neq 0$. We accept this fact in the following result.

THEOREM III. *The absolute value of the quotient of two complex numbers, where the divisor is not 0, is the quotient of their absolute values, and an amplitude for the quotient of the complex numbers is the amplitude of the dividend minus the amplitude of the divisor.*

Proof. 1. Consider $[r(\cos \alpha + i \sin \alpha)]/[s(\cos \beta + i \sin \beta)]$, and multiply both numerator and denominator by $(\cos \beta - i \sin \beta)$:

$$\frac{r(\cos \alpha + i \sin \alpha)}{s(\cos \beta + i \sin \beta)} = \frac{r}{s} \cdot \frac{(\cos \alpha + i \sin \alpha)(\cos \beta - i \sin \beta)}{(\cos \beta + i \sin \beta)(\cos \beta - i \sin \beta)}$$

$$= \frac{r}{s} \cdot \frac{(\cos \alpha + i \sin \alpha)[\cos (- \beta) + i \sin (- \beta)]}{\cos^2 \beta + \sin^2 \beta}, \qquad (3)$$

because $\cos (- \beta) = \cos \beta$ and $\sin (- \beta) = - \sin \beta$.

2. In (3), apply Theorem II and recall that $\sin^2 \beta + \cos^2 \beta = 1$:

$$\frac{r(\cos \alpha + i \sin \alpha)}{s(\cos \beta + i \sin \beta)} = \frac{r}{s} \cdot [\cos (\alpha - \beta) + i \sin (\alpha - \beta)]. \qquad (4)$$

ILLUSTRATION 2. $\qquad \dfrac{15(\cos 350° + i \sin 350°)}{5(\cos 240° + i \sin 240°)} = 3(\cos 110° + i \sin 110°).$

THEOREM IV. **(De Moivre's Theorem)** *If n is any positive integer, then*

$$[r(\cos \theta + i \sin \theta)]^n = r^n(\cos n\theta + i \sin n\theta). \qquad (5)$$

ILLUSTRATION 3. From (2) with θ_1, θ_2, and θ_3 replaced by θ, and r_1, r_2, and r_3 replaced by r,

$[r(\cos \theta + i \sin \theta)]^3$

$$= r(\cos \theta + i \sin \theta) \cdot r(\cos \theta + i \sin \theta) \cdot r(\cos \theta + i \sin \theta)$$

$$= r \cdot r \cdot r \cdot [\cos (\theta + \theta + \theta) + i \sin (\theta + \theta + \theta)]$$

$$= r^3(\cos 3\theta + i \sin 3\theta).$$

Proof of (5).   The left-hand side in (5) indicates the product of n factors $r(\cos \theta + i \sin \theta)$. Hence, the absolute value of the nth power is the product of n factors r, or r^n, and an amplitude is the sum of n amplitudes θ, or $n\theta$. Hence, (5) is true.

EXAMPLE 1.   Find $(1 - i)^4$ by use of De Moivre's Theorem.

SOLUTION.   1. Express $(1 - i)$ in polar form:

$$r = \sqrt{2}; \qquad \tan \theta = -1, \text{ with } \theta \text{ in quadrant IV, so that } \theta = 315°.$$

2. Hence, we obtain

$$(1 - i)^4 = [\sqrt{2}(\cos 315° + i \sin 315°)]^4$$

$$= (\sqrt{2})^4(\cos 1260° + i \sin 1260°) = 4(\cos 180° + i \sin 180°) = -4.$$

In the preceding details, we noticed that $1260° = 3 \cdot 360° + 180°$ and used the periodicity of the sine and cosine functions.

EXERCISE 91

Give the result in polar form, except when the final sine and cosine are known without using tables; in that case, express the result in the form $(x + yi)$. Compute any power by use of De Moivre's Theorem.

1. $3(\cos 18° + i \sin 18°) \cdot 4(\cos 42° + i \sin 42°)$.

2. $6(\cos 25° + i \sin 25°) \cdot 3(\cos 125° + i \sin 125°)$.

3. $2(\cos 85° + i \sin 85°) \cdot 6(\cos 310° + i \sin 310°)$.

4. $4(\cos 140° + i \sin 140°) \cdot 5(\cos 275° + i \sin 275°)$.

5. $[2(\cos 15° + i \sin 15°)]^3$.   6. $[3(\cos 60° + i \sin 60°)]^4$.

7. $[2(\cos 45° + i \sin 45°)]^6$.   8. $[5(\cos 250° + i \sin 250°)]^3$.

9. $(2 + 2i)^4$.   10. $(-3 - 3i)^5$.   11. $(-1 + i\sqrt{3})^5$.   12. $(i + \sqrt{3})^6$.

13. $(-\sqrt{3} - i)^4$.   14. $(1 - i\sqrt{3})^3$.   15. $(-4 + 4i)^3$.   16. $(3 + 4i)^3$.

17. $\dfrac{6(\cos 140° + i \sin 140°)}{2(\cos 30° + i \sin 30°)}$.   18. $\dfrac{5(\cos 250° + i \sin 250°)}{20(\cos 310° + i \sin 310°)}$.

19. $\dfrac{15(\cos 150° + i \sin 150°)}{1 + i}$.   20. $\dfrac{25(\cos 250° + i \sin 250°)}{5\sqrt{2} - 5i\sqrt{2}}$.

21. $\dfrac{2 - 2i\sqrt{3}}{3(\cos 150° + i \sin 150°)}$.   22. $\dfrac{15(\cos 150° + i \sin 150°)}{5(\cos 30° - i \sin 30°)}$.

★23. If $z = r(\cos \theta + i \sin \theta)$, where $r \neq 0$, and if n is a positive integer, prove that $z^{-n} = r^{-n}[\cos(-n\theta) + i \sin(-n\theta)]$, so that *De Moivre's Theorem holds if the exponent is a negative integer.*

★24. In the complex plane with the origin at O, let U be the unit point on the real axis and let P and Q represent $r(\cos \alpha + i \sin \alpha)$ and $s(\cos \beta + i \sin \beta)$, respectively.   Construct $\triangle UOP$ and $\angle QOM = \alpha$; complete $\triangle QOM$ similar to $\triangle UOP$.   (Give the figure for α and β acute, for convenience.)   Prove that M represents the product of the given complex numbers.

149. The *n*th roots of a complex number

In this section, n always represents a *positive integer*. Then, to say that R is an *n*th root of a complex number z means that $z = R^n$.

EXAMPLE 1. Find the cube roots of $8(\cos 150° + i \sin 150°)$.

SOLUTION. 1. Let $r(\cos \alpha + i \sin \alpha)$ be any cube root. Then,

$$8(\cos 150° + i \sin 150°) = [r(\cos \alpha + i \sin \alpha)]^3.$$

Or, by De Moivre's Theorem,

$$8(\cos 150° + i \sin 150°) = r^3(\cos 3\alpha + i \sin 3\alpha). \tag{1}$$

2. If two complex numbers are equal, their absolute values are *equal* and their amplitudes *differ at most by some integral multiple of* 360°. Hence, from (1), the values of r and α which give cube roots satisfy

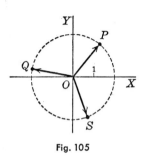

Fig. 105

$$r^3 = 8, \quad or \quad r = 2;$$

$$3\alpha = 150° + k \cdot 360°, \; or$$

$$\alpha = 50° + k \cdot 120°, \tag{2}$$

where k is any integer. On placing $k = 0$, 1, and 2 in (2), we obtain 50°, 170°, and 290° as the values of α. These give the following cube roots:

$$2(\cos 50° + i \sin 50°);$$

$$2(\cos 170° + i \sin 170°);$$

$$2(\cos 290° + i \sin 290°).$$

Comment. If $k = 3$ in (2), then $\alpha = 50° + 360°$, equivalent to the amplitude 50°. If $k = -1$, then $\alpha = 50° - 120° = -70° = 290° - 360°$, equivalent to 290°. Similarly, if k has any integral value in (2), the value found for α is equivalent to one of (50°, 170°, 290°). Hence, the roots obtained in Step 2 are the *only* cube roots. The cube roots are represented by P, Q, and S in Figure 105. These points lie on a circle whose radius is 2, because 2 is the modulus of each of the roots. Moreover, P, Q, and S divide the circumference into *three equal parts* because the amplitudes of the roots are 50°, 170°, and 290°, where adjacent angles differ by 120°.

THEOREM V. *If n is any positive integer, and $R > 0$, any complex number $R(\cos \theta + i \sin \theta)$ has just n distinct nth roots.*

Proof. 1. Suppose that $0 \leqq \theta < 360°$. Let $r(\cos \alpha + i \sin \alpha)$ be any *n*th root. Then, by De Moivre's Theorem,

$$R(\cos \theta + i \sin \theta) = [r(\cos \alpha + i \sin \alpha)]^n = r^n(\cos n\alpha + i \sin n\alpha). \tag{3}$$

2. From (3), $r^n = R$, or $r = \sqrt[n]{R}$; and $n\alpha = \theta + k \cdot 360°$, or

$$\alpha = \frac{\theta}{n} + k \cdot \frac{360°}{n}, \tag{4}$$

where k is any integer. On placing $k = 0, 1, 2, \cdots, (n-1)$ in (4), we obtain the following n distinct values for α, all less than $360°$:

$$\frac{\theta}{n}; \quad \left(\frac{\theta}{n} + \frac{360°}{n}\right); \quad \left(\frac{\theta}{n} + 2\frac{360°}{n}\right); \quad \cdots ; \quad \left[\frac{\theta}{n} + (n-1)\frac{360°}{n}\right]. \tag{5}$$

Corresponding to (5), we obtain the following n distinct nth roots:

$$\sqrt[n]{R}\left(\cos\frac{\theta}{n} + i\sin\frac{\theta}{n}\right); \quad \sqrt[n]{R}\left[\cos\left(\frac{\theta}{n} + \frac{360°}{n}\right) + i\sin\left(\frac{\theta}{n} + \frac{360°}{n}\right)\right]; \quad etc.$$

3. If k has any integral value other than $0, 1, 2, \cdots, (n-1)$ in (4), we obtain a value for α differing from some amplitude in (5) by an integral multiple of $360°$. Hence, in (5) we have the only distinct amplitudes which give nth roots. Thus, $R(\cos\theta + i\sin\theta)$ has *exactly* n distinct nth roots, as obtained in Step 2.

SUMMARY.   *The nth roots of $R(\cos\theta + i\sin\theta)$ are obtained by placing $k = 0, 1, 2, \cdots, (n-1)$ in the formula*

$$\sqrt[n]{R}\left[\cos\left(\frac{\theta}{n} + k\cdot\frac{360°}{n}\right) + i\sin\left(\frac{\theta}{n} + k\cdot\frac{360°}{n}\right)\right]. \tag{6}$$

To obtain the nth roots of a complex number given in the form $(a + bi)$, that is, to solve $z^n = a + bi$ for z, express $(a + bi)$ in polar form and then use (6).

ILLUSTRATION 1.   The 4th roots of $16(\cos 80° + i\sin 80°)$ are

$$2(\cos 20° + i\sin 20°), \qquad 2(\cos 110° + i\sin 110°),$$
$$2(\cos 200° + i\sin 200°), \qquad 2(\cos 290° + i\sin 290°).$$

ILLUSTRATION 2.   To find the 5th roots of -32, or to solve $z^5 = -32$, first write -32 in polar form:

$$-32 = 32(\cos 180° + i\sin 180°).$$

Hence, the five values of z which satisfy $z^5 = -32$ are

$$2(\cos 36° + i\sin 36°), \qquad 2(\cos 108° + i\sin 108°),$$
$$2(\cos 180° + i\sin 180°), \text{ etc.}$$

We notice that the root with amplitude $180°$ is -2.

Note 1.   ABRAHAM DE MOIVRE (1667–1754) was a French mathematician who was compelled to leave France for religious reasons. He settled in London, where he earned a precarious living by miscellaneous mathematical work, partly by solving problems associated with games of chance. He is particularly noted for his work entitled *The Doctrine of Chances,* which was published in 1718 and dedicated to SIR ISAAC NEWTON.

★*Note 2.*   Let m and n be integers, with $n > 0$ and m/n in lowest terms. We defined $a^{m/n}$ on page 49 as the principal nth root of a^m in case a is real and a^m has a *real* nth root. Also, we defined $\sqrt{-P}$ or $(-P)^{\frac{1}{2}}$ as $i\sqrt{P}$ if $P > 0$. Otherwise, *no meaning has been given to* $a^{m/n}$. Now, if $z = R(\cos\theta + i\sin\theta)$, define $z^{m/n}$ *as an n-valued symbol* to represent *any one of the nth roots of z^m*. Then $z^m = R^m(\cos m\theta + i\sin m\theta)$. Hence, all values of $z^{m/n}$ are given by (6) with θ replaced by $m\theta$. In particular, with $k = 0$ in (6), we obtain

$$z^{m/n} = R^{m/n}\left(\cos\frac{m\theta}{n} + i\sin\frac{m\theta}{n}\right), \tag{7}$$

which is the same as obtained from (5) on page 263 in De Moivre's Theorem with n replaced by m/n. That is, this theorem holds for *rational exponents* in the sense that the theorem gives *one of the values of $z^{m/n}$*, as in (7). In (6), with $k = 0$, we have one value of $z^{1/n}$.

EXERCISE 92

Leave any result in polar form, unless its amplitude is an angle for which the values of the trigonometric functions are known without tables; in the latter case, give the result in the form $(a + bi)$. In each problem, find all of the specified roots, and plot them as vectors in a plane.

1. 4th roots of $81(\cos 160° + i\sin 160°)$.

2. Cube roots of $125(\cos 60° + i\sin 60°)$.

3. Cube roots of $27(\cos 228° + i\sin 228°)$.

4. 5th roots of $32(\cos 210° + i\sin 210°)$.

5. Square roots of $9i$.   **6.** Square roots of $-25i$.

7. Cube roots of 27.   **8.** Cube roots of -1.   **9.** 5th roots of $32i$.

10. Cube roots of i.   **11.** 4th roots of 81.   **12.** 4th roots of -16.

13. 4th roots of $(8\sqrt{2} - 8i\sqrt{2})$.   **14.** Square roots of $(-2 + 2i\sqrt{3})$.

15. 4th roots of $(8 - 8i\sqrt{3})$.   **16.** Cube roots of $(-4\sqrt{2} - 4i\sqrt{2})$.

17. 4th roots of $(-8\sqrt{3} + 8i)$.   **18.** Square roots of $(7 - 24i)$.

For the given equation, find all roots in polar forms, or otherwise.

19. $z^4 = 16$.   **20.** $z^5 = 243$.   **21.** $z^6 - 64 = 0$.   **22.** $z^4 + 81i = 0$.

Theory of Equations

150. Polynomials and equations of the *n*th degree

From page 77, we recall that an *integral rational function* $f(x)$ of degree n in a variable x, or a *polynomial* of degree n in x, is of the form

$$f(x) = a_0x^n + a_1x^{n-1} + a_2x^{n-2} + \cdots + a_{n-1}x + a_n, \qquad (1)$$

where $n \geqq 0$ and $a_0, a_1, \cdots, a_n$ are constants, with $a_0 \neq 0$. An *integral rational equation* of degree n in x is an equation which, by transposition of terms if necessary, can be written in the form

$$a_0x^n + a_1x^{n-1} + a_2x^{n-2} + \cdots + a_{n-1}x + a_n = 0, \qquad (2)$$

or $f(x) = 0$ with $f(x)$ as in (1), with $n \geqq 1$. We call (2) the general equation of degree n. Polynomials of degrees 1, 2, 3, and 4 are called *linear, quadratic, cubic,* and *quartic functions*, respectively. Equations of degrees 1, 2, 3, and 4 in x are called *linear, quadratic, cubic,* and *quartic equations*, respectively. In this chapter, any functional symbol such as $f(x)$, $H(x)$, etc., will represent a *polynomial* in x. Unless otherwise stated, any theorem or proof will apply when the coefficients are any complex numbers. Also, in any polynomial (1), we shall assume that $n \neq 0$, unless $n = 0$ is included explicitly.

151. Certain fundamental theorems

REMAINDER THEOREM. *If r is a constant, and if a polynomial $f(x)$ is divided by $(x - r)$ until a constant remainder is obtained, then this remainder is equal to $f(r)$.*

Proof. After $f(x)$ is divided by $(x - r)$, let $q(x)$ represent the quotient, and let R be the constant remainder. Then, since

$$dividend \equiv (divisor) \cdot (quotient) + remainder,$$

$$f(x) \equiv (x - r)q(x) + R. \qquad (1)$$

Since (1) is true for all values of x, we may use $x = r$ in (1). Then,

$$f(r) = 0 \cdot q(r) + R \quad or \quad R = f(r).$$

ILLUSTRATION 1. The following division of $(5x^2 - 3x + 7)$ by $(x - 2)$ checks the Remainder Theorem.

$$
\begin{array}{r}
5x + 7 = q(x) \\
x - 2 \overline{)\, 5x^2 - 3x + 7} \\
5x^2 - 10x \\
\hline
7x + 7 \\
7x - 14 \\
\hline
21 = R
\end{array}
$$

By substitution, if
$f(x) = 5x^2 - 3x + 7$, *then*
$f(2) = 5(4) - 3(2) + 7$, *or*
$f(2) = 21$, *which checks.*

ILLUSTRATION 2. If $f(x) = 5x^3 - 11x^2 - 14x - 10$, and if $f(x)$ is divided by $(x + 2)$, where we recognize $x + 2 = x - (-2)$, then the constant remainder is

$$f(-2) = 5(-2)^3 - 11(-2)^2 - 14(-2) - 10 = -66.$$

Note 1. To say that r is a *root* of an equation $f(x) = 0$ *means that* $f(r) = 0$. Thus, if $f(x) = x^2 - x - 2$, we find that 2 is a root of $f(x) = 0$, or $x^2 - x - 2 = 0$, because $f(2) = 4 - 2 - 2 = 0$.

FACTOR THEOREM. *If $f(r) = 0$ then $(x - r)$ is a factor of $f(x)$. That is, if r is a root of $f(x) = 0$, then $(x - r)$ is a factor of $f(x)$.*

Proof. In (1), $R = f(r)$; hence, by our hypothesis, $R = 0$ and the division of $f(x)$ by $(x - r)$ is exact. Or, from (1),

$$f(x) \equiv (x - r)q(x),$$

which states that $(x - r)$ is a factor of $f(x)$.

CONVERSE OF THE FACTOR THEOREM. *If $(x - r)$ is a factor of $f(x)$, then $f(r) = 0$, or r is a root of the equation $f(x) = 0$.*

Proof. If $f(x)$ is divided by $(x - r)$, the division is exact and yields an integral rational quotient $q(x)$ such that $f(x) \equiv (x - r)q(x)$. Thus $f(r) = 0 \cdot q(r) = 0$, and hence r is a root of the equation $f(x) = 0$.

EXAMPLE 1. Is $(x + 3)$ a factor of $3x^3 - 2x + 5$?

SOLUTION. 1. Let $f(x) = 3x^3 - 2x + 5$, and notice that

$$x + 3 = x - (-3); \qquad f(-3) = 3(-27) + 6 + 5 = -70 \neq 0.$$

2. Hence, by the preceding theorem, $(x + 3)$ is *not* a factor of $f(x)$.

Let $f(x)$ be a given polynomial and let r be a constant. Then, to say that $x = r$ is a **zero** of the function $f(x)$ means that $f(r) = 0$, which also means that $x = r$ satisfies $f(x) = 0$. Thus, *the zeros of the function $f(x)$ are the roots of the equation $f(x) = 0$.*

ILLUSTRATION 3. If $f(x) = x^2 - 5x + 6$, we verify that

$$x^2 - 5x + 6 = 0 \quad gives \quad x = 3 \quad and \quad x = 2.$$

Or, 3 and 2 are the zeros of the function $f(x)$ and the roots of $f(x) = 0$.

EXERCISE 93

Divide $f(x)$ until the remainder is a constant. Also, compute the indicated value of $f(x)$ by substitution, to verify a preceding theorem.

1. $f(x) = 3x^2 + 14x + 8$; divide by $(x - 3)$, and also compute $f(3)$; divide by $(x + 2)$ and also compute $f(-2)$.

2. $f(x) = 2x^2 - 7x + 5$; divide by $(x - 4)$ and also compute $f(4)$.

Answer by computing a value of $f(x)$ and applying the Factor Theorem or its converse. If the answer is yes, find another factor by division.

3. If $f(x) = x^3 + 3x^2 - 5x + 2$, is $(x - 2)$ a factor of $f(x)$?

4. If $f(x) = 2x^3 + 6x^2 - x + 12$, is $(x + 2)$ a factor of $f(x)$?

5. Is $(x - 3)$ a factor of $x^3 - 27$; of $x^3 + 27$?

6. Is $(x + 2)$ a factor of $x^5 - 32$; of $x^5 + 32$?

7. Is $(x + u)$ a factor of $x^4 - u^4$; of $x^4 + u^4$?

Find the values of k for which $(x - 2)$ is a factor of $f(x)$.

8. $f(x) = 3x^2 + 4kx - 5$.   **9.** $f(x) = k^2x^2 + 2kx - 3$.

152. Synthetic division

A telescopic method for division, with detached coefficients, is available for dividing a polynomial $f(x)$ by a binomial $(x - r)$. The method is referred to as *synthetic division*. A background for its development is as follows.

ILLUSTRATION 1. Let us divide $5x^3 - 11x^2 - 14x - 10$ by $x - 3$, in (I).

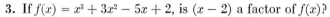

I.

$$5x^2 + 4x - 2 = quotient$$

$$\begin{array}{r} 5x^3 - 11x^2 - 14x - 10 \enspace \big|\underline{x - 3} \\ \hline \star 5x^3 - 15x^2 \\ \hline 4x^2 - 14x\star \\ \star 4x^2 - 12x \\ \hline -2x - 10\star \\ \star - 2x + 6 \\ \hline Remainder = -16 \end{array}$$

II.

$$5x^2 \quad + \; 4x \quad - \; 2 = quotient$$

$5x^3$	$-11x^2$	$-14x$	-10	$x-3$
	$-15x^2$	$-12x$	$+6$	
	$4x^2$	$-2x$	-16	

III.

5	-11	-14	-10	1	-3
	-15	-12	$+6$		
5	4	-2	-16		

In $(x - 3)$, the coefficient of x is 1; hence, at each stage in the division, the coefficient of the highest power of x in the remainder is the next coefficient in the quotient. We obtain (II) by omitting each "$\star$" term in (I) and then condensing (I) into three lines. We obtain (III) from (II) by writing only the coefficient in place of each term; we introduce "5" into the third line so that all coefficients of the quotient appear in that line, and then omit writing the quotient. (III) suggests (IV), which illustrates synthetic division. In (IV) we use "$+3$" instead of "-3" as a multiplier so that we may *add* instead of *subtract* in the third row.

IV.

$$\begin{array}{r|r|r|r|r}
5 & -11 & -14 & -10 & +3 \\
& +15 & +12 & -6 & \\
\hline
5 & +4 & -2 & -16 &
\end{array}$$

Quotient $= 5x^2 + 4x - 2$.   Remainder $= -16$.

SUMMARY. *Routine for synthetic division of $f(x)$ by $(x - r)$.*

1. *Arrange $f(x)$ in descending powers of x, supplying each missing power with zero as a coefficient. Then, arrange the following details in three lines.*

2. *In the first line, write the coefficients a_0, a_1, a_2, $\cdots$, a_n of $f(x)$ in this order. Write a_0 in the first place in the third line.*

3. *Multiply a_0 by r, add the product ra_0 to a_1, and write the sum in the third line; multiply this sum by r, add the product to the next coefficient, a_2, and write the sum in the third line; etc., to the last coefficient of $f(x)$.*

4. *The last number in the third line is the remainder, and the other numbers in the third line are the coefficients of the powers of x in the quotient, arranged in descending powers of x.*

EXAMPLE 1. Divide $(2x^4 - 12x^2 - 5)$ by $(x + 3)$, or $[x - (-3)]$.

SOLUTION.

$$\begin{array}{r|r|r|r|r|r}
2 & 0 & -12 & 0 & -5 & -3 \\
& -6 & +18 & -18 & +54 & \\
\hline
2 & -6 & +6 & -18 & +49 &
\end{array}$$

Quotient $= 2x^3 - 6x^2 + 6x - 18$.   Remainder $= 49$:

$$\frac{2x^4 - 12x^2 - 5}{x + 3} = 2x^3 - 6x^2 + 6x - 18 + \frac{49}{x + 3}. \tag{1}$$

In Example 1, by the Remainder Theorem, it follows that $+49$ is the value of $2x^4 - 12x^2 - 5$ when $x = -3$. This illustrates the following important use of synthetic division.

$$\left\{ \begin{array}{l} \textit{To find the value of a polynomial } f(x) \textit{ when } x = r, \textit{ divide} \\ f(x) \textit{ by } (x - r) \textit{ by synthetic division; the remainder is } f(r). \end{array} \right\} \tag{2}$$

EXAMPLE 2. If $f(x) = 3x^3 + 2x - 3$, find $f(-2)$.

SOLUTION. Divide by $[x - (-2)]$ or $(x + 2)$:

$$\begin{array}{r|r|r|r|l}
3 & 0 & 2 & -3 & -2 \\
& -6 & 12 & -28 & \\
\hline
3 & -6 & 14 & -31 & = f(-2).
\end{array}$$

EXERCISE 94

By synthetic division, find the quotient and the remainder, and summarize as in (1) on this page. In Problem 1, also divide by ordinary long division.

1. $(4x^2 + 3 - 2x) \div (x - 3)$.   **2.** $(3x - 7 + 2x^2) \div (x + 4)$.

3. $(3x^3 - x^2 + 2x - 7) \div (x - 2)$.

4. $(-2x^3 - 4x^2 + 3x - 5) \div (x - 3)$.   **5.** $(2x^3 - 5x^2 + 7) \div (x + 2)$.

6. $(-3x^3 + 2x - 75) \div (x + 3)$.   **7.** $(2x^3 + 5x^2 - 4x - 5) \div (x + \frac{1}{2})$.

Solve by synthetic division.

8. If $f(x) = 3x^4 - 2x^3 + x^2 - x + 7$, find $f(2)$; $f(-3)$.

9. If $f(x) = -2x^4 + 5x^3 - 2x^2 - 7x + 5$, find $f(3)$; $f(-2)$.

10. Find $(x^4 - 12x^3 + 46x^2 - 60x + 9) \div (x - 3)^2$, by dividing twice.

11. Prove that $(x - 1)$ is a factor of $(x^7 - 1)$, without division, by the Factor Theorem. Then, find the other factor by synthetic division.

12. Prove that $(x + c)$ is a factor of $(x^6 - c^6)$, and proceed as in Problem 11.

★13. Prove Properties (I), (II), (III), and (IV) of Section 16, pages 26–27, by use of theorems on page 269. Then, find any implied second factors by use of synthetic division.

153. Graphs of polynomials

The graph of a polynomial $f(x)$ is the graph of the equation $y = f(x)$. In obtaining the graph, synthetic division may be used in computing values of $f(x)$. Whenever we refer to the graph of a polynomial, we assume that its coefficients are real numbers.

ILLUSTRATION 1. A graph of the function $f(x) = x^3 - 12x + 3$ is given in Figure 106; this graph was obtained on page 79. On the graph, point M (where $x = -2$) is higher than any neighboring point of the curve. Hence, we call M a *maximum point* of the curve. We say that $f(x)$ has a *relative maximum* at $x = -2$ because $f(-2)$ is greater than any other value of $f(x)$ if x *is sufficiently near* $x = -2$. Point m (where $x = 2$) is *lower* than any neighboring point of the graph, and is called a *minimum point* of the graph. Also, we say that the function $f(x)$ has a *relative minimum* when $x = 2$.

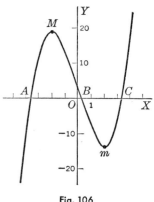

Fig. 106

Note 1. Figure 106, and curves I, II, and III in Figure 107 illustrate the different types met as the graphs of cubic functions. Curve IV in Figure 107 is the graph of a certain quartic function.

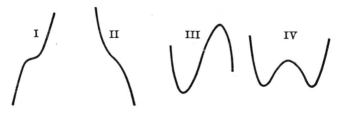

Fig. 107

In more advanced mathematics, it is proved that the graph of a polynomial $f(x)$ of degree n is *a continuous curve, with at most* $(n-1)$ *relative maxima and minima*. Also, the graph is proved to be a *smooth curve*, that is, it has *no sharp corners*. A polynomial $f(x)$ is called a *continuous function* because of its properties which lead us to call its graph a continuous curve.

Recall that the real roots of the equation $f(x) = 0$ are the x-intercepts of the graph of the equation $y = f(x)$.

EXAMPLE 1. Solve graphically: $x^3 + 3 = 12x.$ (1)

SOLUTION. 1. Subtract $12x$: $x^3 - 12x + 3 = 0.$

2. Let $f(x) = x^3 - 12x + 3$. A graph of the equation $y = f(x)$ is given in Figure 106. At the points A, B, and C, the value of $f(x)$ is *zero*. Hence, the abscissas of these points are the real roots of (1). These roots are, approximately, $x = -3.6$, $x = .3$, and $x = 3.3$. Later, we shall refine the graphical method so that it will yield real roots to any desired degree of accuracy.

EXERCISE 95

Graph each polynomial.

1. x^3.   **2.** $-x^3$.   **3.** x^4.   **4.** $-x^4$.

5. $x^3 + 2x^2 - 3x + 4$.   **6.** $-x^3 + 2x^2 - x + 1$.

7. $-x^3 - 3x^2 + 6x + 7$.   **8.** $x^3 - 3x^2 + 4x + 7$.

9. $x^4 + 3x^3 - 6x^2 + 16x - 5$.   **10.** $-x^4 + 24x^2 - 12x + 4$.

Obtain approximate values of the real roots graphically.

11. $x^3 - 4x^2 - 3x + 7 = 0$.   **12.** $x^3 + x^2 - 7x - 8 = 0$.

13. $x^3 + 3x^2 + 3x - 2 = 0$.   **14.** $2x^4 - 11x^2 + 10 = 0$.

154. Consequences of the Fundamental Theorem of Algebra

The following result was proved first in 1799 by the great German mathematician JOHANN KARL FRIEDRICH GAUSS (1777–1855). The proof is beyond the scope of this book.

FUNDAMENTAL THEOREM OF ALGEBRA. *Every integral rational equation of degree $n > 0$ in a single variable has at least one root.*

By use of the preceding result, we then establish the following sequence of theorems, where the coefficients in any polynomials or their factors are allowed to be any complex numbers.

THEOREM I. *If $f(x)$ is a polynomial of degree n in x, where $n > 0$, there exist n factors, linear in x, whose product is $f(x)$.*

Proof. 1. Suppose that $f(x) = a_0 x^n + a_1 x^{n-1} + \cdots + a_n.$

2. By the Fundamental Theorem, the equation $f(x) = 0$ has at least one root. Let r_1 be this root; then, by the Factor Theorem, $f(x)$ has $(x - r_1)$ as a factor.

If we let $Q_1(x) = [f(x) \div (x - r_1)]$, then $Q_1(x)$ is a polynomial whose term of highest degree is $a_0 x^{n-1}$:

$$f(x) = (x - r_1)Q_1(x). \tag{1}$$

3. By the Fundamental Theorem, the equation $Q_1(x) = 0$ has a root, r_2. Therefore, $Q_1(x) = (x - r_2)Q_2(x)$, where $Q_2(x)$ is a polynomial whose term of highest degree is $a_0 x^{n-2}$. On using the expression for $Q_1(x)$, from (1) we obtain $f(x) = (x - r_1)(x - r_2)Q_2(x)$.

4. On continuing this process through n steps, we obtain n numbers $r_1, r_2, \cdots, r_n$ and a function $Q_n(x)$ such that

$$f(x) = (x - r_1)(x - r_2) \cdots (x - r_n)Q_n(x), \tag{2}$$

where a_0 is the coefficient of the term of highest degree in $Q_n(x)$. Moreover, the degree of $Q_n(x)$ is $(n - n)$ or zero. That is, $Q_n(x)$ is a constant and hence $Q_n(x) = a_0$. Therefore,

$$f(x) = a_0(x - r_1)(x - r_2) \cdots (x - r_n), \tag{3}$$

where $r_1, r_2, \cdots, r_n$ may not all be distinct, and some may be imaginary.

THEOREM II. *Any equation $f(x) = 0$ of degree $n > 0$ has at most n distinct roots.*

Proof. 1. By Theorem I, $f(x) = a_0(x - r_1)(x - r_2) \cdots (x - r_n)$. Hence, by the converse of the factor theorem, each of $r_1, r_2, \cdots, r_n$ is a root of $f(x) = 0$. These roots may not all be distinct.

2. If r is any number different from all of $r_1, r_2, \cdots, r_n$, then

$$f(r) = a_0(r - r_1) \cdots (r - r_n) \neq 0,$$

because no factor is zero. Therefore, r is not a root of $f(x) = 0$, and hence $f(x) = 0$ has no roots other than $r_1, r_2, \cdots, r_n$.

If a root R occurs just once among $r_1, r_2, \cdots, r_n$, then R is called a **simple root.** If R occurs exactly h times or, in other words, *if $(x - R)^h$ is the highest power of $(x - R)$ which is a factor of $f(x)$,* R is called a **multiple root** of $f(x) = 0$, whose **multiplicity** is h. Roots of multiplicities 2 and 3 are called **double** and **triple roots,** respectively. The preceding theorem may be restated as follows:

Every equation of degree $n > 0$ has exactly n roots $r_1, r_2, \cdots, r_n$, where a root of multiplicity h is counted as h roots.

COROLLARY 1. *If two polynomials*

$$a_0 x^n + a_1 x^{n-1} + \cdots + a_n,$$

and $\qquad\qquad b_0 x^n + b_1 x^{n-1} + \cdots + b_n,$

each of degree not greater than n, are equal in value for more than n distinct values of x, then the polynomials are identical term by term; that is, $a_0 = b_0$, $a_1 = b_1, \cdots, a_n = b_n$, and hence the polynomials are equal for all values of x.

Proof. By assumption, the equation

$$a_0x^n + a_1x^{n-1} + \cdots + a_n - (b_0x^n + b_1x^{n-1} + \cdots + b_n) = 0, \qquad (4)$$

or,

$$(a_0 - b_0)x^n + (a_1 - b_1)x^{n-1} + \cdots + (a_n - b_n) = 0, \qquad (5)$$

has more than n distinct roots. If any one of the coefficients $(a_0 - b_0)$, $(a_1 - b_1)$, $\cdots$, $(a_n - b_n)$ in (5) were *not* zero, then (5) would be an equation of degree n or less, with more than n distinct roots. This fact would contradict the preceding theorem. Hence, all coefficients in (5) must be zero; that is,

$$a_0 = b_0, \; a_1 = b_1, \cdots, \; a_n = b_n.$$

From Theorem II and (3), any equation $f(x) = 0$, of degree n, with the roots $r_1, r_2, \cdots, r_n$, can be written in the form

$$a_0(x - r_1)(x - r_2)(x - r_3) \cdots (x - r_n) = 0, \qquad (6)$$

where $a_0 \neq 0$, and a_0 may be chosen arbitrarily.

EXAMPLE 1. Form an equation with the following roots, and no others: -2, 4 as a triple root, $(3 \pm i\sqrt{2})$.

SOLUTION. By use of (6) with $a_0 = 1$, one equation is

$$(x + 2)(x - 4)^3[x - (3 + i\sqrt{2})][x - (3 - i\sqrt{2})] = 0, \; or$$
$$(x + 2)(x - 4)^3[(x - 3) - i\sqrt{2}][(x - 3) + i\sqrt{2}] = 0, \; or$$
$$(x + 2)(x - 4)^3(x^2 - 6x + 11) = 0.$$

Note 1. If a polynomial $f(x)$ is given as a product of real linear factors, a useful graph of $f(x)$ can be obtained quickly by use of the zeros of $f(x)$.

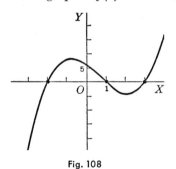

Fig. 108

EXAMPLE 2. Solve graphically:

$$f(x) = (x - 3)(x + 2)(x - 1) > 0. \qquad (7)$$

SOLUTION. A graph of the equation $y = f(x)$ is shown in Figure 108. The graph was obtained by use of $f(3), f(-2)$, and $f(1)$, each of which is zero, and values of y when x is $-3, 0, 2,$ and 4. From Figure 108, $f(x) > 0$ when $-2 < x < 1$ and when $x > 3$. The set of numbers on these intervals forms the solution of (7).

155. Occurrence of imaginary roots in pairs

Recall that, with i as the imaginary unit, i^k is a real number, $+1$ or -1, when k is an even positive integer, and i^k is either $+i$ or $-i$ when k is an odd positive integer. Moreover,

if k is odd,

$$(-i)^k = [(-1)(i)]^k = (-1)^k i^k = -i^k; \qquad (1)$$

if k is even,

$$(-i)^k = (-1)^k i^k = i^k. \qquad (2)$$

We shall use the preceding facts in the following proof.

THEOREM III. *If an imaginary number $(a + bi)$ is a root of an integral rational equation $f(x) = 0$ with real coefficients, then the conjugate imaginary $(a - bi)$ also is a root.*

ILLUSTRATION 1. If $f(x)$ has real coefficients and if $(3 + 2i)$ is a root of $f(x) = 0$, then $(3 - 2i)$ also is a root.

Proof of Theorem III. 1. On substituting $x = a + bi$ in $f(x)$, we obtain

$$f(a + bi) = h_1(a, b) + ih_2(a, b), \tag{3}$$

where h_1 and h_2 are polynomials in a and b with real coefficients. In the expansion of the left-hand side in (3), since the coefficients in $f(x)$ are real, the terms involving *even* powers of i give $h_1(a, b)$, and the terms involving *odd* powers of i give $h_2(a, b)$.

2. Since $x = a + bi$ is a root of $f(x) = 0$, we have $f(a + bi) = 0$. Hence, by (2) on page 256, $\qquad h_1(a, b) = 0 \quad and \quad h_2(a, b) = 0. \tag{4}$

3. To obtain $f(a - bi)$, we note that the result can be found *by replacing i by $- i$* in the expansion of $f(a + bi)$. By (1) and (2), this change will have no effect on the *even* powers of i, and will multiply all *odd* powers of i by $- 1$. Hence, from (3) and (4),

$$f(a - bi) = h_1(a, b) - ih_2(a, b) = 0 + 0i = 0. \tag{5}$$

Therefore $x = a - bi$ also is a root of the equation $f(x) = 0$.

COROLLARY 1. *Every polynomial $f(x)$ with real coefficients can be expressed as a product of real linear and real quadratic factors.*

Proof. 1. If $r_1, r_2, \cdots, r_n$ are the *roots* of $f(x) = 0$, or the *zeros* of $f(x)$, then

$$f(x) = a_0(x - r_1)(x - r_2) \cdots (x - r_n). \tag{6}$$

2. By Theorem III, if the function $f(x)$ has an imaginary factor $[x - (a + bi)]$, then $[x - (a - bi)]$ also is a factor. Since

$$[x - (a + bi)][x - (a - bi)] = x^2 - 2ax + a^2 + b^2,$$

which has real coefficients, all imaginary factors can be combined by pairs to give real quadratic factors.

EXERCISE 96

Solve without multiplying the factors.

1. $(x - 3)(x + 4)(x - 8) = 0.$ $\qquad\qquad$ **2.** $(2x^2 - 5x)(x^2 + 3x + 7) = 0.$

Form an equation, with integral coefficients, which has the given roots.

3. $1, 1, - 3, 2.$ $\qquad$ **4.** $2, 3, 3, - 2.$ $\qquad$ **5.** $2, (1 \pm \sqrt{3}).$

6. $6, \frac{3}{2}, \pm 2i.$ $\qquad$ **7.** $\frac{2}{3}, \frac{2}{3}, \pm 3i.$ $\qquad$ **8.** $4, (2 \pm \sqrt{2}).$

9. $2, (3 \pm i).$ $\qquad$ **10.** $- 3, (2 \pm i\sqrt{2}).$ $\qquad$ **11.** $\pm 4, - \frac{3}{2}, 2.$

12. 2 as a triple root. $\qquad\qquad$ **13.** $- 3$ as a root of multiplicity 4.

14. $- 2$ as a double root and $\pm \frac{1}{2}$ as simple roots.

Form an equation $f(x) = 0$ with real coefficients having the given character.

15. A cubic equation, with 2 and $(1 + 2i)$ as roots.

16. A cubic equation, with -3 and $(2 - 5i)$ as roots.

17. A quartic equation, with $(2 + 3i)$ and $(3 - i\sqrt{2})$ as roots.

18. Prove that a cubic equation with real coefficients has either three real roots, or one real and two imaginary roots. Also, state and prove similar theorems for equations of degrees 4 and 5.

Solve the inequality.

19. $(x - 2)(x + 3)(x - 6) < 0.$ **20.** $(x + 3)(2 - x)(x + 4) > 0.$

21. $(x - 2)(x + 3)(x - 4)(x - 6) < 0.$

22. $(x - 2)^2(x - 3)(x + 5)(x - 2) > 0.$ [Need $(x - 2)^2$ be retained?]

156. The roots of $f(-x) = 0$

Let $r_1, r_2, \cdots, r_n$ be the roots of the equation $f(x) = 0$. If we place $x = -X$ in $f(x) = 0$, we obtain $f(-X) = 0$, which is satisfied if and only if

$$-X = r_1, \quad -X = r_2, \quad \cdots, \quad -X = r_n, \; or$$

$$X = -r_1, \quad X = -r_2, \quad \cdots, \quad X = -r_n.$$

Or, the roots of $f(-X) = 0$ are the *negatives* of the roots of $f(x) = 0$. Usually, there is no object in using the new letter X for the new unknown. Thus, we have the following conclusion.

THEOREM IV. *To obtain an equation whose roots are the negatives of those of a given equation $f(x) = 0$, replace x by $-x$ in the equation. Or, the roots of $f(-x) = 0$ are the negatives of the roots of $f(x) = 0$.*

ILLUSTRATION 1. The roots of $x^2 - 5x + 6 = 0$ are $x = 3$ and $x = 2$. On replacing x by $-x$ in the given equation, we obtain

$$(-x)^2 - 5(-x) + 6 = 0, \quad or \quad x^2 + 5x + 6 = 0. \tag{1}$$

From (1), $(x + 3)(x + 2) = 0$, which has the roots $x = -3$ and $x = -2$.

Note 1. The following rule is easily established:

To obtain the equation $f(-x) = 0$ whose roots are the negatives of those of $f(x) = 0$, change the sign of the coefficient of each term of odd degree.

In any particular case, we prefer to proceed directly by use of Theorem IV, which leads naturally to the preceding rule without memorization.

EXAMPLE 1. Obtain the equation whose roots are the negatives of the roots of the equation

$$x^5 - 4x^4 + 3x^3 + 2x^2 - 5x - 7 = 0. \tag{2}$$

SOLUTION. We replace x by $-x$ in (2), which gives

$$(-x)^5 - 4(-x)^4 + 3(-x)^3 + 2(-x)^2 - 5(-x) - 7 = 0, \; or$$

$$-x^5 - 4x^4 - 3x^3 + 2x^2 + 5x - 7 = 0. \tag{3}$$

ORAL EXERCISE 97

Find an equation whose roots are the negatives of those of the given equation.

1. $2x^4 - 3x^3 + 4x^2 - 6x = 5.$ 2. $4x^3 + 2x^2 - 3x = 7.$

3. $2x^3 + 5x^2 + 7x - 3 = 0.$ 4. $4x^5 - x^3 + x^2 - 5x = 8.$

5. $5x^6 - 4x^4 - x^2 + 7 = 0.$ 6. $3x^4 - 2x^3 - 2x + 6 = 0.$

7. $2x^5 - 3x^4 - x^3 = 3x - 1.$ 8. $5x^5 - 3x^3 + 2x^2 - 7x = 9.$

157. Signs of the roots

Let $f(x)$ have real coefficients and be arranged in descending powers of x. Then, if two successive terms differ in sign, there is said to be a **variation of sign.** In counting the variations, zero coefficients (missing powers of x) are disregarded.

ILLUSTRATION 1. $(x^4 - 5x^3 + 6x^2 - 9)$, shows three variations of sign.

We shall use the following interesting theorem without proof. Its demonstration is found in more advanced texts.

DESCARTES' RULE OF SIGNS.   *If $f(x)$ is a polynomial with real coefficients, the number of positive roots of the equation $f(x) = 0$ cannot exceed the number of variations of sign in $f(x)$, and, in any case, differs from the number of variations by an even integer.*

The roots of $f(-x) = 0$ are the negatives of the roots of $f(x) = 0$. Hence, the *negative* roots of $f(x) = 0$ give rise to the *positive* roots of $f(-x) = 0$. Therefore, we obtain the following result.

COROLLARY 1.   *The number of negative roots of $f(x) = 0$ cannot exceed the number of variations of sign in $f(-x)$, etc.*

Without actually solving an equation, we can obtain useful information about its roots by use of Descartes' rule of signs and other theorems.

EXAMPLE 1.   Without solving, investigate the roots of

$$2x^4 + 5x^2 - 4x - 1 = 0. \tag{1}$$

SOLUTION.   1. Let $f(x)$ represent the left-hand member; $f(x)$ has one variation of sign. Hence, by Descartes' rule, there *cannot be more than one positive root*. The possibility of *no* positive root does not enter, because $1 - 0 = 1$, which is *not an even integer*. Hence, there is *exactly one positive root*.

2. We obtain $f(-x) = 2x^4 + 5x^2 + 4x - 1$, which has one variation of sign. Hence, as in Step 1, (1) has *exactly one negative root*.

3. Since (1) has four roots, there are two imaginary roots, one positive root, and one negative root.

EXAMPLE 2.   State what can be learned about the roots of the equation $2x^5 - 3x^4 + 2x - 5 = 0$ without solving it.

SOLUTION. 1. Let $f(x)$ represent the left-hand side. Then, $f(x)$ has three variations of sign. Hence, the equation has one or three positive roots.

2. $f(-x) = -2x^5 - 3x^4 - 2x - 5$, with no variations of sign. Hence, there are *no negative roots.*

3. There are four imaginary roots and one positive root, or three positive roots and two imaginary roots, because imaginary roots occur in pairs.

EXERCISE 98

Without solving the equation, investigate the roots by use of general theorems.

1. $2x^2 - 3x - 5 = 0.$ **2.** $2x^3 - 5x^2 + 2x = 4.$ **3.** $x^4 - 3x = 2.$

4. $x^4 + x^2 + 1 = 2x^3.$ **5.** $3x^5 - 4x^3 + 2x^2 = 3.$ **6.** $4x^4 + 3x^2 = 2.$

7. $x^4 + 5x^3 + x^2 = 6.$ **8.** $x^3 + 2x^2 = 5.$ **9.** $x^3 + 3 = 0.$

10. $x^5 + 2x^3 = 4.$ **11.** $x^3 + 3x = 4.$ **12.** $x^6 + 4 = 0.$

13. $x^7 - x^3 = 1 - x.$ **14.** $x^5 + 2x^2 - x = 3.$ **15.** $x^7 + 5 = 0.$

16. $x^6 + 3x^4 + 2x^3 = 5.$ **17.** $3x^6 - 2x^4 - 15 = 0.$

Given that all roots are real, determine their nature.

18. $x^3 + 4x^2 - 20x = 48.$ **19.** $x^6 - 6x^4 + 12x^2 - 8 = 0.$

20. $4x^3 - 12x^2 + 11x = 3.$ **21.** $x^5 - 2x^4 - 13x^3 + 39x^2 = 24x.$

158. Bounds for the real roots

Suppose that the coefficients in the polynomial $f(x)$ are real. Then, if no real root of $f(x) = 0$ is *greater than* some number L, we call L an **upper bound** for the real roots of $f(x) = 0$. If no real root is *less than* some number l, we call l a **lower bound** for the real roots. An upper bound can be found from the following theorem, which we easily justify in each application. In applying the theorem to an equation $f(x) = 0$ where the coefficient of the highest power of $f(x)$ is negative, usually we would multiply both sides by -1.

THEOREM V. *If $k > 0$, and if all numbers in the 3d row of the synthetic division of $f(x)$ by $(x - k)$ are of the* **same sign or zero,** *then no real root of $f(x) = 0$ is greater than k.*

A lower bound for the roots of $f(x) = 0$ can be found by applying Theorem V to $f(-x) = 0$, whose roots are the *negatives* of those of $f(x) = 0$, and then taking the *negative of the upper bound thus found.*

EXAMPLE 1. Find bounds for the real roots of

$$f(x) = x^3 + 3x^2 - 12x - 9 = 0. \tag{1}$$

SOLUTION. 1. On dividing $f(x)$ by $(x - 3)$ by synthetic division, all numbers in the third line are found to be positive, and $f(3) = 9$.

$$
\begin{array}{r|rrr|r}
1 & 3 & -12 & -9 & \underline{3} \\
  & 3 & 18 & 18 & \\
\hline
1 & 6 & 6 & 9 &
\end{array}
$$

Hence, if we should divide $f(x)$ by $(x - a)$, where a is any number *greater* than 3, we would find that $f(a) > 9$, because each number in the second row in this new division would be greater than the corresponding number in the division by $(x - 3)$. Hence, if $a > 3$, then a is not a root of $f(x) = 0$; or, 3 is an *upper* bound for the real roots of $f(x) = 0$.

2. To find a lower bound, consider

$$f(- x) = - x^3 + 3x^2 + 12x - 9 = 0, \text{ or}$$
$$x^3 - 3x^2 - 12x + 9 = 0.$$

By the method of Step 1, we find that 6 is an upper bound for the roots of $f(- x) = 0$. Hence, $- 6$ is *less* than any root of $f(x) = 0$, or $- 6$ is a *lower* bound for the roots.

★*Note 1.* Instead of the method of the preceding solution in finding a lower bound for the roots, the student might desire to use the following result. In such a case, he should prove the theorem, or justify each application as in Step 1 of the solution of Example 1.

THEOREM VI. *If $k < 0$, and if the numbers in the 3d row of the synthetic division of $f(x)$ by $(x - k)$* **alternate in sign,** *then k is a lower bound for the roots of $f(x) = 0$.*

EXERCISE 99

Find bounds for the real roots of the equation.

1. $x^3 + 3x^2 - 14x + 7 = 0.$ 2. $4x^3 + 2x^2 - 17x + 10 = 0.$
3. $2x^4 - 3x^3 - 17x^2 = 55.$ 4. $x^4 - 2x^2 - 80 = 0.$
5. $x^3 - 5x^2 - 90 = 0.$ 6. $2x^5 - 8x^3 + 2x^2 = 45.$
7. $x^3 - 3x^2 = 43x - 17.$ 8. $3x^4 - 12x^3 + 10x^2 = 19.$
9. $x^5 - 4x^4 - 25x = 85.$ 10. $x^4 - 18x^3 + 35x = 28.$
11. $x^5 - 6x^4 + 15x^3 - 17x^2 - 8x = 25.$

159. Rational roots

We may obtain rational roots of an integral rational equation by a trial and error process based on the following result.

THEOREM VII. *If an equation*

$$a_0 x^n + a_1 x^{n-1} + a_2 x^{n-2} + \cdots + a_{n-1} x + a_n = 0, \tag{1}$$

with integral coefficients and $a_0 \neq 0$, has a rational root c/d, where c/d is in lowest terms, then c is a factor of a_n and d is a factor of a_0.

Proof. 1. By hypothesis, c and d are integers with no common factor except ± 1. On substituting c/d for x in (1), we obtain

$$a_0 \frac{c^n}{d^n} + a_1 \frac{c^{n-1}}{d^{n-1}} + a_2 \frac{c^{n-2}}{d^{n-2}} + \cdots + a_{n-1} \frac{c}{d} + a_n = 0. \tag{2}$$

2. On multiplying both sides of (2) by d^n we find

$$a_0c^n + a_1c^{n-1}d + a_2c^{n-2}d^2 + \cdots + a_{n-1}cd^{n-1} + a_nd^n = 0, \text{ or} \tag{3}$$

$$d(a_1c^{n-1} + a_2c^{n-2}d + \cdots + a_{n-1}cd^{n-2} + a_nd^{n-1}) = -a_0c^n. \tag{4}$$

3. In (4), all letters represent integers and d is a factor on the left. Hence, d is a factor of a_0c^n. But, unless $d = \pm 1$, d is not a factor of c^n because d is not a factor of c. Hence, d is a factor of a_0.

4. On subtracting a_nd^n from both sides in (3), we obtain

$$a_0c^n + a_1c^{n-1}d + \cdots + a_{n-1}cd^{n-1} = -a_nd^n. \tag{5}$$

In (5), c is a factor of the left-hand side and hence is a factor of a_nd^n. But, unless $c = \pm 1$, c is not a factor of d^n. Hence, c is a factor of a_n.

COROLLARY 1. *Any rational root of an equation*

$$x^n + b_1x^{n-1} + b_2x^{n-2} + \cdots + b_{n-1}x + b_n = 0, \tag{6}$$

with integral coefficients, is an integer and an exact divisor of b_n.

Proof. By the theorem, if c/d is a root of (6), then d is a factor of the coefficient of x^n, and c is a factor of b_n. Since the coefficient of x^n is 1, hence $d = \pm 1$, and therefore c/d is an integer, $\pm c$, which is a factor of b_n.

Note 1. For reference, one may say that equation (6) is in the **b-form;** its essential feature is that the coefficient of x^n is 1.

In solving an equation, whenever a rational root is found, *depress* the degree of the original equation $f(x) = 0$ by removing the factor of $f(x)$ corresponding to the known root. Then, continue the solution by finding the roots of the **depressed equation,** with Theorem VII used again if the depressed degree is at least 3.

EXAMPLE 1. Find all rational roots of

$$f(x) = x^4 - 6x^3 + 3x^2 + 24x - 28 = 0.$$

SOLUTION. 1. By Corollary 1, the possible rational roots are the integral divisors of -28, or $\pm 1, \pm 2, \pm 4, \pm 7, \pm 14$, and ± 28.

2. By inspection of $f(x)$, we find $f(1) = -6$; hence, 1 is not a root. Also, $f(-1) = -42$ and -1 is not a root.

3. From synthetic division by $(x - 2)$, we find $f(2) = 0$, and

$$f(x) = (x - 2)(x^3 - 4x^2 - 5x + 14).$$

1	-6	3	24	-28	2
	2	-8	-10	28	
1	-4	-5	14	0	

Hence, 2 is a root. The other roots of $f(x) = 0$ are the roots of the *depressed equation* $x^3 - 4x^2 - 5x + 14 = 0$.

4. Let $Q(x) = x^3 - 4x^2 - 5x + 14$. Then, the possible rational roots of $Q(x) = 0$ are $\pm 1, \pm 2, \pm 7, \pm 14$. From Step 2, ± 1 are not roots. From

synthetic division of $Q(x)$ by $(x + 2)$, we find $Q(-2) = 0$ and

$$Q(x) = (x + 2)(x^2 - 6x + 7).$$

$$\begin{array}{r|rrr|r} 1 & -4 & -5 & 14 & \underline{-2} \\ & -2 & 12 & -14 & \\ \hline 1 & -6 & 7 & 0 & \end{array}$$

Hence, -2 is a root. The depressed equation is $x^2 - 6x + 7 = 0$, whose solutions, obtained by the quadratic formula, are $x = 3 \pm \sqrt{2}$, which are irrational. Hence, 2 and -2 are the only rational roots of $f(x) = 0$.

EXAMPLE 2. Find all roots of $\qquad f(x) = 3x^3 + 2x^2 - 3x - 2 = 0$.

SOLUTION. 1. By Theorem VII, if c/d is a root, the possible values of c are ± 1 and ± 2; the possible values of d are ± 1 and ± 3. On forming all possible fractions c/d from these values, we find the following as the possible rational roots: $\pm 1;\ \pm 2;\ \pm \frac{1}{3};\ \pm \frac{2}{3}$.

2. From synthetic division by $(x - 1)$, we find that $f(1) = 0$, and that

$$f(x) = (x - 1)(3x^2 + 5x + 2).$$

$$\begin{array}{r|rrr|r} 3 & 2 & -3 & -2 & \underline{1} \\ & 3 & 5 & 2 & \\ \hline 3 & 5 & 2 & 0 & \end{array}$$

Hence, 1 is a root; the depressed equation is $3x^2 + 5x + 2 = 0$. From this equation, we find that the other roots are -1 and $-\frac{2}{3}$.

EXERCISE 100

Find all rational roots and, if their determination leads to a depressed equation which is a quadratic, find all the roots. In case there are no rational roots, this fact must be demonstrated thoroughly.

1. $x^3 - 7x + 6 = 0$.
2. $x^3 + 3x^2 + 12 = 16x$.
3. $2x^3 - 3x^2 - 7x = 6$.
4. $x^3 - 3x - 2 = 0$.
5. $x^3 - x^2 = 8x - 12$.
6. $x^3 + 2x^2 - 9x = 4$.
7. $x^4 - 4x^3 - 5x^2 = 36 - 36x$.
8. $x^4 + 10x + 24 = 15x^2$.
9. $x^3 + x^2 - 6x = 2$.
10. $x^4 - 6x^2 + 15x = 4$.
11. $2x^3 + 5x^2 - 8x = 6$.
12. $5x^3 + 6x + 4 = 8x^2$.
13. $2x^3 + 7x^2 + 6x = 5$.
14. $4x^3 - 25x^2 + 50x = 11$.
15. $3x^3 + 2x^2 - 3x = 1$.
16. $4x^3 - 19x^2 + 32x = 15$.
17. $2x^3 + 5x^2 - 14x = 8$.
18. $3x^3 - 2x^2 = 2x - 8$.
19. $8x^3 + 18x^2 + 3x = 2$.
20. $x^4 - 3x^3 - 12x = 16$.

★*Find bounds for the roots and then obtain all rational roots. Make use of the bounds and general theorems in rejecting possibilities.*

21. $x^3 + 4x^2 - 36x = 72$.
22. $x^4 - x^2 - 32x + 3x^3 = 87$.
23. $x^4 - 3x^3 - 16x^2 = 48x - 168$.
24. $x^3 + 18x^2 + 72x = 54$.
25. $x^4 + 4x^3 + 10x^2 - 41x = 156$.
26. $x^4 + 16x + 30 = 23x^2$.
27. $4x^4 + 3x^3 - 180x = x^2 - 45$.
28. $x^4 - 2x^3 - 21x^2 - 94x = 136$.

160. Separation of real roots

In the graphical method for solving an equation $f(x) = 0$, we focus on the following result, which applies when the graph of $f(x)$ is a continuous curve.

LOCATION THEOREM. *If a and b are real numbers for which $f(a)$ and $f(b)$ have unlike signs, then the equation $f(x) = 0$ has at least one root between $x = a$ and $x = b$.*

Proof. On a graph of $y = f(x)$, as in Figure 109, the points P and Q corresponding to $x = a$ and $x = b$ are on opposite sides of the x-axis. Since the graph is a continuous curve joining P and Q, the graph must cross the x-axis *at least once*, and in any case an *odd number* of times, between P and Q. To each intersection with the x-axis, there corresponds a real root of $f(x) = 0$.

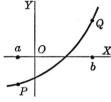

Fig. 109

161. Real roots from successive graphs

Consider an equation $f(x) = 0$, where the function $f(x)$ is *not necessarily integral and rational*. We assume that the graph of $y = f(x)$ is a continuous curve. Then, the essential features of the following method would apply in obtaining the real roots of $f(x) = 0$.

EXAMPLE 1. Solve: $\qquad x^3 - 3x^2 - 2x + 5 = 0.$ $\qquad$ (1)

SOLUTION. 1. By the method of Section 159, we find that (1) has no rational root. Let $f(x)$ represent the left-hand member of (1). By synthetic division, we compute the values of $f(x)$ in the following table, observe the changes in sign for $f(x)$, and conclude that there is a real root of (1) between -2 and -1; between 1 and 2; between 3 and 4. These facts are verified from the graph of $y = f(x)$ drawn in Figure 110 by use of the table.

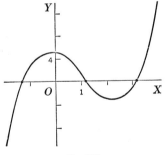

Fig. 110

WHEN x =	-2	-1	0	1	2	3	4
THEN $f(x)$ =	-11	3	5	1	-3	-1	13

2. From Figure 110, the roots are approximately -1.3, 1.2, 3.2.

3. **To obtain more accurately the root r_1 near 3.2:**

A. *To bracket the root r_1 between successive tenths.* By synthetic division we compute $f(x)$ at $x = 3.2$, because 3.2 is our best estimate for r_1, and find $f(3.2) = +.65$. From Figure 110, where we think of the root r_1 as unknown but near 3.2, we see that

$$f(x) > 0 \quad if \quad x > r_1.$$

Hence, $r_1 < 3.2$, because $f(3.2) > 0$. Therefore, we compute $f(x)$ *at* $x = 3.1$, *rather than at* $x = 3.3$. Since $f(3.1) = -.24$, we become *certain* that r_1 lies between 3.1 and 3.2:

When x =	3.1	3.2
Then $f(x)$ =	$-.24$	$+.65$

B. *Enlarge the graph between* $x = 3.1$ *and* $x = 3.2$, by use of the preceding values of $f(x)$. The graph, in Figure 111, is taken as a straight line, because we used just two points to determine it, and act as if a small segment of the

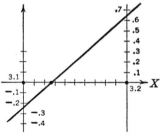

Fig. 111

graph is well approximated by a straight line. From Figure 111, we estimate $r_1 = 3.13$.

C. *To bracket the root* r_1 *between successive hundredths.* First, we compute $f(3.13) = +.014$. Then, after inspection of Figure 111, we decide that $r_1 < 3.13$ and hence compute $f(3.12) = -.073$. We conclude that r_1 lies between 3.12 and 3.13.

When x =	3.12	3.13
Then $f(x)$ =	$-.073$	$+.014$

D. By use of the preceding values, we draw a straight line approximation to the graph of $y = f(x)$ between $x = 3.12$ and $x = 3.13$ on an enlarged scale, in Figure 112, and estimate $r_1 = 3.128$. The final 8 is doubtful, but could be verified by computing $f(x)$ for values of x to successive thousandths near $x = 3.128$.

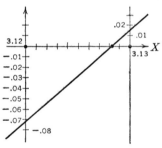

Fig. 112

4. Similarly, we find the other roots, -1.330 and 1.202.

★*Note 1.* The result, 3.13, obtained from Figure 111 can be found *without a figure* by use of **simple interpolation,** as used for instance with logarithm tables. In this method, we first notice that, if r is the unknown root, then $f(r) = 0$. From the following data, we assume that, since 0 is 24/89 of the

When x =	3.1	r	3.2
Then $f(x)$ =	$-.24$	0	.65

$3.2 - 3.1 = .1; \quad 0 - (-.24) = .24;$
$.65 - (-.24) = .89.$

numerical distance from $-.24$ to .65, then r is *the same proportion of the way from 3.1 to 3.2.* Or, we assume that

$$r = 3.1 + \frac{24}{89}(.1) = 3.1 + .027 = 3.13, \text{ } approximately.$$

The preceding assumption is *exactly* equivalent to assuming that the graph of $f(x)$ between $x = 3.1$ and $x = 3.2$ is a *straight line*. This statement can be proved by drawing appropriate triangles in Figure 111 and then using properties of similar triangles.

SUMMARY. *To find irrational roots of $f(x) = 0$ as accurately as desired.*

1. *Establish the general location of the real roots, by computing $f(x)$ for integral values of x, or values spaced moderately otherwise.*

2. *From a graph of $y = f(x)$, estimate the value of each root to the nearest tenth. Let one of these estimates be x_1, for a particular unknown root r_1. Then, improve on the estimate as follows.*

3. *Bracket r_1 between successive tenths by computing $f(x)$ first for $x = x_1$, and then for successive tenths in the values of x, on whichever side of x_1 is appropriate, as judged by the graph which was used in Step 2.*

4. *Graph $f(x)$ on an enlarged scale, for values of x between the tenths of the bracket found in Step 3, with a straight line as the approximate curve. From this graph, read an estimate x_2 of the root r_1 to the nearest hundredth.*

5. *Bracket the root r_1 between successive hundredths by computing $f(x)$ at $x = x_2$, and at other neighboring values of x, expressed to hundredths. Etc.; continue by the method of Step 4 to obtain r_1 as accurately as desired.*

Each step of the preceding method accurately specifies the *next to the last decimal place* in the estimate being obtained. Hence, to determine the root accurately to k decimal places, we obtain the estimate to $(k + 1)$ places, where *the last place remains in doubt.*

Note 2. In a diagram such as Figure 111, use generous scales. To aid accuracy in estimating the point where the line graph crosses the x-axis, it is desirable that the scale units should cause the acute angle between the line and the x-axis to be greater than $30°$.

To obtain the real roots of an integral rational equation $F(x) = 0$ of degree $n > 2$, Descartes' rule of signs and other general theorems should be applied first. Then the rational roots, if any, should be found. If $f(x) = 0$ is the depressed equation after removal of factors corresponding to all rational roots, then the method of the Summary should be applied to obtain the irrational real roots.

EXERCISE 101

Obtain the results accurate to two decimal places, unless otherwise specified. Find any specified root by starting with a graph over just one x-unit.

1. The root of $2x^3 - 11x^2 + 15x - 1 = 0$ between 2 and 3.
2. The root of $x^3 - 10x^2 + 32x + 66 = 0$ between -2 and -1.
3. The root of $x^3 + x^2 - 10x + 4 = 0$ between 0 and 1.
4. The root of $x^4 + x^3 + x^2 - 2x = 6$ between 1 and 2.

5. The two roots of $x^3 - 7x + 7 = 0$ between 1 and 2.

HINT. Start from a graph using $x = 1$, $x = 1.5$, and $x = 2$.

6. The two roots of $5x^3 + 6x^2 - 7x + 1 = 0$ between 0 and 1.

Find all real roots.

7. $x^3 + 3x^2 + 3x = 10$.   **8.** $x^3 - 3x^2 + 3x = 14$.

9. $x^3 - 2x^2 = x - 1$.   **10.** $x^3 - 2x^2 = 5x - 4$.

11. $x^3 + 2x^2 = 7x - 1$.   **12.** $x^4 - 6x^3 + 12x^2 = 10x + 2$.

13. $4x^3 - 12x^2 + 8x = 1$.   **14.** $3x^4 + 5x^3 - x^2 - 4x = 1$.

15. $x^4 - 2x^3 + 3x^2 = 11x - 10$.   **16.** $x^3 - 2x^2 = 14x + 13$.

Find the indicated principal root.

17. $\sqrt[4]{10}$.   **18.** $\sqrt[3]{185}$.   **19.** $\sqrt[3]{-62}$.   **20.** $\sqrt[5]{-148}$.

HINT for Problem 17. We desire the positive root of $x^4 - 10 = 0$.

The equation has no rational roots. Find the real roots.

21. $x^3 - 4.57x^2 + 6.14x = 2.139$.   **22.** $x^4 + 4x^3 + 6x^2 + 384x = 1063$.

23. An open box is to be made from a rectangular piece of cardboard, 12″ long and 8″ wide, by cutting equal squares from the corners and turning up the sides. Find the length of a side of these squares if the box is to contain 56 cubic inches.

24. It is known that the maximum safe load S in pounds for a beam of a certain material and specified length, supported at both ends, is given by $S = 15d^2x$, where x is the breadth and d is the depth, in inches. The beam is to be cut from a log 10 inches in diameter. Find the breadth correct to one decimal place, if $S = 3500$ pounds.

25. The relation $M = x - e \sin x$, called **Kepler's equation,** holds between the *mean anomaly* M and the *eccentric anomaly* x of a planet at any point in its path; e is the eccentricity of the path, and M and x are measured in radians. If $e = .4$ and $M = 4$, find x.

★162. Coefficients in terms of the roots

Let $f(x) = 0$ be an integral rational equation where the coefficients in $f(x)$ are any complex numbers. Then, we find that the coefficients can be expressed in terms of the roots of $f(x) = 0$.

ILLUSTRATION 1. Let r_1, r_2, and r_3 be the roots of

$$x^3 + b_1x^2 + b_2x + b_3 = 0. \qquad (1)$$

From page 274,

$$x^3 + b_1x^2 + b_2x + b_3 \equiv (x - r_1)(x - r_2)(x - r_3)$$
$$\equiv x^3 - (r_1 + r_2 + r_3)x^2 + (r_1r_2 + r_1r_3 + r_2r_3)x - r_1r_2r_3. \qquad (2)$$

As a consequence of Corollary 1, page 274,

$$b_1 = -(r_1 + r_2 + r_3); \qquad b_2 = r_1r_2 + r_1r_3 + r_2r_3; \qquad b_3 = -r_1r_2r_3. \qquad (3)$$

Similarly, we find that, if $r_1, r_2, \cdots, r_n$ are the roots of

$$x^n + b_1 x^{n-1} + b_2 x^{n-2} + \cdots + b_n = 0, \tag{4}$$

the following equations are true:

$$\left.\begin{aligned}
b_1 &= -(r_1 + r_2 + \cdots + r_n), \\
b_2 &= r_1 r_2 + r_1 r_3 + \cdots + r_1 r_n + r_2 r_3 + \cdots + r_{n-1} r_n, \\
b_3 &= -(r_1 r_2 r_3 + r_1 r_2 r_4 + \cdots), \\
&\;\cdot\;\cdot\;\cdot\;\cdot\;\cdot\;\cdot\;\cdot\;\cdot\;\cdot\;\cdot\;\cdot\;\cdot\;\cdot\;\cdot\;\cdot\;\cdot \\
b_n &= (-1)^n r_1 r_2 r_3 \cdots r_n.
\end{aligned}\right\} \tag{5}$$

Or, $b_1 = -$ *(the sum of all the roots)*,

$b_2 = +$ *(the sum of the products of the roots, two at a time)*,

$b_3 = -$ *(the sum of the products of the roots, three at a time)*,

$\quad\cdot\;\cdot\;\cdot\;\cdot\;\cdot\;\cdot\;\cdot\;\cdot\;\cdot\;\cdot\;\cdot\;\cdot\;\cdot\;\cdot\;\cdot\;\cdot\;\cdot\;\cdot\;\cdot$

$b_n = (-1)^n \cdot$ *(the product of the roots)*.

If we divide both sides of

$$a_0 x^n + a_1 x^{n-1} + a_2 x^{n-2} + \cdots + a_n = 0 \tag{6}$$

by a_0, we obtain $x^n + \dfrac{a_1}{a_0} x^{n-1} + \dfrac{a_2}{a_0} x^{n-2} + \cdots + \dfrac{a_n}{a_0} = 0.$

Hence, from (5), if $(r_1, r_2, \cdots, r_n)$ are the roots of (6), then

$$\frac{a_1}{a_0} = -(r_1 + r_2 + \cdots + r_n);$$

$$\frac{a_2}{a_0} = +(r_1 r_2 + r_1 r_3 + \cdots); \text{ etc.}$$

Note 1. An *algebraic formula* is one involving only a finite number of the operations of addition, subtraction, multiplication, division, and the extraction of roots, and no other operations. Let $f(x) = 0$ represent the *general equation* of degree n in a single unknown number x. We know that an algebraic formula can be written easily for the single solution when $n = 1$, and for the two solutions (by the quadratic formula) when $n = 2$. Complicated methods are available giving the three solutions when $n = 3$, and the four solutions when $n = 4$. If $n > 4$, it can be proved, by very advanced methods, that *no algebraic formulas* (in terms of the coefficients) *exist which would give the solutions of $f(x) = 0$ if $n \geqq 5$.* This famous result was proved first in 1824 by the Norwegian mathematician NIELS HENRIK ABEL (1802–1829). The essential elements of the solution of the general cubic ($n = 3$) were first published by GIROLAMO CARDANO (1501–1576) in 1545, although he had received the solution under a pledge of secrecy from NICCOLÒ TARTAGLIA (1506–1557). The general quartic ($n = 4$) was first solved by LODOVICO FERRARI (1522-1560). The last three mathematicians were Italians.

★EXERCISE 102

1. By the method of Illustration 1, page 286, derive equations (5) of page 287 for the case of $x^4 + b_1x^3 + b_2x^2 + b_3x + b_4 = 0$.

By use of (5) on page 287, obtain an equation with the specified roots.

2. $2, 3, -4$.   **3.** $\pm \sqrt{3}, 2, -3$.   **4.** $\pm 3i, 2, -4$.

In the remaining problems, x is the unknown.

5. Find the third root of $x^3 + ax^2 + bx - 40 = 0$ if 2 and -5 are known to be roots.

6. Find the third root of $x^3 + hx^2 - 14x + k = 0$ if -3 and 4 are roots.

7. Find the roots of $9x^3 - 30x^2 + bx + c = 0$ if one root is 2 and the other roots differ by 2.

8. Find all roots of $x^4 - 2x^3 - 11x^2 + hx + 36 = 0$ if it has two double roots.

9. Find all roots of $x^3 + 4x^2 + kx - 18 = 0$ if it has one simple real root and one double real root.

Solve the equation if the roots in some order form an A.P.

10. $x^3 - 3x^2 - x + h = 0$.   **11.** $9x^3 + 18x^2 + 11x + k = 0$.

Solve the equation if the roots in some order form a G.P.

12. $x^3 + 3x^2 - 6x + k = 0$.   **13.** $8x^3 + 18x^2 - 27x + k = 0$.

14. Prove that, if $x^3 + qx^2 + rx + s = 0$ has one root the negative of another, then $qr = s$, and conversely.

Note 1. If a function $f(x)$ is defined by a formula, we refer to f as an **algebraic function** if the formula involves just operations of algebra applied to the value of x. More generally, if the function $g(x, y)$ is integral and rational in x and y, and if $y = f(x)$ gives a solution of $g(x, y) = 0$ for y in terms of x at all values of x on a certain range, then f is called an *algebraic function*. In view of Note 1 on page 287, it can be established that, if $g(x, y)$ is of degree $n > 4$ in y alone, an algebraic function $y = f(x)$ may satisfy $g(x, y) = 0$ but it may be *impossible to obtain an algebraic formula for $f(x)$*. If a function $f(x)$ is *not* algebraic, it is called a **transcendental function.** Thus, all functions are classified as either *algebraic* or *transcendental*. Examples of transcendental functions are the trigonometric functions, the exponential function a^x, and the logarithm function $\log_a x$, as met in this text. Other types of transcendental functions arise in later mathematics.

Permutations and Combinations

163. Fundamental principle

The present chapter will develop methods for finding how often specified events can occur, if they are of appropriate types. The following result, and its extension to more than two events, is useful in many situations.

PRINCIPLE I. **Successive or simultaneous events.** *If one event can occur in h ways* * *and if, after its occurrence or at the same time, a second event can occur in k ways, then the two events can occur in the stated fashion in hk different ways.*

Proof. For each occurrence of the 1st event there are k ways for the two events to occur. Hence, since there are h ways in which the 1st event can occur, there are hk ways in which the two events can occur.

ILLUSTRATION 1. If there are 5 ways of going from A to B and 4 ways of going from B to C, then we can go from A to B to C in $5 \cdot 4$ or 20 ways.

Note 1. In this chapter and the next, unless otherwise specified, the word *number* will refer to a *positive integer*.

EXAMPLE 1. How many numbers of three different digits each can be formed by use of the digits 1, 2, 3, 5, 8, and 9.

SOLUTION. We can choose any one of the six digits for the units' place, indicated by 6 in the adjoining right-

(4)	(5)	(6)

hand box; then, any one of the five remaining digits for the tens' place; then, any one of the four remaining digits for the hundreds' place. Hence, by Principle I, we can form $6 \cdot 5 \cdot 4$ or 120 different numbers of the specified type.

In applying Principle I with a complicated act, try to *analyze it into two or more successive or simultaneous acts of a more simple nature.* Then, apply the principle first to each of the simpler acts, and finally to their combination.

EXAMPLE 2. In how many ways can 4 boys and 3 girls be seated in a row of 7 seats if the end seats are to be occupied by boys?

* In referring to *ways* we shall mean *different ways*.

SOLUTION. The 1st seat can be
filled in 4 ways; then, the 7th seat

(4)	(5)	(4)	(3)	(2)	(1)	(3)

in 3 ways, by any one of the 3 re-
maining boys; then, the 2d seat in 5 ways, by any one of the 5 remaining
boys and girls; then, the 3d seat in 4 ways, etc., as in the diagram. Hence,
the 7 seats can be filled in $4 \cdot 3 \cdot 5 \cdot 4 \cdot 3 \cdot 2 \cdot 1$ or 1440 ways.

EXAMPLE 3. In how many ways can 3 men be assigned consecutive seats
in a row of 7 seats?

SOLUTION. 1. *Analysis.* To seat the men in any one of the ways,

(a) *choose 3 consecutive seats, and then*

(b) *seat the men in the 3 seats just chosen.*

2. We can perform act (a) in 5 ways (think first of the 3 seats being at the
left-hand end, and then move to the right-hand end, in 4 steps).

3. After any choice of 3 seats, by Principle I, the 3 men can be assigned
these seats in $3 \cdot 2 \cdot 1$ ways, or (b) can be performed in 6 ways.

4. Hence, by Principle I, (a) and (b) can be done in succession, or the men
can be seated, in $5 \cdot 6$ or 30 ways.

164. Permutations

We can think of any set * of things as being arranged in a set of numbered
places, for instance, in places numbered 1, 2, 3, $\cdots$. Any such ordered
arrangement of any part of a set of things is called a **permutation** of them.
If r of the things occur in the arrangement, it is called a permutation of the
things *taken r at a time.*

ILLUSTRATION 1. The permutations of the letters a, b, and c, taken two at
a time, are *ab, ba, ac, ca, bc,* and *cb;* their permutations, taken three at a time,
are *abc, acb, bac, bca, cab,* and *cba.*

EXAMPLE 1. Find the number of permutations of seven different things
taken three at a time.

SOLUTION. In forming permutations, we can fill the first place in 7 ways,
then the second place with any one of the 6 things remaining after the first
place is filled, and finally the last place in 5 ways. Hence, there are $7 \cdot 6 \cdot 5$ or
210 permutations of the specified kind.

EXERCISE 103

1. From the digits 1, 2, 3, 4, 5, 7, and 8, (a) how many numbers of four
   different digits each can be formed; (b) how many odd numbers of this
   character can be formed?

2. In how many ways can 4 people seat themselves in 6 given seats?

* We shall always mean a *finite* set in such a reference. The class may wish to read parts of
Chapter 17 at this point.

3. Each of 3 departments in a store needs a secretary. There are 6 applicants for the positions. In how many ways can the positions be filled?

4. Two cubical dice, each with its faces numbered 1, 2, 3, 4, 5, and 6, are tossed. In how many ways can they fall?

5. How many permutations (*numbers*) can be formed from the digits 2, 3, 4, 7, and 8 taken three at a time? Write out these permutations.

6. Find an expression for the number of permutations of n different things taken 4 at a time; taken 8 at a time, assuming that $n > 7$.

7. In how many ways can 3 students choose sections in registering for a course where 6 sections are taught at the same hour?

8. How many permutations are there of the letters a, d, h, k, and w taken three at a time? Write out all of these permutations.

9. If all possible numbers of five different digits each are formed from the digits 1, 2, 3, 4, 5, 6, 7, 8, and 9, (*a*) how many are formed? Also, find how many are (*b*) even; (*c*) divisible by 5; (*d*) begin with an even digit and end with an odd digit.

10. From the letters of the word "decimal," all permutations of 5 different letters each will be formed. (1) How many of them are formed? Also, how many (2) begin and end with a *consonant;* (3) have d or c in the center; (4) have consonants and vowels alternating?

11. How many numbers without repeated digits can be formed by use of the digits 1, 2, 3, 4, 5, and 6?

12. In how many ways can 4 men choose movies to attend, if 6 different movies are being shown?

13. In how many ways can 6 men be arranged in a row for a minstrel show if just 4 men are capable of acting as end men?

14. How many flag signals can be shown by a ship if the signal mast has five positions, the flags have different colors, and any signal with less than five flags uses the top positions on the pole? Five flags are available.

15. Four travelers arrive in a town with five hotels. In how many ways can they (*a*) take up quarters; (*b*) take up quarters, each traveler at a different hotel?

16. (*a*) How many numbers of four different digits each can be formed from the digits 0, 2, 3, 5, 6, and 9? Of these numbers, how many (*b*) are even; (*c*) are divisible by 5?

17. In how many ways can 7 people be assigned consecutive positions in a receiving line if the first 2 positions must be filled by selections from 4 of the people?

18. In how many ways can 4 girls and 4 boys be assigned seats in a row at a theater if boys and girls are to alternate?

19. In how many ways can 4 different novels and 3 different mystery stories be arranged in a row on a shelf, with books of the same variety together?

165. Formulas for permutations of different things

Let $_nP_r$ represent the number of permutations of n different things taken r at a time.

ILLUSTRATION 1. We read "$_5P_3$" as "*the number of permutations of 5 things* * *taken 3 at a time.*"

THEOREM I. *The number of permutations of n different things taken r at a time is* $n(n - 1)(n - 2) \cdots (n - r + 1)$, *or*

$$_nP_r = n(n - 1)(n - 2) \cdots (n - r + 1). \tag{1}$$

Proof. In any permutation, we can fill the 1st place by any one of the n things, then the 2d place by any of the $(n - 1)$ things remaining after the 1st place is filled, then the 3d place by any one of the $(n - 2)$ things remaining, $\cdots$, finally the rth place by any one of the $[n - (r - 1)]$ things remaining after the $(r - 1)$th place is filled. Hence, by Principle I, all r places in a permutation of the n things, taken r at a time, can be filled in

$$n(n - 1)(n - 2) \cdots (n - r + 1) \text{ different ways.}$$

COROLLARY 1. *The number of permutations of n different things, taken n at a time, is* $n!$.

Proof. We place $r = n$ in (1) and obtain

$$_nP_n = n(n - 1)(n - 2) \cdots 3 \cdot 2 \cdot 1 = n!. \tag{2}$$

ILLUSTRATION 2. $_7P_4 = 7 \cdot 6 \cdot 5 \cdot 4 = 840$; $_nP_3 = n(n - 1)(n - 2)$.

Note 1. The student should remember that Principle I has wider application than (1) and (2), which were derived by use of the principle.

EXAMPLE 1. In how many relative orders can 7 people take seats at a round table?

SOLUTION. Think of *a particular one* of the people as being seated, and consider his position permanently fixed. Since only *relative* order is involved, it does not matter where he is located. Then, the number of different orders for the 7 people is the number of ways in which six of them can be arranged in *the other 6 seats*, which is $_6P_6$ or $6!$, or 720 ways.

In Example 1, we dealt with **cyclical permutations,** or arrangements in a *ring*. In contrast, permutations as otherwise described can be referred to as **linear permutations,** or arrangements in ordered places in a line. By the method of Example 1, we obtain the following result, because the number of *cyclical* permutations of n different things is equal to the number of *linear* permutations of $(n - 1)$ of the things.

THEOREM II. *The number of cyclical permutations of n different things taken n at a time is* $(n - 1)!$.

* Understood to be *different* things if nothing is said to the contrary.

EXAMPLE 2. In how many ways can 4 boys and 3 girls be seated in a row of 7 seats with the girls in consecutive seats?

FIRST SOLUTION. 1. *Analysis.* We may seat the boys and girls by performing the following successive acts:

(a) *Select 3 consecutive seats.*

(b) *Arrange the girls in these 3 seats.*

(c) *Arrange the boys in the remaining 4 seats.*

2. We can perform (a) in 5 ways. The number of ways for performing (b) is $_3P_3$ or 3!, and for (c) is $_4P_4$ or 4!. Hence, by Principle I, we can perform (a), (b), and (c) in 5(3!)(4!) or 720 ways.

SECOND SOLUTION. 1. *Analysis.* At first, think of the girls as if tied together, giving 5 things for arrangement, the girls as a unit and 4 boys. Then, to seat them we may proceed as follows:

(a) *Choose seats for the 4 boys and the "unit" of girls.*

(b) *Seat the 3 girls in the 3 seats chosen for them.*

2. The number of ways for performing (a) is $_5P_5$ or 5!, for (b) is $_3P_3$ or 3!, and for (a) and (b) is 5!(3!) or 720 ways.

166. Permutations of things not all different

It is easily seen that there are fewer permutations of *like* things than of *unlike* things. For instance, there are 6 permutations of (a, b, c) taken all at a time, whereas the only permutation of the three letters (a, a, a), taken all at a time, is *aaa*.

EXAMPLE 1. Find the number of permutations of (a, a, a, b, c) taken five at a time.

SOLUTION. 1. Let P be the desired number of permutations.

2. Consider (a_1, a_2, a_3, b, c) where all letters are different; their number of permutations taken five at a time is 5!. We can obtain these as follows:

I. *Take in turn each distinct permutation of* (a, a, a, b, c).

II. *Replace the a's in all possible ways by* (a_1, a_2, a_3).

We can perform (I) in P ways, (II) in 3! ways, and hence (I) and (II) in $P(3!)$ ways. Therefore,

$$P(3!) = 5!, \quad or \quad P = \frac{5!}{3!} = 20.$$

THEOREM III. *If P represents the number of distinct permutations of n things taken all at a time when, of the n things, there are u alike, v others alike, w others alike, etc., then*

$$P = \frac{n!}{u!v!w!\cdots}. \tag{1}$$

Proof. 1. For concreteness, let the n things consist of u like things represented by a's, and v other like things represented by b's.

2. Replace the u letters "a" by u different letters $a_1, a_2, \cdots, a_u$ and the v letters "b" by v different letters $b_1, b_2, \cdots, b_v$, thus obtaining n *different* letters. We can create all of their permutations taken n at a time as follows:

i. Take in turn each permutation of the given u letters "a" and v letters "b."

ii. Then, replace the u letters "a" of the permutation in all possible ways by the u different letters $a_1, a_2, \cdots, a_u$.

iii. Replace the v letters "b" in all possible ways by the v different letters $b_1, b_2, \cdots, b_v$.

We can do (*i*) in P ways, (*ii*) in $u!$ ways, and (*iii*) in $v!$ ways. Hence, we can do (*i*), (*ii*), and (*iii*) in succession in $P(u!)(v!)$ ways. But, this is equal to the number of permutations of the n different letters taken n at a time, or $n!$. Hence,

$$P(u!)(v!) = n!, \quad or \quad P = \frac{n!}{u!\,v!}. \tag{2}$$

ILLUSTRATION 1. The number of permutations of the letters in *attention* taken all at a time is $\dfrac{9!}{3!\,2!}$, because there are three t's and two n's.

EXERCISE 104

Read the symbol and compute its value.

1. $_6P_3$. **2.** $_7P_4$. **3.** $_4P_4$. **4.** $_8P_6$. **5.** $_{10}P_3$.

Find the number of distinct permutations of the letters or digits, taken all at a time.

6. $(d, d, c, c, c, c, b, b, b)$. **7.** $(3, 3, 3, 3, 2, 5, 5, 5, 6, 6)$.

8. How many distinct permutations can be made of the letters of the word *commotion*, taken all at a time?

9. How many different numbers of eight digits each can be formed by use of three 1's, two 4's, one 5, and two 7's?

10. With 5 green hats and 3 red hats, all alike except for color, in how many distinct ways can 8 boys be provided with hats?

11. (*a*) In how many relative orders can a host seat himself and 4 guests around a table? (*b*) In how many ways can the host seat his guests after he has chosen his own seat?

12. In how many ways can 4 pennies, 5 nickels, and 3 dimes be distributed among 12 children, if each is to receive one coin?

13. In how many distinguishable ways can 9 similar spherical beads of different colors be strung on a circular wire?

14. How many numbers of five different digits each can be formed by use of 2, 3, 5, 7, and 8, with 2, 3, and 5 consecutive in each number?

15. By use of 8 flags, identical except for color, how many signals can be formed by arranging all of the flags in 8 positions on a pole, if 3 flags are red, 3 are green, and 2 are yellow?

16. By use of 3 different red flags, and 4 different green flags, how many different signals can be formed by flying all of the flags from seven positions on a pole, if flags of the same color are to be consecutive?

17. How many permutations can we form by use of (a, b, c, d, e, h) taken all at a time, with (a, b, e, h) consecutive?

18. In how many ways can 2 men, 3 boys, and 4 girls be seated in a row of 9 seats, with a man at each end and with the boys and girls, respectively, in consecutive seats?

19. In how many different relative orders can 4 men and 4 women be seated around a table, with men and women alternating?

20. In how many ways can we seat 3 girls and 2 boys in a row of 5 seats if the boys are *not* to sit in consecutive seats?

167. Combinations

A *combination* of a set of things is a group of all or of any part of the things, **without regard to the order of the things in this group.** A combination involving r of the things is called a combination of the things *taken r at a time.*

ILLUSTRATION 1. The different combinations of a, b, c, and d, taken 3 at a time, are (a, b, c), (a, b, d), (a, c, d), and (b, c, d). From each combination we can form 3! or 6 different permutations of the 4 letters taken 3 at a time. Thus, from (a, b, c) we can form the permutations abc, acb, bac, bca, cab, and cba. In other words, there are only *four combinations*, whereas there are $4 \cdot 6$, or 24, *permutations* of the 4 letters taken 3 at a time.

We use the symbol $_nC_r$ to denote the number of combinations of n different things taken r at a time.

THEOREM IV. *The number of combinations of n different things taken r at a time is equal to the number of permutations of n different things, taken r at a time, divided by r!.*

Proof. With each combination containing r of the things, we can form $r!$ permutations of the things taken r at a time. Hence, since there are $_nC_r$ different combinations, there are $_nC_r \cdot (r!)$ different permutations. That is,

$$_nC_r \cdot (r!) = {_nP_r}, \; or$$

$$_nC_r = \frac{_nP_r}{r!}. \tag{1}$$

Note 1. We agree that, when we refer to an *arrangement* of a set of things, we shall mean a *permutation* of them. On the other hand, whenever we refer to a *group* formed from a set of things, we shall mean that *no order* is assigned to the members of the group. Thus, a *group* will be a *combination* of things.

EXAMPLE 1. From 10 people, in how many ways can we (a) select a group of 6 people; (b) fill 6 different offices in a club?

SOLUTION. (a) The number of groups which can be formed is the number of combinations of 10 things taken 6 at a time, or $_{10}C_6$. From (1),

$$_{10}C_6 = \frac{_{10}P_6}{6!} = \frac{10 \cdot 9 \cdot 8 \cdot 7 \cdot 6 \cdot 5}{1 \cdot 2 \cdot 3 \cdot 4 \cdot 5 \cdot 6} = 210. \tag{2}$$

(b) The result is $_{10}P_6$ or 151,200.

When we *pick a group* of r things from n things, we *leave a group* of $(n - r)$ things. Thus, *the number of combinations of the n things r at a time is the same as the number of combinations $(n - r)$ at a time, or*

$$_nC_r = {_nC_{n-r}}. \tag{3}$$

We may use (3) to compute $_nC_r$ *if r is close to n.*

ILLUSTRATION 2. $_{50}C_{48} = {_{50}C_2} = \dfrac{50 \cdot 49}{2} = 1225.$

Formula (1) is useful for computation, as seen in (2). However, other convenient formulas for $_nC_r$ can be obtained. Thus, by use of Theorem I, page 292, formula (1) gives

$$_nC_r = \frac{n(n - 1)(n - 2) \cdots (n - r + 1)}{r!}. \tag{4}$$

If both numerator and denominator in (4) are multiplied by $(n - r)!$, the new numerator is

$$1 \cdot 2 \cdot 3 \cdots (n - r)(n - r + 1) \cdots (n - 2)(n - 1)n,$$

or $n!$, and therefore

$$_nC_r = \frac{n!}{r!(n - r)!}. \tag{5}$$

We may prove (3) by use of (5). Thus, from (5),

$$_nC_{n-r} = \frac{n!}{(n - r)![n - (n - r)]!}$$

$$= \frac{n!}{(n - r)!r!} = {_nC_r}.$$

ILLUSTRATION 3. From (5), $_7C_3 = \dfrac{7!}{3!4!} = \dfrac{5 \cdot 6 \cdot 7}{6} = 35.$

EXAMPLE 2. If 7 coins are tossed, in how many ways can it happen that 5 coins fall tails?

SOLUTION. For any way of picking a group of 5 coins from the 7 coins, there is just *one way* of placing the group with tails up, and the other coins with heads up. Hence, the number of ways in which 5 coins can fall tails is equal to $_7C_5$, or 21 ways.

168. Mutually exclusive events

If a certain two events cannot occur simultaneously, we call them *mutually exclusive events*. For such events, we observe the following simple result. It merely states that, if two sets of h objects and k objects, respectively, include no duplications, the total number of objects in the two sets is $(h + k)$.

PRINCIPLE II. *If a first event can occur in h ways and a second event in k ways, and if the events are mutually exclusive, then one or the other of the events can occur in (h + k) ways.*

ILLUSTRATION 1. Suppose that a bag contains 5 white, 6 black, and 4 red balls. By Principle II, we can draw a white ball **OR** a black ball from the bag in $(5 + 6)$ or 11 ways. On the other hand, by the fundamental Principle I for successive events, we can draw a white ball **AND** a black ball in $5 \cdot 6$ or 30 ways. The key words AND and OR are the essential clues leading to the use of Principles I and II, respectively.

EXAMPLE 1. From 6 men and 5 women, in how many ways can we select a group of (a) 4 men alone *or* 3 women alone; (b) 4 men *and* 3 women?

SOLUTION. 1. The number of ways of selecting a group of 4 men is $_6C_4$ or 15 ways, and the number of ways for a group of 3 women is $_5C_3$ or 10 ways.

2. By Principle II, the number of ways for selecting a group of 4 men alone OR 3 women alone is $(15 + 10)$ or 25 ways.

3. By Principle I, the number of ways for selecting a group of 4 men AND 3 women is $15 \cdot 10$ or 150 ways.

169. Miscellaneous methods

In finding the number of ways of performing a complicated act, it is advisable to make a preliminary analysis of the act into either *successive simpler acts* or into various *mutually exclusive simpler acts*. After the numbers of ways of performing the simpler acts have been found, Principles I and II can be employed to obtain the final result.

EXAMPLE 1. How many numbers of five different digits each can be formed if each number involves three odd and two even digits and no digit 0?

SOLUTION. 1. *Analysis.* In forming a number, we must

(a) *select a group of three odd digits from* (1, 3, 5, 7, 9),

(b) *select a group of two even digits from* (2, 4, 6, 8), *and then*

(c) *form a permutation of the five digits selected in* (a) *and* (b).

2. The number of ways for performing (a) is $_5C_3$ or 10 ways, and for (b) is $_4C_2$ or 6 ways. For each way of performing (a) and (b), the number of ways for performing (c) is $_5P_5$ or 5! ways. Hence, by Principle I, the number of ways for performing (a), (b), and (c) is $10 \cdot 6 \cdot 5!$ or 7200 ways.

EXAMPLE 2. How many numbers greater than 5000, with no repeated digits, can be formed by use of the digits 0, 3, 6, 7, 4, 2?

SOLUTION. 1. *Analysis.* The desired numbers are of the following three mutually exclusive types:

(a) *Numbers of six digits each.*

(b) *Numbers of five digits each.*

(c) *Numbers of four digits each.*

2. *For type* (a): the left-hand end can be filled in just 5 ways (with 3, 6, 7, 4, or 2); then the next place in 5 ways, because 0 is now eligible; etc.; the number of these numbers is $5 \cdot 5 \cdot 4 \cdot 3 \cdot 2 \cdot 1$, or 600 numbers. Similarly, there are 600 numbers of type (b).

3. *For type* (c): the left-hand end can be filled in just 2 ways (with 6 or 7); then the next place in 5 ways; etc.; we find $2 \cdot 5 \cdot 4 \cdot 3$ or 120 numbers of type (c).

4. The number of numbers of all types is $(600 + 600 + 120)$ or 1320, by Principle II.

EXAMPLE 3. A bag contains 7 black and 6 white balls. In how many ways can we draw from the bag groups of 5 balls involving *at least* 3 black balls?

SOLUTION. 1. We obtain *at least* 3 black balls if we obtain

(a) EXACTLY 3 black balls and 2 white balls; OR

(b) EXACTLY 4 black balls and 1 white ball; OR

(c) EXACTLY 5 black balls.

2. Since (a), (b), and (c) are *mutually exlcusive events*, we *add* their numbers of ways of occurrence and obtain the following final result:

$$(_7C_3)(_6C_2) + (_7C_4)(_6C_1) + {}_7C_5 = 756 \; ways.$$

Comment. Notice the preliminary analysis of "AT LEAST" into various mutually exclusive possibilities involving "EXACT" situations, to which our methods apply more easily. A similar analysis is usually advisable in any problem involving "AT MOST" in its statement.

Note 1. In mathematical literature, in place of the symbol $_nP_r$ we frequently meet $P_r{}^{(n)}$ or $P_{n,r}$; in place of $_nC_r$, we may meet $C_r{}^{(n)}$, $C_{n,r}$, $\binom{n}{r}$, or other forms.

MISCELLANEOUS EXERCISE 105

1. Write out (a) all the combinations of (H, K, M, N) taken three at a time; (b) all the permutations of (H, K, M, N) taken three at a time.

2. Read each symbol and compute it: $_9C_3$; $_8C_6$; $_{12}C_5$.

3. From a group of 8 people, how many different committees may be appointed consisting of (a) 4 people each; (b) 4 or 5 people each?

4. From a cent, a nickel, a dime, a quarter, and a half dollar, how many sums can be formed of (a) 3 coins each; (b) at least 3 coins each?

5. (a) How many triangles can be drawn with their vertices chosen from 10 given points in a plane, if no three of the points are in a line? (b) How many of these triangles have any specified point as a common vertex?

6. Use the formula $_nC_r = _nC_{n-r}$ to compute $_{500}C_{498}$.

7. How many different groups of 2000 people each could be formed from 2003 people?

8. From a suit of 13 playing cards, (a) how many hands of 5 cards each can be dealt to a player; (b) how many of these hands will include the king?

9. If 5 coins are tossed, in how many ways can they fall?

10. A bag contains 6 black, 7 white, and 8 green balls.* In how many ways can we select groups of balls where each group consists of (a) 4 black or 4 white balls; (b) 4 black and 4 white balls; (c) 4 balls all of the same color; (d) 4 balls of each color?

11. In how many ways can a hostess select 6 luncheon guests from 10 women, if she is to avoid having a particular two of the women together at the luncheon?

12. From a group of 7 girls and 8 boys, how many committees of six each can be formed, involving (a) 3 girls and 3 boys; (b) 6 girls or 6 boys; (c) at least 5 girls?

13. From the digits (1, 2, 3, 4, 5, 6, 7), how many numbers of four different digits each can be formed, if each number involves two odd and two even digits?

14. In how many ways can 6 different presents be given to 5 children?

15. In how many ways can we fill 7 numbered seats with 3 men and 4 women, by selections from 6 men and 5 women?

16. In how many ways can 7 boys choose places in a row of 10 seats?

17. From a bag containing 5 white and 9 black balls, in how many ways can we form a group of 5 balls involving (a) exactly 3 white balls; (b) at least 3 white balls?

18. In how many ways can 9 different books be divided among A, B, and C, so that they receive 4, 3, and 2 books, respectively?

19. From the digits (1, 2, 3, 4, 5, 6, 7, 8, 9), how many numbers of 7 different digits each can be formed in which odd and even digits alternate?

20. If two dice † are tossed, in how many ways can they show a total of 6?

21. In how many ways can 8 people be arranged with 4 people at each of two round tables, and with only relative order of importance at any table?

* Indistinguishable except as to color. This assumption will persist in all problems with similar data in this book.
† Any die referred to in a problem is a cube, with the faces numbered 1, 2, 3, 4, 5, and 6, respectively.

22. How many committees of 6 men each can be selected from 9 men, if a certain 2 men refuse to serve together on any committee?

23. If 6 coins are tossed together, in how many ways can it result that (*a*) all fall heads; (*b*) just two fall heads; (*c*) at least four fall heads?

24. If 7 coins are tossed together, in how many ways can they fall with at most 3 heads?

25. In how many relative orders can we seat 7 people at a round table, with a certain 3 people (*a*) side by side; (*b*) not in consecutive chairs?

26. One bag contains 6 white and 8 black balls, and a second bag contains 3 white and 6 black balls. How many groups of 6 balls each can be selected consisting of 4 black and 2 white balls, (*a*) if all balls come from the same bag; (*b*) if the white balls come from one bag and the black balls from the other bag; (*c*) if there is no restriction in regard to the bags from which the balls come?

27. From the letters of the word *restitution*, how many distinguishable permutations can be formed if all letters are used?

28. In how many ways can two numbers whose sum is even be chosen from (1, 2, 3, 8, 9, 10, 11)?

29. From a suit of 13 cards, in how many ways can we select a group of 5 cards including the king, or the jack, or both?

30. How many distinguishable combinations can be formed of the digits (2, 2, 2, 3, 4, 5, 6), taken three at a time?

31. In how many ways can 10 convention guests be divided, with 3 guests going to a theater, 4 guests to a dance, and 3 guests to a concert?

32. From the letters (*a, o, e, i, r, s, t*), how many permutations of 5 different letters each can be formed, if each permutation involves 2 consonants and 3 vowels?

33. From a group of 7 different books, in how many ways can we choose groups of (*a*) exactly 4 books each; (*b*) at least 4 books each; (*c*) at most 4 books each?

34. From a group of 6 representatives of labor, 5 representatives of business, and 8 representatives of the general public, how many committees of six can be formed consisting of 2 people from each group?

35. In how many ways can 12 different presents be distributed to 4 children, with each to receive 3 presents?

36. From a group of 5 freshmen, 6 sophomores, and 8 seniors, how many committees can be formed if each consists of 3 members of one class and 3 members of another class?

37. How many parallelograms are formed if a set of 4 parallel lines is met by another set of 6 parallel lines, not parallel to the 1st set?

38. In how many ways can 7 dice fall, with all of 1, 2, 3, 4, 5, 6 up?

39. In how many ways can a total of 8 be thrown if 3 dice are tossed?

40. How many combinations of 3 letters each can be formed by use of (a, b, c, d, e) if repetitions are allowed?

41. (*a*) How many different hands of 13 cards each can be made from a usual deck of 52 cards? (*b*) In how many ways can 4 players in a game be dealt hands of 13 cards each? Leave the results in factored form.

170. Proof of the binomial formula

On page 134, we met the expansion of $(x + y)^n$, where n is a positive integer, but no proof was given for the result. We shall prove that

$$\left. \begin{array}{l} (x + y)^n = x^n + {}_nC_1 x^{n-1}y + {}_nC_2 x^{n-2}y^2 + \cdots \\ \qquad + {}_nC_r x^{n-r}y^r + \cdots + {}_nC_{n-1}xy^{n-1} + {}_nC_n y^n, \end{array} \right\} \tag{1}$$

and then compare the coefficients in (1) with the expressions on page 134.

Proof of (1). 1. By definition,

$$(x + y)^n = (x + y)(x + y) \cdots (x + y). \tag{2}$$

The expansion of the product of the n factors $(x + y)$ in (2) on the right consists of the sum of the results obtained by taking, *in all possible ways,* one term out of each of the factors and multiplying the selected terms.

2. We obtain x^n in the expansion of (2) by selecting x out of *each* factor $(x + y)$; since this can be done in just *one way*, we obtain x^n with the coefficient 1 in the expansion, in agreement with (1).

3. We obtain a term of the type $x^{n-1}y$ in the expansion of (2) by selecting y out of just *one factor* on the right, which can be done in n *ways*, and x out of the remaining $(n - 1)$ factors. Thus we get the term $x^{n-1}y$ exactly n *times*, or we obtain $nx^{n-1}y$ on the right in (1). We note that $n = {}_nC_1$. *Etc.*

4. We obtain a term of the type $x^{n-r}y^r$ in expanding on the right in (2) by selecting y out of r of the factors $(x + y)$ and x out of the other $(n - r)$ factors. The number of ways of selecting r letters y out of the n factors is ${}_nC_r$ (the number of *combinations* of r letters y out of n letters y, because the *order of selection is of no importance*). Hence, the term $x^{n-r}y^r$ is obtained ${}_nC_r$ times; or, in other words, ${}_nC_r$ is the coefficient of $x^{n-r}y^r$ in the expansion of $(x + y)^n$.

Note 1. We verify that ${}_nC_1 = n$, ${}_nC_2 = \frac{1}{2}n(n - 1)$, and observe the expression for ${}_nC_r$ in (4) on page 296. Then, on comparing (1) on page 134 with (1) of this section, we see that the results on page 134 were correct. Also, notice the successive terms, the $(r + 1)$th term and the $(r + 2)$th term counting from the left in (1):

$$_nC_r x^{n-r}y^r \quad and \quad {}_nC_{(r+1)}x^{n-r-1}y^{r+1}, \; where \tag{3}$$

$$_nC_{r+1} = \frac{n - r}{r + 1}\, {}_nC_r. \tag{4}$$

The student may verify that (4) proves rule (IV) on page 133. In (1), we refer to $_nC_r x^{n-r} y^r$ as the **general term**, or the term involving y^r.

ILLUSTRATION 1. From (1),

$$(x - y)^5 = x^5 - {}_5C_1 x^4 y + {}_5C_2 x^3 y^2 - {}_5C_3 x^2 y^3 + {}_5C_4 x y^4 - {}_5C_5 y^5, \text{ or}$$

$$(x - y)^5 = x^5 - 5x^4 y + 10x^3 y^2 - 10x^2 y^3 + 5xy^4 - y^5.$$

ILLUSTRATION 2. By use of the general term in (1), the term involving y^{10} in the expansion of $(x^3 + 2y^2)^7$ is

$$_7C_5 (x^3)^{7-5} (2y^2)^5 = {}_7C_2 x^6 (2^5 y^{10}) = 21(32) x^6 y^{10} = 672 x^6 y^{10}.$$

Note 2. If we place $x = 1$ and $y = 1$ in (1), we obtain

$$2^n = 1 + {}_nC_1 + {}_nC_2 + \cdots + {}_nC_r + \cdots + {}_nC_n, \text{ or}$$

$$_nC_1 + {}_nC_2 + \cdots + {}_nC_n = 2^n - 1.$$

Thus, *the total number of combinations of n things taken 1 at a time, or 2 at a time, $\cdots$, or n at a time, is $(2^n - 1)$.*

Note 3. The use of $_nC_r$ as in (1) is so important that, frequently, $_nC_r$ is called the *r*th *binomial coefficient* in the expansion of $(x + y)^n$, without mentioning the meaning of $_nC_r$ as a *number of combinations.*

EXERCISE 106

Write out the expansion of the power by use of combination symbols and then compute the coefficients.

1. $(x + y)^6$. 　　**2.** $(x - y)^5$. 　　**3.** $(x^3 - 3y^2)^5$. 　　**4.** $(2x^2 + y^3)^6$.

Find only the specified term in the expansion by use of the general term, $_nC_r x^{n-r} y^r$, in (1) on page 301.

5. $(x + y)^8$; term involving y^6. 　　**6.** $(2y - x)^{10}$; term involving y^6.

7. $(x - 2z^{\frac{1}{2}})^{12}$; term involving z^4. 　　**8.** $(x^{\frac{1}{3}} + w^2)^7$; term involving $x^{\frac{5}{3}}$.

9. Without computing coefficients, write out the expansion of $(x + y)^{12}$ by use of (1) on page 301. On the basis of past experience with the sizes of binomial coefficients, compute $_{12}C_r$ for that value of r which gives the *maximum result.*

10. For what values of r does $_{17}C_r$ have its maximum value? Find this value.

11. Recall the property $_nC_r = {}_nC_{n-r}$. What property of the coefficients in the expansion of $(x + y)^n$ is proved by the preceding equality?

12. How many committees of one or more people can be made up from a group of 7 people?

13. How many sums of money can be made up by use of combinations of a cent, a nickel, a dime, a quarter, a dollar, a $5 bill, a $10 bill, and a $100 bill?

★14. Obtain the expansion of $(x + y + z)^n$ by use of combination symbols for the coefficients. Use the method of proof employed for (1) on page 301.

Introduction to Set Terminology *

171. The concept of a set of objects

In referring to a *set* of things, we shall take the word **set** as an *undefined term*. Each object in a set will be called an **element** of it, or one of its **members**. A **subset** S of a set T is a set consisting of *some* (*possibly all*) *of the members of* T.

ILLUSTRATION 1. We may refer to the set T of people who are members of the United States Senate. The two senators from Minnesota form a subset, S, of T.

If all elements of a set T can be placed in a one-to-one correspondence with the positive integers from 1 to some number n, inclusive, we say that T is a *finite set* with n members. If T is *not a finite set*, then T is said to be an *infinite set*. In such a case, for every positive integer n, *more than n members can be found in* T.

ILLUSTRATION 2. The set of all positive integers is an infinite set. If $a < b$, the set of all numbers x where $a \leq x \leq b$ is an infinite set of numbers. In a certain sense, investigated in advanced mathematics, there are "*more*" members in this infinite set than in the set of positive integers.

If S is a subset of the set T, we say that S is **included** in T, and write "$S \subset T$," read "S *is included in* T." We have $T \subset T$. If all members of S are members of T, and if all members of T also are members of S, then S and T consist of the *same members* and we write $S = T$. It proves convenient to introduce the so-called **empty set,** or **null set,** consisting of *no* members, and represented by $\emptyset$. We agree to say that $\emptyset$ is included in every set. That is, for any set S, we have $\emptyset \subset S$.

Note 1. If the student should reread the earlier parts of this text, or other mathematics at the same or even lower levels, he would find that the word *set*

* Only Sections 171 and 172 are essential for the fundamental parts of the next chapter.

has occurred informally with intuitive meaning on many occasions. This fact is particularly true in the initial discussion of variables and functions. Thus, the abstract notion of a set of objects is one of the most fundamental concepts of mathematics, and many other fields. Intuitional reactions to sets have been sufficient for our purposes thus far. We now have arrived at a point where a moderate discussion of set operations becomes desirable. Our remarks will be limited mainly to facts which will be useful in the next chapter.

Note 2. If $S \subset T$ and $S \neq T$, we say that S is a **proper subset** of T. In such a case, there is at least one element of T which is not in S.

172. The operations of complement, union, and intersection for sets

Suppose that all sets to which we shall refer are included in a certain set T, which we shall call the **basic space.**

DEFINITION I. *If T is the basic space, the* **complement,** *H', of any set H is the set of elements of T which are not in H.*

Although the elements of T are thought of at present as abstract objects r, let us visualize them as points in a plane. Also, let T be thought of as all points of the plane inside or on some simple closed curve, such as C in Figure 113. Then, let H be the set of points inside or on the boundary of some curve, as in Figure 113 where H is not cross-hatched. With this representation, the complement of H is the set H' which *is cross-hatched* in T. This interpretation of a set as points in a plane is extremely useful; a corresponding figure like Figure 113 sometimes is called a **Venn diagram.**

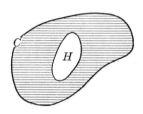

Fig. 113

ILLUSTRATION 1. If T is the interval of numbers x such that $2 \leq x \leq 7$, and H is the subset of T where $3 \leq x \leq 5$, then H' consists of the interval $2 \leq x < 3$ and the interval $5 < x \leq 7$.

ILLUSTRATION 2. If S is the set of points covered by horizontal rulings in Figure 114, and T is the whole plane, then S' is indicated by the radial lines.

DEFINITION II. *The* **union** *of any number of sets is the set consisting of all elements which are in one or more of the sets.*

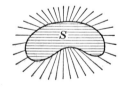

Fig. 114

If A and B are sets, "*the union of A and B*" is represented by $A \cup B$. The order in which the sets are described is of no importance in Definition II. Thus, $A \cup B = B \cup A$. The union of three sets, A, B, and C is represented by $A \cup B \cup C$, or any similar expression with the letters in any desired order. The symbol "$\cup$" may be read "*union*" wherever met.

ILLUSTRATION 3. Let T be the set of all points in the plane in Figure 115, and let A and B represent the sets of points indicated by the vertical and horizontal rulings, respectively. Then $A \cup B$ consists of all ruled points; this set includes some points which are in *both sets*, and thus have double rulings. In general, $A \cup B$ consists of all elements in A alone, or in B alone, or in both A and B.

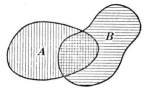

Fig. 115

DEFINITION III. *The **intersection** of any number of given sets is the set of elements belonging to all of the given sets.*

If A and B are sets, "*the intersection of A and B*" is denoted by "$A \cap B$;" it consists of all elements in *both A and B*. In Figure 115, $A \cap B$ consists of all points in the doubly ruled region. To denote "*the intersection of A, B, and C,*" we write $A \cap B \cap C$, where the order of the letters is immaterial. The symbol "$\cap$" may be read "*intersection*" wherever met.

DEFINITION IV. *To say that two sets A and B are **mutually exclusive,** or **disjoint,** means that they have no element in common, or $A \cap B = \emptyset$. To say that certain sets A, B, C, $\cdots$ are mutually exclusive, means that the intersection of any two of the sets is the empty set.*

Fig. 116

ILLUSTRATION 4. In Figure 116, A and B are mutually exclusive sets of points in the plane.

EXERCISE 107

1. If the basic space T consists of all students in a class, and H is the set of all girls in the class, what is the complement of H?

Let the basic space T be the numbers x where $-5 \leq x \leq 10$. Find the specified set corresponding to the given data.

2. If H is all x such that $2 \leq x \leq 4$, describe the complement H'.

3. With H from Problem 2, and K as all x such that $-1 \leq x \leq 3$, describe $H \cup K$; $H \cap K$.

Let the basic space T be the points (x, y) in an xy-plane for which $(-2 \leq x \leq 6$ and $-2 \leq y \leq 8)$. Describe the specified sets in the problems.

4. If H is the square where $(|x| \leq 2, |y| \leq 2)$, show H' in a figure.

5. For H as in Problem 4, and K as the rectangle where $0 \leq x \leq 3$ and $0 \leq y \leq 4$, draw a figure and indicate the sets $H \cup K$ and $H \cap K$.

6. With H and K from Problems 4 and 5, let W be the set of points where $(0 \leq x \leq 5, 0 \leq y \leq 1)$. Describe $H \cup K \cup W$ and $H \cap K \cap W$.

7. If T is the set of all points on an x-axis, what statement can you make concerning the sets of points H: $(2 < x < 5)$ and K: $(8 < x < 10)$?

8. If the basic space T is the set of letters (a, b, c, d, e), write down all subsets of T.

9. Without writing down the sets, compute the number of subsets of T, in Problem 8, containing (i) 3 letters; (ii) any number of letters (including the case of no letters). Note that a subset is a *combination* of the letters. Thus, $_nC_r$ is *the number of subsets of r elements each which can be formed from a set of n elements.*

10. If the basic space T is the set of figures $(1, 2, 3, 4, 5, 6)$, write out all subsets consisting of three of the figures.

11. If the basic space T has 6 elements, how many subsets of T exist? How many exist if T has n elements?

Note 1. The graph of an equation (or inequality) involving just two variables x and y has been described as the *set* of points in an xy-plane whose coordinates (x, y) satisfy the equation (or inequality). In the terminology of this chapter, the *set of solutions* of a system of equations and/or inequalities can be described as the *intersection* of their graphs, where "intersection" is used as in Definition III on page 305. Fortunately, this usage is consistent with the elementary meaning of "intersection of curves."

Show the solution for each system in a figure.

12. $\begin{cases} 3x - y - 3 < 0, \\ x < 4, \\ y > 2. \end{cases}$

13. $\begin{cases} x - y - 2 < 0, \\ x + 2y < 4, \\ x + y > 2. \end{cases}$

14. $\begin{cases} x + 2y + 2 < 0, \\ x - y = 1. \end{cases}$

15. $\begin{cases} x^2 + 4y^2 < 16, \\ x + y < 1. \end{cases}$

★173. Elementary algebra of sets

Sometimes, the *union* of sets A and B is referred to as their *sum*, and the *intersection* of A and B is called their *product*. Also, we have a definition of *equality* for two sets. Thus, we have a basis for development of what may be called an *algebra of sets* where the operations of union, $\cup$, and intersection, $\cap$, play roles similar to those indicated by "$+$" and "$\times$," respectively, in ordinary algebra. We verify the following results, where T is the basic space.

(*Commutative laws*): $A \cup B = B \cup A;$ $A \cap B = B \cap A.$ (1)

(*Associative law for* $\cup$): $A \cup B \cup C = (A \cup B) \cup C = A \cup (B \cup C).$ (2)

(*Associative law for* $\cap$): $A \cap B \cap C = (A \cap B) \cap C = A \cap (B \cap C).$ (3)

($\cap$ *is distributive with respect to* $\cup$):

$$A \cap (B \cup C) = (A \cap B) \cup (A \cap C). \qquad (4)$$

($\cup$ *is distributive with respect to* $\cap$):

$$A \cup (B \cap C) = (A \cup B) \cap (A \cup C). \qquad (5)$$

(*Properties of null set*): $A \cup \emptyset = A;$ $A \cap \emptyset = \emptyset.$ (6)

(Transitive property of $\subset$):   "$A \subset B$ and $B \subset C$"   *implies* $A \subset C.$ (7)

(T acts like a unit in intersections): $T \cap A = A \cap T = A.$ (8)

Results (1), (2), and (3) are true because, in Definitions II and III, the order in which the sets are mentioned is of no importance. We accept (6) because the empty set $\emptyset$ has *no member*. The student will prove (5), (7), and (8) in the next exercise.

Proof of (4). 1. If α is an element in $A \cap B$, then α is in A and in B, and hence is in $(B \cup C)$; therefore α is in $A \cap (B \cup C)$. Similarly, if α is in $A \cap C$, then α is in C and hence is in $B \cup C$; therefore, α is in $A \cap (B \cup C)$. Thus, any element in the right-hand set in (4) is in the set on the left.

2. Suppose that α is in $A \cap (B \cup C)$. Then, α is in A. Also, α is in $B \cup C$ and hence is in B alone or in C alone or in both B and C. Hence, α is in *both A and B*, or in *both A and C*. That is, α is in $(A \cap B) \cup (A \cap C)$, or each element α in the set on the left in (4) is in the set on the right. Hence, (4) is a true set equality.

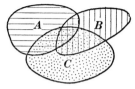

Fig. 117

ILLUSTRATION 1. In Figure 117, for sets A, B, and C in the plane, $A \cap (B \cap C)$, or $(A \cap C) \cap B$, or $(B \cap C) \cap A$, etc., is represented by the region which is dotted and also is crossed by both vertical and horizontal lines.

DEFINITION V. *The **difference** of two sets A and B, represented by * $A \setminus B$, read A minus B, is the set of all points of A which are not in B.*

We may refer to "$\setminus$" as a sign for *set subtraction*. It is important to notice that this operation is not as simple as subtraction in ordinary algebra.

ILLUSTRATION 2. For any set H in the basic space T, we have $H' = T \setminus H$. In Figure 118, where A is the set inside the outer curve and B is the set inside the inner curve, the difference $A \setminus B$ is the set of points covered just by vertical rulings. If $W = A \setminus B$, we verify that $A = W \cup B$, because $W \cup B$ merely replaces those points of A which were removed by subtracting B. Also, $B \setminus A = \emptyset$, because all points of B are in A; in this case, we do *not* have $B = \emptyset \cup A$ because $\emptyset \cup A = A$ and $B \neq A$.

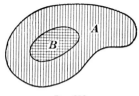

Fig. 118

ILLUSTRATION 3. In Figure 115 on page 305, $A \setminus B$ is the set covered just by vertical rulings. Again, if $W = A \setminus B$, we do *not* have $A = W \cup B$, because this set contains all of the points of B which are not in A.

---

* Frequently in mathematical literature, we find "$-$" used in place of "$\setminus$," which has been introduced in some recent research.

Various peculiarities are exhibited by results of set algebra, as compared to ordinary algebra [with $(+, \times, \leqq)$ thought of in place of $(\cup, \cap, \subset)$]. For instance, if A and B represent any sets in the basic space,

$$A \cup A = A; \quad A \cap A = A; \quad (A \cap B) \subset A;$$
$$if \ A \subset B \quad then \quad A \cup B = B.$$

★174. Area as a set function

Let T be a basic space, and let H be any one of a certain class D of subsets of T. For every set H of D, suppose that a number $M(H)$ is determined. Thus, we have defined a *function M whose domain is a class of sets, D*. We then refer to M as a *set function*. In particular, let T be the set of points in a part of a plane, and let D be the class of all subsets $\{H\}$ of T of such a type that H has an area * $M(H) \geqq 0$. The student may permit himself to visualize H as a region inside and on the boundary of some simple closed curve, as in the case of regions A and B of Figure 116 on page 305. Hereafter, let M be this area function. We define $M(\emptyset) = 0$. We make the following postulates concerning M and D.

If A is in D, then the complement A' is in D.   (1)

If A and B are in D, then $A \cup B$ and $A \cap B$ are in D.   (2)

If A and B are in D and $A \cap B = \emptyset$, then

$$(A \cap B = \emptyset) \qquad\qquad M(A \cup B) = M(A) + M(B). \qquad (3)$$

Since $T = A \cup A'$, it follows from (1) and (2) that T is in D; that is, T has an *area*, $M(T)$. Also, from (1) and (2), the student will prove later that, if A and B are in D, then $A \setminus B$ is in D.

THEOREM I. *If A and B are sets for which M is defined, then*

$$M(A \cup B) = M(A) + M(B) - M(A \cap B). \qquad (4)$$

Proof. 1. If A and B are mutually exclusive, or $A \cap B = \emptyset$, we have the situation illustrated in Figure 116 on page 305. Then, the area of $A \cup B$ is equal to the area of A plus the area of B, or (3) is true, which is a special case of (4) since $M(A \cap B) = 0$.

2. If $A \cap B \neq \emptyset$, as in Figure 119, then we verify that $A \cap B = W$ is the cross-ruled region. Let $A_1 = A \setminus W$ and $B_1 = B \setminus W$. Then, A_1, B_1, and W are mutually exclusive sets, and

$$A \cup B = A_1 \cup W \cup B_1;$$
$$A = A_1 \cup W; \qquad B = B_1 \cup W.$$

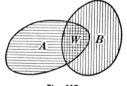

Fig. 119

---

* The notion of *area* of a region H is defined with moderate completeness in elementary integral calculus, and more rigorously in advanced mathematics. The student may think of area in the usual intuitional fashion.

Hence, on considering areas in Figure 119, from (3) we obtain

$$M(A) = M(A_1) + M(W); \qquad M(B) = M(B_1) + M(W);$$
$$M(A \cup B) = M(A_1) + M(W) + M(B_1)$$
$$= [M(A_1) + M(W)] + [M(B_1) + M(W)] - M(W)$$
$$= M(A) + M(B) - M(W),$$

which proves (4).

Note 1. Equation (3) states that M is an *additive function of sets,* that is, the value of M for the union (sum) of two disjoint sets is the sum of the values of M for the two sets. Property (3) extends to any finite number of sets. Thus, if A_1, A_2, A_3, $\cdots$ are mutually exclusive sets, then

$$M(A_1 \cup A_2 \cup A_3 \cdots) = M(A_1) + M(A_2) + M(A_3) + \cdots. \qquad (5)$$

In the next chapter, with M replaced by P, meaning *probability* as defined on page 311, it will be found that (1), (2), and (3) hold for P. That is, P is an *additive set function.* At a more advanced level, an important class of set functions called **measure functions** are introduced which have property (5) for an *infinite number* of sets A_1, A_2, A_3, $\cdots$, in the domain of definition of M. The probability function P, in a proper setting, is found to be a measure function.

★EXERCISE 108

Let T be the basic space. All other letters represent subsets of T. First try to prove the relation by stating facts about an appropriate Venn diagram. After that, if directed by the teacher, prove the result by statements in words. Any result is available, if useful, to prove later results.

1. The complement of the complement of H is H. Or, $(H')' = H$.
2. For any sets A and B, $(A \cup B)' = A' \cap B'$. (Consider two cases, $A \cap B = \emptyset$ and $A \cap B \neq \emptyset$.)
3. For any sets A and B, $(A \cap B)' = A' \cup B'$.
4. $H \cap H' = \emptyset$.   5. $T' = \emptyset$.
6. If $H \subset K$ then $H \cap K' = \emptyset$.
7. If $H \cap K' = \emptyset$, then $H \subset K$.
8. For any sets A and B, we have $A = (A \cap B) \cup (A \cap B')$.
9. Set subtraction is expressible in terms of *union and taking of complement,* or of *intersection and taking of complement.* That is,

$$A \setminus B = (A' \cup B)' = A \cap B'.$$

10. By use of Problem 9, if A and B are in the class D of Section 174, prove that $A \setminus B$ is in D.
11. Prove (5), (7), and (8) of pages 306 and 307 verbally. Check where possible by use of Venn diagrams. Show that the analog of (5) is not true in ordinary algebra.

Probability

175. The role of probability

The word *probability* is in common use colloquially, usually as a means for expressing varying degrees of confidence, not clearly defined, in the possibility of the occurrence of some uncertain event. Whenever the word *probability* is introduced mathematically, an explicit definition of its meaning should be given. The importance of probability as a part of applied mathematics comes from its application to concrete situations. Let us refer to the typical application as an *experiment*, directed by some experimenter. In his use of probability terminology and theory, his procedure should involve two fundamental steps, as follows:

1. *A decision that a certain completely abstract* **mathematical model for defining probability** *will be satisfactory as a basis for later decisions, when the elements in this model are thought of as items related to the experiment.*

2. *Computation of probabilities based on the abstract model and interpretation of these results in terms of the elements of the experiment.*

These steps are the logical basis for any sound procedure in the field called *statistical inference*. Hence, the study of probability is a necessary preliminary to appreciation of that field. We proceed to define *probability* for certain simple models.

176. Probability defined for a finite sample space

Consider a set T consisting of N distinct elements, r, where N is a positive integer. The power of our future definition will come from the fact that these elements r are merely symbols for *abstract entities with no concrete significance*. However, it will be an aid to intuition, and keep future applications in view, if we refer to each element r of T as an **outcome of a fundamental experiment** (ideal and abstract), which may produce any one of N outcomes whenever it is performed. Thus, T is the set of all possible outcomes $\{r\}$ of the experiment. We shall refer to T as the basic **sample space.** We shall talk of each outcome r as being a possible result of a **trial** of the experiment. We call T a *finite sample space* because it has just a finite number, N, of elements.

Let H represent a subset of T; that is, H consists of a certain number, say S, of the N possible outcomes of T. Let $F = N - S$. We shall refer to H as an **event,** made possible by any trial of the experiment. When we examine a particular outcome $\hat{r}$ of T, we shall say that H **occurs** *if $\hat{r}$ is in H* and shall call the outcome $\hat{r}$ a **success.** If a particular outcome $\hat{r}$ *is not in H*, we shall refer to $\hat{r}$ as a **failure** *relative to H.* Thus, the sample space T consists of S outcomes (those *in H*) which are *successes* and F outcomes (those *not in H*) which are *failures* relative to H. These F outcomes make up a set H', called the **complement** of H. H and H' are *mutually exclusive sets*, and the *union* of H and H' is the *whole space* T, or $T = H \cup H'$ and $H \cap H' = \emptyset$.

ILLUSTRATION 1. A bag contains 4 white and 3 black balls. Let an experiment consist of drawing 2 balls together from the bag, and identify the concrete possible outcomes of this experiment as the set T mentioned above. Then, the total number of outcomes is $N = {}_7C_2$ or $N = 21$. Let H_1 be the event of obtaining a black ball and a white ball at any trial; the number of outcomes of this variety is $S_1 = 4(3) = 12$. Let H_2 be the event of obtaining 2 black balls at any trial; the number of outcomes in H_2 is $S_2 = {}_3C_2 = 3$.

ILLUSTRATION 2. Let the fundamental experiment be the drawing of 2 balls in succession from the bag in Illustration 1, with the first ball being replaced before the second is drawn. Then, there are 7×7 outcomes in T.

DEFINITION I. *To each outcome r of the sample space T, let there be assigned arbitrarily a* **nonnegative number** p_r, *to be called the* **probability of r,** *where the sum of the numbers p_r for all outcomes of T is 1. Then, the* **probability of any event** H *is the sum of the probabilities of those outcomes of the sample space which belong to H.*

We use $P(H)$ to represent the probability of H. Sometimes, we may call $P(H)$ the *probability of success for H at any trial of the experiment.* Thus, we have defined a **probability function P,** whose *domain* is all subsets $\{H\}$ of T. That is, P is a *set function*, or a function of *sets of outcomes*. If $\emptyset$ as usual denotes the empty set, containing no outcomes of T, we define $P(\emptyset) = 0$. The range of P is all numbers from 0 to 1, inclusive.

In any acceptance of Definition I as the model for probability, an experimenter would first identify the possible *concrete outcomes* of his experiment as the elements r of the sample space T. Then, on the basis of past experience with the experiment, or theoretical knowledge of its nature, the experimenter would *arbitrarily select the individual probabilities of the outcomes.* Thereafter, he would use the result $P(H)$ given by Definition I.

ILLUSTRATION 3.   Let the ideal experiment be identified as the concrete action of tossing a die, numbered as usual, and observing which number falls up.   First, suppose that the experimenter assigns the probability $\frac{1}{6}$ to each of the 6 possible outcomes.   In this case, he would say that he considers them "*equally likely*," in a colloquial sense.   Let H be the event that, at a trial of the experiment, the die falls with a face up *which is numbered greater than* 4. Then, H consists of two outcomes, 5 up and 6 up, and $P(H) = \frac{1}{6} + \frac{1}{6} = \frac{1}{3}$. Next, as a new basis, suppose that the experimenter knows that the die is *biased* or *loaded*, and accordingly assigns the probability $\frac{1}{3}$ to each of faces 1 and 6, and $\frac{1}{12}$ to each of faces 2, 3, 4, and 5.   Let H be the event that, at any throw of the die, it will fall with a face up *numbered less than* 3; H consists of the outcomes where faces 1 and 2 fall up; $P(H) = \frac{1}{3} + \frac{1}{12} = \frac{5}{12}$.

For any event H, there is the **complementary event** "*not H*," denoted by H', consisting of all outcomes of the sample space T which are *failures* relative to H.   We shall refer to $P(H')$ as *the probability of failure of H*.

THEOREM I.   *For any event H, the sum of the probabilities of success and failure is* 1.   *That is,*

(H' *means not H*) $$P(H) + P(H') = 1. \tag{1}$$

Proof.   The outcomes in H and those which are in H' (that is, *not in H*) make up *all* of the outcomes of T.   Hence, $P(H) + P(H')$ is just the sum of the probabilities of *all outcomes*, and hence is equal to 1.

We shall say that H is *certain to occur* at any trial of the experiment in case $P(H) = 1$.   If no outcome r of T has $p_r = 0$, then the condition $P(H) = 1$ is equivalent to stating that H consists of all outcomes of T, so that $H = T$. If $P(H) = 1$, it follows from (1) that $P(H') = 0$, or *the probability of failure for H is zero*.   To say that H is *certain to fail* at any trial will mean that $P(H) = 0$.   In this case, from (1), $P(H') = 1$, or the *probability of success is zero* and *of failure is* 1.

If all of the N outcomes in the sample space T are assigned *equal probabilities*, we shall say that the outcomes are **equally likely**.   In such a case, each outcome r has the probability $1/N$.

THEOREM II.   *Suppose that the N outcomes of the sample space T are equally likely, and that H is an event consisting of S outcomes (successes), with F outcomes (failures) not in H, where $F = N - S$.   Then, at any trial of the experiment, the probability of success for H is*

$$P(H) = \frac{S}{N} = p, \tag{2}$$

and the probability of H failing to occur is

$$P(H') = \frac{F}{N} = q. \tag{3}$$

Proof. By Definition I, with each outcome having the probability $1/N$, the sum of the probabilities of the S outcomes of H is $S \cdot (1/N)$, or $P(H)$ is given by (2). Similarly, the sum of the probabilities of the F failures in H' is $F \cdot (1/N)$, or the probability of failure of H is $P(H') = F/N$, as in (3).

Hereafter in this chapter, a moderate number of problems will occur where the outcomes of the sample space are *not* equally likely; this case is absolutely essential for the development of statistics. However, unless otherwise stated in a problem, Theorem II will apply. In any concrete experiment, "*to draw*" or "*to perform an act*" will imply that this is done "*at random*" in the colloquial sense. Then, we shall assume that the possible concrete outcomes are to be taken as the sample space T of Definition I with the outcomes considered as *equally likely*.

ILLUSTRATION 4. If a bag contains 7 black and 3 white balls, the probability that a ball drawn at random will be black is $\frac{7}{10}$.

Note 1. As a special case of (1), from (2) and (3) we obtain $p + q = 1$. If the event H is *certain to occur*, then $p = 1$ and $q = 0$. If H is *certain to fail*, then $p = 0$ and $q = 1$.

In using (2), we first decide on the *fundamental experiment* which produces the outcomes. Then, with an event H, we compute separately the number, S, of successful outcomes, and the total number, N, of outcomes for the act.

EXAMPLE 1. A bag contains 5 red and 6 white balls. If we draw 4 balls *together* (or, *in succession without replacement*), find the probability that (*a*) two are red and two are white; (*b*) all are of the same color; (*c*) at least three are white.

SOLUTION. 1. The *fundamental act* is that we draw 4 balls. The number of outcomes for this act is $_{11}C_4$, or $N = 330$.

2. Let H_1 be event (*a*). *Successful outcomes:* the number of ways of drawing 2 reds and 2 whites is $(_5C_2)(_6C_2) = 150$, or H_1 contains 150 outcomes. Hence, $P(H_1) = \frac{150}{330} = \frac{5}{11}$.

3. Let H_2 be event (*b*). *Successful outcomes:* the number of ways of drawing 4 reds is $_5C_4$ or 5, and of drawing 4 whites is $_6C_4$ or 15; hence, by Principle II on page 297, the number of ways of drawing 4 balls of the *same color* is $(5 + 15)$ or 20, the number of outcomes in H_2. Hence, $P(H_2) = \frac{20}{330} = \frac{2}{33}$.

4. Let H_3 be event (*c*). *Successful outcomes:* at least 3 of the 4 balls are white if (*i*) exactly 3 are white or (*ii*) exactly 4 are white.

(*i*) *The number of ways of drawing exactly 3 white balls, and hence just 1 red ball, is* $(_6C_3)(_5C_1)$ *or 100 ways.*

(*ii*) *The number of ways of drawing 4 whites is* $_6C_4$ *or 15 ways.*

By page 297, the number of outcomes in H_3 is $(100 + 15)$; $P(H_3) = \frac{115}{330} = \frac{23}{66}$.

EXAMPLE 2. A number of five different digits is built at random from the digits (1, 2, 3, 4, 5, 6, 8). Find the probability that the number will have even digits at each end.

SOLUTION. 1. *The fundamental experiment* is the building of a number of five different digits. The number of ways of doing this is $_7P_5$, or $N = 2520$.

2. *Successful outcomes.* By Principle I, page 289, the number of ways in which we can build a number of five different digits having even digits at the ends is $4 \cdot 3 \cdot 5 \cdot 4 \cdot 3$, or $S = 720$.

3. From (2), the desired probability is $p = \frac{720}{2520}$, or $p = \frac{2}{7}$.

Probability as described in Definition I is referred to as "*a priori*" probability because, in any application to a concrete experiment, it is assumed that, in advance of a trial, we know the number and nature of the possible outcomes.

Note 2. In the mathematical model used as a basis for probability in Definition I, the "*probability of an outcome*" is an *undefined term*, subject only to the restriction that the sum of the probabilities of all outcomes is 1. However, the experimenter is at liberty to think of the probability which he assigns to any outcome as a measure of a subjective impression, which he might call his confidence in the appearance of the outcome at any trial. Then, in any resulting application of the theory, the desirability of the whole procedure is judged by the results obtained.

EXERCISE 109

1. An experimenter will throw a loaded die at random. He assigns the probabilities $\frac{1}{6}$, $\frac{1}{12}$, $\frac{1}{4}$, $\frac{1}{3}$, $\frac{1}{12}$, and $\frac{1}{12}$ to the faces 1, 2, 3, 4, 5, and 6, respectively, as possible outcomes for the face up on a throw. Let H be the event of obtaining, at any trial, a face numbered (*a*) less than 5; (*b*) more than 2. In each case find $P(H)$ and $P(H')$ where H' represents the complement of H, or "*not H.*"

2. An experimenter will throw, together, a *warped coin* and a *loaded die*. For the coin thought of alone, he would assign a probability of $\frac{1}{3}$ to obtaining a head, and $\frac{2}{3}$ to obtaining a tail at any throw. For the die alone, he would assign the probability $\frac{1}{12}$ to each of faces 1, 2, 3, and 4, and $\frac{1}{3}$ to each of faces 5 and 6, as outcomes of any throw. For the *joint experiment* of throwing *the coin and the die*, he decides to assign to each joint outcome a probability equal to *the product of the probabilities of the particular face on the coin and the face on the die* which land up. (Thus, to the outcome heads and 3 on the die, he assigns the probability $\frac{1}{3} \cdot \frac{1}{12}$ or $\frac{1}{36}$.) (*a*) Make up a table with 2 rows and 6 columns showing the probability of each outcome of the experiment, and verify that the sum of the assigned probabilities is 1. (*b*) Let H be the event of obtaining, at any trial, a tail and at least 3 on the die; find $P(H)$ and $P(H')$.

3. A bag contains 5 white, 6 red, and 15 green balls. If 1 ball is drawn, find the probability that it will be (a) red; (b) white or green.

4. If a die is tossed, what is the probability that it will show (a) 3 or 4; (b) at least 4?

5. From a deck of 52 cards, 1 card is to be drawn. What is the probability that it will be (a) a queen; (b) an ace, king, or jack?

6. A bag contains 3 white and 5 red balls. If 2 balls are drawn together, find the probability that (a) both balls are white; (b) both are red; (c) one is white and one is red; (d) all are of the same color.

7. From 5 men and 7 women, a committee of four is chosen by lot. Find the probability that the committee will involve (a) 4 men; (b) 2 men and 2 women; (c) all men or all women; (d) at least 3 women.

8. In a single toss with two dice, find the probability of throwing a total of (a) 7; (b) 9; (c) 11; (d) at most 5.

9. From a deck of 52 cards, 4 cards will be drawn together. Find the probability that those drawn will be (a) spades; (b) all of the same suit; (c) all face cards or aces.

10. If a number of six different digits is built at random by use of the digits (1, 2, 3, 4, 5, 6, 7), find the probability that the number will be (a) odd; (b) even; (c) divisible by 5; (d) greater than 500,000.

11. Four roads meet at an intersection. If each of 2 people chooses a road at random, find the probability that they will choose the same road.

12. A 1st group consists of 4 men and 2 women, and a 2d group consists of 5 men and 10 women. If 1 person is chosen by lot from each group, find the probability that (a) both are women; (b) both are men; (c) one is a man and one is a woman; (d) at least one is a man.

13. If 5 coins are tossed together (or, if one coin is tossed 5 times), find the probability that they will fall with (a) just 3 heads; (b) just 3 heads or just 2 heads.

14. If a hand of 13 cards is dealt from a deck of 52 cards, find the probability that the hand will contain all of the aces and kings.

15. A 1st bag contains 4 red and 6 green balls, and a 2d bag contains 5 red and 8 black balls. If we draw a ball from each bag, find the probability that we obtain (a) a red ball and a black ball; (b) a red ball and one not red; (c) at least 1 red ball.

16. If 2 balls are drawn together from each bag in Problem 15, find the probability of obtaining (a) 2 red and 2 black balls; (b) just 1 red ball from each bag; (c) no red ball.

17. A bag contains 10 black and 5 red balls. If we draw 2 balls in succession, find the probability that both are black, if the 1st ball drawn (a) *is replaced* before the 2d is drawn; (b) *is not replaced*. If we draw 3 balls in succession, without replacement, find the probability that (c) all are red; (d) the 1st and 2d balls drawn are black and the 3d is red.

18. If 3 men and 3 women are seated at random at a round table, find the probability that (a) men and women will alternate; (b) a certain man and his wife, in the group, will be seated side by side.

19. A wholesaler's stock of 80 motors contains 8 defective motors. If 5 motors are selected at random for shipment to a purchaser, find the probability that (a) none of these is defective; (b) at most one motor in the shipment is defective. Logarithms would be useful.

20. In a matching question on an examination, 8 events in history are to be matched with 8 specified dates, where each item is to be used just once. A student is sure of 4 dates, and chooses to match the others at random. Find his probability of matching correctly (a) all items; (b) at least 6 dates.

21. Six dice are tossed. Find the probability that all of the numbers 1, 2, 3, 4, 5, and 6 will appear.

22. A 1st bag contains 5 white and 10 black balls, and a 2d bag contains 20 white and 10 black balls. The experiment consists of selecting a bag at random and then drawing a ball. We decide to use $\frac{1}{2}$ as the probability in equal shares for all outcomes from any bag. Thus, each *outcome* (a *ball*) from the 1st bag has the probability $\frac{1}{2} \cdot \frac{1}{15}$ or $\frac{1}{30}$, and $\frac{1}{2} \cdot \frac{1}{30}$ or $\frac{1}{60}$ for each outcome from the 2d bag. By use of Definition I, find the probability of drawing (a) a white ball; (b) a white ball from the 1st bag; (c) a black ball.

23. A first die is biased so that, at any toss of this die alone, the probabilities of throwing 1, 2, 3, 4, 5, or 6 would be chosen as, respectively, $\frac{1}{12}, \frac{1}{12}, \frac{1}{12}, \frac{1}{3}, \frac{1}{12}$, and $\frac{1}{3}$. For a second biased die, the corresponding probabilities are $\frac{1}{4}, \frac{1}{12}, \frac{1}{12}, \frac{1}{4}, \frac{1}{4}$, and $\frac{1}{12}$. The experiment will consist, now, of throwing the dice together. (a) Define *sensible* probabilities for each of the 36 possible outcomes, and show them in a table. (b) Find the probabilities of throwing each of the following totals at any trial: (i) 9, consisting of 4 on the 1st die and 5 on the 2d die; (ii) 3; (iii) at least 9; (iv) 8.

177. Sigma notation

We introduce capital sigma, Σ, the *sign of summation*, in abbreviating sums of notationally similar terms. Thus, we write

$$u_1 + u_2 + \cdots + u_n = \Sigma_{i=1}^n u_i, \tag{1}$$

where the right-hand side is read "*the sum of u_i from $i = 1$ to $i = n$.*" In (1), we call i the **index** or **variable of summation.** We think of Σ as abbreviating the word "*sum.*"

ILLUSTRATION 1. $\Sigma_{j=1}^6 v_j = v_1 + v_2 + v_3 + v_4 + v_5 + v_6 = \Sigma_{i=1}^6 v_i.$ (2)

$$\Sigma_{x=1}^n x^2 = 1^2 + 2^2 + 3^2 + \cdots + n^2.$$

We infer that the *letter* used for an index of summation is immaterial.

ILLUSTRATION 2. $\displaystyle\sum_{i=1}^{3} (x_i - 2) = (x_1 - 2) + (x_2 - 2) + (x_3 - 2) = \sum_{i=1}^{3} x_i - 6.$

$\Sigma_{i=1}^{n} (x_i - c) = (x_1 - c) + (x_2 - c) + \cdots + (x_n - c) = \Sigma_{i=1}^{n} x_i - nc.$

178. A simple random variable

Let T be any sample space, as in Definition I, consisting of N elements, or outcomes $r_1, r_2, \cdots, r_N$, where the general element will be denoted by r_i, with i having the range $i = 1, 2, 3, \cdots, N$. Then, corresponding to each r_i in T, suppose that a real number x_i is specified. Thus, we have a set of N pairs

$$(r_1, x_1), (r_2, x_2), \cdots, (r_i, x_i), \cdots, (r_N, x_N), \tag{1}$$

where the first elements are the *outcomes* (not numbers) of T, with no repetitions, and the second member of each pair is a *number*, x_i for the general or ith pair. The set of ordered pairs in (1) form a *function*, whose *domain* is the set T of outcomes $\{r_i\}$, and whose *range* is the set of distinct numbers among $x_1, x_2, \cdots, x_N$. Let X represent this function; its general value is $X(r_i) = x_i$. We call X a **random variable** defined on the sample space T. We summarize this important terminology as follows.

DEFINITION II. *Let T be a sample space with N elements $r_1, \cdots, r_N$. Then, a* **random variable,** X, *is a* **real-valued function whose domain is T.** *That is, for each r_i in T, there is defined a value x_i where $X(r_i) = x_i$.*

ILLUSTRATION 1. Let the fundamental experiment consist of drawing one ball at random from a bag containing 4 white and 6 black balls; the 10 outcomes in T are taken as equally likely. Consider a gambling game, where the person making the draw will be paid \$2 if he draws a white ball and \$3 if he draws a black ball. For each outcome r_i, define $X(r_i) = x_i$, where x_i is the number of dollars in the payoff corresponding to r_i. Thus, we have defined a random variable X on the sample space; the range of X, with numbers of dollars as elements, consists of just two numbers, 2 and 3.

The concept of a random variable is combined with a second notion, below, to produce a very important concept of the field of statistics.

DEFINITION III. *Let X be a random variable defined on a sample space T, where the outcomes $\{r_i\}$ of T have been assigned the corresponding probabilities $\{p_i\}$, with $\Sigma_{i=1}^{N} p_i = 1$ and $X(r_i) = x_i$. Then, the* **expected value of X,** *denoted by $E(X)$, is defined by*

$$E(X) = p_1 x_1 + p_2 x_2 + \cdots + p_N x_N = \Sigma_{i=1}^{N} p_i x_i. \tag{2}$$

Note 1. From (2), if the outcomes $\{r_i\}$ are equally likely, then $p_i = 1/N$ and, from (2),

$$E(X) = \frac{\Sigma_{i=1}^{N} x_i}{N}. \tag{3}$$

Thus, in this case, $E(X)$ is merely the *average* of the values of X. In any case, from (2), $E(X)$ can be thought of as a *weighted average* of the values $\{x_i\}$. In statistics, $E(X)$ is called the **mean** of X, and is denoted by $\bar{x}$.

ILLUSTRATION 2. In Illustration 1, we have

the outcomes,	$r_1,$	$r_2,$	$r_3,$	$r_4,$	$r_5,$	$r_6,$	$r_7,$	$r_8,$	$r_9,$	$r_{10};$
their probabilities,	$\frac{1}{10},$	$\frac{1}{10},$	$\frac{1}{10},$	$\frac{1}{10},$	$\frac{1}{10},$	$\frac{1}{10},$	$\frac{1}{10},$	$\frac{1}{10},$	$\frac{1}{10},$	$\frac{1}{10};$
the values of X,	2,	2,	2,	2,	3,	3,	3,	3,	3,	3.

Hence, $E(X) = \frac{2}{10} + \frac{2}{10} + \frac{2}{10} + \frac{2}{10} + \frac{3}{10} + \frac{3}{10} + \frac{3}{10} + \frac{3}{10} + \frac{3}{10} + \frac{3}{10} = 2.6.$

Thus, $\$E(X) = \$2.60$. The total of the possible payoffs is $4(\$2) + 6(\$3)$ or $\$26$. The *average payoff* per outcome is $\$2.6 = \$E(X)$.

Suppose that each outcome r in the sample space T for an experiment (thought of as a *game*) has a payoff value $\$X(r)$ for the experimenter. Then, the *expected value of the payoff function*, or $E(X)$, is called the **mathematical expectation** of the player. In dollars, the value of this expectation is $\$E(X)$. Thus, in Illustration 2, the dollar value of the mathematical expectation is $\$2.60$.

Let H be any event in T, where H consists of the outcomes $(r_1, r_2, \cdots, r_S)$, with probabilities $p_1, p_2, \cdots, p_S$; their sum is $P(H)$. Suppose that the experimenter is promised $\$W$ if H occurs at a trial of the game, and *no payment otherwise*. Then, for the payoff function X, each $X(r_i) = W$, and X has the value 0 at all outcomes *not in H*. Then, by (2),

$$E(X) = p_1 W + p_2 W + \cdots + p_S W = W(p_1 + p_2 + \cdots + p_S) = WP(H).$$

Hence, if a player is promised $\$W$ in case a certain event H occurs at the playing of a game, his mathematical expectation is $WP(H)$, *number of dollars in the prize multiplied by the probability of winning it.*

179. Empirical probability

Consider a concrete experiment, with its outcomes $\{r\}$ forming a sample space T, where the experimenter has no knowledge of * T on which to base a selection of probabilities for the outcomes, as in Definition I. Let H be an event consisting of a well-defined subset of T. Assume that the experimenter has observed N trials of the experiment and has determined that the outcome was in H, or that H *occurred*, in exactly S of these N trials. We shall call S/N the observed **relative frequency** of successes in the N trials. Under certain reasonable assumptions as to the experiment, it can be shown that S/N is a desirable approximation to the unknown number $p = P(H)$, which,

---

* We do not restrict our meaning of probability here to the basis in Definition I. We even allow for the possibility that T might consist of infinitely many outcomes, and then that probability for an event H has been defined in some manner which makes subsequent remarks have meaning. Such matters are discussed in detail in mathematical statistics.

theoretically, would be the best value for the experimenter to choose. Moreover, it can be shown that S/N becomes increasingly desirable as an approximation for p as N grows large. Hence, in applications of statistics, the observed relative frequency of H in past trials often is taken as the definition of the phrase "*probability of H at any trial*" in the future. We then refer to S/N as an *empirical* or *experimental probability*. Also, S/N sometimes is called an "*a posteriori*" probability, because it is determined from data observed in the past. Hereafter, when we refer to a *probability*, p, without a qualifying description, p may be either an *empirical probability* or an *a priori* probability found by use of Definition I.

Note 1. In the remainder of this chapter, we agree that, in any result which we shall prove or state for the case of *a priori* probabilities, based on Definition I, we shall permit use of the result also for empirical probabilities. In particular, the definition of mathematical expectation will be employed when $P(H)$ is an empirical probability, S/N.

ILLUSTRATION 1. The Commissioners Standard Ordinary Mortality Table (Table IX, abbreviated CSO Table) embodies the results of extensive observation of the ages at death of people who have carried life insurance. The table may be thought of as a record of the year in which death occurred for each of 1,023,102 people who were born at the same time. A mortality table can be used as the basis for obtaining empirical probabilities concerning living and dying for a person of any given age.

EXAMPLE 1. If a man is alive at age 30, find the probability that he will live at least 14 years.

SOLUTION. In Table IX, we observe 924,609 men alive at age 30, and 859,464 of these remain alive 14 years later. Hence, the (empirical) probability of living at least 14 years is $p = 859,464/924,609$, or $p = .9295$, by logarithms.

180. The expected number of successes in *n* trials

Consider a certain fundamental experiment, and an associated event H whose probability at any trial is p. Later, in Section 183, we shall think of a set of n *trials* of the experiment as constituting a *single trial* of a *new experiment*, which can be taken as a *new basis* for probability. Then, if n trials of the original experiment are to be made, there will exist a probability of occurrence for each particular number, k, of successes in the n trials. Let that number of successes having the *largest probability* be called the *most probable number of successes*. Then, for n trials, it can be proved that the most probable number, S, of successes (under reasonable hypotheses) is approximately equal to pn. Sometimes, pn is called the **expected number of successes** in

n trials (because pn is found to be the *expected value* of a *random variable* X on a certain sample space where the *value* of X at any point is a *corresponding number of successes in n trials*).

Suppose that n trials of the fundamental experiment are to be made, and let k be the number of trials where event H will occur. Then, a famous theorem, called the **law of large numbers,*** causes us to expect that the relative frequency k/n will be near p if n is large. However, if n is small, we would not have any reason to expect k/n to be near p. Even when n is large, the theorem allows for the possibility that k/n might differ substantially from p, although this would be anticipated as a rare occurrence.

ILLUSTRATION 1. Suppose that $\frac{3}{5}$ is the probability that Jones will win a certain game whenever he plays. If, for instance, Jones plays 1000 games, the most probable number of wins is $\frac{3}{5}(1000)$ or 600. Since 1000 is large, we would expect the relative frequency of his wins to be approximately $\frac{3}{5}$. If he plays only a few games, we would not be surprised if the relative frequency of his wins differed largely from $\frac{3}{5}$.

ILLUSTRATION 2. If a man plays a game where the prize is $100, and the probability of winning is $\frac{3}{5}$, his mathematical expectation in dollars is $\frac{3}{5}(\$100)$ or $60. Now, suppose that a professional gambler offers to play this game against any man who will pay his expectation ($60) as a fee for playing. If a great many players enter the game, the professional operator may feel safe † in assuming that the relative frequency of wins will be approximately $\frac{3}{5}$, or that about $\frac{3}{5}$ of the players will win. Thus, if 100 players enter, they pay $6000 in fees; if $\frac{3}{5}(100)$ or 60 players win, they collect $6000, and in this case the operator has no gain or loss. To avoid possible loss, however, the operator should charge more than the mathematical expectation as a fee because more than $\frac{3}{5}$ of the players may win.

EXAMPLE 1. An insurance policy written for a man, A, aged 30 promises to pay him an endowment of $1000 at age 50 if he is alive then. What is his mathematical expectation?

SOLUTION. Let p be the probability that A will be alive at age 50. From the CSO Table IX, $p = 810,900/924,609$, or $p = .877$, which is the probability of the payment being made. Hence, the value of the mathematical expectation of A in dollars is $1000(.877) or $877, payable at age 50.

The principle involved in Illustration 1 is important in the conduct of a life insurance company, or of any financial enterprise involving the sharing of

---

* The language of limits is required for the exact statement of the result: "*For any assigned number* $\epsilon > 0$, *however small* ϵ *may be, the limit as* $n \to \infty$ *of the probability that* $\left| \dfrac{k}{n} - p \right| < \epsilon$ *is equal to* 1." The word "*probability*" in this statement refers to probability *associated with the new experiment*, consisting of n trials of the given experiment.

† This attitude is encouraged by the law of large numbers.

natural risks by a group of people. The fact that the risks are unavoidable, instead of being assumed voluntarily, as in a game of chance, does not alter the nature of the problem essentially. The financial safety of the operating company demands that the fees charged shall be more than the corresponding mathematical expectations and that a large number of people should be induced to join the enterprise.

EXERCISE 110

1. Find the mathematical expectation of a man whose probability of winning $500 is $\frac{1}{20}$.

2. On a *"bank night"* at a chain of theaters, the pot contains $3500, and each of 15,000 patrons has an equal probability of winning the pot. Find the mathematical expectation of each person.

Note 1. In Theorem II, page 312, we say that the **odds** are S to F *in favor* of the event if $S > F$, and S to F *against* the event if $S < F$.

3. If the odds are 5 to 3 in favor of a man receiving $100 if a certain act is performed, find the probability of his (*a*) receiving $100; (*b*) not receiving $100. Also, find his mathematical expectation.

4. If the odds are 5 to 7 against a man receiving $50, find (*a*) his probability of receiving it; (*b*) his mathematical expectation.

5. A game consists of drawing 2 balls together from a bag containing 6 white and 4 black balls. The player will receive $5 if he draws 2 balls of the same color. Find his mathematical expectation at one draw.

Find the probability of the event by use of the mortality table. Leave the result as a fraction, except as directed by the instructor. If decimal values are desired, logarithms should be used.

6. That a boy aged 10 will be alive 30 years later.

7. That a man aged 24 will live at least 20 years.

8. (*a*) That a person aged 30 will live at least 35 years; (*b*) that he will die between ages 65 and 70.

9. That a person aged 21 will die (*a*) within 5 years, (*b*) during the 5th year.

10. That a person aged 20 will die (*a*) within 1 year; (*b*) during his 36th year.

11. That a person aged 65 will die within 1 year.

12. An insurance policy, written for a man now aged 30, promises an endowment of $1000 to him at the end of 20 years if he is alive then. Find his mathematical expectation to the nearest dollar, in terms of money due at the end of 20 years.

13. Let the sample space T consist of the 6 outcomes of the experiment of tossing a die, where the outcomes (face up) 1, 2, 3, 4, 5, and 6 are assigned the probabilities $\frac{1}{12}$, $\frac{1}{12}$, $\frac{1}{3}$, $\frac{1}{3}$, $\frac{1}{12}$, and $\frac{1}{12}$, respectively, and where the corresponding values of a random variable X are 12, 10, 8, 6, 4, and 2. Find $E(X)$.

14. A game consists of drawing two balls together from a bag containing 6 white balls and 4 black balls. The player will receive \$2 if he draws 2 white balls, \$3 if he draws 2 black balls, and \$1 if he draws one ball of each color. Define appropriately the value of a payoff random variable X, and find $E(X)$.

★*Expand the sum. Find its value if possible.*

15. $\displaystyle\sum_{i=1}^{3} i^2.$ **16.** $\displaystyle\sum_{k=1}^{4} k.$ **17.** $\displaystyle\sum_{j=1}^{4} j^3.$ **18.** $\displaystyle\sum_{i=1}^{5} \tfrac{1}{2}i^2.$ **19.** $\displaystyle\sum_{i=1}^{4} x_i.$

20. $\displaystyle\sum_{k=1}^{5} x_i y_i.$ **21.** $\displaystyle\sum_{i=1}^{4} x_i^2.$ **22.** $\displaystyle\sum_{i=1}^{5} 3x_i.$ **23.** $\displaystyle\sum_{i=1}^{n} x_i^3.$ **24.** $\displaystyle\sum_{i=1}^{n} (x_i - y_i).$

25. If $(x_1, x_2, \cdots, x_5)$ consists of $(2, 3, 6, 5, 9)$, find

$$\sum_{i=1}^{5} x_i; \quad \sum_{i=1}^{5} (x_i - 3); \quad \sum_{i=1}^{5} (x_i - 2)^2.$$

26. Simplify somewhat: $\sum_{i=1}^{n} (x_i - 2);$ $\sum_{i=1}^{n} 3(x_i - 2).$

★*Note 2.* If X is a random variable on a sample space T, then X^2 also is a random variable on T. In general, any function of a random variable on T also is a random variable on T. For a given random variable X, let $\bar{x} = E(X)$ and $\sigma^2 = E(X - \bar{x})^2$. Then, in statistics, $\bar{x}$ is called the **mean** and σ^2 is called the **variance** of X. The positive square root of σ^2, or σ, is called the **standard deviation** of X.

★**27.** (*a*) In Problem 13, find $E(X - \bar{x})$ and σ^2. (*b*) For any sample space T as in Definition I on page 311, prove that $E(X - \bar{x}) = 0$.

★**28.** Repeat (*a*) of Problem 27 for Problem 14.

181. Probability of mutually exclusive events

Consider a fundamental experiment, whose outcomes form a sample space T, as in Definition I, where the outcomes are *not* assumed to be equally likely. Let H_1 and H_2 be two mutually exclusive events, either of which may occur at a trial of the experiment. That is, H_1 and H_2 are two mutually exclusive, or disjoint, subsets of outcomes of T, or $H_1 \cap H_2 = \emptyset$.

ILLUSTRATION 1. A bag contains 3 white, 7 black, and 10 yellow balls. Let the experiment consist of drawing one ball from the bag. Let H_1 be the event of obtaining a white ball and H_2 the event of obtaining a black ball. Then T consists of 20 outcomes; H_1 consists of 3 outcomes; H_2 consists of 7 outcomes. Also, H_1 and H_2 cannot occur simultaneously, or H_1 and H_2 are *mutually exclusive sets of outcomes*. The event (H_1 or H_2) would mean the event of obtaining *either a white ball or a black ball* on the draw. The set (H_1 or H_2) consists of 10 outcomes, that is the total outcomes in H_1 or in H_2, because there are no duplications between their outcomes. Instead of writing (H_1 or H_2), we may write $H_1 \cup H_2$.

THEOREM III. *Let T be the sample space of outcomes of a fundamental experiment, and let H_1 and H_2 be* **mutually exclusive events** *which are possibilities when the experiment is performed. Then, the probability of the event $(H_1 \text{ or } H_2)$ is equal to the sum of the probabilities of H_1 and H_2. That is,*

(H_1 and H_2 **mutually exclusive**) $P(H_1 \text{ or } H_2) = P(H_1) + P(H_2)$.   (1)

★*Note 1.* In place of (1) we may write

$$H_1 \cap H_2 = \emptyset \quad \text{implies that} \quad P(H_1 \cup H_2) = P(H_1) + P(H_2). \qquad (2)$$

Proof of (1). Since H_1 and H_2 are mutually exclusive, the outcomes in $(H_1 \text{ or } H_2)$ consist of all those in H_1 and all those in H_2, where there are no duplications. Hence, by Definition I on page 311, $P(H_1 \text{ or } H_2)$ is equal to the sum of the probabilities of *all outcomes in H_1*, plus the sum of the probabilities of *all outcomes in H_2*, or $P(H_1 \text{ or } H_2)$ is equal to the sum $P(H_1) + P(H_2)$.

ILLUSTRATION 2. In Illustration 1, let the outcomes of the experiment be taken as *equally likely.* Then, the probability of drawing a white ball is $P(H_1) = \frac{3}{20}$; of drawing a black ball is $P(H_2) = \frac{7}{20}$. Hence, without added inspection, by use of Theorem III, the probability of drawing a white or a black ball is given by $P(H_1 \text{ or } H_2) = \frac{7}{20} + \frac{3}{20} = \frac{10}{20}$.

182. Independent experiments

Consider two experiments, Z_1 with sample space T_1 consisting of outcomes $\{r\}$, and Z_2 with sample space T_2 consisting of outcomes $\{s\}$, where probability is defined separately for events in T_1 and T_2, as in Definition I. Let H_1 be a subset of T_1, or an *event* corresponding to Z_1, with probability $P_1(H_1)$; let H_2 be an *event* for Z_2 with probability $P_2(H_2)$. Suppose that Z_1 and Z_2 can be performed either *in succession or simultaneously*, with the joint outcomes (r, s) where any r of T_1 may be paired with any s of T_2. Let Z denote this compound experiment, which we shall write (*and read*) $Z = (Z_1, Z_2)$. Its sample space T consists of all possible pairs (r, s); let $T = (T_1, T_2)$. One subset of T will be the set H consisting of all pairs (r, s) where r is in H_1 and s is in H_2; let $H = (H_1, H_2)$. According to Definition I, we might define probabilities in T *arbitrarily.* However, the following agreement appears most natural in applications.

$$\left\{ \begin{array}{l} \textit{In the sample space } T = (T_1, T_2) \textit{ of the experiment} \\ Z = (Z_1, Z_2), \textit{ define the probabilities of outcomes so} \\ \textit{that, for any events } H_1 \textit{ of } T_1 \textit{ and } H_2 \textit{ of } T_2, \textit{ the event} \\ H = (H_1, H_2) \textit{ will have the following probability:} \\ \qquad P(H) = P(H_1, H_2) = P_1(H_1)P_2(H_2). \end{array} \right\} \qquad (1)$$

That is, to find $P(H_1, H_2)$, *multiply the probabilities of H_1 and H_2 as given for the separate experiments.* We may refer to (H_1, H_2) as a *compound event.*

★*Note 1.* It should be proved that it is possible to assign probabilities to the outcomes in T so that (1) is true. Suppose that T_1 and T_2 are sample spaces of the variety met in Definition I; let $p_1(r)$ and $p_2(s)$ denote the probabilities of outcome r in T_1 and outcome s in T_2, respectively. Then, if each outcome (r, s) of T is assigned the probability $p(r, s) = p_1(r)p_2(s)$, it can be proved that $P(T) = 1$ and also that (1) is true. We omit this proof. Also, (1) can be obtained for other types of sample spaces.

We agree to use (1) when Z_1 and Z_2 are interpreted as concrete acts or experiments, which can be performed either *simultaneously or in succession, with the outcome of neither experiment having any effect on the other experiment.* That is, we shall use (1) when Z_1 and Z_2 are *independent in the colloquial sense.* We shall employ (1) when $P_1(H_1)$ and $P_2(H_2)$ are given either as stated probabilities, with no background, or as relative frequencies from past observations, or as consequences of Definition I as applied to the sample spaces of outcomes of Z_1 and Z_2. Also, we shall use the analogue of (1) for three or more events. Thus,

$$P(H_1, H_2, H_3) = P_1(H_1)P_2(H_2)P_3(H_3). \qquad (2)$$

Or, for any finite number of experiments $Z_1, Z_2, Z_3, \cdots$, with corresponding events $H_1, H_2, H_3, \cdots$

$$P(H_1, H_2, H_3, \cdots) = P_1(H_1)P_2(H_2)P_3(H_3) \cdots. \qquad (3)$$

EXAMPLE 1. A 1st bag contains 4 white and 6 black balls, and a 2d bag contains 5 white and 7 green balls. If a ball is drawn from each bag, find the probability (*a*) of obtaining a black ball and a green ball; (*b*) of obtaining a black ball (with no specification about the second ball).

SOLUTION. (*a*) We can analyze the experiment as consisting of act Z_1, *the drawing of a ball from the* 1st *bag,* and act Z_2, *the drawing of a ball from the* 2d *bag.* Let H_1 be the event of obtaining a black ball when Z_1 is performed, and H_2 the event of obtaining a green ball when Z_2 is performed. Then, with all outcomes equally likely for each experiment, $P_1(H_1) = \frac{3}{5}$ and $P_2(H_2) = \frac{7}{12}$. Hence, by (1), with "*P*" meaning probability based on (Z_1, Z_2),

$$P(a \ black \ and \ a \ green \ ball) = \tfrac{3}{5} \cdot \tfrac{7}{12} = \tfrac{7}{20}.$$

(*b*) Let T_2 be the event of any outcome of Z_2 occurring. Then, $P_2(T_2) = 1$. Hence, $P(a \ black \ ball \ and \ any \ ball \ from \ 2d \ bag) = \frac{3}{5} \cdot 1 = \frac{3}{5}$.

Suppose that an event H may occur at any trial of a concrete experiment Z, whose sample space T is a basis for probability. Assume that, in *repeated trials of Z,* the outcome at any trial is not affected by the outcomes at other trials. Then, we agree that any specified finite number of repetitions of Z will be considered as *independent identical experiments* to which we can apply (1), (2), and their extension to any number of successive events $H_1, H_2, \cdots$, all associated with Z.

EXAMPLE 2. The probability that Jones will win in a certain game when he plays is $\frac{1}{3}$. If he plays twice, find the probability that he will win just once.

SOLUTION. 1. He plays twice (*two independent acts*). He wins just once if

(a) *he wins the* 1st *game and loses the* 2d *game; or, if*

(b) *he loses the* 1st *game and wins the* 2d *game.*

2. Each of the mutually exclusive compound events (a) and (b) has a probability which can be obtained by use of (1) on page 323. The probability that Jones will lose in any game is $\frac{2}{3}$. Hence, with "*P*" meaning probability based on the outcome space for *two successive games*,

$$P[(a)] = \tfrac{1}{3} \cdot \tfrac{2}{3} = \tfrac{2}{9}; \qquad P[(b)] = \tfrac{2}{3} \cdot \tfrac{1}{3} = \tfrac{2}{9}.$$

By Theorem III on page 323,

$$P[(a) \ or \ (b)] = \tfrac{2}{9} + \tfrac{2}{9} = \tfrac{4}{9}.$$

EXAMPLE 3. A bag contains 10 white and 30 black balls. We draw 2 balls together, replace them, and then draw 2 more balls together. Find the probability of obtaining 2 white, and then 1 white and 1 black ball.

SOLUTION. 1. Let Z be the act of drawing 2 balls from the bag, and let P_1 refer to probability based on the outcome space for Z, where the outcomes are equally likely. Then,

$$p_1 = P_1(2 \ white) = \frac{_{10}C_2}{_{40}C_2} = \frac{3}{52} ;$$

$$p_2 = P_1(1 \ white \ and \ 1 \ black) = \frac{10 \cdot 30}{_{40}C_2} = \frac{15}{39} .$$

2. We have Z repeated twice, to give a compound experiment (Z, Z). Then, with $H_1 = (event \ of \ 2 \ white)$ and $H_2 = (event \ of \ 1 \ white \ and \ 1 \ black)$, and P meaning probability based on two repetitions of Z, we use (1):

$$P(H_1, H_2) = p_1 p_2 = \tfrac{3}{52} \cdot \tfrac{15}{39} = \tfrac{15}{676}.$$

EXERCISE 111

Use Theorem II of page 312 *only for simple events. Obtain the probability of any compound event by use of Sections* 181 *and* 182.

1. In a game where only one player can win, the probability that Smith will win is $\frac{1}{4}$ and that Johnson will win is $\frac{1}{3}$. Find the probability that one of them will win.

2. The probability that Jones will win a certain game is $\frac{1}{4}$ and that Smith will win another game is $\frac{1}{3}$. If each man plays his game, find the probability that (a) both will win; (b) Smith will win and Jones will lose; (c) just one of the men will win.

3. Find the probability of throwing 5 heads in 5 tosses of a coin.

4. If a coin and a die are tossed, find the probability of obtaining (a) a tail and 3 on the die; (b) a head and at least 5 on the die.

5. Find the probability of throwing 11 each time in 3 tosses of 2 dice.

6. If a coin is tossed twice, find the probability that one fall is a head and the other is a tail.

7. The probability that Hansen will win a certain game whenever he plays is $\frac{1}{4}$. If he plays twice, find the probability that (a) he will win the 1st game and lose the 2d game; (b) he will win just one game; (c) he will win at least one game; (d) he will lose both games. [Why are results (c), and (d) related simply?]

8. The probability that a certain man will live 10 years is $\frac{1}{3}$, and that his wife will live 10 years is $\frac{3}{4}$. Find the probability that (a) the wife will live and the man will not live 10 years; (b) just one of them will remain alive at the end of 10 years.

A 1st bag contains 5 black and 10 white balls. A 2d bag contains 3 white and 5 black balls. Find the probability of the specified event.

9. If we draw a ball from each bag, we shall obtain (a) 2 white balls; (b) 2 balls of the same color; (c) 1 white and 1 black ball.

10. If 2 balls are drawn in succession from the 1st bag, *with replacement* of the 1st ball before the 2d ball is drawn, then (a) both will be white; (b) just one will be white; (c) at most one will be white.

11. If 2 balls are drawn together from each bag, (a) all balls obtained will be white; (b) 1 white and 1 black ball will be obtained from each bag; (c) all obtained will be of the same color; (d) 3 white balls and 1 black ball will be obtained.

12. From a deck of 52 cards, we draw 3 cards in succession, with each one replaced before the next draw. Find the probability that we draw (a) all spades or clubs; (b) all of one suit; (c) all aces or jacks.

13. From a deck of 52 cards, we draw 2 cards together, replace them, and repeat this act again. Find the probability that (a) all cards obtained are hearts; (b) all are of the same suit.

14. Johnson's probability of winning a certain game is $\frac{1}{4}$, and Jackson's probability of winning a different game is $\frac{1}{2}$. If each of them plays his game, find the probability that at most one will win.

15. Robert's probability of winning a certain game whenever he plays it is $\frac{1}{3}$. If he plays the game 3 times, find his probability of (a) winning each time; (b) winning twice and losing once.

HINT for (b). He may (i) *win, win, lose;* (ii) *win, lose, win;* (iii) *lose, win, win.* Events (i), (ii), and (iii) are mutually exclusive.

16. Jordan's probability of winning a certain game whenever he plays it is $\frac{1}{4}$. If he plays the game 4 times, find his probability of (a) losing each time; (b) winning just 3 times.

17. In answering true-false questions on an examination, a student chooses responses at random. Find his probability of answering the first 6 questions correctly and the next 4 questions incorrectly.

18. To determine who gets a prize, A tosses a coin with B, the winner tosses with C, and the winner tosses with D. The last winner obtains the prize. Find each person's probability of receiving the prize.

★19. Let H and K be *any* subsets of T in Definition I on page 311. Find the probability of the event $M = (H \cup K)$ in terms of the probabilities of H, K, and $(H \cap K)$. See page 308 for a contact.

183. Successive trials of an experiment

Let Z be a concrete experiment whose set of outcomes $\{r\}$ form the sample space T which is a basis for probability, as in Definition I. Let H be a subset of T; that is, H is an event made possible by Z. We have mentioned, in Section 182, that *successive trials* of Z qualify as *independent experiments*. Then, on successive trials of Z, the probability of any specified sequence of successes and failures for H can be found by (3) on page 324, with all $H_i = H$.

EXAMPLE 1. The probability that Jones will win whenever he plays a certain game is $\frac{1}{4}$. If he plays 6 times, find his probability of winning 4 games and losing 2 games.

SOLUTION. 1. He might have wins and losses as follows, where each subscript indicates the number of the game which is won or lost:

$$W_1, W_2, L_3, L_4, W_5, W_6; \qquad L_1, W_2, W_3, L_4, W_5, W_6; \; etc. \qquad (1)$$

The number of mutually exclusive possibilities, as in (1), is equal to the number of ways of selecting 4 games to be won out of 6 games to be played,* which gives $_6C_4$ or 15 ways. Two of these are seen in (1). The student should write a few of the other possibilities.

2. The probability that Jones will lose in any game is $(1 - \frac{1}{4})$ or $\frac{3}{4}$.

3. We shall apply (3) on page 324, say for the first sequence of wins and losses in (1). For any trial Z_i, we have $P_i(L_i) = \frac{3}{4}$ and $P_i(W_i) = \frac{1}{4}$. Hence, with P meaning *probability based on 6 repetitions of the game* Z,

$$P(W_1, W_2, L_3, L_4, W_5, W_6) = \frac{1}{4} \cdot \frac{1}{4} \cdot \frac{3}{4} \cdot \frac{3}{4} \cdot \frac{1}{4} \cdot \frac{1}{4} = (\tfrac{1}{4})^4(\tfrac{3}{4})^2.$$

Clearly, the order of the 4 wins and 2 losses is unimportant. The probability of any one of the 15 mutually exclusive cases in which Jones wins just 4 games is $(\tfrac{1}{4})^4(\tfrac{3}{4})^2$. Hence, by Theorem III on page 323, the probability that one or another of the 15 cases will occur is the sum of 15 probabilities, each equal to $(\tfrac{1}{4})^4(\tfrac{3}{4})^2$, or

$$P(4 \; wins \; and \; 2 \; losses) = 15(\tfrac{1}{4})^4(\tfrac{3}{4})^2 = 15\tfrac{9}{4096} = \tfrac{135}{4096}.$$

THEOREM IV. *If the probability that an event H will occur at any trial of an experiment Z is p, and that H will not occur is q, then the probability that H will occur exactly k times in n trials is*

$$_nC_kp^kq^{n-k}. \qquad (2)$$

* Or, is the number of permutations of 4 W's and 2 L's, six at a time.

Proof. 1. By (3) on page 324, the probability that any particular k trials will be successful and the other $(n - k)$ trials will fail is

$$(p \cdot p \cdots \text{to } k \text{ factors}) \cdot [q \cdot q \cdots \text{to } (n - k) \text{ factors}], \quad \text{or} \quad p^k q^{n-k}. \tag{3}$$

2. The number of ways for stipulating k successes out of n trials is $_nC_k$. The probability of each of these mutually exclusive combinations of k successes and $(n - k)$ failures is $p^k q^{n-k}$, by (3). Hence, by Theorem III, the probability that k successes will occur in one or another of the mutually exclusive ways (whose number is $_nC_k$) is $_nC_k p^k q^{n-k}$.

COROLLARY 1. *The probability that H will occur at least k times in n trials of the experiment Z is*

$$p^n + {_nC_{n-1}}p^{n-1}q + {_nC_{n-2}}p^{n-2}q^2 + \cdots + {_nC_k}p^k q^{n-k}. \tag{4}$$

Proof. In (4), the 1st term is the probability of *exactly* n successes in n trials; the 2d term is the probability of *just* $(n - 1)$ successes, etc.; the last term is the probability of *just* k successes. By Theorem III, (4) is the probability of k *or more successes.*

Note 1. From (1), page 301, recognize that $_nC_k p^k q^{n-k}$ is the term in the expansion of $(p + q)^n$ which contains p^k as a factor. Also, (4) consists of *the first* $(n - k + 1)$ *terms in the expansion of* $(p + q)^n$.

Note 2. The most probable number of successes in n trials is the value of k for which $_nC_k p^k q^{n-k}$ is greatest. An investigation of $_nC_k p^k q^{n-k}$ would show that *the most probable number of successes is approximately np.*

EXAMPLE 2. A bag contains 5 white and 10 black balls. If we draw 5 balls in succession, replacing each one before the next is drawn, find the probability that (*a*) just three drawn will be black; (*b*) at least three will be black.

SOLUTION. 1. At any draw, since replacement occurs, the probability of obtaining a black ball is $\frac{2}{3}$. Hence, we have repeated trials, where $p = \frac{2}{3}$ and $q = \frac{1}{3}$ in Theorem IV.

2. For (*a*), the probability is $_5C_3(\frac{2}{3})^3(\frac{1}{3})^2$, or $80/243$. From (4),

$$P[(b)] = {_5C_3}(\tfrac{2}{3})^3(\tfrac{1}{3})^2 + {_5C_4}(\tfrac{2}{3})^4(\tfrac{1}{3}) + (\tfrac{2}{3})^5 = \tfrac{64}{81}.$$

Note 3. Theorem IV is of fundamental importance in connection with the *binomial probability distribution* in statistics.

EXERCISE 112

1. The probability of Jones's winning whenever he plays a certain game is $\frac{1}{3}$. If he plays 4 times, find the probability that he wins (*a*) just twice; (*b*) at least twice; (*c*) at most twice.

2. The probability of Hansen's winning whenever he plays a certain game is .2. If he plays 5 times, find the probability that he wins (*a*) exactly 4 games; (*b*) at least 4 games; (*c*) at most 2 games.

3. If 6 coins are tossed (or, 1 coin is tossed 6 times), find the probability of tossing (a) just 3 heads; (b) at least 3 heads; (c) at most 2 heads.

4. If 3 dice are tossed, find the probability of throwing (a) just 2 aces (the number 1 is referred to as an ace); (b) at least 2 aces.

5. A bag contains 2 white and 6 black balls. If we draw 4 balls in succession, with each replaced before the next is drawn, find the probability that, of those drawn, (a) exactly three are white; (b) at least two are white.

6. Find the probability of throwing just three 7's in 4 throws with 2 dice.

7. From a group of 2 men and 4 women, we make 5 random selections of a committee of 2 persons. Find the probability that exactly three of the committees consist entirely of men.

8. A bag contains 3 black and 2 white balls. We draw 2 balls together from the bag, replace the balls, and repeat the act until 4 draws of 2 balls each have been made. Find the probability that just 3 draws yield 1 black and 1 white ball.

9. An examination of multiple-choice type has 10 problems, each with 3 responses, where just one is correct. If a student chooses a response at random for each problem, find the probability that he answers correctly in just (a) 4 problems; (b) 6 problems.

10. Find the probability that, of 4 men, each of age 25, just three will remain alive at age 40. Use Table IX and logarithms.

11. Find the probability that, from 3 classmates each of age 21, just two will be alive 30 years later.

12. For a certain type of biological cell, the empirical probability that the cell will survive for a given time is .3. Find the probability that just 4 out of 6 cells will survive for this time.

13. If 7 coins are tossed, find the most probable number of heads, and the corresponding probability, by writing down all terms in a binomial expansion, as mentioned in Note 1, page 328.

14. A coin is to be tossed repeatedly. Find the probability that the 5th head will appear at the 8th toss.

15. A coin is to be tossed repeatedly. Find the probability that (a) the 3d head will appear on the 9th toss; (b) the kth head will appear on the nth toss.

★184. Conditional probability

Let Z be a fundamental experiment, whose outcomes $\{r\}$ form a sample space T which is a basis for probability, as in Definition I. Let H_1 and H_2 be two events (subsets of T). Then, the *intersection* of H_1 and H_2, or $H_1 \cap H_2$, consists of the outcomes in both H_1 and H_2, as shown schematically in Figure 120, where $W = H_1 \cap H_2$. We wish to develop a method for computing $P(H_1 \cap H_2)$.

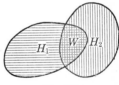

Fig. 120

Suppose that $P(H_1) \neq 0$. Then, we define the "**conditional probability of H_2, given H_1,**" in symbols, $P(H_2, \text{ given } H_1)$, as follows:

$$P(H_2, \text{ given } H_1) = \frac{P(H_1 \cap H_2)}{P(H_1)}. \tag{1}$$

More colloquially, $P(H_2, \text{ given } H_1)$ is read "*the probability of H_2 if H_1 is known to have occurred.*"

ILLUSTRATION 1. Consider a bag containing 3 black and 7 white balls, and 5 black and 10 white cubes. Let Z be the act of drawing an object at random from the bag, with all outcomes taken equally likely. Let H_1 be the event of *obtaining a ball* and H_2 the event of *obtaining a black object*. Then, $P(H_1) = \frac{10}{25}$; $P(H_2) = \frac{8}{25}$. We verify that $H_1 \cap H_2$ consists of 3 black balls and $P(H_1 \cap H_2) = \frac{3}{25}$; from (1),

$$P(H_2, \text{ given } H_1) = \frac{\frac{3}{25}}{\frac{10}{25}} = \frac{3}{10}.$$

Suppose that we now think of H_1, the 10 balls, as a *new sample space*, to form a *basis for probability*. Then, in H_1, there are 3 black objects, and the probability of this set would be $\frac{3}{10}$. Thus, $P(H_2, \text{ given } H_1)$ is equal to the probability of the set of black objects in H_1, where we think of H_1 as a new basis for probability. Notice that

$$P(H_2) = \frac{8}{25} \neq P(H_2, \text{ given } H_1) = \frac{3}{10}.$$

In Definition I on page 311, for *any subset H in T*, we could have defined $P(H)$ as *the ratio of the total probability of the outcomes of H to the total probability of T* (whose probability is 1). Similarly, in (1), $P(H_2, \text{ given } H_1)$ is defined as *the ratio of the total probability of the outcomes in $H_1 \cap H_2$ to the total probability of H_1*. Hence, it is sensible to think of $P(H_2, \text{ given } H_1)$ as an *ordinary probability* of the set $H_1 \cap H_2$, with *probability based on H_1 as if it were a new sample space*. We met a special case of this fact in Illustration 1. The fact is very useful as a means to compute $P(H_2, \text{ given } H_1)$, from which we then obtain a formula for computing $P(H_1 \cap H_2)$ by use of (1):

$$P(H_1 \cap H_2) = P(H_1)\, P(H_2, \text{ given } H_1). \tag{2}$$

That is, when it is convenient to compute $P(H_1)$ *and the conditional probability* $P(H_2, \text{ given } H_1)$, we then have a means for computing $P(H_1 \cap H_2)$.

Let H_1, H_2, and H_3 be three subsets of T. Then, as in (1), we define the conditional probability

$$P(H_3, \text{ given } H_1 \cap H_2) = \frac{P(H_1 \cap H_2 \cap H_3)}{P(H_1 \cap H_2)}. \tag{3}$$

In words, (3) states that the conditional probability of H_3, given $H_1 \cap H_2$, is equal to the probability of the set of outcomes common to H_1, H_2, and H_3, divided by $P(H_1 \cap H_2)$. From (2) and (3),

$$P(H_1 \cap H_2 \cap H_3) = P(H_1)\,P(H_2, \text{given } H_1)\,P(H_3, \text{given } H_1 \cap H_2). \quad (4)$$

In (3), $P(H_3, \text{given } H_1 \cap H_2)$ can be thought of as an ordinary probability of the set of outcomes common to H_1, H_2, and H_3 based on a *new sample space* composed of the outcomes common to H_1 and H_2.

DEFINITION IV.   *If* $P(H_1 \cap H_2) = P(H_1)P(H_2)$, *then the events* H_1 *and* H_2 *are said to be* **independent in the probability sense.** *If the events are not independent, they are said to be* **dependent.**

From (1), if H_1 and H_2 are independent, $P(H_2, \text{given } H_1) = P(H_2)$.

ILLUSTRATION 2.   Consider a bag containing 3 black and 7 white balls, and 6 black and 14 white cubes. Let Z be the drawing of an object from the bag, with the outcomes of Z forming a basis for probability, where the outcomes are taken as equally likely. Let H_1 be the event of *obtaining a ball*, and H_2 be the event of *obtaining a black object*. Then, we find $P(H_1) = \frac{1}{3}$; $P(H_2) = \frac{3}{10}$; $P(H_1 \cap H_2) = \frac{1}{10}$, because $H_1 \cap H_2$ consists of 3 black balls. From (1),

$$P(H_2, \text{given } H_1) = \frac{P(H_1 \cap H_2)}{P(H_1)} = \frac{\frac{1}{10}}{\frac{1}{3}} = \frac{3}{10}.$$

Thus, $P(H_2, \text{given } H_1) = P(H_2)$ and, from (1), $P(H_1 \cap H_2) = P(H_1)P(H_2)$. Hence, H_1 and H_2 are *independent events*. In Illustration 1, H_1 and H_2 are *not* independent events.

★185. Dependent events

Consider an experiment Z, with outcomes $\{r\}$ forming a sample space T. Suppose that Z is equivalent to a sequence of two experiments, Z_1 followed by Z_2 where the nature and outcomes of Z_2 may be affected by the preceding outcome of Z_1. We shall call Z_1 and Z_2 **dependent experiments.**

ILLUSTRATION 1.   A 1st bag contains 5 white and 10 black balls, and a 2d bag contains 20 white and 10 black balls. Let Z be the experiment of *(drawing a ball from a bag selected at random)*. We decide to consider each outcome as a ball; there are 45 outcomes. We obtain all of them by analyzing Z into the acts $(Z_1, \text{then } Z_2)$, where Z_1 is *(select a bag at random)* and Z_2 is *(after selecting a bag, draw a ball)*. Consider the event $H = $ *(obtaining a white ball from the 1st bag)*. We are tempted to proceed as follows: with Z_1 thought of *alone*, the probability of selecting the 1st bag is $p_1 = \frac{1}{2}$. After this bag is selected, the probability of drawing a white ball is $p_2 = \frac{5}{15}$ or $p_2 = \frac{1}{3}$. Then, we conclude that $P(H) = \frac{1}{2} \cdot \frac{1}{3} = \frac{1}{6}$. We shall justify this result.

With an experiment $Z = (Z_1, \text{then } Z_2)$, possessing the set T of outcomes $\{r\}$, there will be a sample space T_1 of outcomes $\{\alpha\}$ for Z_1 alone. Let A_1 be a particular event which may occur when Z_1 is performed and let $p_1 = P_1(A_1)$, where P_1 denotes probability based on T_1. After each outcome α of A_1, then

Z_2 is performed, and there results, for all α in A_1, a corresponding set, H_1, of outcomes $\{r\}$ in * T. We agree that *probabilities are assigned in T so that $P(H_1)$, based on T, will equal p_1;* that is, by definition,* $P(H_1) = p_1$. Let H_2 be an event, or subset of T, which may occur if Z_2 is performed after A_1 occurs. Then, H_2 is a subset of H_1. Consider H_1 *by itself* as a sample space for Z_2, and let p_2 be the probability of H_2 as a subset of H_1, based on Definition I for Z_2. However, with all outcomes in H_1 finally considered to have probabilities applying in T for the experiment Z, p_2 also can be described as the *conditional probability* $P(H_2, \text{ given } H_1)$. Thus, we have

$$p_1 = P(H_1) = P_1(A_1); \qquad p_2 = P(H_2, \text{ given } H_1).$$

The succession of events $(A_1, \text{ then } H_2)$ produces the set of outcomes H_2 in T, and also can be described as *the set of outcomes common to H_1 and H_2,* or their *intersection* $H_1 \cap H_2$. From (2) on page 330, with all probabilities based on T for $Z = (Z_1, \text{ then } Z_2)$, and "$(A_1, \text{ then } H_2)$" meaning just the set H_2,

$$P(A_1, \text{ then } H_2) = P(H_1 \cap H_2) = P(H_1)P(H_2, \text{ given } H_1), \text{ or} \qquad (1)$$

$$\mathbf{P(A_1, \text{ then } H_2) = p_1 p_2.} \qquad (2)$$

In (2), we think of p_1 and p_2 as easy to define in a satisfactory fashion, and thus have a means to compute $P(A_1, \text{ then } H_2)$. A similar result for any finite number of successive acts, and corresponding events, is described as follows. The second event, H_2, in (1) will be referred to hereafter as A_2, for symmetry.

SUMMARY. *Suppose that the events A_1, A_2, A_3, $\cdots$ may occur in succession at a trial of the sequence of corresponding dependent experiments Z_1, Z_2, Z_3, $\cdots$. Let p_1, p_2, p_3, $\cdots$ be the probabilities, respectively, of A_1, of A_2 if A_1 occurs, of A_3 if A_2 occurs, $\cdots$, as based on sample spaces for the separate experiments. Then, in the sample space T for experiment $Z = (Z_1, \text{ then } Z_2, \text{ then } Z_3, \cdots)$, we agree to assign probabilities to the outcomes so that, with P meaning probability based on T,*

$$P(A_1, \text{ then } A_2, \text{ then } A_3, \cdots) = p_1 p_2 p_3 \cdots. \qquad (3)$$

ILLUSTRATION 2. The work in Illustration 1 made use of (2). In Illustration 1, notice that A_1 of (2) is (*obtain 1st bag*); hence, in the discussion preceding (2), we would have $H_1 = (set \text{ of } 15 \text{ outcomes in } 1st \text{ bag})$. Since $P(H_1) = p_1 = \frac{1}{2}$, the method assigns $\frac{1}{2}$ as the total probability, in equal shares, to the 15 outcomes. Hence, as an outcome of Z, each ball in the 1st bag has *probability* $\frac{1}{15} \cdot \frac{1}{2}$ or $\frac{1}{30}$. Similarly, each ball in the 2d bag has probability $\frac{1}{30} \cdot \frac{1}{2}$ or $\frac{1}{60}$. Thus, our method in arriving at (1) or (2) frequently implies that the outcomes of the complex experiment are *not* taken as equally likely.

---

* Although only H_1 is of interest to us, for completeness we specify all outcomes of T as consisting of H_1 and the outcomes A_1' of Z_1, where we assume that, if A_1' occurs, no additional action is taken. Also, we assign to each outcome in A_1', as an outcome of T, precisely the probability possessed by the outcome as an element of T_1: this gives $P(A_1') = P_1(A_1')$ and hence $P(T) = P(H_1) + P(A_1') = P_1(A_1) + P_1(A_1') = 1$.

EXAMPLE 1. There are 5 white and 10 black balls in a 1st bag, and 20 white and 10 black balls in a 2d bag. If a bag is selected at random, and then a ball is drawn, find the probability of obtaining a black ball.

SOLUTION. 1. At any trial, the desired event occurs if either of the following mutually exclusive compound events occurs:

(a) *The* 1st *bag is selected, and then a black ball is drawn.*

(b) *The* 2d *bag is selected, and then a black ball is drawn.*

2. We apply (2) to (a) and (b) separately and use Theorem III. For (a),

$p_1 = prob.$ *(of drawing* 1st *bag)* $= \frac{1}{2}$; $p_2 = prob.$ *(black, if* 1st *bag)* $= \frac{2}{3}$.

Hence, by (2), $P[(a)] = \frac{1}{2} \cdot \frac{2}{3} = \frac{1}{3}$.

For (b), $p_1 = prob.$ *(of drawing* 2d *bag)* $= \frac{1}{2}$;

                 $p_2 = prob.$ *(of black, if* 2d *bag)* $= \frac{1}{3}$.

Hence, $P[(b)] = \frac{1}{2} \cdot \frac{1}{3} = \frac{1}{6}$. Then, $P[(a)$ or $(b)] = \frac{1}{3} + \frac{1}{6} = \frac{1}{2}$.

EXAMPLE 2. A bag contains 10 white and 5 black balls. If 3 balls are drawn in succession without replacement, find the probability that *(black, black, white)* are obtained, in that order.

SOLUTION. We apply (3) for 3 *dependent* acts *(successive draws without replacement)*. The probability of a black at the 1st draw is $p_1 = \frac{5}{15}$. If the 1st draw is black, there remain 4 black and 10 white balls. Hence,

$$p_2 = prob. \text{ (2d } black \text{ if 1st } is \text{ } black) = \frac{4}{14}.$$

If the 2d draw is black, there remain 3 black and 10 white balls. Hence, from (3),   *prob. (black, black, white)* $= \frac{5}{15} \cdot \frac{4}{14} \cdot \frac{10}{13} = \frac{20}{273}$.

Note 1. We refer to the event $(A_1,$ *then* $A_2, \cdots)$ in (2) as a *compound event.* If we bring in sets $H_1, H_2, \cdots$ of T corresponding to $A_1, A_2, \cdots$, as in the discussion preceding the Summary, then $p_2, p_3, \cdots$ in (3) can be written as conditional probabilities $P(H_2,$ *given* $H_1), P(H_3,$ *given* $H_2), \cdots$.

★EXERCISE 113

A 1st *bag contains* 5 *white and* 10 *green balls, a* 2d *bag contains* 4 *white and* 2 *black balls, and a* 3d *bag contains* 6 *black and* 4 *green balls. Find the probability of the specified event.*

1. If a ball is drawn from the 1st bag, and a ball from the 2d bag, both balls will be white.

2. If a bag is selected at random, and then a ball is drawn, it will be (a) white; (b) white or green.

3. If a bag is selected at random, and then 2 balls are drawn together, both will be (a) white; (b) green; (c) of the same color.

4. If 2 balls are drawn in succession from the 1st bag and not replaced, the balls drawn will be white and green, in any order.

5. If 3 balls are drawn in succession from the 1st bag, then all will be white, under the assumption that (*a*) none are replaced; (*b*) each is replaced before the next one is drawn.

6. If 3 balls are drawn in succession from the 1st bag, and none are replaced, then they will appear (white, green, white), (*a*) in that order as drawn; (*b*) in any order.

7. One box contains 5 lemons and 8 oranges; a second box contains 4 lemons and 3 oranges. A man selects a box at random and then a piece of fruit at random. Let *H*, *K*, and *W* be the events of obtaining a lemon from the 1st box, a lemon from the 2d box, and a lemon, respectively. Find $P(H)$, $P(K)$, and $P(W)$. Also, if he obtains a lemon, find the probability that it came from the second box.

8. A 1st bag contains 5 red and 8 white balls, and a 2d bag contains 9 red and 3 white cubes. Let *Z* be the experiment of drawing an object from a bag selected at random. Let *H* be the event of (*obtaining a ball*) and *K* be the event of (*obtaining a red object*). Let H' and K' be "*not H*" and "*not K*," respectively. Find $P(H)$; $P(K)$; $P(H')$; $P(K')$; $P(H \cap K)$; $P(K, given\ H)$. Prove that *H* and *K* are *not* independent.

9. Repeat Problem 8 if the 2d bag contains 10 red and 16 white cubes, but in this case prove that *H* and *K* are independent events.

10. A bag contains two markers numbered 1, and three markers numbered 2. A box, numbered 1, contains 4 white and 3 black balls. A box, numbered 2, contains 2 white and 4 black balls. A marker is drawn from the bag, and then a ball is drawn from that box having the number on the marker. (*a*) Find the probability of obtaining a white ball. (*b*) If a white ball is obtained, find the probability that it came from box 1.

11. A committee consists of 5 men and 9 women. In order to fill the positions of chairman, secretary, and treasurer for the committee, first a chairman will be selected by lot, then a secretary by lot, and then a treasurer by lot. Find the probability that the chairman and treasurer will be women and the secretary a man.

12. A bag contains 3 white and 7 black balls. We draw 2 balls, replace them by green balls, and then draw 2 more balls. Find the probability that all balls drawn will have the same color.

13. Consider the data preceding Problem 1. Suppose that 2 bags are selected at random, and then 1 ball is drawn from each of these bags. Find the probability that each of these balls is green.

14. For a certain type of biological cell, the empirical probability of survival for 1 hour is .8. If the cell survives, then fission occurs, and the cell splits into two new cells of the same type. If a single cell starts the creation of a population of cells, find the probability that, at the end of 2 hours, there will be (*a*) 4 cells; (*b*) just 2 cells. (*c*) Check by computing the probability for no cells at the end of 2 hours. Assume that the survival of any cell is not affected by any coexisting cell.

Mathematical Induction

186. A property of positive integers and mathematical induction

In this chapter, the word *integer* always will refer to a *positive integer*. In a logical foundation of the number system, we find that the following axiom or some equivalent postulate about the positive integers is of basic importance. We shall use the property stated by the axiom.

AXIOM OF INDUCTION. *If T is a set of positive integers with the following two properties, then T consists of* **all positive integers:**

I. *The integer 1 belongs to T.*

II. *If the integer k belongs to T, then $(k + 1)$ belongs to T.*

This axiom becomes the foundation for a powerful method of proof called *mathematical induction*, which we proceed to illustrate.

Note 1. If (I) of the Axiom is changed to read "*the integer h belongs to T*," the conclusion would be that T consists of all integers $\geq h$.

EXAMPLE 1. By use of the axiom of induction, prove that, if the first term of an A.P. is a and the common difference is d, then the nth term is

$$[a + (n - 1)d].$$

Proof. 1. Let $l_n = a + (n - 1)d$. Let T be the set of all integers n for which l_n is the nth term of the A.P. We wish to prove that T consists of *all* integers n.

2. *Verification of property* (I). If $n = 1$, the first term is known to be a, and we verify that $l_1 = a + 0d = a$. Hence, T contains the integer 1 (that is, the stated result is true when $n = 1$).

3. *Verification of property* (II). Our *hypothesis* is that the kth term of the A.P. is given by $l_k = a + (k - 1)d$. We wish to *prove* that the $(k + 1)$th term also is given by the formula for l_n. By the definition of an A.P.,

$$[(k + 1)\text{th } term] = l_k + d = a + (k - 1)d + d$$
$$= a + kd = a + [(k + 1) - 1]d. \tag{1}$$

In (1), notice that the result is that which is obtained if $n = k + 1$ in

$$l_n = a + (n - 1)d.$$

Hence, we have proved that, if the stated result of Example 1 is true when $n = k$, then the result also is true when $n = k + 1$.

4. We have shown that T satisfies (I) and (II) of the Axiom. Hence, T contains *all* integers, or the nth term is $a + (n - 1)d$ for *all* values of n.

The method of proof in Example 1 is called *mathematical induction*. A proof by this method may be compared to climbing a ladder, where each rung corresponds to a special case of the theorem. In the proof, in verifying (I) of the Axiom, we show that we can climb onto the 1st rung (or, we may feel more comfortable if we verify that we can climb up the first few rungs). Then, in proving (II) of the Axiom, we show that we are able to pass *from rung to rung*. The conclusion, justified by the Axiom, is that we can reach *all* rungs of the ladder.

Let the sequence $\{H_n\}$ represent a theorem which has H_1, H_2, H_3, $\cdots$, H_n, $\cdots$ as its special cases. That is, we are dealing with a theorem whose special cases can be arranged in a one-to-one correspondence with the set of all * positive integers, 1, 2, 3, $\cdots$, n, $\cdots$. We refer to H_n as the nth *case*, or the *general case* of the theorem. Mathematical induction sometimes can be used to prove that H_n is true for all values of n.

SUMMARY. *Proof of a theorem $\{H_n\}$ for all values of n by mathematical induction.*

A. *Let T be the set of integers $\{n\}$ for which $\{H_n\}$ is true. Verify that H_n is true when $n = 1$ (and perhaps $n = 2$ and $n = 3$ for appreciation of the nature of the theorem).*

B. *Proof of an* **auxiliary theorem** *which states that, if the kth case H_k is true then the $(k + 1)$th case H_{k+1} is true.*

Conclusion. *A clear statement that (B) showed the truth of (II) of the Axiom of Induction for the set T, and hence that T contains all integers, or H_n is true for all values of n.*

EXAMPLE 2. *If n is any positive integer, prove that*

$$2 + 4 + 6 + \cdots + 2n = n(n + 1), \tag{2}$$

or, the sum of the first n positive even integers is $n(n + 1)$.

Note 2. There are n terms on the left in (2), and $2n$ is not only the nth *term* but also is a formula from which any term may be computed. Hence, we refer to $2n$ as the *general term* in (2).

Proof of (2). The theorem $\{H_n\}$ is summarized in (2). Let T be the set of all integers n for which (2) is true.

---

* Or, with all of them from a certain point on.

Part A. *Verification of special cases.*

When we place $n = 1$ in (2): $\qquad\qquad\qquad$ $2 = 1(1+1),$ *or* $2 = 2.$

When we place $n = 2$ in (2): $\qquad\qquad\qquad$ $2+4 = 2(2+1),$ *or* $6 = 6.$

When we place $n = 3$ in (2): $\qquad\qquad$ $2+4+6 = 3(3+1),$ *or* $12 = 12.$

Hence, equation (2) is true when n is 1, 2, or 3. The verification of these special cases may create a *presumption* that all cases of the theorem are true but, *by itself, the verification of any number of special cases does not prove a general theorem.* We have verified that T contains the integers $n = 1, 2,$ and 3, or (I) of the Axiom is true for T.

Part B. Auxiliary Theorem. *If k is a value of n for which equation* (2) *is true, then it is true also when* $n = k + 1.$

Proof. 1. By hypothesis, equation (2) is true when $n = k$, or

$$2 + 4 + 6 + \cdots + 2k = k(k+1). \tag{3}$$

By use of (3), we wish to prove that

$$2 + 4 + 6 + \cdots + 2(k+1) \overset{?}{=} (k+1)[(k+1)+1]$$
$$\overset{?}{=} (k+1)(k+2), \tag{4}$$

which results from (2) when $n = k + 1$. In (4), we place "?" over "=" because the equality is not yet proved. Recognize that

$$2 + 4 + \cdots + 2(k+1) = 2 + 4 + \cdots + 2k + 2(k+1), \tag{5}$$

since the sum of $(k+1)$ terms is the sum of k terms plus the $(k+1)$th term. By (5), the equation (4) which we wish to establish becomes

$$2 + 4 + 6 + \cdots + 2k + 2(k+1) \overset{?}{=} (k+1)(k+2). \tag{6}$$

Our *hypothesis* is stated by equation (3); by means of it we desire *to prove* that equation (6) is true.

2. Add $2(k+1)$ to both sides of (3):

$$2 + 4 + 6 + \cdots + 2k + 2(k+1) = k(k+1) + 2(k+1)$$

(factoring) $\qquad\qquad\qquad\qquad\qquad\quad = (k+1)(k+2). \tag{7}$

Hence, each side in (7) is the same as the corresponding side of (6). Therefore, (6) is true if (3) is true, which proves the auxiliary theorem.

Conclusion. We have shown that the set T of all values of n for which (2) is true contains the integer $n = 1$ and, also, that (II) of the Axiom is true. Hence, by the Axiom, T contains *all integers*, or (1) is true for *all values of n.*

Example 3. *If n is any positive integer, prove that*

$$1 \cdot 2 + 2 \cdot 3 + \cdots + n(n+1) = \tfrac{1}{3}n(n+1)(n+2). \tag{8}$$

Proof of (8). The theorem $\{H_n\}$ is summarized in (8). Let T be the set of all integers n for which (8) is true.

Part A. *Verification of special cases.* We verify (8) when $n = 1$ and $n = 2$:

When $n = 1$, $\qquad\qquad\qquad\qquad$ $1 \cdot 2 = \frac{1}{3}(1)(1 + 1)(1 + 2)$, $\quad or \quad 2 = 2$.

When $n = 2$, $\qquad\qquad\qquad$ $1 \cdot 2 + 2 \cdot 3 = \frac{1}{3}(2)(2 + 1)(2 + 2)$, $\quad or \quad 8 = 8$.

Hence, the set T contains the integers $n = 1$ and $n = 2$.

Part B. AUXILIARY THEOREM. *If k is any value of n for which equation (8) is true, then it is true also when $n = k + 1$.*

Proof. 1. By hypothesis, (8) is true when $n = k$, or

$$1 \cdot 2 + 2 \cdot 3 + \cdots + k(k + 1) = \tfrac{1}{3}k(k + 1)(k + 2). \tag{9}$$

Under this hypothesis we wish to show the truth of the following equation, which is obtained by placing $n = k + 1$ in (8):

$$\left. \begin{aligned} 1 \cdot 2 + 2 \cdot 3 + \cdots + (k + 1)[(k + 1) + 1] \\ \overset{?}{=} \tfrac{1}{3}(k + 1)[(k + 1) + 1][(k + 1) + 2]. \end{aligned} \right\} \tag{10}$$

2. On explicitly indicating the kth term on the left in (10), we obtain

$$\left. \begin{aligned} 1 \cdot 2 + 2 \cdot 3 + \cdots + k(k + 1) + (k + 1)(k + 2) \\ \overset{?}{=} \tfrac{1}{3}(k + 1)(k + 2)(k + 3). \end{aligned} \right\} \tag{11}$$

To establish (11), add $(k + 1)(k + 2)$ to both sides of (9):

$$\left. \begin{aligned} 1 \cdot 2 + 2 \cdot 3 + \cdots + k(k + 1) + (k + 1)(k + 2) \\ = \tfrac{1}{3}k(k + 1)(k + 2) + (k + 1)(k + 2). \end{aligned} \right\} \tag{12}$$

In (12), when the right-hand side is simplified, we obtain

$$\frac{k(k + 1)(k + 2) + 3(k + 1)(k + 2)}{3} = \frac{1}{3}(k + 1)(k + 2)(k + 3).$$

Since each side of (12) is the same as the corresponding side of (11), we have shown that (10) is true if (9) is true. The student now should supply a concluding statement, as in Example 2.

Both Part A and Part B of a proof by mathematical induction are necessary. Thus, Part A alone would be insufficient, because verification of any number of special cases of a theorem would not prove that all of its cases are true.

ILLUSTRATION 1. It can be verified that $(n^2 - n + 41)$ is a prime number when $n = 1, 2, 3, \cdots, 40$. Hence, it might be inferred, incorrectly, that $(n^2 - n + 41)$ is a prime integer for all values of the integer n. This result is *not* true because, if $n = 41$,

$$n^2 - n + 41 = (41)^2 - 41 + 41 = (41)^2,$$

which is not a prime integer (being 41×41).

We note also that Part B, alone, of a proof by mathematical induction would not constitute a proof.

ILLUSTRATION 2. If we should forget the necessity for Part A (verification of special cases), apparently we could prove the false statement that, *if n is any positive integer, then*

$$2 + 4 + 6 + \cdots + 2n = 20 + n(n + 1). \qquad (13)$$

When we compare this equation with (2) on page 336, we see that the present equation (1) is *not* true for any value of n. Nevertheless, we can prove the auxiliary theorem of Part B, which would state that, if

$$2 + 4 + 6 + \cdots + 2k = 20 + k(k + 1), \qquad (14)$$

then $\qquad 2 + 4 + 6 + \cdots + 2(k + 1) = 20 + (k + 1)(k + 2). \qquad (15)$

We could verify (15) by adding $2(k + 1)$ on both sides of (14).

The student must not infer that mathematical induction applies only when the theorem is stated by means of an *equation*. In the next example, no equation is written to summarize the statement (although this could be done).

EXAMPLE 4. *Prove that, if n is any positive integer, then* $(x^{2n} - y^{2n})$ *has* $(x + y)$ *as a factor.*

SOLUTION. A. When $n = 1$, $(x^{2n} - y^{2n})$ becomes $(x^2 - y^2)$, which is seen to have $(x + y)$ as a factor. If $n = 2$, $(x^{2n} - y^{2n})$ becomes $(x^4 - y^4)$, which has $(x + y)$ as a factor:

$$x^4 - y^4 = (x + y)(x^3 - x^2y + xy^2 - y^3).$$

B. AUXILIARY THEOREM. *If* $(x^{2n} - y^{2n})$ *has* $(x + y)$ *as a factor when* $n = k$, *then* $(x^{2n} - y^{2n})$ *has* $(x + y)$ *as a factor also when* $n = k + 1$.

Proof. 1. If $(x^{2n} - y^{2n})$ has $(x + y)$ as a factor when $n = k$, then

$$x^{2k} - y^{2k} = (x + y)F, \qquad (16)$$

where we let F represent the other factor. When $n = k + 1$, $(x^{2n} - y^{2n})$ becomes $(x^{2k+2} - y^{2k+2})$. On dividing $(x^{2k+2} - y^{2k+2})$ by $(x^{2k} - y^{2k})$, we find

$$x^{2k+2} - y^{2k+2} = x^2(x^{2k} - y^{2k}) + y^{2k}(x^2 - y^2). \qquad (17)$$

2. Hence, by use of (16) and (17), we obtain

$$x^{2k+2} - y^{2k+2} = x^2(x + y)F + y^{2k}(x + y)(x - y) \qquad (18)$$
$$= (x + y)[x^2F + y^{2k}(x - y)].$$

Therefore, $(x^{2k+2} - y^{2k+2})$ has the factor $(x + y)$ if $(x^{2k} - y^{2k})$ has the factor $(x + y)$, and hence the auxiliary theorem has been proved. The student should supply the concluding statement for the solution.

Note 3. In the natural sciences, a general conclusion often is reached, although not demonstrated in the mathematical sense, by a consideration of what happens in a number of special cases. Such reasoning is called *ordinary*, or *incomplete*, induction. In contrast to it, mathematical induction often is called *complete* induction.

EXERCISE 114

*By use of mathematical induction, prove that each equation, or verbal statement,
is true for all positive integral values of n.*

1. Suppose that a geometric progression has the first term a and common ratio r. Prove that the nth term, l_n, is given by the formula $l_n = ar^{n-1}$.

2. $4 + 8 + 12 + \cdots + 4n = 2n(n + 1)$.

3. $1 + 2 + 3 + \cdots + n = \dfrac{n(n + 1)}{2}$.

4. The sum of the first n positive integral multiples of 3 is $\frac{3}{2}n(n + 1)$.

5. The sum of the first n positive integral multiples of 6 is $3n(n + 1)$.

6. Prove that the sum of the first n terms of the A.P. in Example 1 on page 335 is $\frac{1}{2}n[2a + (n - 1)d]$.

7. Prove that the sum of the first n terms of the G.P. of Problem 1 is $(a - ar^n)/(1 - r)$.

8. $1 + 3 + 5 + \cdots + (2n - 1) = n^2$. (State this theorem in words.)

9. $1 + 5 + 9 + \cdots + (4n - 3) = n(2n - 1)$.

10. $3 + 3^2 + 3^3 + \cdots + 3^n = \frac{1}{2}(3^{n+1} - 3)$.

11. $1 + 2 + 2^2 + \cdots + 2^{n-1} = 2^n - 1$.

12. $1 + 6 + 6^2 + \cdots + 6^{n-1} = \frac{1}{5}(6^n - 1)$.

13. $1^2 + 2^2 + 3^2 + \cdots + n^2 = \dfrac{n}{6}(n + 1)(2n + 1)$.

14. $1^3 + 2^3 + 3^3 + \cdots + n^3 = \dfrac{n^2}{4}(n + 1)^2$.

15. $1 \cdot 3 + 2 \cdot 4 + 3 \cdot 5 + \cdots + n(n + 2) = \frac{1}{6}n(n + 1)(2n + 7)$.

16. $\dfrac{1}{1 \cdot 2} + \dfrac{1}{2 \cdot 3} + \dfrac{1}{3 \cdot 4} + \cdots + \dfrac{1}{n(n + 1)} = \dfrac{n}{n + 1}$.

17. If n is any integer, prove that $\frac{1}{3}(n^3 + 2n)$ is an integer.

18. The sum of the cubes of the first n positive even integers is $2n^2(n + 1)^2$.

19. If n is a positive integer, then $(x^n - y^n)$ has $(x - y)$ as a factor.

20. If n is a positive integer, $(x^{2n-1} + y^{2n-1})$ has $(x + y)$ as a factor.

★21. Prove that, for every positive integer n, $(x + y)^n$ is given by the expansion (1) on page 134. That is, prove the binomial theorem by mathematical induction.

Comment. The resulting demonstration is one of the classical proofs of mathematics. However, the natural complexity of the proof compares very unfavorably with the simple demonstration of the theorem on page 301. In Part B of the requested proof, the expansion of $(x + y)^k$ must be written, with both the hth and the $(h - 1)$th terms given explicitly. Then, after multiplication by $(x + y)$ to obtain $(x + y)^{k+1}$, it must be shown that the term involving $x^h y^{k-h+1}$ has the correct coefficient.

General Systems of Linear Equations

187. Systems of n linear equations in n variables

Let any system of n linear equations in n variables be written in the following form, illustrated for $n = 3$, with the variables x, y, and z:

$$
(A) \begin{cases} a_1x + b_1y + c_1z = k_1, & (1) \\ a_2x + b_2y + c_2z = k_2, & (2) \\ a_3x + b_3y + c_3z = k_3. & (3) \end{cases}
$$

In (A), the characteristic feature is that all terms in the variables, *in a definite order*, are in the left-hand members, and the constant term (possibly zero) in each equation is on the right. A solution of (A) is a set of values of the variables which satisfy all of the equations. The *system* (or its *set of equations*) is called **consistent** if there is *a solution* (at least one), and otherwise is called **inconsistent.** We shall assume that the remarks of Note 1 on page 99, as extended to a system of any number of equations, justify the following statement.

FUNDAMENTAL PRINCIPLE. *A system of n linear equations in any number of variables is equivalent to (has the same solutions as) the new system which results on replacing any given equation, $H = W$, by the new equation $R = S$ obtained as follows:*

$$
(B) \begin{cases} \textit{Multiply both sides of } H = W \textit{ by a constant, not zero;} \\ \textit{multiply both sides of a second equation, } U = V, \textit{ of} \\ \textit{the system by a constant, not zero; add corresponding} \\ \textit{sides of the two new equations to obtain } R = S. \end{cases}
$$

In some form, (B) is applied again and again in many of the methods available for solving (A), for any number of variables.

188. Triangular form for a system, and matrices

Let us phrase our remarks for the case of a system (A) on this page, for three variables. On the basis of (B) on this page, we may eliminate one variable, say z, by use of (1) and (2) of (A) to obtain a new equation (1)′ to replace (1). By use of (2) and (3), we may eliminate z again, to obtain a new equation (2)′ in x and y to replace (2). Then, we consider [(1)′, (2)′, (3)] as the new system. Here, we may use (1)′ and (2)′ to eliminate y and obtain a new equation (1)″ to replace (1)′; equation (1)″ will involve *only* x. Then, in general, the system [(1)″, (2)′, (3)] is immediately solvable. For a reason evident in the following example, this system is said to be a **triangular system,** equivalent to the given system (A).

Note 1. Instead of having (1)″ involving x, we might equally well choose to have (1)″ involve y, or z, as proves convenient, which amounts merely to altering the order in which we refer to the variables.

EXAMPLE 1. Solve for x, y, and z:
$$\begin{cases} 3x + y - z = 11, & (1) \\ x + 3y - z = 13, & (2) \\ x + y - 3z = 11. & (3) \end{cases}$$

SOLUTION. 1. Subtract,* (2) from (1): $\qquad\qquad 2x - 2y = -2.$ $\qquad$ (4)

Multiply by 3 in (2): $\qquad\qquad\qquad\qquad\qquad 3x + 9y - 3z = 39.$ $\qquad$ (5)

Subtract, (3) from (5): $\qquad\qquad\qquad\qquad\qquad\qquad 2x + 8y = 28.$ $\qquad$ (6)

Subtract, (4) from (6): $\qquad\qquad\qquad\qquad\qquad\qquad\qquad 10y = 30.$

Thus, system [(1), (2), (3)] is equivalent to the following system, which is in the triangular form.
$$\begin{cases} 10y = 30, & (7) \\ 8y + 2x = 28, & (8) \\ y + x - 3z = 11. & (9) \end{cases}$$

2. From (7), $y = 3$; then, from (8), we have $2x = 28 - 24$ or $x = 2$; then, from (9), we have $3z = 3 + 2 - 11 = -6$ or $z = -2$. Thus, the given system has the single solution ($x = 2$, $y = 3$, and $z = -2$).

We shall refer to the preceding method as a solution by *changing to a triangular form.*

A **matrix** (of numbers) with h rows and k columns is a set of hk numbers, each called an **element** of the matrix, arranged in h rows and k columns. If $h = k$, the matrix is said to be a **square matrix.**

ILLUSTRATION 1. The coefficients of the variables in [(1), (2), (3)] in the order (x, y, z) form a square matrix; these coefficients, with an *added column* consisting of the *constant terms* on the right in the equations, form a rectangular matrix of three rows and four columns. Thus, we have two matrices:

$$\begin{bmatrix} 3 & 1 & -1 \\ 1 & 3 & -1 \\ 1 & 1 & -3 \end{bmatrix}; \qquad \begin{bmatrix} 3 & 1 & -1 & 11 \\ 1 & 3 & -1 & 13 \\ 1 & 1 & -3 & 11 \end{bmatrix}. \qquad (10)$$

* Meaning, *subtract corresponding sides in the stated order.*

We call the matrix at the left in (10) the **coefficient matrix** and the matrix at the right the **augmented matrix** for the given system.

Recall the nature of Step 1 of the solution of Example 1, and our switch of y to the place of honor as the "1st *variable*" in writing (7), (8), and (9). We conclude that the following operations on the augmented matrix in (10) lead to a new matrix of 3 rows and 4 columns, which is *the augmented matrix for a system equivalent to* [(1), (2), (3)], where we refer to these equations as if they formed a general system.

I. *Interchange any two rows.*

II. *Interchange any two columns of the coefficient matrix.*

III. *Multiply the elements of any row by a constant, not zero.*

IV. *After applying* (III) *to any two specified rows, add* (*or subtract*) *their corresponding elements, and use the result as a replacement for any one of the two specified rows.*

Note 2. Operation (I) is equivalent to rewriting the system with the equations in a different order. Operation (II) is equivalent to altering the order in which the variables are written in the equations. Operation (III) is equivalent to replacing any equation by a new equivalent equation obtained by multiplying both of its sides by a nonzero constant. Operation (IV) is equivalent to operation (B) of page 341. Instead of the solution given for Example 1, we could proceed as follows, to obtain a new augmented matrix where the matrix of coefficients (consisting of the first 3 columns) is in triangular form (*zeros* above the so-called "**main diagonal**," starting at the *upper left-hand corner*).

MATRIX SOLUTION OF EXAMPLE 1. We write the matrices (10). Instead of saying "*eliminate z*," we shall say "*manipulate the augmented matrix*" to obtain zeros in two places in the 3d column. We subtract the elements of the 2d row from those of the 1st row; then multiply elements of the 2d row by 3 and subtract the elements of the 3d row from the new elements in the 2d row. We thus obtain

$$\begin{bmatrix} 2 & -2 & 0 & -2 \\ 1 & 3 & -1 & 13 \\ 1 & 1 & -3 & 11 \end{bmatrix}; \quad then \quad \begin{bmatrix} 2 & -2 & 0 & -2 \\ 2 & 8 & 0 & 28 \\ 1 & 1 & -3 & 11 \end{bmatrix}. \tag{11}$$

In the matrix at the right in (11), multiply the elements of the 1st row by 4, and then add to these elements the corresponding elements of the 2d row, to obtain a triangular form for the coefficient matrix (3 columns at the left):

$$\begin{bmatrix} 10 & 0 & 0 & 20 \\ 2 & 8 & 0 & 28 \\ 1 & 1 & -3 & 11 \end{bmatrix} \quad for \quad \begin{cases} 10x & = 20, \\ 2x + 8y & = 28, \\ x + y - 3z = 11. \end{cases} \tag{12}$$

From (12), we obtain $(x = 2, y = 3, z = -2)$. For variety, we arranged to get a different triangular form in (12) than in [(7), (8), (9)].

Note 3. With practice, the matrix manipulations may be preferred in place of the method of the 1st solution of Example 1. The convenience of the matrix method becomes more apparent as the number of equations increases.

The remarks at the end of Note 1 on page 99 apply to a system of n equations in n variables, for any positive integer n, in recognizing that the equations are inconsistent. If the equations, in our process of solution, lead to a contradictory statement $c = 0$, where $c \neq 0$, the given system is *inconsistent.* If we are led to an identity $0 = 0$ as one new equation, we thus are left with a system containing fewer equations than variables. In such a case, the equations of the given system would be called **dependent,** but nevertheless they might be inconsistent; usually, however, the system would have infinitely many solutions, as discussed later in this chapter.

Note 4. Suppose that the triangular method is used, with matrices involved. Then, the method leads to a unique solution of the given system if all numbers in the main diagonal of the coefficient matrix, in triangular form, are *not zero.* In such a case, each corresponding equation in the final form determines uniquely the value of one of the variables.

SUMMARY. *To change the augmented matrix of a system of n linear equations in n variables to a form where the coefficient matrix is triangular.*

1. *Manipulate rows by use of* (III) *and* (IV) *of page 343 to obtain 0 in the nth column, 1st row. Repeat, to obtain 0 in all places in the nth column above the last row.*

2. *Use* (III) *and* (IV) *to obtain 0 in the $(n - 1)$th column in all rows except the last two rows. Continue until each element is 0 above the main diagonal of the coefficient matrix.*

EXERCISE 115

Solve by changing to the triangular form by matrix manipulations. In Problem 1, also solve as in Example 1 on page 342.

1. $\begin{cases} 6x + 4y - z = 3, \\ x + 2y + 4z = -2, \\ 5x + 4y = 0. \end{cases}$

2. $\begin{cases} x + y - 2z = 7, \\ 2x - 3y = 2z, \\ x - 2y - 3z = 3. \end{cases}$

3. $\begin{cases} 2s + 4y - 5t = 1, \\ s + 2y - 3t = 1, \\ s - 3t = 2. \end{cases}$

4. $\begin{cases} 3x + 4y + z = -1, \\ 2x - y + 2z + 1 = 0, \\ x + 3y - z = 2. \end{cases}$

5. $\begin{cases} x + y - z = 1, \\ 12x - 2y + 3z = 3, \\ 3x + y - 3z = 6. \end{cases}$

6. $\begin{cases} 9x + 2y + 3z = 3, \\ y - 12x - 12z + 6 = 0, \\ 2z - y - 2x = 4. \end{cases}$

7. $\begin{cases} x - 2y + z + 3w = 7, \\ x + y + 3z + 2w = 6, \\ x + y - 2z + w = 9, \\ 3x + 4y + 4z + 2w = 16. \end{cases}$

8. $\begin{cases} 6y - 4z - w + 3 = 0, \\ 2x + y - z - 2w = 7, \\ x - 2y + 8z = 7, \\ 3x - 4y + 4z - w = 12. \end{cases}$

9. $\begin{cases} 2y + z = 0, \\ -x + 3y + 5z = 0, \\ 3x + 4y - z = 0. \end{cases}$

10. $\begin{cases} x - 3y + 2z = 0, \\ 2x + y + 4z = 0, \\ -2x + y + 3z = 0. \end{cases}$

11. $\begin{cases} 3x + 3y - 7z = 7, \\ x + 2y - 3z = 3, \\ x - y - z = 2. \end{cases}$

12. $\begin{cases} 2x + 6y + 2z = 11, \\ 2x + y - z = 2, \\ x - 2y - 2z = -2. \end{cases}$

13. $\begin{cases} 2x - y + 3z - w = 9, \\ x - 4y + z = 11, \\ 3x - 5z + 2w = 13, \\ 8x + y + 4z - 2w = 30. \end{cases}$

14. $\begin{cases} 3x - 4y + 12z + 4w + 2v = 0, \\ 5 + 2y + 3v + 2w = 0, \\ z + v + 1 = 0, \\ 4 - x + 4y - 4z - 4w + 2v = 0, \\ x - 4y + 8z - 6w = 4. \end{cases}$

15. $\begin{cases} 2x + 6y + 2z - u + 2v + 3 = 0, \\ -6y + 8z + 2u - 2v = 1, \\ 2x + y + z - v = -1, \\ 6x + 4y - 2z + u = 4, \\ -8y + 6z - u + 4v = 3. \end{cases}$

189. Determinants of the second order

If $ad - bc \neq 0$, by elementary means we find that the system

$$\begin{cases} ax + by = e, & \quad (1) \\ cx + dy = f, & \quad (2) \end{cases}$$

has the solution

$$x = \frac{de - bf}{ad - bc}; \quad y = \frac{af - ce}{ad - bc}. \quad (3)$$

The symmetrical nature of the numerators and denominators in (3) was noticed by early mathematicians, and led to the introduction of the following notation which, in its later extensions, proves to be one of the most useful tools of advanced mathematics.

The symbol on the left in the following equality is called a **determinant** and is an abbreviation for $ad - bc$. Or, by definition,

$$\begin{vmatrix} a & b \\ c & d \end{vmatrix} = ad - bc. \quad (4)$$

We read (4) by *rows* as follows: "*the determinant a, b, c, d is equal to ad − bc.*"
We call a, b, c, and d the **elements** and $ad − bc$ the **expansion** of the determinant. This determinant is said to be of the *second* order because it has two rows and two columns.

ILLUSTRATION 1. $\begin{vmatrix} 3 & 2 \\ -4 & -5 \end{vmatrix} = 3(-5) - (-4)(2) = -15 + 8 = -7.$

By the definition of a determinant, if $ad − bc \neq 0$, the solution of system [(1), (2)] in (3) can be written as follows:

$$x = \frac{\begin{vmatrix} e & b \\ f & d \end{vmatrix}}{\begin{vmatrix} a & b \\ c & d \end{vmatrix}}; \quad y = \frac{\begin{vmatrix} a & e \\ c & f \end{vmatrix}}{\begin{vmatrix} a & b \\ c & d \end{vmatrix}}. \tag{5}$$

We refer to [(1), (2)] as the *standard form* for a system of two linear equations in two variables. In this form, the terms in the variables are in the left-hand members, with the order of the variables *the same in both equations.* The terms in the right-hand members then are called the *constant terms.* The solution in (5), for a system in standard form, is summarized by the following rule, due to the Swiss mathematician CRAMER (1704–1752). This rule will be extended later to systems of more than two equations.

CRAMER'S RULE. *In a system of linear equations where there are just as many equations as variables, suppose that* **the determinant of the coefficients of the variables is not zero.** *Then, the system has a single solution. In it, the value of each variable can be written as the quotient of two determinants as follows:*

1. *The denominator is the determinant of the coefficients of the variables.*

2. *For any variable, the numerator is obtained from the denominator by replacing the coefficients of the variable by the constant terms.*

ILLUSTRATION 2. In (5), the constant terms e and f are in the 1st column in the numerator for x, and in the 2d column for y.

EXAMPLE 1. Solve by determinants: $\begin{cases} 2x - 4y = -14, \\ 3x + 7y = 5. \end{cases}$

SOLUTION. From (5), $x = \dfrac{\begin{vmatrix} -14 & -4 \\ 5 & 7 \end{vmatrix}}{\begin{vmatrix} 2 & -4 \\ 3 & 7 \end{vmatrix}}$, and $y = \dfrac{\begin{vmatrix} 2 & -14 \\ 3 & 5 \end{vmatrix}}{\begin{vmatrix} 2 & -4 \\ 3 & 7 \end{vmatrix}}.$

On computing the determinants, we obtain $x = \dfrac{-78}{26} = -3$; $y = \dfrac{52}{26} = 2.$

Note 1. As far as the Western world is concerned, determinants were invented in 1693 by the German mathematician LEIBNIZ (1646–1716). However, determinants were invented at least ten years earlier by SEKI-KOWA (1642–1708), the great Japanese mathematician. The work of SEKI-KOWA had no influence on mathematical development outside of Japan.

Note 2. In the system [(1), (2)] we refer to the array $\begin{bmatrix} a & b \\ c & d \end{bmatrix}$ as the *matrix* (square) *of the coefficients.* Then, the determinant at the left in (4) is called the *determinant of the square matrix* of coefficients. A matrix, whether square or not, with real numbers as elements, is *not assigned any value*, as a real number. However, the *determinant* of a square matrix of 2 rows and 2 columns has a *value.* Later, we shall define the determinant of any square matrix.

EXERCISE 116

Find the expansion of the determinant.

1. $\begin{vmatrix} 2 & 1 \\ 4 & -5 \end{vmatrix}$.
2. $\begin{vmatrix} 5 & 7 \\ 8 & 2 \end{vmatrix}$.
3. $\begin{vmatrix} c & 3 \\ 3 & -1 \end{vmatrix}$.
4. $\begin{vmatrix} h & m \\ k & n \end{vmatrix}$.

Solve by determinants, if possible.

5–15. Solve Problems 5–15, respectively, on page 100.

Solve for x and y by determinants.

16. $\begin{cases} cx + by = 1, \\ bx - ay = 1. \end{cases}$
17. $\begin{cases} dx - hy = k, \\ fx + by = h. \end{cases}$
18. $\begin{cases} 2bx - 3ay = 4b^2, \\ x + 3y = 4b + a. \end{cases}$

190. Determinants of any order

Consider a square matrix. Then, if we enclose the matrix by two vertical bars, we call the resulting symbol the **determinant** *of the matrix,* and assign to this determinant a *value* in accordance with a later definition. The *elements of the matrix* also are called the *elements of the determinant.* If the matrix has n rows and n columns, its determinant is spoken of as a determinant of **order n.** Thus, a determinant of order n has n^2 *elements.* The elements in the diagonal running from the upper left-hand to the lower right-hand corner are referred to as forming the **main diagonal** of the determinant.

ILLUSTRATION 1. If a_1, a_2, a_3, b_1, c_1, $\cdots$ are any numbers, the following symbols are determinants of the 3d order and 4th order, respectively.

$$D = \begin{vmatrix} a_1 & b_1 & c_1 \\ a_2 & b_2 & c_2 \\ a_3 & b_3 & c_3 \end{vmatrix}; \qquad H = \begin{vmatrix} a_1 & b_1 & c_1 & d_1 \\ a_2 & b_2 & c_2 & d_2 \\ a_3 & b_3 & c_3 & d_3 \\ a_4 & b_4 & c_4 & d_4 \end{vmatrix}. \tag{1}$$

DEFINITION I. *In a determinant, if the row and column containing a given element, say* α, *are deleted,* * *the determinant, M, of the remaining matrix of elements, arranged in natural order, is called the* **minor** *of* α.

* That is, *blotted out,* or *removed.*

ILLUSTRATION 2. In the determinant D of (1), the minor of any element is a determinant of the 2d order. Thus, the minor

$$\text{of } a_2 \text{ is } \begin{vmatrix} b_1 & c_1 \\ b_3 & c_3 \end{vmatrix}; \qquad \text{of } b_3 \text{ is } \begin{vmatrix} a_1 & c_1 \\ a_2 & c_2 \end{vmatrix}.$$

In the determinant H of (1), the minor of any element is a determinant of the 3d order. Thus, the minor of b_2 is

$$\begin{vmatrix} a_1 & c_1 & d_1 \\ a_3 & c_3 & d_3 \\ a_4 & c_4 & d_4 \end{vmatrix}.$$

DEFINITION II. *In a determinant of any order, let α be the element which is in row i and column j, and let M be the minor of α. Then, the cofactor, C, of α is defined by $C = (-1)^{i+j}M$. That is, C is $+ M$ if $(i+j)$ is an* **even** *integer, and $C = -M$ if $(i+j)$ is* **odd.**

ILLUSTRATION 3. In D of (1), if M_2 represents the *minor* of a_2, then the *cofactor* C_2 of a_2 is given by $C_2 = (-1)^{2+1}M_2 = -M_2$. For any determinant, the signs to attach to the minors of the elements in the various locations, to obtain the cofactors, can be remembered by use of the adjoining diagram. The signs *alternate* in proceeding *to the right in any row* or *moving down in any column*. The sign for the leading element at the top in the main diagonal is $+$; that is, $C = +M$ for this element.

$$\begin{vmatrix} + & - & + & . & . & . & . \\ - & + & - & . & . & . & . \\ + & - & + & . & . & . & . \\ - & + & - & . & . & . & . \\ . & . & . & . & . & . & . \end{vmatrix}$$

ILLUSTRATION 4. For the following determinant of the 2d order, the minor of a_1 is b_2 and of a_2 is b_1. The cofactor, C_1, of a_1 is $+ b_2$; the cofactor, C_2, of a_2 is $- b_1$. We verify, from page 345, that

$$\begin{vmatrix} a_1 & b_1 \\ a_2 & b_2 \end{vmatrix} = a_1 b_2 - a_2 b_1 = a_1 C_1 + a_2 C_2. \tag{2}$$

We proceed to define the value of *any* determinant of *order n* in terms of *determinants of order $(n-1)$*. From (2), the following definition is seen to give the value as previously defined for a determinant of order $n = 2$. Then, the Axiom of Induction on page 335 assures us that the definition has meaning for all values $n \geq 2$, because the definition has meaning for the value $n = k+1$ if there is a well-defined meaning when $n = k$.

DEFINITION III. *Let D be a determinant of any order. For any column of D, with the elements, say, p_1, p_2, p_3, $\cdots$,*

1. *multiply each element p_i by its* **cofactor,** *C_i;*

2. *form the sum $p_1 C_1 + p_2 C_2 + \cdots$, for all elements in the column. Then, this sum is called the* **value of D,** *and we write*

$$D = p_1 C_1 + p_2 C_2 + p_3 C_3 + \cdots. \tag{3}$$

We refer to (3) as the **expansion of D** with respect to the elements of the specified column. We shall accept the following theorem without proof, and merely verify the result for the case $n = 3$.

THEOREM I. *The value of D as obtained by the expansion (3) for any column is the same as for any other column. Also, the value of D as given by (3) is correct if p_1, p_2, p_3, $\cdots$ represent the elements of any row.*

On the basis of Theorem I, we may expand any determinant by cofactors of any row, or column, as we please.

ILLUSTRATION 5. For the determinant D of (1), if we expand by cofactors of the 1st column, and use (2), we obtain

$$\begin{vmatrix} a_1 & b_1 & c_1 \\ a_2 & b_2 & c_2 \\ a_3 & b_3 & c_3 \end{vmatrix} = a_1 \begin{vmatrix} b_2 & c_2 \\ b_3 & c_3 \end{vmatrix} - a_2 \begin{vmatrix} b_1 & c_1 \\ b_3 & c_3 \end{vmatrix} + a_3 \begin{vmatrix} b_1 & c_1 \\ b_2 & c_2 \end{vmatrix}$$

$$= a_1(b_2c_3 - b_3c_2) - a_2(b_1c_3 - b_3c_1) + a_3(b_1c_2 - b_2c_1), \text{ or}$$

$$\begin{vmatrix} a_1 & b_1 & c_1 \\ a_2 & b_2 & c_2 \\ a_3 & b_3 & c_3 \end{vmatrix} = a_1b_2c_3 + a_3b_1c_2 + a_2b_3c_1 - a_3b_2c_1 - a_1b_3c_2 - a_2b_1c_3. \quad (4)$$

On expanding by cofactors of the 2d row, we obtain

$$D = -a_2 \begin{vmatrix} b_1 & c_1 \\ b_3 & c_3 \end{vmatrix} + b_2 \begin{vmatrix} a_1 & c_1 \\ a_3 & c_3 \end{vmatrix} - c_2 \begin{vmatrix} a_1 & b_1 \\ a_3 & b_3 \end{vmatrix}$$

$$= -a_2(b_1c_3 - b_3c_1) + b_2(a_1c_3 - a_3c_1) - c_2(a_1b_3 - a_3b_1),$$

which we verify is the same as in (4). The student should verify that (4) is obtained by expanding by cofactors in a few other ways.

ILLUSTRATION 6. For the following determinant, we expand by cofactors of the 1st column.

$$\begin{vmatrix} 1 & 5 & 2 \\ 4 & 7 & 3 \\ 2 & -3 & 6 \end{vmatrix} = 1 \begin{vmatrix} 7 & 3 \\ -3 & 6 \end{vmatrix} - 4 \begin{vmatrix} 5 & 2 \\ -3 & 6 \end{vmatrix} + 2 \begin{vmatrix} 5 & 2 \\ 7 & 3 \end{vmatrix}$$

$$= (42 + 9) - 4(30 + 6) + 2(15 - 14) = -91.$$

ILLUSTRATION 7. We expand according to the elements of the 2d row:

$$\begin{vmatrix} 3 & -1 & 5 & 0 \\ -1 & 0 & -4 & 2 \\ 2 & 3 & -2 & 6 \\ 4 & -2 & -3 & -1 \end{vmatrix}$$

$$= -(-1) \begin{vmatrix} -1 & 5 & 0 \\ 3 & -2 & 6 \\ -2 & -3 & -1 \end{vmatrix} + 0 - (-4) \begin{vmatrix} 3 & -1 & 0 \\ 2 & 3 & 6 \\ 4 & -2 & -1 \end{vmatrix} + 2 \begin{vmatrix} 3 & -1 & 5 \\ 2 & 3 & -2 \\ 4 & -2 & -3 \end{vmatrix}.$$

EXERCISE 117

1. Expand by minors according to the elements of the 1st column; of the 2d column; of the 3d row.

$$\begin{vmatrix} c_1 & m_1 & v_1 \\ c_2 & m_2 & v_2 \\ c_3 & m_3 & v_3 \end{vmatrix}.$$

Evaluate by expansion by cofactors.

2. $\begin{vmatrix} 1 & 4 & 2 \\ 4 & 3 & 3 \\ 2 & -5 & 6 \end{vmatrix}.$ **3.** $\begin{vmatrix} 4 & 3 & -2 \\ 1 & -1 & 4 \\ -2 & 0 & 3 \end{vmatrix}.$ **4.** $\begin{vmatrix} -2 & 0 & 2 \\ -3 & -3 & 3 \\ 4 & -2 & 3 \end{vmatrix}.$

5. $\begin{vmatrix} 5 & 4 & 2 \\ -6 & 0 & -5 \\ 6 & -3 & 4 \end{vmatrix}.$ **6.** $\begin{vmatrix} a & c & b \\ 2a & 2 & 3 \\ c & b & 8a \end{vmatrix}.$ **7.** $\begin{vmatrix} 1 & x & y \\ 1 & x^2 & y^2 \\ 1 & x^3 & y^3 \end{vmatrix}.$

8. $\begin{vmatrix} 1 & 2 & 3 & 1 \\ 3 & 0 & 0 & 2 \\ -2 & -1 & 4 & -3 \\ 1 & 3 & 2 & -4 \end{vmatrix}.$ **9.** $\begin{vmatrix} 2 & -1 & 2 & 3 \\ -1 & 1 & 0 & -2 \\ 5 & 3 & 0 & 1 \\ 7 & 2 & 4 & -5 \end{vmatrix}.$

10. If the determinant D of (1) on page 347 is expanded finally into a *polynomial in the elements of D*, verify from (4) on page 349 that there are 6 (or 3!) terms in the expansion. Then, by proper remarks, *without expanding*, prove that the determinant H of the 4th order in (1) on page 347 is equal to a polynomial consisting of 4! terms.

★11. By mathematical induction, prove that the expansion of a determinant D of order n into a polynomial in the elements of D contains $n!$ terms.

★*Note 1.* A determinant D of order n can be defined as the sum of all terms where *each term* is a product of *just one element from each row and from each column,* and where the term has an attached sign, $+$ or $-$, according to the following rule: *the sign is "$+$" if, after the factors of a term are written in their natural* **row order,** *it is possible to place the factors in their natural* **column order** *by an even number of interchanges of neighboring factors, and otherwise the attached sign is "$-$"* (*the number of interchanges is odd*).

191. Properties of determinants

A few of the properties of determinants are obtained quickly by use of (3) on page 348. However, the most fundamental properties require elaborate proofs which will not be given. All of the properties can be verified easily for determinants of order 3. We shall give proofs only where convenient.

I. *The value of a determinant is unchanged if corresponding rows and columns are interchanged.*

ILLUSTRATION 1. If we let $\;D = \begin{vmatrix} a_1 & b_1 & c_1 \\ a_2 & b_2 & c_2 \\ a_3 & b_3 & c_3 \end{vmatrix},\;$ *and* $\;D' = \begin{vmatrix} a_1 & a_2 & a_3 \\ b_1 & b_2 & b_3 \\ c_1 & c_2 & c_3 \end{vmatrix},$

then Property I states that $D = D'$. The reader can verify this special case of Property I by expanding D and D' by Definition III on page 348.

From Property I, it follows that, *for every theorem concerning the columns of a determinant, there is a corresponding theorem concerning the rows.* Hence, we shall state the following properties as true for both rows and columns, but shall give verification or proof only for the case referring to columns.

II. *If all elements of a column (or row) of a determinant D are multiplied by the same number k, the value of the determinant is multiplied by k.*

Proof. Consider the expansion (3) of page 348 for D,

$$D = p_1 C_1 + p_2 C_2 + p_3 C_3 + \cdots. \tag{1}$$

If each element of the column of p's is multiplied by k, then the new determinant D has the value obtained from (1) by replacing each p_i by kp_i, which multiplies the sum on the right by k. Hence, $D' = kD$.

ILLUSTRATION 2. By Property II, $\quad k \begin{vmatrix} 3 & 4 \\ 5 & 7 \end{vmatrix} = \begin{vmatrix} 3 & 4k \\ 5 & 7k \end{vmatrix}.$

A special case of the following result is observed in Illustration 2. The general result is an immediate consequence of Property II.

III. *A common factor of all elements of a column (or row) may be removed and written before the determinant.*

IV. *If each element of a column (or row) is zero, the value of the determinant is zero.*

Proof. In the expansion (3) of page 348 by cofactors according to the elements of the column of zeros, each term on the right in (3) is zero, so that $D = 0$.

V. *If two columns (or rows) are interchanged, the sign of the determinant is changed.*

ILLUSTRATION 3. If $\quad D = \begin{vmatrix} a_1 & b_1 & c_1 \\ a_2 & b_2 & c_2 \\ a_3 & b_3 & c_3 \end{vmatrix}$ and $D' = \begin{vmatrix} c_1 & b_1 & a_1 \\ c_2 & b_2 & a_2 \\ c_3 & b_3 & a_3 \end{vmatrix},$

then Property V states that $D = -D'$. The reader can verify this by expanding D and D'; each term of D' is the negative of a term of D.

VI. *If two columns (or rows) of a determinant D are identical, then $D = 0$.*

Proof. Interchange the identical columns in D. By Property V, the value of the new determinant is $-D$. But, since the columns were identical, the new determinant is the same as D. Hence, $D = -D$, or $2D = 0$, or $D = 0$.

ILLUSTRATION 4. By Property VI, $\quad \begin{vmatrix} a & x & x \\ b & y & y \\ c & z & z \end{vmatrix} = 0.$

VII. *If each element of some column (or row) is expressed as the sum of two or more numbers, the determinant may be expressed as the sum of two or more determinants.*

ILLUSTRATION 5. From Property VII,

$$\begin{vmatrix} a_1 & (b_1 + d_1) & c_1 \\ a_2 & (b_2 + d_2) & c_2 \\ a_3 & (b_3 + d_3) & c_3 \end{vmatrix} = \begin{vmatrix} a_1 & b_1 & c_1 \\ a_2 & b_2 & c_2 \\ a_3 & b_3 & c_3 \end{vmatrix} + \begin{vmatrix} a_1 & d_1 & c_1 \\ a_2 & d_2 & c_2 \\ a_3 & d_3 & c_3 \end{vmatrix}. \tag{2}$$

To verify (2), let B_1, B_2, and B_3 be the cofactors of the elements in the 2d column in the determinant at the left in (2). Since these cofactors depend *only on the* 1st *and* 3d *columns,* B_1, B_2, and B_3 also are the cofactors of the 2d column in *all* determinants in (2). Hence, on the left in (2) we have the value

$$(b_1 + d_1)B_1 + (b_2 + d_2)B_2 + (b_3 + d_3)B_3, \text{ or}$$
$$(b_1B_1 + b_2B_2 + b_3B_3) + (d_1B_1 + d_2B_2 + d_3B_3),$$

which is the sum of the values of the determinants on the right in (2).

VIII. *The value of a determinant is not changed if to each element of any column (or row) we add k times the corresponding element of some other column (or row).*

Proof. 1. For convenience in details, consider only the special case which states that D and D' below are equal.

$$D = \begin{vmatrix} a_1 & b_1 & c_1 \\ a_2 & b_2 & c_2 \\ a_3 & b_3 & c_3 \end{vmatrix}. \qquad D' = \begin{vmatrix} a_1 & (b_1 + kc_1) & c_1 \\ a_2 & (b_2 + kc_2) & c_2 \\ a_3 & (b_3 + kc_3) & c_3 \end{vmatrix}.$$

2. We apply Property VII and then Property III to D':

$$D' = \begin{vmatrix} a_1 & b_1 & c_1 \\ a_2 & b_2 & c_2 \\ a_3 & b_3 & c_3 \end{vmatrix} + \begin{vmatrix} a_1 & kc_1 & c_1 \\ a_2 & kc_2 & c_2 \\ a_3 & kc_3 & c_3 \end{vmatrix} = D + k \begin{vmatrix} a_1 & c_1 & c_1 \\ a_2 & c_2 & c_2 \\ a_3 & c_3 & c_3 \end{vmatrix} = D,$$

because the last determinant is equal to zero, by Property VI.

192. Evaluation of determinants

A determinant of the 2d order should be computed by the method of page 345. If the order of a determinant D is greater than 2, usually it is convenient to proceed as follows:

1. *By use of Property* VIII, *reduce all except a few of the elements of some particular column (or row) to zeros, and thus obtain an equal determinant D'.*

2. *Expand D' by cofactors according to the elements of the column (or row) containing the zeros. For each minor, if its order is greater than 2, proceed as in the first stage.*

EXAMPLE 1. Compute the value of the determinant

$$D = \begin{vmatrix} 5 & 7 & 8 & 6 \\ 11 & 16 & 13 & 11 \\ 14 & 24 & 20 & 23 \\ 7 & 13 & 12 & 2 \end{vmatrix}.$$

SOLUTION. 1. Subtract the 1st row * from the 4th row, twice the 1st row from the 2d row, and three times the 1st row from the 3d row. Then,

$$D = \begin{vmatrix} 5 & 7 & 8 & 6 \\ 1 & 2 & -3 & -1 \\ -1 & 3 & -4 & 5 \\ 2 & 6 & 4 & -4 \end{vmatrix} = 2 \begin{vmatrix} 5 & 7 & 8 & 6 \\ 1 & 2 & -3 & -1 \\ -1 & 3 & -4 & 5 \\ 1 & 3 & 2 & -2 \end{vmatrix}.$$

In the final determinant, Property III was used in removing the factor 2 from the elements of the last row of the preceding determinant.

2. In the last determinant, subtract the 2d row from the 4th row, and five times the 2d row from the 1st row; add the 2d row to the 3d row; then, expand by cofactors according to the elements of the first column; finally compute the determinant of the 3d order below by use of cofactors:

$$D = 2 \begin{vmatrix} 0 & -3 & 23 & 11 \\ 1 & 2 & -3 & -1 \\ 0 & 5 & -7 & 4 \\ 0 & 1 & 5 & -1 \end{vmatrix} = 2\left\{ -(1) \cdot \begin{vmatrix} -3 & 23 & 11 \\ 5 & -7 & 4 \\ 1 & 5 & -1 \end{vmatrix} \right\}$$

$$= 2(-598) = -1196.$$

Note 1. Sometimes it may be convenient to evaluate a determinant by first changing it to triangular form, as in the case of the matrix method of Section 188, where *all elements above the main diagonal are zeros.* Then, the determinant is equal to *the product of the numbers in the final main diagonal.*

EXERCISE 118

1–4. Compute the determinants in Problems 2–5, respectively, of Exercise 117 by first arranging to have two zeros in some row or column. Apply the method of Note 1 above in at least one problem.

5–6. Compute the determinants in Problems 8 and 9, respectively, of Exercise 117, by first arranging to have three zeros in some row or column.

Evaluate the determinant.

7.
$$\begin{vmatrix} 1 & -2 & 3 & 7 \\ -1 & -1 & 5 & 8 \\ 2 & 6 & -2 & -4 \\ 4 & 7 & 3 & 3 \end{vmatrix}.$$

8.
$$\begin{vmatrix} 2 & -1 & 2 & 3 \\ 1 & 0 & 2 & 1 \\ 5 & 3 & 0 & 1 \\ 7 & 2 & 4 & -5 \end{vmatrix}.$$

---

* That is, subtract each element of the 1st row from the corresponding element of the 4th row.

9. $\begin{vmatrix} 2 & -1 & 3 & 7 \\ 3 & 1 & 5 & 8 \\ 6 & -2 & -2 & -4 \\ 8 & -4 & -3 & 3 \end{vmatrix}.$

10. $\begin{vmatrix} 2 & 3 & 1 & 4 \\ 3 & -5 & -1 & -1 \\ 0 & 1 & 2 & -5 \\ 3 & 3 & 2 & 3 \end{vmatrix}.$

11. Without expanding, show that the adjoining equation is satisfied when $x = 2$ and $x = 3$. Hence, what factors has the determinant? Check by expanding. $\begin{vmatrix} 1 & 3 & 2 \\ 1 & x & 2 \\ 1 & 2 & x \end{vmatrix} = 0.$

12. Without expanding, show that the adjoining determinant has the factors $(x - y)$, $(y - w)$, and $(x - w)$, and find a factored expression for the determinant. $\begin{vmatrix} 1 & 1 & 1 \\ x & y & w \\ x^2 & y^2 & w^2 \end{vmatrix}$

13. Without expanding the determinant, prove that the adjoining equation is the equation of the line through the points (x_1, y_1) and (x_2, y_2). Then, use this form to obtain the line through the points $(2, -3)$ and $(4, 1)$. $\begin{vmatrix} 1 & x & y \\ 1 & x_1 & y_1 \\ 1 & x_2 & y_2 \end{vmatrix} = 0.$

193. A property of cofactors

In any determinant D, as in (1) below, let the cofactor of each element be represented by the corresponding *capital* letter, with a subscript as on the element. For illustration, consider

$$D = \begin{vmatrix} a_1 & b_1 & c_1 \\ a_2 & b_2 & c_2 \\ a_3 & b_3 & c_3 \end{vmatrix}, \tag{1}$$

with cofactors A_1, A_2, A_3, B_1, etc.

THEOREM II. *In the expansion of a determinant D by cofactors according to the elements of a given column (or row), if its elements are replaced by any numbers, the result is the expansion of a new determinant obtained by replacing the given column by the new numbers.*

Proof, with remarks specialized to D in (1). Consider the expansion of D according to the cofactors of any column, for instance,

$$\begin{vmatrix} a_1 & b_1 & c_1 \\ a_2 & b_2 & c_2 \\ a_3 & b_3 & c_3 \end{vmatrix} = b_1 B_1 + b_2 B_2 + b_3 B_3. \tag{2}$$

In the *identity* (2), replace b_1, b_2, and b_3 on both sides by any numbers k_1, k_2, and k_3. Then, we obtain the following equality, which proves Theorem II:

$$\begin{vmatrix} a_1 & k_1 & c_1 \\ a_2 & k_2 & c_2 \\ a_3 & k_3 & c_3 \end{vmatrix} = k_1 B_1 + k_2 B_2 + k_3 B_3. \tag{3}$$

THEOREM III. *In the expansion of a determinant D by cofactors according to the elements of a given column (or row), if its elements are replaced by the corresponding elements of another column (or row), the result is identically zero.*

Proof. If k_1, k_2, k_3 in (3) are the elements of another column, not the column used in (2), then the determinant in (3) has two identical columns, and hence is equal to zero.

194. Solution of linear systems by determinants

Let any system of n linear equations in n variables be written in the following normal form, illustrated for the case $n = 3$, with the variables x, y, and z:

$$\text{I.} \begin{cases} a_1x + b_1y + c_1z = k_1, & (1) \\ a_2x + b_2y + c_2z = k_2, & (2) \\ a_3x + b_3y + c_3z = k_3. & (3) \end{cases}$$

In system (I), the characteristic feature is that all terms in the variables, *in a definite order*, are in the left-hand members, and the constant term (possibly zero) in each equation is on the right. In (I), let

$$\Delta = \begin{vmatrix} a_1 & b_1 & c_1 \\ a_2 & b_2 & c_2 \\ a_3 & b_3 & c_3 \end{vmatrix}, \tag{4}$$

to be called the *determinant of the coefficients of the variables*, where each column consists of the coefficients of a corresponding variable. In connection with (I), let K_1, K_2, and K_3 be defined as follows:

$$K_1 = \begin{vmatrix} k_1 & b_1 & c_1 \\ k_2 & b_2 & c_2 \\ k_3 & b_3 & c_3 \end{vmatrix}; \quad K_2 = \begin{vmatrix} a_1 & k_1 & c_1 \\ a_2 & k_2 & c_2 \\ a_3 & k_3 & c_3 \end{vmatrix}; \quad K_3 = \begin{vmatrix} a_1 & b_1 & k_1 \\ a_2 & b_2 & k_2 \\ a_3 & b_3 & k_3 \end{vmatrix}. \tag{5}$$

THEOREM IV. **Cramer's Rule,** *as stated on page 346, applies for a system of n linear equations in n variables.*

Proof, for the case $n = 3$, with system (I). 1. First, let us show that, **IF** (x, y, z) satisfy (I), then

$$\Delta \cdot x = K_1; \qquad \Delta \cdot y = K_2; \qquad \Delta \cdot z = K_3. \tag{6}$$

2. For Δ, let capital letters A_1, B_1, etc., as in Section 193, represent the *cofactors* of the elements. Then, to establish, for instance, $\Delta \cdot y = K_2$, multiply both sides of (1), (2), and (3), respectively, by B_1, B_2, and B_3, which gives

$$a_1B_1x + b_1B_1y + c_1B_1z = k_1B_1, \tag{7}$$
$$a_2B_2x + b_2B_2y + c_2B_2z = k_2B_2, \tag{8}$$
$$a_3B_3x + b_3B_3y + c_3B_3z = k_3B_3. \tag{9}$$

On adding corresponding members of (7), (8), and (9) and collecting terms, the coefficient of y is found to be

$$b_1B_1 + b_2B_2 + b_3B_3, \tag{10}$$

which is seen to be Δ, expanded according to the elements of its 2d column. The coefficient of x is $(a_1B_1 + a_2B_2 + a_3B_3)$, which is the same as (10) except that a's replace the b's in (10). Hence, by Theorem III, the coefficient of x is zero. Similarly, the coefficient of z is zero. Thus, on adding in (7), (8), and (9), we obtain

$$\Delta \cdot y = k_1 B_1 + k_2 B_2 + k_3 B_3. \tag{11}$$

In (11), the right-hand side is the same as (10), except that the b's are replaced by the k's. Hence, by Theorem II, the right-hand side in (11) is the expansion of the determinant obtained on replacing the b's by the k's in D, which gives K_2. Thus, (11) becomes $\Delta \cdot y = K_2$.

3. To establish $\Delta \cdot z = K_3$, we would multiply in (1), (2), and (3) by the cofactors C_1, C_2, and C_3, respectively, and then add. To obtain $\Delta \cdot x = K_1$, we would multiply in (1), (2), and (3) by A_1, A_2, and A_3, respectively, and add. Thus, (6) is true, regardless of the value of Δ, zero or not, for any values of (x, y, z) satisfying (I).

4. IF $\Delta \neq 0$, from (6) we obtain

$$x = \frac{K_1}{\Delta}, \quad y = \frac{K_2}{\Delta}, \quad \text{and} \quad z = \frac{K_3}{\Delta}. \tag{12}$$

That is, IF $\Delta \neq 0$, and IF *system* (I) *has any solution*, then there is *just one solution* and it is given by (12).

5. For a complete proof, now we should substitute (12) in system (I) and show that the equations are satisfied. We shall omit this step.*

EXAMPLE 1. Solve: II.
$$\begin{cases} 2x - y + 2z + w = 12, & (13) \\ 2x - y + 3z - 4w = 5, & (14) \\ 5x + y + z = 6, & (15) \\ -2y + z + w = 9. & (16) \end{cases}$$

SOLUTION. We use Cramer's Rule.

$$\Delta = \begin{vmatrix} 2 & -1 & 2 & 1 \\ 2 & -1 & 3 & -4 \\ 5 & 1 & 1 & 0 \\ 0 & -2 & 1 & 1 \end{vmatrix} = 48; \quad K_3 = \begin{vmatrix} 2 & -1 & 12 & 1 \\ 2 & -1 & 5 & -4 \\ 5 & 1 & 6 & 0 \\ 0 & -2 & 9 & 1 \end{vmatrix} = 144.$$

Hence, $z = (K_3/\Delta) = 3$. Similarly, $y = -2$. Instead of using determinants to find the values of x and w, it is convenient to proceed as follows:

Substitute $(y = -2, z = 3)$ *in* (15) *and* (16): from (15), $x = 1$; from (16), $w = 2$. The solution of (II) is $(x = 1, y = -2, z = 3, w = 2)$.

Let us understand that the notations for system (I) are to extend similarly to a corresponding system of n linear equations in n variables, with Δ as the determinant of the coefficients of the variables. The complete discussion of the solution of such a system when $\Delta = 0$ is too complicated for treatment in

* See page 145, *Elementary Theory of Equations*, by L. E. Dickson (New York: John Wiley and Sons, Inc., 1914).

this text. The system may be consistent (have solutions), and then can be proved to have *infinitely many solutions*. Usually, however, the system is inconsistent if $\Delta = 0$. The most simple condition for inconsistency in this case is as follows.

THEOREM V. *A system of the form* (I) *in n variables, where* $\Delta = 0$, *is inconsistent if at least one of the numerator determinants* K_1, K_2, K_3, $\cdots$ *from Cramer's Rule is not equal to zero.*

Proof, for the case of system (I). **IF** system (I) **is consistent** and if (x, y, z) represents any solution, then (6) is true. Since $\Delta \cdot x = K_1$, it follows that, if $\Delta = 0$, then $K_1 = 0$; similarly, $K_2 = K_3 = 0$. Hence, if $\Delta = 0$ and if any one of (K_1, K_2, K_3) is *not* zero, the system *cannot* be consistent.

EXERCISE 119

1–15. Solve Problems 1–15, respectively, on pages 344–345, if possible, by use of determinants.

195. Homogeneous equations

A linear equation is said to be *homogeneous* in case the constant term in it is equal to zero. Thus, in (I) on page 355, to say that the equations are homogeneous means that $k_1 = k_2 = k_3 = 0$. By substitution, we see that any system of homogeneous linear equations is satisfied when each variable has the value zero. Frequently, such a solution is useless, and hence it is called the **trivial solution**. To say that a solution of the system is **nontrivial** means that, in it, *at least one of the variables is not equal to zero.*

THEOREM VI. *If a system of n homogeneous linear equations in n variables has a nontrivial solution, then the determinant of the coefficients of the variables is equal to zero.*

Proof. 1. Consider system (I), with $k_1 = k_2 = k_3 = 0$. By hypothesis, (I) has a nontrivial solution. We shall refer by numbers to equations on pages 355–356.

2. (*Indirect argument*) Let us assume that, in (4), $\Delta \neq 0$. From (5), $K_1 = K_2 = K_3 = 0$, because each determinant has a column of zeros. Hence, since $\Delta \neq 0$, from (12) we find that the only solution of (I) is $x = y = z = 0$. This contradicts the hypothesis that (I) has a *nontrivial* solution. Hence, the assumption that $\Delta \neq 0$ is false, and thus $\Delta = 0$.

THEOREM VII. *In a system of n homogeneous linear equations in n variables, if* $\Delta = 0$ *then the system has infinitely many nontrivial solutions.*

Note 1. The proof of Theorem VII is beyond the scope of this text. However, for a homogeneous system as in Theorem VII, nontrivial solutions usually can be obtained as follows.

1. *Solve* $(n-1)$ *of the equations for* $(n-1)$ *of the variables in terms of the other variable, call it* x.

2. *Assign any value, not zero, to* x *and compute the values of the other variables by use of the results of Step 1. Each set of corresponding values of the* n *variables thus obtained is a solution of the system.*

EXAMPLE 1. Discuss the system

$$\begin{cases} 3x + 2y - 3z = 0, & (1) \\ 4x - y + 7z = 0, & (2) \\ x - 3y + 10z = 0. & (3) \end{cases}$$

SOLUTION. 1. The determinant of the coefficients of the *variables* is

$$\begin{vmatrix} 3 & 2 & -3 \\ 4 & -1 & 7 \\ 1 & -3 & 10 \end{vmatrix} = 0.$$

Hence, by Theorem VII, the system has nontrivial solutions.

2. On solving (1) and (2) for x and y in terms of z, we obtain $x = -z$ and $y = 3z$. By substitution, it is found that these expressions for x and y satisfy (3) for every value of z.

3. From the preceding details, if $z = 2$, then $x = -2$ and $y = 6$, so that $(-2, 6, 2)$ is one solution. Similarly, corresponding to any value of z, we obtain a solution for the system. Thus, it has infinitely many solutions, given by $(x = -h, y = 3h, z = h)$, for any value of h.

196. More variables than equations

A system of m linear equations in n variables, where $n > m$, usually has *infinitely many solutions* but may be inconsistent. Generally, we can obtain solutions by solving the m equations for m of the variables in terms of the others and then substituting values arbitrarily for them.

ILLUSTRATION 1. Consider the system $\qquad \begin{cases} 3x - y - 2z = 1, \\ 2x + y - 3z = -1. \end{cases}$ (1)

In (1), the determinant of the coefficients of x and y is not equal to zero. Hence, we can solve (1) for x and y in terms of z by use of determinants, to obtain $(x = z, y = z - 1)$. Then, if $z = 2$, we find $x = 2$ and $y = 1$; thus, $(2, 1, 2)$ is a solution of (1). Similarly, for any value of h, with $z = h$ we obtain the solution $(x = h, y = h - 1, z = h)$ for (1). Thus, (1) has infinitely many solutions.

197. More equations than variables

A system of m linear equations in n variables, with $m > n$, usually is *inconsistent*. However, suppose that we can solve a certain n of the equations for the variables. If the values thus obtained also satisfy the other $(m - n)$ equations, then the system is consistent.

ILLUSTRATION 1. In the system

$$x - 2y + 7 = 0, \\ 3x + 7y - 5 = 0, \\ x + y + 1 = 0, \tag{1}$$

the first two equations have the single solution $(x = -3, y = 2)$. By substitution, these values are found to satisfy the third equation in (1). Hence, the system has just one solution.

A system of n linear equations in $(n - 1)$ variables can be written in the standard form (illustrated for $n = 3$)

$$a_1x + b_1y + c_1 = 0, \\ a_2x + b_2y + c_2 = 0, \\ a_3x + b_3y + c_3 = 0. \tag{2}$$

THEOREM VIII. *In a system of n linear equations in $(n - 1)$ variables, in the standard form (2), if the determinant formed from the coefficients of the variables and the constant terms is not equal to zero, then the given system is inconsistent.*

Proof, for the case $n = 3$. 1. Let Δ be the determinant of the coefficients a_1, b_1, c_1, etc., in (2). By hypothesis, $\Delta \neq 0$.

2. In (2), change c_1, c_2, c_3 to c_1z, c_2z, c_3z, respectively, to obtain a homogeneous system in x, y, and z:

$$a_1x + b_1y + c_1z = 0, \\ a_2x + b_2y + c_2z = 0, \\ a_3x + b_3y + c_3z = 0. \tag{3}$$

3. (*Indirect argument*) Assume that (2) is *consistent*. Then, (2) has a solution $(x = h, y = k)$. Hence, (3) has the *nontrivial* solution $(x = h, y = k, z = 1)$, because (3) becomes (2) when $z = 1$. Thus, by Theorem VI, page 357, $\Delta = 0$. But, this contradicts the hypothesis that $\Delta \neq 0$. Hence, the assumption that (2) is *consistent* is *false*, or (2) is *inconsistent*. The preceding remarks also prove the following result.

COROLLARY 1. *If system (2) is consistent, then $\Delta = 0$.*

EXERCISE 120

Find two nontrivial solutions or prove that none exist.

1. $\begin{cases} x - 4y - 6z = 0, \\ 3x + 10y + 4z = 0, \\ 3x - y - 7z = 0. \end{cases}$
2. $\begin{cases} 3u - 2v - 13w = 0, \\ u + 4v + 5w = 0, \\ 2u + v - 4w = 0. \end{cases}$

3. $\begin{cases} 2x - 3y + 3z = 0, \\ 4x - 6y + 5z = 0, \\ 3x - 4y + 3z = 0. \end{cases}$
4. $\begin{cases} x + 3y + z = 0, \\ 3x - y - 2z = 0, \\ 2x - 4y - 3z = 0. \end{cases}$

Find two solutions of the system.

5. $\begin{cases} 2x - 3y = z - 8, \\ x + 2y - 4z = 3. \end{cases}$

6. $\begin{cases} 3x - y - 2z = 4, \\ 2x + 5y - 7z = 3. \end{cases}$

Prove inconsistent, or find a solution.

7. $\begin{cases} 2x + 9y - 12 = 0, \\ x - 2y + 7 = 0, \\ 3x + 7y = 5. \end{cases}$

8. $\begin{cases} x - 3y - 2 = 0, \\ x - 2y + 5 = 0, \\ 3x + 5y + 2 = 0. \end{cases}$

9. $\begin{cases} 4x - 7y = 13, \\ x - 2y = 3, \\ 2x - 3y = 7. \end{cases}$

10. $\begin{cases} x - 2y + 2 = 0, \\ 2x - 4y + 7 = 0, \\ 3x - y + 5 = 0. \end{cases}$

Given that the system is consistent, find the value of the constant k.

11. $\begin{cases} kx + 2y + k = 0, \\ 3x + 14ky - 5k = 0, \\ 2kx + 5y + k = 0. \end{cases}$

12. $\begin{cases} x - y + k = 0, \\ 6kx + ky - 2 = 0, \\ 2x + y + 2 = 0. \end{cases}$

Given that nontrivial solutions exist, find the value of the constant k.

13. $\begin{cases} kx - y + 2kz = 0, \\ 8x + 10y + kz = 0, \\ 2x + 2y + z = 0. \end{cases}$

14. $\begin{cases} 3kx - 2y + 2w = 0, \\ 4y + kw = 0, \\ kx + 6y - w = 0. \end{cases}$

If (x, y, z) represents any solution of the system, find numbers g, h, k such that $x : y : z = g : h : k$.

15. $\begin{cases} x - 2y + 3z = 0, \\ 2x + 4y - z = 0. \end{cases}$

16. $\begin{cases} 3x - y + z = 0, \\ 2x + 3y - 2z = 0. \end{cases}$

Inverse Functions

198. The general notion of an inverse function

Consider a function * f of the independent variable x, and let $y = f(x)$. Suppose that the domain, D, of f is the interval $a \leq x \leq b$ and the range, R, of f is the interval $c \leq y \leq d$. Then, by Definition III on page 71, to each number x in D there corresponds just one number y in R. Now, suppose also that, *to each number y in R, there corresponds just one number x*, as in (1):

$$\left\{ \begin{array}{l} \textit{For each value of } x \textit{ on the interval } a \leq x \leq b, \textit{ the equation} \\ y = f(x) \textit{ defines a single value } y \textit{ on the interval } c \leq y \leq d. \\ \textit{And, for each value of } y \textit{ on this interval, there exists} \\ \textit{just one value of } x \textit{ on } a \leq x \leq b \textit{ satisfying } y = f(x). \end{array} \right\} \quad (1)$$

Statements (1) are true, for instance, if the value of $f(x)$ *increases steadily* (or, *decreases steadily*) if x changes continuously from $x = a$ to $x = b$. With moderate modifications, the preceding sentence states the situation which exists whenever (1) is true. Hence, the student may base his intuitions for the remainder of our present discussion on the inference that (1) is equivalent to an assumption that *the graph of the equation $y = f(x)$ has the appearance shown in Figure 121 or in Figure 122.*

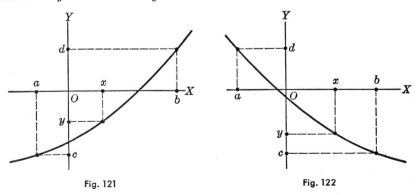

Fig. 121   Fig. 122

* Meaning a *single-valued* function as usual.

With f satisfying (1), consider the equation $y = f(x)$ in the variables x and y. For each value of y, let $g(y)$ represent the single value of x satisfying $y = f(x)$. Thus, we meet a (single-valued) *function* g such that

$$y = f(x) \quad \text{is equivalent to} \quad x = g(y). \tag{2}$$

Each of the equations $y = f(x)$ and $x = g(y)$ is satisfied by *the same set of pairs of numbers* (x, y). In (2), f is a function with the domain D and range R, whereas R is the domain and D is the range for g. We call g the **inverse** of the function f, and f the inverse of g. *Jointly, we call f and g inverse functions.* On account of (2), the graphs of the equations $y = f(x)$ and $x = g(y)$ on the same xy-plane are *identical*.

ILLUSTRATION 1. Let y be the function of x defined by $y = 3x + 7$. Then, $x = \frac{1}{3}y - \frac{7}{3}$. In this case, with the notation of (2), $f(x) = 3x + 7$ and $g(y) = \frac{1}{3}y - \frac{7}{3}$. The graph of either $y = f(x)$ or $x = g(y)$ in this case would be the line $y = 3x + 7$, with slope 3 and y-intercept 7 if the x-axis is horizontal.

★ILLUSTRATION 2. Let us call N^{-1}, or $1/N$, the *inverse of N*, for a present analogy. Then, we verify that "*the inverse of the inverse*" of N is N, or $[1 \div 1/N] = N$. A somewhat similar situation arises from (2). Since $x = g(y)$ is the solution of $y = f(x)$, we have $f(g(y)) = y$, or the value of "*the inverse function, f, of its inverse function, g,*" at any value of y is y. Similarly, $g(f(x)) = x$. Thus, in a symbolic sense, the *composite function* $f(g)$, as an operator on y, *leaves y unchanged*, or g acts like a *reciprocal* of f as applied to y.

199. The inverse sine function

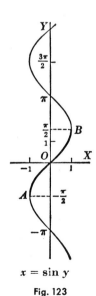

$x = \sin y$

Fig. 123

The graph of the equation $x = \sin y$ is the sine curve along the y-axis in Figure 123. For each eligible value of x, the equation $x = \sin y$ is satisfied by *infinitely many values of y*. Thus, if $x = \frac{1}{2}$, we obtain $\sin y = \frac{1}{2}$, which is satisfied by

$$y = \tfrac{1}{6}\pi + 2n\pi \quad \text{and} \quad y = \tfrac{5}{6}\pi + 2n\pi, \tag{1}$$

for all integral values of n. It can be said that the equation $x = \sin y$ defines y as an *infinitely many-valued function of x*. However, this complicated function has no essential merit for use in trigonometry or calculus. Hence, we proceed as follows to arrive at a *single-valued inverse* for the sine function.

In Figure 123 notice that arc AB has the characteristic appearance observed in Figure 121 on page 361. Accordingly, we consider the restricted relation

$$\left\{ \begin{array}{l} x \text{ on } D: \quad -1 \leqq x \leqq 1; \\ y \text{ on } R: \quad -\tfrac{1}{2}\pi \leqq y \leqq \tfrac{1}{2}\pi. \end{array} \right\} \qquad x = \sin y, \tag{2}$$

whose graph is AB in Figure 123, transferred also to Figure 124, with enlarged scale. For each number x in D, there exists *just one number y in R*. Hence, (2) *defines y as a (single-valued) function of x*, to be called the **Arcsine function**, with the value Arcsin x for any number x in D. That is,

$$\left\{ \begin{array}{l} with -1 \leq x \leq 1, \\ -\tfrac{1}{2}\pi \leq y \leq \tfrac{1}{2}\pi \end{array} \right\} \quad x = \sin y \quad is\ equivalent\ to \quad y = \text{Arcsin } x. \qquad (3)$$

Thus, for the restricted range of y in (2), the Arcsine function is the *inverse of the sine function*. It is important to remember that

$$(for\ all\ x) \qquad -\tfrac{1}{2}\pi \leq \text{Arcsin } x \leq \tfrac{1}{2}\pi. \qquad (4)$$

The graph of $y = $ Arcsin x is the same as the graph of $x = \sin y$ with y restricted to lie on the interval $-\tfrac{1}{2}\pi \leq y \leq \tfrac{1}{2}\pi$, as in Figure 124. To find Arcsin x at any value of x, we use (3).

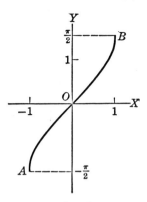

$y = $ **Arcsin** x

Fig. 124

ILLUSTRATION 1. To find Arcsin $(-\tfrac{1}{2})$, let $y = $ Arcsin $(-\tfrac{1}{2})$; then we obtain $\sin y = -\tfrac{1}{2}$ and $-\tfrac{1}{2}\pi \leq y \leq \tfrac{1}{2}\pi$. Hence, $y = -\tfrac{1}{6}\pi$.

ILLUSTRATION 2. To construct a table of values for graphing the function $y = $ Arcsin x, first use (3); thus $x = \sin y$. Then, to make up the following table, assign values to y on the range in (3) and compute x. The student may check the table against the graph in Figure 124.

x	-1	$-.87$	$-.5$	0	$.5$	$.87$	1
$y = $ Arcsin x	$-\tfrac{1}{2}\pi$	$-\tfrac{1}{3}\pi$	$-\tfrac{1}{6}\pi$	0	$\tfrac{1}{6}\pi$	$\tfrac{1}{3}\pi$	$\tfrac{1}{2}\pi$
y, *dec. form*	-1.57	-1.05	$-.52$	0	$.52$	1.05	1.57

ILLUSTRATION 3. By the definition in (3),

$$x = \sin (\text{Arcsin } x); \quad also \quad y = \text{Arcsin } (\sin y). \qquad (5)$$

For the moment, interpret Arcsin x as the measure of an *angle* in radians. Then, sometimes, "Arcsin x" is referred to as "*an angle whose sine is x*," which is equivalent to "$\sin$ (Arcsin x) = x," in (5).

EXAMPLE 1. Find $\sin [\text{Arcsin } \tfrac{1}{2} + \text{Arcsin } (-\tfrac{3}{5})]$.

SOLUTION. 1. Let $\alpha = $ Arcsin $\tfrac{1}{2}$; then $\sin \alpha = \tfrac{1}{2}$ and $0 < \alpha < \tfrac{1}{2}\pi$. Let $\beta = $ Arcsin $(-\tfrac{3}{5})$; then $\sin \beta = -\tfrac{3}{5}$, $-\tfrac{1}{2}\pi < \beta < 0$. We desire $\sin (\alpha + \beta)$.

2. We obtain $\cos \alpha = \sqrt{1 - \tfrac{1}{4}} = \tfrac{1}{2}\sqrt{3}$; $\cos^2 \beta = 1 - \sin^2 \beta = 1 - \tfrac{9}{25} = \tfrac{16}{25}$. Hence, $\cos \beta = \pm \tfrac{4}{5}$ but, since $-\tfrac{1}{2}\pi < \beta < 0$, we take $\cos \beta = \tfrac{4}{5}$. By the addition formula for the sine on page 156,

$$\sin (\alpha + \beta) = \tfrac{1}{2}(\tfrac{4}{5}) + \tfrac{1}{2}\sqrt{3}(-\tfrac{3}{5}) = \tfrac{1}{10}(4 - 3\sqrt{3}).$$

★*Note 1.* In some texts, we first find a definition of the *complete* or *infinitely many-valued* function $y = $ arcsin x (written with *small "a"* in *arcsin*), introduced as equivalent to the relation $x = \sin y$, with no limitation on the range for y. In such a case, our function Arcsin x (written in many texts with *capital* A as here) is called the **principal value** of the complete arcsine function. Thereafter, in calculus, *all applications refer to the principal value function.* In the present text, we have eliminated the complete arcsine function because it has negligible utility and also is a source for student errors. We use capital A in Arcsin so that the student will not be forced to a change in notation if he reads a text where our function Arcsin x is met after a different introduction.

★*Note 2.* In certain books, instead of "**Arcsin** x" we find "**sin^{-1} x**," which then is read "*inverse sine x.*" We prefer not to use sin^{-1} because of possible confusion with exponents applied to the sine function.

EXAMPLE 2. Find all trigonometric functions of Arcsin $(-\frac{2}{3})$.

SOLUTION. 1. Let $y = $ Arcsin $(-\frac{2}{3})$. Then, $\sin y = -\frac{2}{3}$ and $-\frac{1}{2}\pi < y < 0$ because $\sin y$ is negative. If, for the moment, we interpret y as an angle of y radians, and let z be the reference angle for y, then $0 < z < \frac{1}{2}\pi$ and $\sin z = \frac{2}{3}$.

2. From the reference triangle for z in Figure 125, and knowledge of the signs of the trigonometric functions in quadrant IV,

$$\cos z = \frac{\sqrt{5}}{3}, \qquad \tan z = \frac{2}{\sqrt{5}}, \qquad \cot z = \frac{\sqrt{5}}{2}, \quad etc.;$$

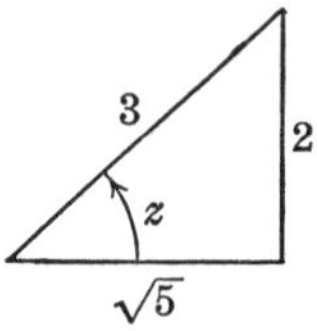

hence, $\cos y = \frac{1}{3}\sqrt{5}$, $\tan y = -\frac{2}{5}\sqrt{5}$, $\cot y = -\frac{1}{2}\sqrt{5}$, *etc.*

Fig. 125

ILLUSTRATION 4. To find Arcsin $(-.444)$, let $y = $ Arcsin $(-.444)$. Then, $\sin y = -.444$ and, from (4), $-\frac{1}{2}\pi < y < 0$. Let z be such that $\sin z = .444$ and $0 < z < \frac{1}{2}\pi$; that is, z is the reference number for y. Then, from the "Rad." column of Table IV, z is between .454 and .471. We interpolate:

$$.017 \left[d \begin{bmatrix} \sin .454 = .438 \\ \downarrow \sin z \quad\;\; = .444 \downarrow \\ \sin .471 = .454 \end{bmatrix} 6 \right] 16 \qquad \frac{d}{.017} = \frac{6}{16};$$
$$d = \tfrac{3}{8}(.017) = .006.$$
$$z = .454 + d = .454 + .006 = .460.$$

Since $\sin y = -\sin z$, we have $y = -z$, or Arcsin $(-.444) = -.460$.

EXAMPLE 3. Prove that the following equation is an identity for all values of u on the interval $-1 \leqq u \leqq 1$:

$$\textbf{Arcsin } (-u) = -\textbf{ Arcsin } u. \tag{6}$$

SOLUTION. 1. From Figure 124 on page 363, if y_1 and y_2 are two values of y on the range $-\frac{1}{2}\pi \leqq y \leqq \frac{1}{2}\pi$, and if $\sin y_1 = \sin y_2$, then $y_1 = y_2$.

2. To prove (6) for any value of u as specified, take the sines of the numbers on the two sides:

on the left, by (5), $\sin [\text{Arcsin} (- u)] = - u.$ (7)

on the right, by use of (5) and the identity $\sin (- \theta) = - \sin \theta,$

$$\sin [- \text{Arcsin } u] = - \sin (\text{Arcsin } u) = - u. \qquad (8)$$

From Step 1 of the proof, (7) and (8) show that (6) is true.

200. The inverse tangent function

The complete graph of the equation $x = \tan y$ consists of the branch in Figure 126 and its repetitions above and below without end. To define a single-valued inverse for the tangent function, we consider the restricted relation

$$\begin{cases} x \text{ on } D: & -\infty < x < \infty; \\ y \text{ on } R: & -\tfrac{1}{2}\pi < y < \tfrac{1}{2}\pi \end{cases} \qquad x = \tan y, \qquad (1)$$

whose graph is in Figure 126. We notice that *y increases steadily if the value of x increases steadily.* Hence, (1) defines y as a *single-valued function of x,* to be called the **Arctangent** function, with the value **Arctan** x, read "*arctangent x,*" at any point x in D. That is, by definition

$$\begin{cases} \text{with} - \infty < x < \infty, \\ -\tfrac{1}{2}\pi < y < \tfrac{1}{2}\pi \end{cases} \qquad x = \tan y \quad \text{is equivalent to} \quad y = \text{Arctan } x. \quad (2)$$

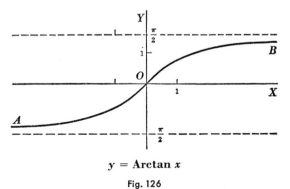

$$y = \textbf{Arctan } x$$

Fig. 126

From (2), the Arctangent function, with the domain D of (1), is the *inverse of the tangent function,* whose domain is R of (1). It is important to remember

$$-\tfrac{1}{2}\pi < \text{Arctan } x < \tfrac{1}{2}\pi. \qquad (3)$$

From (2), the graph of $y = \text{Arctan } x$ is one branch of the graph of $x = \tan y$, with the range for y in (1). To find the value $y = \text{Arctan } x$ for any particular value of x, we use (2) and write $x = \tan y$; then we solve this equation for y with x known. From (2),

$$x = \tan (\text{Arctan } x); \qquad y = \text{Arctan } (\tan y). \qquad (4)$$

ILLUSTRATION 1. To find Arctan $\sqrt{3}$, let $y = $ Arctan $\sqrt{3}$. Then $\tan y = \sqrt{3}$ and $-\frac{1}{2}\pi < y < \frac{1}{2}\pi$. Hence, $y = \frac{1}{3}\pi$.

ILLUSTRATION 2. To obtain the graph of $y = $ Arctan x in Figure 126, we use (2) to obtain $x = \tan y$. Then, we form a table of values of x and y by selecting values of y on the range $-\frac{1}{2}\pi < y < \frac{1}{2}\pi$. Since $|\tan y| \rightarrow \infty$ when $y \rightarrow \frac{1}{2}\pi$, and also as $y \rightarrow -\frac{1}{2}\pi$, the graph in Figure 126 has the lines $y = \frac{1}{2}\pi$ and $y = -\frac{1}{2}\pi$ as **asymptotes.** Since $\tan y < 0$ if $-\frac{1}{2}\pi < y < 0$, it follows that $\tan y \rightarrow -\infty$ as y approaches $-\frac{1}{2}\pi$ on this range.

x	$x \rightarrow -\infty$	-1.7	-1	0	1	1.7	$x \rightarrow \infty$
$y = $ Arctan x	$y \rightarrow -\frac{1}{2}\pi$	$-\frac{1}{3}\pi$	$-\frac{1}{4}\pi$	0	$\frac{1}{4}\pi$	$\frac{1}{3}\pi$	$y \rightarrow \frac{1}{2}\pi$
y, dec. value	-1.57	-1.05	$-.79$	0	$.79$	1.05	1.57

EXAMPLE 1. Find $\tan (2 \text{ Arctan } x)$.

SOLUTION. Let $y = $ Arctan x; then $\tan y = x$ and we desire $\tan 2y$. From (IX) on page 237,

$$\tan (2 \text{ Arctan } x) = \tan 2y = \frac{2 \tan y}{1 - \tan^2 y} = \frac{2x}{1 - x^2}.$$

EXERCISE 121

Graph the function, with the same unit for distance used on both axes.

1. $y = $ Arcsin x.   2. $y = $ Arctan x.

Find each function value either from memory or by use of the "Rad." column in Table IV.

3. Arcsin $\frac{1}{2}$.   4. Arctan 1.   5. Arcsin 0.   6. Arctan 0.

7. Arcsin $\frac{1}{2}\sqrt{3}$.   8. Arcsin $\frac{1}{2}\sqrt{2}$.   9. Arctan $\sqrt{3}$.   10. Arctan $\frac{1}{3}\sqrt{3}$.

11. Arcsin $(-\frac{1}{2})$.   12. Arctan (-1).   13. Arctan $(-\sqrt{3})$.

14. Arcsin $(-\frac{1}{2}\sqrt{3})$.   15. Arctan $(-\frac{1}{3}\sqrt{3})$.   16. Arcsin $(-\frac{1}{2}\sqrt{2})$.

17. Arcsin .407.   18. Arctan .839.   19. Arcsin .423.

20. Arcsin $(-.946)$.   21. Arctan .683.   22. Arctan (-1.160).

Find the value of the expression without using a table.

23. sin Arcsin $\frac{1}{3}$.   24. tan Arctan (-2).   25. sin Arcsin $(-\frac{2}{5})$.

26. tan Arctan $2z$.   27. sin Arcsin $(-3x)$.   28. sin Arcsin u^2.

29. cos Arcsin $(-\frac{1}{2})$.   30. tan Arcsin $(-\frac{1}{2})$.   31. sin Arctan $\sqrt{3}$.

32. cos Arctan (-1).   33. cot Arcsin $(-\frac{1}{2}\sqrt{2})$.   34. sin Arctan (-1).

Find sin $(y + z)$, cos $(y + z)$, sin 2y, cos 2y, *and* tan 2y *for the data.*

35. $y = $ Arcsin $\frac{1}{2}$; $z = $ Arcsin $\frac{1}{2}\sqrt{3}$.

36. $y = $ Arcsin (-1); $z = $ Arcsin $(-\frac{1}{2})$.

37. $y = $ Arcsin $\frac{3}{5}$; $z = $ Arctan $(-\sqrt{3})$.

38. $y = $ Arcsin $\frac{5}{13}$; $z = $ Arcsin $(-\frac{7}{25})$.

39. $y = \text{Arctan } 2$; $z = \text{Arcsin } \frac{1}{2}\sqrt{2}$.   **40.** $y = \text{Arctan } (-\frac{3}{5})$; $z = \text{Arctan } \frac{4}{3}$.

41. $y = \text{Arctan } (-2)$; $z = \text{Arcsin } \frac{1}{4}$.

42. Find all trigonometric functions of $\text{Arcsin } (-\frac{12}{13})$.

43. Find all trigonometric functions of $\text{Arctan } (-\frac{3}{4})$.

44. Prove the identity $\text{Arctan } (-x) = -\text{Arctan } x$.

45. Solve for the unknown number x: $\text{Arcsin } 4x = \text{Arcsin } (2x - 1)$.

46. State the interval of numbers where $\text{Arcsin } x$ lies (*a*) in case $x > 0$;
(*b*) $x < 0$. Repeat the problem for $\text{Arctan } x$.

201. Other inverse trigonometric functions

The modern tendency in calculus is to emphasize use of the Arcsine and Arctangent functions. However, occasionally it proves convenient to employ the Arccosine and Arccotangent functions, which we proceed to describe.

With the following restriction on the range for y, the equation $x = \cos y$ defines y as a (single-valued) function of x, called the **Arccosine** function, the *inverse of the cosine function* on the indicated range. Thus, by definition

$$\left\{ \begin{array}{c} with -1 \leq x \leq 1; \\ 0 \leq y \leq \pi \end{array} \right\} \qquad x = \cos y \quad \textit{is equivalent to} \quad y = \textbf{Arccos } x; \qquad (1)$$

that is, for all x, $\qquad\qquad\qquad 0 \leq \textbf{Arccos } x \leq \pi.$ $\qquad\qquad\qquad$ (2)

Similarly, $\text{Arccot } x$ is defined as follows:

$$\left\{ \begin{array}{c} with -\infty < x < \infty; \\ 0 < y < \pi \end{array} \right\} \qquad x = \cot y \quad \textit{is equivalent to} \quad y = \textbf{Arccot } x; \qquad (3)$$

that is, for all x, $\qquad\qquad\qquad 0 < \textbf{Arccot } x < \pi.$ $\qquad\qquad\qquad$ (4)

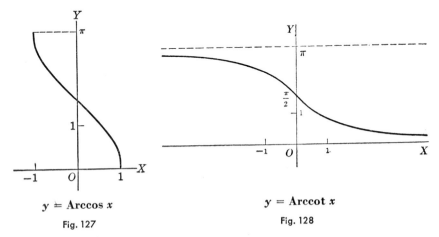

$y = \textbf{Arccos } x$

Fig. 127

$y = \textbf{Arccot } x$

Fig. 128

A graph of $y = \text{Arccos } x$ is the graph of $x = \cos y$ with $0 \leq y \leq \pi$, as seen in Figure 127. A graph of $y = \text{Arccot } x$ is the graph of $x = \cot y$ with $0 < y < \pi$, as seen in Figure 128.

Note 1. For contrast with the *inverse* trigonometric functions arcsine, arccosine, etc., sometimes the functions sin x, cos x, tan x, cot x, sec x, and csc x are called the *direct* trigonometric functions.

Note 2. The Arcsecant and Arccosecant functions are used so seldom that, in this text, treatment of them is restricted to problems in the next exercise.

SUMMARY. *The domain for the independent variable, x, and the range are listed below for each of the important inverse trigonometric functions.*

Domain: $-1 \leq x \leq 1$.	*Range:*	$-\frac{1}{2}\pi \leq \text{Arcsin } x \leq \frac{1}{2}\pi$.	(5)
Domain: $-\infty < x < \infty$.	*Range:*	$-\frac{1}{2}\pi < \text{Arctan } x < \frac{1}{2}\pi$.	(6)
Domain: $-1 \leq x \leq 1$.	*Range:*	$0 \leq \text{Arccos } x \leq \pi$.	(7)
Domain: $-\infty < x < \infty$.	*Range:*	$0 < \text{Arccot } x < \pi$.	(8)

Note 3. Observe that, for any one of the inverse functions in (5)–(8) with $x > 0$, the value, y, of the function at the point x in its domain lies on the interval $0 \leq y \leq \frac{1}{2}\pi$.

EXERCISE 122

1. Graph the function $y = \text{Arccot } x$ on an xy-plane where the same unit for distance is used on both axes.

2. Repeat Problem 1 for $y = \text{Arccos } x$.

Find each function value either from memory or by use of the "Rad." column in Table IV.

3. Arccot $\sqrt{3}$. **4.** Arccos 1. **5.** Arccos $\frac{1}{2}$. **6.** Arccot 1.

7. Arccos (-1). **8.** Arccot $(-\frac{1}{3}\sqrt{3})$. **9.** Arccos $(-\frac{1}{2}\sqrt{2})$.

10. Arccot $(-\sqrt{3})$. **11.** Arccot (-1). **12.** Arccos $(-\frac{1}{2})$.

13. Arccos $(\frac{1}{2}\sqrt{3})$. **14.** Arccos $(-\frac{1}{2}\sqrt{3})$. **15.** Arccot 3.732.

16. Arccos $(.485)$. **17.** Arccos $(-.880)$. **18.** Arccot $(-.842)$.

19. State the interval of numbers where Arccos x lies in case (*a*) $x \geq 0$; (*b*) $x \leq 0$.

20. Repeat Problem 19 for the case of Arccot x.

Note 1. The following definitions for the functions Arcsec x and Arccsc x harmonize with their rare applications in some texts on integral calculus. Thus we define Arcsec x by stating that

$$x = \sec y \quad \text{is equivalent to} \quad y = \text{Arcsec } x, \qquad (1)$$

subject to the restriction that, if $1 \leq x$, then $0 \leq y < \frac{1}{2}\pi$ and, if $x \leq -1$, then $-\pi \leq y < -\frac{1}{2}\pi$, or

$$\left\{\begin{matrix} \text{if } x \geq 1: \\ \text{if } x \leq -1: \end{matrix}\right\} \qquad \begin{matrix} 0 \leq \text{Arcsec } x < \frac{1}{2}\pi; \\ -\pi \leq \text{Arcsec } x < -\frac{1}{2}\pi. \end{matrix} \Bigg\} \qquad (2)$$

$$x = \csc y \quad \text{is equivalent to} \quad y = \text{Arccsc } x, \qquad (3)$$

subject to the restriction that, if $1 \leqq x$, then $0 < y \leqq \frac{1}{2}\pi$ and, if $x \leqq -1$, then $-\pi < y \leqq -\frac{1}{2}\pi$, or

$$\left. \begin{matrix} if \ x \geqq 1: \\ if \ x \leqq -1: \end{matrix} \right\} \qquad \left. \begin{matrix} 0 < \text{Arccsc } x \leqq \frac{1}{2}\pi; \\ -\pi < \text{Arccsc } x \leqq -\frac{1}{2}\pi. \end{matrix} \right\} \tag{4}$$

★21. Draw a graph of $x = \sec y$ and verify that, with the restrictions on y following (1), the equation defines y as a single-valued function of x. Thus, obtain a graph of $y = $ Arcsec x.

★22. Draw a graph of $x = \csc y$ subject to the restrictions on y applying in (4), and repeat Problem 21 for the function $y = $ Arccsc x.

202. The logarithm and exponential functions as inverses

Consider the graph of $y = e^x$ in Figure 129, with $e = 2.71828 \cdots$, a fundamental constant which will arise in calculus as the value of the following limit:

$$e = \lim_{h \to 0} (1 + h)^{\frac{1}{h}}.$$

In calculus, it is found that e^x has particularly simple properties as compared to exponential functions a^x for all other values of $a \neq 1$ with $a > 0$. In Figure 129, notice that y *increases steadily if x increases steadily.* Hence, our discussion on page 361 shows that, for each value of y which is on the range $0 < y < \infty$, the equation $y = e^x$ has *a single solution for x.* Let this value of x, for any y, be denoted by "**ln** y," read "*natural logarithm of y*," meaning "*logarithm of y to the base e.*" Then,

$$y = e^x \quad \text{is equivalent to} \quad x = \ln y.$$

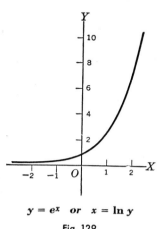

$$y = e^x \quad or \quad x = \ln y$$

Fig. 129

Thus, the standard exponential function $y = e^x$ and the logarithm function $x = \ln y$ are *inverse functions.* This relationship becomes of vital importance later in calculus.

Oblique Triangles

203. Terminology about triangles

An *oblique triangle* is one which has no angle equal to 90°. This chapter bears its indicated name because the objective is to develop formulas applicable to oblique triangles. However, the formulas will apply not only to oblique triangles but also to right triangles, although no essential new information about them is gained. Hence, we proceed to consider *any* triangle *ABC*, as in Figure 130, where α, β, and γ are the measures of the angles at A, B, and C, respectively, and a, b, and c are the lengths of the corresponding opposite sides. Also, we shall use α, β, γ, a, b, and c as symbols for the angles and sides of which these letters are the measures.

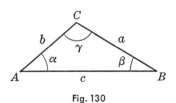

Fig. 130

Note 1. In this chapter, the trigonometric functions will be considered as functions of *angles*, as in Definition I on page 140, with any symbol such as θ in sin θ representing an angle whose degree measure is θ. All angles will be expressed in degree measure.

The angles α, β, and γ, and the sides a, b, and c in $\triangle ABC$ will be called its *parts*. The student should recall from elementary geometry that we can construct $\triangle ABC$ if three of its parts, including at least one side, are given. Such data fall into four categories:

I. *Given two angles and a side.*

II. *Given two sides and an angle opposite one of them.*

III. *Given two sides and the included angle.*

IV. *Given three sides.*

In this chapter, we shall develop methods for computing the unknown parts of a triangle under each of Cases I to IV. The computation of the unknown parts is called the *solution* of the triangle.

204. Law of cosines

In any triangle, the square of any side is equal to the sum of the squares of the other sides minus twice their product times the cosine of their included angle. That is,

$$a^2 = b^2 + c^2 - 2bc \cos \alpha; \tag{1}$$

$$b^2 = a^2 + c^2 - 2ac \cos \beta; \tag{2}$$

$$c^2 = a^2 + b^2 - 2ab \cos \gamma. \tag{3}$$

On solving (1), (2), and (3) for the cosines, we obtain

$$\cos \alpha = \frac{b^2 + c^2 - a^2}{2bc}; \quad \cos \beta = \frac{a^2 + c^2 - b^2}{2ac}; \quad \cos \gamma = \frac{a^2 + b^2 - c^2}{2ab}. \tag{4}$$

Note 1. Suppose that triangle ABC is a *right* triangle with $\gamma = 90°$. Then, $\cos \gamma = 0$, $\cos \alpha = \dfrac{b}{c}$, and $\cos \beta = \dfrac{a}{c}$. Hence, from (1), (2), and (3),

$$a^2 = b^2 + c^2 - 2b^2, \quad or \quad a^2 = c^2 - b^2; \qquad b^2 = c^2 - a^2; \qquad c^2 = a^2 + b^2.$$

Thus, *for a right triangle, the law of cosines is equivalent to the Pythagorean theorem.*

Proof of the law of cosines. 1. Consider any $\triangle ABC$, and place it on an xy-system of coordinates with vertex A at the origin, B on the positive side of the x-axis, and C above the x-axis, as in Figure 131. The coordinates of B are $(c, 0)$. Let (k, h) be the coordinates of C. The radius vector of C is b. Notice that angle α is in its standard position on the coordinate system. Then, from Definition I on page 140, with $C:(k, h)$ as a point on the terminal side of α,

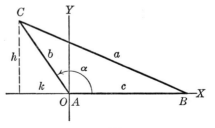

Fig. 131

$$\cos \alpha = \frac{k}{b} \quad and \quad \sin \alpha = \frac{h}{b}; \qquad k = b \cos \alpha \quad and \quad h = b \sin \alpha.$$

2. By use of the distance formula (1) of page 61 as applied to CB, with $C:(b \cos \alpha, b \sin \alpha)$ and $B:(c, 0)$, we obtain

$$a^2 = \overline{CB}^2 = (b \cos \alpha - c)^2 + (b \sin \alpha - 0)^2$$

$$= b^2 \cos^2 \alpha - 2bc \cos \alpha + c^2 + b^2 \sin^2 \alpha$$

$$= b^2 (\sin^2 \alpha + \cos^2 \alpha) - 2bc \cos \alpha + c^2,$$

which gives (1) because $\sin^2 \alpha + \cos^2 \alpha = 1$.

3. Since side a may be referred to as *any* side of the triangle, we obtain (2) and (3) by using (b, β) and (c, γ), respectively, in place of (a, α) as in (1).

205. Application of law of cosines to Case IV in solving triangles

The law of cosines is not well fitted for logarithmic computation. However, the formulas are used frequently without logarithms, particularly in physics. If a table of squares is available, or if convenient numbers are involved, problems of certain types can be solved efficiently by use of the law of cosines and natural values of the trigonometric functions.

OUTLINE. *Application of the law of cosines to solve $\triangle ABC$ under Case IV, that is, to find the angles when all sides are given.*

1. *Find each angle by use of its cosine, from (4) on page 371.*
2. *Check the solution by means of $\alpha + \beta + \gamma = 180°$.*

EXAMPLE 1. Solve $\triangle ABC$ if $a = 5$, $b = 7$, and $c = 11$.

SOLUTION. 1. From (4) on page 371,

$$\cos \alpha = \frac{145}{154} = .9416; \quad \cos \beta = \frac{97}{110} = .8818; \quad \cos \gamma = -\frac{47}{70} = -.6714.$$

2. By use of Table VII, we find $\alpha = 19° \, 41'$; $\beta = 28° \, 8'$.

3. Since $\cos \gamma$ is negative, $\gamma > 90°$. Let θ be the reference angle for γ, so that θ is acute and $\gamma = 180° - \theta$. Then, $\cos \theta = .6714$. From Table VII, $\theta = 47° \, 50'$. Hence, $\gamma = 180° - 47° \, 50' = 132° \, 10'$.

Check. $\qquad \alpha + \beta + \gamma = 19° \, 41' + 28° \, 8' + 132° \, 10' = 179° \, 59'.$

ILLUSTRATION 1. If $a = 5$, $b = 12$, and $\gamma = 60°$, then $\cos \gamma = \frac{1}{2}$ and, from (3) on page 371, we find

$$c^2 = 25 + 144 - 2(5)(12) \cos 60° = 109.$$

By use of logarithms or Table I, $c = \sqrt{109} = 10.4$.

EXERCISE 123

Find the obtuse angle α by use of Table VII.

1. $\sin \alpha = .2447$.   **2.** $\cos \alpha = -.1363$.   **3.** $\cos \alpha = -.7969$.

Solve without trigonometric tables if possible. Otherwise use Table VII.

4. $a = 3$, $b = 2$, $\gamma = 60°$; find c.   **5.** $b = 4$, $c = \sqrt{3}$, $\alpha = 30°$; find a.

6. $b = \sqrt{2}$, $a = 8$, $\gamma = 45°$; find c.   **7.** $b = 7$, $c = \sqrt{2}$, $\alpha = 135°$; find a.

8. $a = \sqrt{3}$, $c = 4$, $\beta = 150°$; find b.   **9.** $a = 2$, $c = 2$, $\beta = 120°$; find b.

10. $a = 3$, $b = 10$, $c = 8$; find γ.   **11.** $a = 7$, $b = 9$, $c = 4$; find α.

12. $a = 5$, $b = 6$, $c = 7$; find β.   **13.** $a = 9$, $b = 10$, $c = 7$; find γ.

14. $a = 13$, $b = 7$, $c = 8$; find α.   **15.** $a = 6$, $b = 12$, $c = 9$; find β.

By use of Table VII, solve $\triangle ABC$ and check, if all sides are given. Otherwise, just find the requested side. Use logarithms where pertinent.

16. $a = 5$, $b = 6$, $c = 4$.   **17.** $a = 8$, $b = 5$, $c = 7$.

18. $a = 6$, $b = 14$, $c = 10$.   **19.** $a = 13$, $b = 6$, $c = 9$.

20. $a = 5$, $b = 7$, $\gamma = 32°$; find c.

21. $a = 6$, $c = 10$, $\beta = 155° \; 30'$; find b.

22. $b = 5$, $c = 12$, $\alpha = 120° \; 40'$; find a.

23. $b = 4$, $c = 11$, $\alpha = 65° \; 38'$; find a.

24. Find the sides of a parallelogram if the lengths of its diagonals are 12 inches and 16 inches and one angle formed by the diagonals is 37°.

25. At 1 P.M., a train leaves a city T at 30 miles per hour in a direction due east, and a second train travels from T in the direction $N \; 20° \; W$ at 40 miles per hour. How far apart are the trains at the end of 2 hours?

26. In a storm cloud, an airplane meets an air current flowing vertically upward at a rate of 100 miles per hour. The pilot aims his plane 58° from the horizontal downward and his instruments show that his airspeed is 250 miles per hour. Find the resultant speed of the plane and the inclination of its path to the horizontal.

Find the magnitude of the resultant of the given forces acting simultaneously on the same object, by solving an oblique triangle.

27. 200 pounds and 300 pounds: angle between their directions is 78°.

28. 150 pounds and 250 pounds: angle between their directions is 67°.

29. 40 pounds and 70 pounds: angle between their directions is 123°.

206. Law of sines

In any triangle, the lengths of the sides are proportional to the sines of the opposite angles. That is,

$$a : b : c = \sin \alpha : \sin \beta : \sin \gamma, \; or \tag{1}$$

$$\frac{a}{\sin \alpha} = \frac{b}{\sin \beta} = \frac{c}{\sin \gamma}. \tag{2}$$

In (2), we are abbreviating three equations:

$$\frac{a}{\sin \alpha} = \frac{b}{\sin \beta}; \qquad \frac{b}{\sin \beta} = \frac{c}{\sin \gamma}; \qquad \frac{c}{\sin \gamma} = \frac{a}{\sin \alpha}. \tag{3}$$

Proof of (3). 1. Let α and β represent any two angles of $\triangle ABC$. At least one of α and β is acute; hence, without loss of generality in our proof, we may assume that the triangle is lettered so that β is acute. Then, let $\triangle ABC$ be placed on an xy-coordinate system, as in Figure 132 with A at the origin, B on the positive side of the x-axis, and C above the x-axis. Thus, α is in its standard position on the coordinate system. Let h be the ordinate of C, in Figure 132.

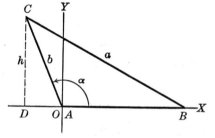

Fig. 132

2. From Definition I on page 140, with C as the point on the terminal side of α, we have $x = h$, $r = b$, and

$$\sin \alpha = \frac{h}{b}, \quad or \quad h = b \sin \alpha. \tag{4}$$

From right $\triangle DBC$, and the formulas of page 150 for acute angles,

$$\sin \beta = \frac{h}{a}, \quad or \quad h = a \sin \beta. \tag{5}$$

From (4) and (5), $a \sin \beta = b \sin \alpha, \quad or \quad \dfrac{a}{\sin \alpha} = \dfrac{b}{\sin \beta},$ (6)

where we divided both sides of $a \sin \beta = b \sin \alpha$ by $\sin \alpha \sin \beta$. Thus, we obtain the equation at the left in (3). Since α and β represented any two angles of $\triangle ABC$, we also claim that our proof justifies the other two equations in (3).

★*Note 1.* Let $k = AD$ be the abscissa of C in Figure 132. Then $\cos \alpha = k/b$, or $k = b \cos \alpha$, and D has the coordinates $(b \cos \alpha, 0)$. Also, B has the coordinates $(c, 0)$. From (4) on page 59 with $x_1 = b \cos \alpha$ and $x_2 = c$, we have

$$\overline{DB} = c - b \cos \alpha. \tag{7}$$

Also, from right $\triangle DBC$, $\cos \beta = \overline{DB}/a$, or $\overline{DB} = a \cos \beta$. Hence, from (7),

$$a \cos \beta = c - b \cos \alpha, \quad or \quad c = a \cos \beta + b \cos \alpha. \tag{8}$$

As a consequence of (8), for a and b on the left as well as c, we have the following results, called **projection formulas:**

$$\left. \begin{array}{ll} c = a \cos \beta + b \cos \alpha; & a = b \cos \gamma + c \cos \beta; \\ b = a \cos \gamma + c \cos \alpha. \end{array} \right\} \tag{9}$$

These formulas are sometimes useful in checking the solution of a triangle.

207. Solution of Case I by the law of sines

To solve $\triangle ABC$ if two angles and a side are given, for instance α, β, and c.

1. *Find the third angle by use of $\alpha + \beta + \gamma = 180°$.*

2. *Find the unknown sides by use of the law of sines:*

$$a = \frac{c \sin \alpha}{\sin \gamma}; \qquad b = \frac{c \sin \beta}{\sin \gamma}. \tag{1}$$

3. *To check, use one of the projection formulas (9) above.*

The solution as just outlined can be carried out without logarithms by use of Table IV or Table VII, or with logarithms by use of Table VI.

EXAMPLE 1.   Solve $\triangle ABC$ if $b = 5$, $\alpha = 65°$, and $\beta = 30°$.

SOLUTION. 1. From (3) on page 373, $\dfrac{a}{\sin 65°} = \dfrac{5}{\sin 30°};$

$$a = \frac{5}{\sin 30°} \, (\sin 65°) = 10(.9063) = 9.063. \qquad (\sin 30° = \tfrac{1}{2}; \text{ Table VII})$$

2. From $\alpha + \beta + \gamma = 180°$, $\gamma = 180° - 95° = 85°$.

From (1), $c/\sin \gamma = b/\sin \beta$, *or* $c = 10 \sin 85° = 9.962$.

The solution gives $\gamma = 85°$, $a = 9.063$, and $c = 9.962$.

EXAMPLE 2. Solve $\triangle ABC$ if $\beta = 37° 6'$, $\gamma = 42° 38'$, and $c = 21.37$.

SOLUTION. We employ the four-place Tables V and VI.

Formulas	Computation
	Data: $c = 21.37$, $\beta = 37° 6'$, $\gamma = 42° 38'$.
$\alpha = 180° - (\beta + \gamma)$.	$\alpha = 180° - (37° 6' + 42° 38') = 100° 16'$.
$\dfrac{b}{\sin \beta} = \dfrac{c}{\sin \gamma}$, *or* $b = \dfrac{c \sin \beta}{\sin \gamma}.$	log c = 1.3298 (Table V) log sin β = 9.7805 − 10 (+) (Table VI) log c sin β = 11.1103 − 10 log sin γ = 9.8308 − 10 (−) log b = 1.2795; $b = 19.03$.
$\dfrac{a}{\sin \alpha} = \dfrac{c}{\sin \gamma}$, *or* $a = \dfrac{c \sin \alpha}{\sin \gamma}.$	sin $100° 16'$ = sin $(180° - 100° 16')$ = sin $79° 44'$. log c = 1.3298 log sin α = 9.9930 − 10 (+) log c sin α = 11.3228 − 10 (−) log sin γ = 9.8308 − 10 (−) log a = 1.4920; $a = 31.04$.
Summary.	$a = 31.04$, $b = 19.03$, $\alpha = 100° 16'$.
Check.	$c = a \cos \beta + b \cos \alpha.$

$\cos \alpha = \cos 100° 16' = - \cos (180° - 100° 16') = - \cos 79° 44'.$

$a \cos \beta = 31.04(.7976) = 24.76.$ (Table VII)

$b \cos \alpha = - 19.03 \cos 79° 44' = - 19.03(.1782) = - 3.39.$

$a \cos \beta + b \cos \alpha = 24.76 - 3.39 = 21.37 \to \leftarrow c = 21.37$; *satisfactory*.

EXERCISE 124

Solve $\triangle ABC$ without logarithms by use of Table VII.

1. $b = 5$, $\alpha = 75°$, $\beta = 30°$.   2. $c = 3$, $\beta = 37°$, $\gamma = 30°$.

3. $a = 50$, $\alpha = 37° 30'$, $\beta = 71° 10'$.   4. $a = 200$, $\alpha = 32° 21'$, $\gamma = 21° 39'$

Solve by use of four-place logarithms. Check when directed by the instructor.

5. $c = 15.67$; $\alpha = 42° 20'$; $\gamma = 53° 40'$.

6. $b = 231.6$; $\alpha = 19° 10'$; $\beta = 82° 40'$.

7. $a = 1.056$; $\beta = 23° 20'$; $\gamma = 53° 50'$.

8. $c = 6019$; $\alpha = 16° 30'$; $\beta = 59° 20'$.

9. $\alpha = 19° 41'$; $\beta = 28° 8'$; $a = 5.37$.

10. $\alpha = 64°\ 9'$; $\beta = 13°\ 0'$; $a = 12.3$.

11. $\alpha = 23°\ 54'$; $\gamma = 85°\ 16'$; $b = .4317$.

12. $\beta = 101°\ 36'$; $\gamma = 21°\ 44'$; $c = .04198$.

13. $\alpha = 23°\ 42'$; $\beta = 98°\ 18'$; $a = .03152$.

14. $\alpha = 31°\ 18'$; $\gamma = 42°\ 32'$; $b = .01571$.

15. A polygon is inscribed in a circle whose radius is 6 inches. One of the sides subtends an angle of 27° at the center of the circle; find the length of this side by use of the law of sines.

16. One side of a parallelogram is 56 inches long. The diagonals of the parallelogram make the angles 35° and 47°, respectively, with this side. Find the lengths of the diagonals.

17. In triangle ABC, suppose that $\gamma = 90°$. Show that in this case the equations of the law of sines give merely the well-known expressions for the sines of the two acute angles of the right triangle ABC.

18. A battery commander B is ordered to shoot at a target T from a position G, from which T is visible. To check on the range GT as found by a range finder, B locates an observation point H from which T is visible. The bearing of T from G is $N\ 12°\ 48'\ E$, of T from H is $N\ 6°\ 23'\ W$, and of H from G is $S\ 82°\ 53'\ E$. From a map, it is found that $GH = 3250$ yards. Find the range of the target from G.

19. From Figure 132 on page 373, prove that the area, K, of $\triangle ABC$ is given by $K = \frac{1}{2}bc \sin \alpha$. Also, after stating this result in words, referring to any two sides and their included angle, write two other formulas for K.

20. By use of the relation $(c/\sin \gamma) = (b/\sin \beta)$ and the results in Problem 19, prove that $K = \dfrac{b^2 \sin \alpha \sin \gamma}{2 \sin \beta}$. Then, state this formula in words and write two other symmetrical formulas for K, where each formula involves just one side and all of the angles.

21–24. Find the areas of the triangles in Problems 1–4, respectively, by use of two formulas, one from Problem 19 and one from Problem 20.

208. Solution of Case II, the ambiguous case

If two sides of a triangle ABC and an angle opposite one of these sides are given, we shall find that there may exist *two* solutions, or just *one* solution, or *no* solution for the triangle, depending on the given values. Since there may be two solutions, Case II is called the *ambiguous case*.

Note 1. Recall that, if k is a positive number less than 1, the equation $\sin \alpha = k$ has *two* positive solutions less than 180°, one *acute* and the other *obtuse*. This existence of *two* solutions is the fact which accounts for the possibility of two triangles as solutions in Case II.

If the given parts of a triangle ABC are a, b, and α, any triangle satisfying the data may be obtained geometrically as follows.

1. *Construct α with one side AD horizontal. On the other side, measure distance b from A to locate vertex C.*

2. *With C as center and radius equal to side a, strike an arc. The vertex B may then be located at any point where this arc cuts AD.*

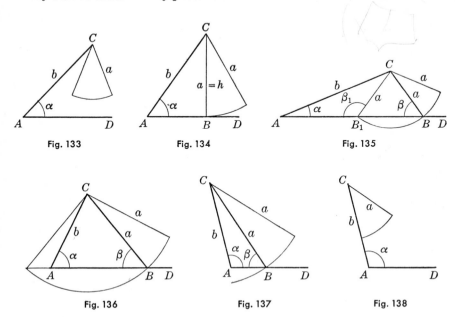

Fig. 133   Fig. 134   Fig. 135

Fig. 136   Fig. 137   Fig. 138

In Figures 133 and 138, the arc does *not meet* AD, and hence there is *no* solution. In Figure 134, the arc is tangent to AD and there is just *one* position for B, with $β = 90°$. In Figure 135, the arc cuts AD twice, at B and B_1; hence there are *two* solutions, triangles AB_1C and ABC. In Figure 136 and in Figure 137, there is just *one* solution.

In a triangle ABC, let h be the perpendicular distance from C to side AB. Then, as in Figure 134, $\sin α = h/b$ or $h = b \sin α$. In Figures 133–135 where $a < b$ and $α < 90°$, we observe that we have *no* solution, *just one* solution, or *two* solutions according as side a, the radius of the arc, is *less than, equal to,* or *greater than h.*

Note 2. The preceding remarks and Figures 133–138 justify the following summary of possibilities in case the given parts under Case II are a, b, and $α$:

$$α < 90° \begin{cases} a < b \sin α; \text{ no solution (Figure 133).} \\ a = b \sin α; \text{ just one solution, with } β = 90° \text{ (Figure 134).} \\ a > b \sin α, \text{ but } a < b; \text{ two solutions (Figure 135).} \\ a \geqq b; \text{ just one solution (Figure 136).} \end{cases}$$

$$α \geqq 90° \begin{cases} a > b; \text{ just one solution (Figure 137).} \\ a \leqq b; \text{ no solution (Figure 138).} \end{cases}$$

Instead of memorizing the preceding summary, the student should *draw a figure roughly to scale for each problem* to learn the number of solutions.

OUTLINE.   *To solve $\triangle ABC$ under Case II, with the given parts a, b, and α:*

1. *Construct the triangle approximately to scale.*
2. *Find β by use of $\sin \beta = (b \sin \alpha)/a$. If this gives*

   $\sin \beta > 1$, *or* $\log \sin \beta > 0$, *there is no solution;*

   $\sin \beta = 1$, *or* $\log \sin \beta = 0$, *then $\beta = 90°$, just one solution;*

   $\sin \beta < 1$, *find one acute and one obtuse value for β.*

3. *Discard any value of β for which $\alpha + \beta \geqq 180°$; for each value of β, compute $\gamma = 180° - (\alpha + \beta)$.*
4. *For each pair of values of β and γ, compute $c = (a \sin \gamma)/\sin \alpha$.*

Note 3. A solution under Case II may be checked as in Case I.

EXAMPLE 1. How many triangles exist with $a = 4$, $b = 8$, and $\alpha = 30°$?

SOLUTION. 1. A figure for this problem would look like Figure 134.

2. To find β: $\sin \beta = \dfrac{b \sin \alpha}{a} = \dfrac{8 \sin 30°}{4} = \dfrac{8(\frac{1}{2})}{4}.$

Hence, $\sin \beta = 1$ and $\beta = 90°$. There is just *one* solution, a right $\triangle$.

EXAMPLE 2. Solve $\triangle ABC$ if $a = 20$, $b = 10$, and $\alpha = 30°$.

SOLUTION. A figure like Figure 136 indicates just one solution.

Formulas	Computation
	Data: $a = 20$, $b = 10$, $\alpha = 30°$.
$\dfrac{\sin \beta}{b} = \dfrac{\sin \alpha}{a}$, or $\sin \beta = \dfrac{b \sin \alpha}{a}.$	$\sin \beta = \dfrac{10 \sin 30°}{20} = .2500.$ $\beta = 14° 29'.$ (Table VII)

Comment. We also obtain $\beta = 180° - 14° 29'$, or $\beta = 165° 31'$. Figure 136 on page 377 shows that this value cannot be used because there is only one solution, with β acute. To prove this otherwise, we compute

$$\alpha + \beta = 30° + 165° 31' = 195° 31';$$

since $195° 31' > 180°$, $\beta = 165° 31'$ is impossible.

$\gamma = 180° - (\alpha + \beta).$	$\gamma = 180° - (30° + 14° 29') = 135° 31'.$
$\dfrac{c}{\sin \gamma} = \dfrac{a}{\sin \alpha}$, or $c = \dfrac{a \sin \gamma}{\sin \alpha}.$	$\sin 135° 31' = \sin (180° - 135° 31') = \sin 44° 29'.$ $c = \dfrac{20 \sin 44° 29'}{\sin 30°} = 28.03.$ (Table VII)
Summary. One solution:	$c = 28.03$, $\beta = 14° 29'$, $\gamma = 135° 31'.$

EXAMPLE 3. Solve $\triangle ABC$ if $b = 4.157$, $c = 3.446$, and $\gamma = 51° 48'$.

SOLUTION. From Figure 139 below, without computation it appears that there are two solutions.

Formulas	Computation
	Data: $b = 4.157$, $c = 3.446$, $\gamma = 51° 48'$.
$\dfrac{\sin \beta}{b} = \dfrac{\sin \gamma}{c}$, or $\sin \beta = \dfrac{b \sin \gamma}{c}$.	$\log b = 0.6188$ (Table V) $\log \sin \gamma = 9.8953 - 10 \ (+)$ (Table VI) $\overline{\log b \sin \gamma = 10.5141 - 10}$ $\log c = 0.5373 (-)$ $\overline{\log \sin \beta = 9.9768 - 10;\ \beta = 71° 26'.}$ (Table VI) $Hence, \quad \beta_1 = 180° - \beta = 108° 34'.$
	Solution for $\triangle ABC$, Figure 139
$\alpha = 180° - (\beta + \gamma).$	$\alpha = 180° - (71° 26' + 51° 48') = 56° 46'.$
$\dfrac{a}{\sin \alpha} = \dfrac{c}{\sin \gamma}$, or $a = \dfrac{c \sin \alpha}{\sin \gamma}$.	$\log c = 0.5373$ $\log \sin \alpha = 9.9224 - 10 \ (+)$ $\overline{\log c \sin \alpha = 10.4597 - 10}$ $\log \sin \gamma = 9.8953 - 10 \ (-)$ $\overline{\log a = 0.5644;} \quad a = 3.668.$
	Solution for $\triangle AB_1C$, Figure 139
$\alpha_1 = 180° - (\beta_1 + \gamma).$	$\alpha_1 = 180° - (108° 34' + 51° 48') = 19° 38'.$
$a_1 = \dfrac{c \sin \alpha_1}{\sin \gamma}.$	$\log c = 0.5373$ $\log \sin \alpha_1 = 9.5263 - 10 \ (+)$ $\overline{\log c \sin \alpha_1 = 10.0636 - 10}$ $\log \sin \gamma = 9.8953 - 10 \ (-)$ $\overline{\log a_1 = 0.1683;} \quad a_1 = 1.473.$
Summary.	First solution: $\quad a = 3.668, \quad \alpha = 56° 46', \quad \beta = 71° 26'.$ Second solution: $\quad a_1 = 1.473, \quad \alpha_1 = 19° 38', \quad \beta_1 = 108° 34'.$

EXAMPLE 4. Solve $\triangle ABC$ if $a = 2$, $b = 6$, and $\alpha = 30°$.

SOLUTION *without logarithms.*

$$\sin \beta = \frac{b \sin \alpha}{a} = \frac{6(\frac{1}{2})}{2} = 1.5 > 1.$$

Hence, there is *no solution* because no value of the sine function exceeds 1. A figure for this problem would look like Figure 133 on page 377.

SOLUTION *with logarithms.* If the logarithm of a number is *positive*, the number is *greater*

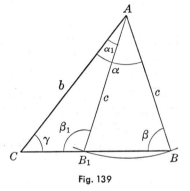

Fig. 139

than 1. Hence, on finding log sin β = 0.1762 below, we see that sin β > 1, which is *impossible*. Therefore, there is *no solution*.

$$\sin \beta = b \, \frac{\sin \alpha}{a} :$$

$$\log b = 0.7782$$
$$\underline{\log \sin \alpha = 9.6990 - 10 \ (+)}$$
$$\overline{\log b \sin \alpha = 0.4772}$$
$$\underline{\quad \log a = 0.3010 \qquad (-)}$$
$$\overline{\log \sin \beta = 0.1762, \textit{which is positive; no solution.}}$$

EXERCISE 125

Solve $\triangle ABC$ *without logarithms by use of Table* VII.

1. $\beta = 30°$, $a = 4$, $b = 5$.   2. $\gamma = 22° \ 20'$, $a = 50$, $c = 38$.
3. $\gamma = 65° \ 30'$, $b = 97.5$, $c = 91$.   4. $\alpha = 30°$, $b = 3$, $a = 5$.
5. $\gamma = 75°$, $c = 7$, $b = 7$.   6. $\alpha = 150°$, $a = 5$, $c = 8$.
7. $\alpha = 31° \ 20'$, $b = .25$, $a = .13$.   8. $\alpha = 157° \ 40'$, $a = 38$, $b = 25$.
9. $\gamma = 148° \ 40'$, $a = 20$, $c = 26$.   10. $\beta = 114° \ 30'$, $b = 13$, $c = 10$.

Solve by use of four-place logarithms.

11. $\beta = 42° \ 30'$, $b = 16.7$, $c = 12.3$.
12. $\alpha = 67° \ 40'$, $a = 2.39$, $c = 1.67$.
13. $\alpha = 76° \ 19'$, $a = .0572$, $b = .139$.
14. $\alpha = 71° \ 45'$, $a = .9632$, $b = .9632$.
15. $\beta = 36° \ 53'$, $c = .07531$, $b = .05126$.
16. $\gamma = 49° \ 46'$, $b = .9652$, $c = .4738$.
17. $\alpha = 113° \ 20'$, $a = 11.56$, $c = 7.282$.
18. $\gamma = 147° \ 5'$, $b = 19.36$, $c = 15.17$.
19. $\gamma = 127° \ 19'$, $a = .7422$, $c = .9732$.

20. A telegraph pole is supported by two guy wires which run from the top of the pole to the ground on opposite sides. One wire is 53.6 feet long and makes an angle of 65° 20′ with the ground. The other wire is 57.5 feet long. Find the acute angle which the second wire makes with the ground, if both wires are in the same vertical plane.

21. A force of 85 pounds pulls due east on *P*. A second force pulls N 37° W on *P*. The resultant force is 73 pounds. Find the second force and the direction of the resultant.

Without solving the triangle, construct all triangles which satisfy the data, and thus reach a conclusion geometrically concerning the number of solutions. Also, compute a perpendicular h, as referred to in Section 208, and apply a corresponding analytical test about the value of h to verify the geometrical conclusion.

22. $\alpha = 58°$, $a = 42$, $b = 50$.   23. $\gamma = 73°$, $a = 60$, $c = 58$.
24. $\beta = 115°$, $a = 35$, $b = 56$.   25. $\gamma = 41°$, $a = 200$, $c = 135$.

209. Solution of Case III by the laws of cosines and sines

Suppose that two sides and the included angle of a $\triangle ABC$ are known. Then, with any data which extend to, say, only three-figure accuracy, as described on page 203, the following outline gives the solution of $\triangle ABC$ with reasonable convenience.

OUTLINE. *Solution of* Case III *for* $\triangle ABC$ *by the laws of cosines and sines, with the data consisting of the values of b, c, and α.*

1. *Find a^2 by use of $a^2 = b^2 + c^2 - 2bc \cos \alpha$; then compute side a either by use of a table of square roots or by use of logarithms.*

2. *Use $\sin \beta = (b \sin \alpha)/a$ to find β. Then use $\gamma = 180° - \alpha - \beta$.*

3. *If a check is desired, investigate* $\dfrac{\sin \gamma}{c} = \dfrac{\sin \alpha}{a}$.

Note 1. The method of the outline is convenient if slide-rule computation is permitted. In any case, we may state that all cases of solution of $\triangle ABC$ may be treated by use of *just the laws of cosines and sines.*[*]

EXAMPLE 1. Solve $\triangle ABC$ if $\alpha = 78° 50'$, $b = 73$, and $c = 94$, to obtain angles to the nearest 10′ and side a to the nearest integer.

SOLUTION. We solve by use of Tables I, V, and VI.

Data: $\alpha = 78° 50'$, $b = 73$, $c = 94$.		
Formula:	$a^2 = b^2 + c^2 - 2bc \cos \alpha$.	
(+) $\begin{cases} \log 2 = 0.3010 \\ \log b = 1.8633 \\ \log c = 1.9731 \\ \log \cos \alpha = 9.2870 - 10 \end{cases}$ $\log 2bc \cos \alpha = 3.4244;$		*From Table I,* $b^2 = 5,329$ $c^2 = 8,836$ $\overline{b^2 + c^2 = 14,165}$ $2bc \cos \alpha = 2,657 \ (-)$ $\overline{a^2 = 11,508.}$
	From Table V, $\begin{cases} \log 11,510 = 4.0611 \\ \frac{1}{2} \log 11,510 = 2.0306 = \log a \\ a = 107.3. \end{cases}$	
$\sin \beta = \dfrac{b \sin \alpha}{a}$	$\log b = 1.8633$ $(+) \log \sin \alpha = 9.9917 - 10$ $\overline{\log b \sin \alpha = 1.8550}$ $(-) \log a = 2.0306$ $\overline{\log \sin \beta = 9.8244 - 10;}$ $\beta = 41° 50'$ *(to nearest 10′).*	
$\gamma = 180° - (\alpha + \beta)$	$\alpha + \beta = 120° 40'$; $\gamma = 180° - 120° 40' = 59° 20'$.	
Summary.	$\beta = 41° 50'$, $\gamma = 59° 20'$, $a = 107$.	

[*] It follows that, if minimum emphasis on computation is desired, the remaining sections of the chapter devoted to the laws of tangents and half-angle formulas could be omitted.

$cos = \Lambda EG$ in 2nd quad.

EXERCISE 126

Solve $\triangle ABC$ for the given data. Find any unknown sides to three significant digits, and unknown angles to the nearest 10' by use of Tables I, V, VI, and VII, as desired.

1. $a = 12, b = 8, \gamma = 30°$.

2. $b = 30, c = 25, \alpha = 50°$.

3. $a = 50, c = 25, \beta = 110°$.

4. $a = 10, b = 15, \gamma = 150°$.

5. $b = 39, c = 14, \alpha = 68°$.

6. $a = 10, b = 44, \gamma = 43°$.

7. $a = .94, c = .35, \beta = 72°$.

8. $b = .66, c = .32, \alpha = 108°$.

9. $b = 13, c = 23, \alpha = 69° 40'$.

10. $a = 21, b = 9, \gamma = 70° 20'$.

11. The sides of a parallelogram are of lengths 185' and 263', and one angle is 39°. Find the length of the longest diagonal.

12. Two forces whose magnitudes are 341 pounds and 264 pounds act simultaneously on an object. If the angle between the directions of the forces is 64°, find the magnitude of the resultant force.

★210. The law of tangents for a triangle

In a triangle, the difference of any two sides, divided by their sum, is equal to the tangent of one half of the difference of the opposite angles divided by the tangent of one half of their sum:

$$\frac{a - b}{a + b} = \frac{\tan \frac{1}{2}(\alpha - \beta)}{\tan \frac{1}{2}(\alpha + \beta)}; \qquad \frac{c - a}{c + a} = \frac{\tan \frac{1}{2}(\gamma - \alpha)}{\tan \frac{1}{2}(\gamma + \alpha)}; \qquad (1)$$

$$\frac{b - c}{b + c} = \frac{\tan \frac{1}{2}(\beta - \gamma)}{\tan \frac{1}{2}(\beta + \gamma)}. \qquad (2)$$

Proof. 1. Let b and c be any two sides and let us prove (2).

2. By the law of sines, $$\frac{b}{c} = \frac{\sin \beta}{\sin \gamma}. \qquad (3)$$

3. Subtract 1 on both sides of (3); also, add 1 on both sides:

$$\frac{b}{c} - 1 = \frac{\sin \beta}{\sin \gamma} - 1; \; or \qquad \frac{b - c}{c} = \frac{\sin \beta - \sin \gamma}{\sin \gamma}. \qquad (4)$$

$$\frac{b}{c} + 1 = \frac{\sin \beta}{\sin \gamma} + 1; \; or \qquad \frac{b + c}{c} = \frac{\sin \beta + \sin \gamma}{\sin \gamma} \qquad (5)$$

4. Divide each side of (4) by the corresponding side of (5); then use (XVIII) and (XIX) from page 240:

$$\frac{b - c}{b + c} = \frac{\sin \beta - \sin \gamma}{\sin \beta + \sin \gamma} = \frac{2 \sin \frac{1}{2}(\beta - \gamma) \cos \frac{1}{2}(\beta + \gamma)}{2 \cos \frac{1}{2}(\beta - \gamma) \sin \frac{1}{2}(\beta + \gamma)}.$$

Hence, $$\frac{b - c}{b + c} = \tan \frac{1}{2}(\beta - \gamma) \cot \frac{1}{2}(\beta + \gamma) = \frac{\tan \frac{1}{2}(\beta - \gamma)}{\tan \frac{1}{2}(\beta + \gamma)}.$$

Note 1. Corresponding to (1) and (2), we obtain equivalent equations by changing the order of the letters. Thus, instead of (2), we find

$$\frac{c-b}{c+b} = \frac{\tan \frac{1}{2}(\gamma - \beta)}{\tan \frac{1}{2}(\gamma + \beta)}. \tag{6}$$

In any application, we use (6) if $c > b$ and (2) if $c < b$, in order to keep *the differences positive* for convenience in the formula employed.

We may solve a problem under Case III by use of the law of tangents.

OUTLINE. *Solution of $\triangle ABC$ with given parts a, b, and γ.*

1. *Compute $\frac{1}{2}(\alpha + \beta) = \frac{1}{2}(180° - \gamma)$.*
2. *Find $\frac{1}{2}(\alpha - \beta)$ by use of the formula of the law of tangents involving a, b, α, β.*
3. *Compute $\alpha = \frac{1}{2}(\alpha + \beta) + \frac{1}{2}(\alpha - \beta)$; $\beta = \frac{1}{2}(\alpha + \beta) - \frac{1}{2}(\alpha - \beta)$.*
4. *Find c from the law of sines.*
5. *Check by a formula of the law of sines not used in solving.*

EXAMPLE 1. Solve $\triangle ABC$ if $\alpha = 78° 48'$, $b = 726$, and $c = 938$.

SOLUTION. We solve by use of the four-place Tables V and VI.

Formulas	Computation
	Data: $\alpha = 78° 48'$, $b = 726$, $c = 938$.
$\frac{1}{2}(\gamma + \beta) = \frac{1}{2}(180° - \alpha)$.	$\frac{1}{2}(\gamma + \beta) = \frac{1}{2}(180° - 78° 48') = 50° 36'$.
$\dfrac{\tan \frac{1}{2}(\gamma - \beta)}{\tan \frac{1}{2}(\gamma + \beta)} = \dfrac{c-b}{c+b}$; or $\tan \frac{1}{2}(\gamma - \beta) = \dfrac{(c - b) \tan \frac{1}{2}(\gamma + \beta)}{c + b}$.	$c - b = 212$; $\quad c + b = 1664$. $\log (c - b) = \quad 2.3263$ $\log \tan \frac{1}{2}(\gamma + \beta) = \quad 0.0855 \ (+)$ $\log$ numerator $= 12.4118 - 10$ $\log (c + b) = \quad 3.2211 \ (-)$ $\log \tan \frac{1}{2}(\gamma - \beta) = \quad 9.1907 - 10$ $\frac{1}{2}(\gamma - \beta) = \quad 8° 49'$. \quad (Table VI)
$\beta = \frac{1}{2}(\gamma + \beta) - \frac{1}{2}(\gamma - \beta)$. $\gamma = \frac{1}{2}(\gamma + \beta) + \frac{1}{2}(\gamma - \beta)$.	$\frac{1}{2}(\gamma + \beta) = 50° 36' \left.\right\}$ Add to get γ. $\frac{1}{2}(\gamma - \beta) = \ 8° 49' \left.\right\}$ Subtract to get β. $\gamma = 59° 25'$; $\quad \beta = 41° 47'$.
$\dfrac{a}{\sin \alpha} = \dfrac{c}{\sin \gamma}$, or $a = \dfrac{c \sin \alpha}{\sin \gamma}$.	$\log c = \quad 2.9722$ $\log \sin \alpha = \quad 9.9916 - 10 \ (+)$ $\log c \sin \alpha = 12.9638 - 10$ $\log \sin \gamma = \quad 9.9350 - 10 \ (-)$ $\log a = \quad 3.0288$; $\quad a = 1069$.
Summary.	$\beta = 41° 47'$, $\quad \gamma = 59° 25'$, $\quad a = 1069$.

Check. $\dfrac{a}{\sin \alpha} = \dfrac{b}{\sin \beta}$.

$\log a = 13.0289 - 10$	$\log b = 12.8609 - 10$
$\log \sin \alpha = \ 9.9916 - 10 \ (-)$	$\log \sin \beta = \ 9.8237 - 10 \ (-)$
$\log (a/\sin \alpha) = \quad 3.0373 \longrightarrow$	$\longleftarrow \log (b/\sin \beta) = \quad 3.0372$; *satisfactory.*

Note 2. Refined checks of solutions of triangles obtained under Cases **I**, **II**, and **III** are provided by formulas of the law of tangents.

ILLUSTRATION 1. In Example 1, we could have checked the solution by computing the logarithms of the two sides of either formula of the law of tangents not used in solving Example 1. For instance, we could have tested by use of the formula at the left in (1).

★*Note 3.* It can be proved that, in any $\triangle ABC$,

$$\frac{a-b}{c} = \frac{\sin \frac{1}{2}(\alpha - \beta)}{\cos \frac{1}{2}\gamma}; \qquad \frac{b-c}{a} = \frac{\sin \frac{1}{2}(\beta - \gamma)}{\cos \frac{1}{2}\alpha}; \ etc.; \qquad (7)$$

$$\frac{a+b}{c} = \frac{\cos \frac{1}{2}(\alpha - \beta)}{\sin \frac{1}{2}\gamma}; \qquad \frac{b+c}{a} = \frac{\cos \frac{1}{2}(\beta - \gamma)}{\sin \frac{1}{2}\alpha}; \ etc. \qquad (8)$$

These results are called **Mollweide's equations,** in recognition of their use by a German astronomer KARL MOLLWEIDE (1774–1825), although the formulas were known before his time. Equations (7) and (8) give sensitive checks on the solution of a triangle because each formula involves all parts of the triangle. The proofs of (7) and (8) are similar to the derivation of the law of tangents.

★EXERCISE 127

1–4. Find the unknown angles in Problems 1–4, respectively, of Exercise 126 on page 382 by use of the law of tangents without logarithms.

Solve $\triangle ABC$ by use of four-place logarithms, and check as directed by the instructor.

5. $b = 387, c = 136, \alpha = 68°.$ **6.** $a = 102, b = 437, \gamma = 43°.$

7. $a = .936, c = .348, \beta = 72°.$ **8.** $b = .657, c = .319, \alpha = 108°.$

9. $a = 13.16, c = 22.78, \beta = 69° 40'.$ **10.** $a = 21.45, b = 9.36, \gamma = 70° 25'.$

11. $a = 773.6, c = 993.4, \beta = 120° 30'.$

★211. Tangents of the half-angles

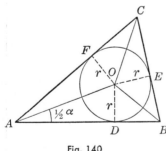

Fig. 140

We recall that the bisectors of the angles of a triangle ABC, as in Figure 140, meet at the center O of the *inscribed circle.* Let r be its radius. Then, in Figure 140,

$$\overline{OD} = \overline{OE} = \overline{OF} = r.$$

Later, we shall obtain a formula for r in terms of sides a, b, c. Let s be one half of the perimeter of triangle ABC:

$$s = \tfrac{1}{2}(a + b + c). \qquad (1)$$

Then, we shall prove the following results:

$$\tan \frac{\alpha}{2} = \frac{r}{s-a}; \quad \tan \frac{\beta}{2} = \frac{r}{s-b}; \quad \tan \frac{\gamma}{2} = \frac{r}{s-c}. \quad (2)$$

Proof. 1. From right $\triangle ADO$ in Figure 140,

$$\tan \frac{\alpha}{2} = \frac{\overline{OD}}{\overline{AD}} = \frac{r}{\overline{AD}}. \quad (3)$$

2. The whole perimeter is

$$2s = (\overline{AD} + \overline{AF}) + (\overline{BE} + \overline{BD}) + (\overline{CE} + \overline{CF}).$$

But, from Figure 140, $\overline{AF} = \overline{AD}; \; \overline{BD} = \overline{BE}; \; \overline{CF} = \overline{CE}.$ Therefore,

$$2s = 2\overline{AD} + 2\overline{BE} + 2\overline{CE}; \; or$$

$$s = \overline{AD} + (\overline{BE} + \overline{CE}).$$

Since $\overline{BE} + \overline{CE} = \overline{BC} = a$, then $s = \overline{AD} + a$, or

$$\overline{AD} = s - a.$$

3. Hence, from (3) we obtain (2) for $\alpha/2$. From symmetry, we obtain the two other formulas in (2).

Note 1. Observe that (2) will not be useful until a formula for r is obtained in the following section, which also gives a second proof for (2).

★212. Sines, cosines, and tangents of the half-angles

Let α be any angle of triangle ABC. Then, without use of the preceding section, we shall show that

$$\sin \frac{\alpha}{2} = \sqrt{\frac{(s-b)(s-c)}{bc}}; \quad \cos \frac{\alpha}{2} = \sqrt{\frac{s(s-a)}{bc}}; \quad \tan \frac{\alpha}{2} = \frac{r}{s-a}. \quad (1)$$

Proof. 1. Since $2s = a + b + c$, then $2s - 2b = a + c - b$. This proves the second equation in (2) below. Each of (3) is proved similarly.

$$a + b + c = 2s; \quad a + c - b = 2(s - b); \quad (2)$$

$$b + c - a = 2(s - a); \quad a + b - c = 2(s - c). \quad (3)$$

2. By the law of cosines, $\quad \cos \alpha = \dfrac{b^2 + c^2 - a^2}{2bc}. \quad (4)$

From XI on page 237, $2 \cos^2 \frac{1}{2}\alpha = 1 + \cos \alpha$. Hence, from (4),

$$2 \cos^2 \frac{\alpha}{2} = 1 + \frac{b^2 + c^2 - a^2}{2bc} - \frac{(b^2 + 2bc + c^2) - a^2}{2bc};$$

$$\cos^2 \frac{\alpha}{2} = \frac{(b+c)^2 - a^2}{4bc} = \frac{(b+c+a)(b+c-a)}{4bc}. \quad (5)$$

On using (2) and (3) in (5), we obtain

$$\cos^2 \frac{\alpha}{2} = \frac{s(s-a)}{bc}, \quad or \quad \cos \frac{\alpha}{2} = \sqrt{\frac{s(s-a)}{bc}}. \quad (6)$$

3. Similarly, since $2 \sin^2 \frac{1}{2}\alpha = 1 - \cos \alpha$, from (4) we derive

$$\sin \frac{\alpha}{2} = \sqrt{\frac{(a - b + c)(a + b - c)}{4bc}} = \sqrt{\frac{(s - b)(s - c)}{bc}}. \tag{7}$$

4. From (6) and (7), $\tan \frac{1}{2}\alpha = \dfrac{\sin \frac{1}{2}\alpha}{\cos \frac{1}{2}\alpha} = \sqrt{\dfrac{(s - b)(s - c)}{s(s - a)}}.$

Multiply numerator and denominator of the radicand by $(s - a)$:

$$\tan \frac{\alpha}{2} = \sqrt{\frac{(s - a)(s - b)(s - c)}{s(s - a)^2}} = \frac{1}{s - a} \sqrt{\frac{(s - a)(s - b)(s - c)}{s}}. \tag{8}$$

If we let $$r = \sqrt{\frac{(s - a)(s - b)(s - c)}{s}}, \tag{9}$$

then $$\tan \frac{\alpha}{2} = \frac{r}{s - a}. \tag{10}$$

In arriving at (10), we made no use of Section 211, and r was introduced in (9) *merely as an abbreviation for a radical.* But, we may now compare equation (10) above with $\tan \frac{1}{2}\alpha$ in (2) in Section 211 on page 385; since the denominators are the *same* in the right-hand members, the numerators must represent the *same quantity.* Hence, we have proved that *the radius r of the inscribed circle of a triangle ABC is given by* (9).

Note 1. By altering the letters in formulas (1) we obtain similar formulas for functions of $\beta/2$ and $\gamma/2$. Thus,

$$\sin \frac{\beta}{2} = \sqrt{\frac{(s - a)(s - c)}{ac}}; \qquad \cos \frac{\gamma}{2} = \sqrt{\frac{s(s - c)}{ab}}.$$

★213. Solution of Case IV by the half-angle formulas

Suppose that all sides of triangle ABC are given. *If just one* of its angles is desired, we may use the preceding formulas for the *sine* or *cosine* of half of the angle, because then it is *unnecessary to find r* or its logarithm. If *all* angles of the triangle are desired, it is best to use tangents of the half-angles, where we proceed as follows.

SUMMARY. *To obtain the angles when the sides are known.*

1. *Compute s, $(s - a)$, $(s - b)$, $(s - c)$, and then log r, by use of*

$$r = \sqrt{\frac{(s - a)(s - b)(s - c)}{s}}.$$

2. *Find α, β, and γ by use of the tangents of the half-angles.*
3. *Check by use of $\alpha + \beta + \gamma = 180°$.*

EXAMPLE 1. Solve $\triangle ABC$ if $a = 173$, $b = 267$, $c = 412$.

SOLUTION. We apply the preceding summary, and use four-place logarithms from Tables V and VI.

Formulas	Computation
$s = \frac{1}{2}(a + b + c)$. To check here, notice that $(s - a) + (s - b) + (s - c)$ $= 3s - (a + b + c) = s$.	$\begin{array}{l}a = 173 \\ b = 267 \\ c = 412\end{array}\Big\}(+)$ $\begin{array}{l}s - a = 253 \\ s - b = 159 \\ s - c = 14\end{array}\Big\}(+)$ $\overline{2s = 852}\longrightarrow$ $\longleftarrow\overline{s = 426}$
$r = \sqrt{\dfrac{(s - a)(s - b)(s - c)}{s}}$; $r^2 = \dfrac{(s - a)(s - b)(s - c)}{s}$. $\log r = \frac{1}{2} \log r^2$.	$\begin{array}{l}\log (s - a) = 2.4031 \\ \log (s - b) = 2.2014 \\ \log (s - c) = 1.1461\end{array}\Big\}(+)$ $\overline{\log \text{ numerator} = 5.7506}$ $\phantom{\log \text{ nume}}\log s = 2.6294 (-)$ $\phantom{\log \text{ num}}\log r^2 = 3.1212; (\div \text{ by } 2)$ $\phantom{\log \text{ nume}}\log r = 1.5606.$
$\tan \dfrac{\alpha}{2} = \dfrac{r}{s - a}$.	$\log r = 11.5606 - 10$ $\log (s - a) = 2.4031 (-)$ $\overline{\log \tan \frac{1}{2}\alpha = 9.1575 - 10};$ $\frac{1}{2}\alpha = 8° 11'; \alpha = 16° 22'.$
Similarly,	$\begin{cases}\frac{1}{2}\beta = 12° 53'; & \beta = 25° 46'; \\ \frac{1}{2}\gamma = 68° 56'; & \gamma = 137° 52'.\end{cases}$
Summary.	$\alpha = 16° 22', \beta = 25° 46', \gamma = 137° 52'.$
Check.	$\alpha + \beta + \gamma = 16° 22' + 25° 46' + 137° 52' = 180° 0';$ *satisfactory.*

★EXERCISE 128

Solve $\triangle ABC$ by use of four-place logarithms.

1. $a = 17, b = 26, c = 25$. **2.** $a = 8, b = 7, c = 11$.

3. $a = 5.26, b = 4.38, c = 9.34$. **4.** $a = .986, b = .726, c = .648$.

5. $a = 136, b = 472, c = 450$. **6.** $a = 4.614, b = 6.213, c = 5.709$.

7. $a = 73.09, b = 91.27, c = 59.86$. **8.** $a = .1931, b = .1137, c = .2625$.

Find the desired angle by use of the sine or cosine of half of the angle.

9. $a = 13, b = 17, c = 9$; find β. **10.** $a = 27, b = 36, c = 42$; find γ.

★214. Heron's formula for the area of a triangle

The great Greek geometer HERON (or HERO) of Alexandria, who lived in the first century A.D., proved the following result for the area, K, of $\triangle ABC$, where $s = \frac{1}{2}(a + b + c)$:

$$K = \sqrt{s(s - a)(s - b)(s - c)}. \tag{1}$$

Proof. 1. From Problem 19 on page 376, $K = \frac{1}{2}bc \sin \alpha$. From (VII) on page 237, we obtain

$$\sin \alpha = 2 \sin \tfrac{1}{2}\alpha \cos \tfrac{1}{2}\alpha, \quad \text{and hence} \quad K = bc \sin \tfrac{1}{2}\alpha \cos \tfrac{1}{2}\alpha. \tag{2}$$

2. By use of (2) and formulas (1) on page 385,

$$K = bc \sqrt{\frac{(s-b)(s-c)}{bc}} \sqrt{\frac{s(s-a)}{bc}} = \sqrt{s(s-a)(s-b)(s-c)}.$$

★215. Summary for logarithmic solution of triangles

I. Given two angles and a side.	Solve by law of sines and check by law of tangents.
II. Given two sides and an opposite angle.	Solve by law of sines, with particular attention to the number of solutions. Check by law of tangents.*
III. Given two sides and the included angle.	1. Find the angles by law of tangents and the third side by law of sines. Check by law of sines or law of tangents.* 2. If **only** the third side is desired, perhaps use law of cosines (not adapted to logarithms).
IV. Given three sides.	1. Solve by half-angle formulas and check by $\alpha + \beta + \gamma = 180°$. 2. Solve by law of cosines (not adapted to logarithms) and check by $\alpha + \beta + \gamma = 180°$.

★MISCELLANEOUS REVIEW EXERCISE 129

Solve $\triangle ABC$ completely except where only one part is requested.
Solve by use of Tables I and VII without logarithms.

1. $b = 20$, $\beta = 30°$, $\gamma = 57°$; find only a.
2. $a = 3$, $b = 5$, $c = 7$; find only β.
3. $a = 4$, $b = 5$, $c = 8$; find only γ.
4. $a = 20$, $\alpha = 30°$, $\gamma = 42° 7'$.   5. $b = 81$, $c = 50$, $\beta = 164° 20'$.
6. $c = 910$, $\gamma = 65° 30'$, $\beta = 100°$.   7. $c = 40$, $\beta = 90°$, $\gamma = 26° 12'$.
8. $a = 50$, $b = 38$, $\beta = 22° 20'$.   9. $a = 76$, $c = 20$, $\alpha = 157° 40'$.
10. $b = 10$, $c = 5$, $\alpha = 74° 20'$; find only a (law of cosines).
11. $a = 12$, $c = 5$, $\beta = 114° 50'$; find only b (law of cosines).

Solve $\triangle ABC$ by use of four-place logarithms, or other tables as desired.

12. $b = 1573$, $c = 6132$, $\beta = 82° 14'$.   13. $a = 2395$, $c = 4647$, $\alpha = 25° 17'$.
14. $a = 863$, $c = 457$, $\gamma = 121° 53'$.   15. $a = 395.6$, $b = 524.7$, $\beta = 73° 6'$.
16. $a = 13.17$, $\alpha = 26° 33'$, $\gamma = 82° 58'$.
17. $a = 31$, $b = 57$, $c = 40$.   18. $b = 22$, $c = 42$, $\alpha = 105°$.

Find the magnitude and direction of the resultant of the given forces which are acting together on an object.

19. 585 pounds directed $N 26° 25' E$; 243 pounds directed $N 78° 47' W$.
20. 41.7 pounds directed $S 17° 5' E$; 39.4 pounds directed $N 21° 14' E$.

* Or, Mollweide's equations; or, formulas like $c = a \cos \beta + b \cos \alpha$.

21. One force of 8 pounds is directed due east. The magnitude of a second force is 12 pounds, and the magnitude of the resultant of these two forces is 15 pounds. Find the direction of the second force if it acts somewhat east of north, and find the direction of the resultant.

22. A telegraph pole, which leans 15° 10′ from the vertical toward the sun, casts a shadow 39.8 feet long when the angle of elevation of the sun is 63° 40′. Find the length of the pole.

23. Along one bank of a river, a surveyor measures

$$AB = 183.5 \text{ feet}, \quad \angle BAC = 67° 45′, \quad and \quad \angle ABC = 43° 26′,$$

where C is a point on the opposite bank. Find the width of the river.

24. A ship is sailing N 23° 25′ W. From A on the ship's track, the navigator sights a point of land P with the bearing N 33° 40′ E. After sailing 2.85 miles farther to a point B, the bearing of P is N 42° 30′ E. Find the distance to P when it is nearest to the ship. (This is said to be the distance at which P is **passed abeam**.)

25. A surveyor runs a line $AB = 1326$ feet in the direction N 37° 28′ E, then $BC = 1184$ feet in a southerly direction, and then $CA = 1016$ feet, back to his starting point. As a check, he measures the direction of CA. Find this direction.

26. A surveyor desires to prolong an east-west line AB due east past an obstruction. He measures $BC = 785.4$ feet, S 23° 17′ E, and then he runs CD in the direction N 47° 53′ E. Find $\overline{CD}$ if D is to be due east of B.

27. In the figure, find the distance between the inaccessible points C and D, on one side of the river, if a surveyor on the other side measures

$AB = 157.8$ feet; $\delta = 32° 26′$;
$\theta = 27° 45′$; $\beta = 40° 29′$;
     $\gamma = 35° 18′$.

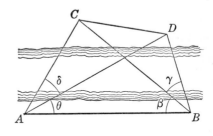

28. A ship heads in the direction with azimuth 141° 35′ at a water-speed of 36 knots; a current is flowing in the direction with azimuth 73° 40′ at a speed of 4 knots. Find the course of the ship and its ground-speed.

29. Prove that the area of any parallelogram is equal to the product of the lengths of a pair of adjacent sides times the sine of their included angle.

30. Prove that the area of any convex quadrilateral is equal to one half of the product of the lengths of its diagonals times the sine of either angle formed by the diagonals.

31. Let R represent the radius of the circumscribed circle for a triangle ABC, whose area is K. Prove that

$$2R = \frac{a}{\sin \alpha} = \frac{b}{\sin \beta} = \frac{c}{\sin \gamma}; \quad R = \frac{abc}{4\sqrt{s(s-a)(s-b)(s-c)}}, \quad or \quad K = \frac{abc}{4R}.$$

Appendix

NOTE 1. THE IRRATIONALITY OF $\sqrt{2}$

If there exists a rational number which is a square root of 2, then there exist two positive integers m and n, such that

$$\sqrt{2} = \frac{m}{n}, \tag{1}$$

where m/n is a fraction in lowest terms. In other words, if $\sqrt{2}$ is rational, there exist two integers m and n, **without a common factor which is an integer, not 1,** such that (1) is true. Let us show that this assumption leads to a contradiction.

1. Square both sides of (1): $\qquad 2 = \frac{m^2}{n^2}; \quad or \quad 2n^2 = m^2. \tag{2}$

We see that 2 is a factor of the left-hand member of $2n^2 = m^2$; hence 2 is a factor of the right-hand member. Therefore 2 is a factor of m because otherwise 2 is not a factor of m^2. Or, $m = 2k$, where k is some positive integer.

2. Place $m = 2k$ in (2): $\qquad 2n^2 = (2k)^2 = 4k^2; \quad or \quad n^2 = 2k^2. \tag{3}$

Consider $n^2 = 2k^2$; since 2 is a factor of the right-hand member, then 2 is a factor of n.

3. We have shown in Steps 1 and 2 that m and n have 2 as a factor. This contradicts our assumption that m and n have no common factor except 1. Hence, the assumed equation (1) has led us to a contradiction, and it follows that (1) itself must be false. Therefore no rational number exists which is a square root of 2, or $\sqrt{2}$ *is an irrational number.*

Comment. We verify that $(1.4)^2 = 1.96$; $(1.41)^2 = 1.9881$; $(1.414)^2 = 1.999396$; $(1.4142)^2 = 1.99996164$; etc. On considering the sequence

$$1.4, \quad 1.41, \quad 1.414, \quad 1.4142, \quad 1.41421, \quad \cdots, \tag{4}$$

we see that the square of each number in (4) is less than 2 but that, on proceeding to the right in (4), the squares of the numbers approach 2 as a limit. Each number in (4) is a rational number, a decimal fraction; we refer to these numbers as the successive decimal approximations to $\sqrt{2}$.

NOTE 2. INTRODUCTION TO TRIGONOMETRIC FUNCTIONS OF NUMBERS WITHOUT PRELIMINARY USE OF ANGLES

We propose to define outright the trigonometric functions of numbers, without any mention of angles. Then, later, we shall show how the geometric trigonometric functions of angles can be introduced as a second-stage event.

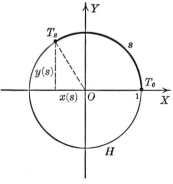

Fig. 141

In Figure 141, a circle H of radius 1 with center at the origin is drawn in an xy-plane where a single unit is used for measuring all distances, and where this unit is the unit for length on the scales for both axes. We assume that the notion of *length of arc* is well defined for arcs on the circle. Let s be any real number. To each value of s, we make correspond a point T_s on the circle, in Figure 141, as follows:

If $s = 0$, T_0 is the point with coordinates $(1, 0)$.

If $s > 0$, T_s is on H and such that arc T_0T_s, measured **counterclockwise,** *has length s.*

If $s < 0$, T_s is on H and such that arc T_0T_s, measured **clockwise,** *has length $|s|$.*

ILLUSTRATION 1. The circumference of H has length 2π, since the radius is 1. Hence, if $s = \frac{1}{2}\pi$, then T_s is the point $(0, 1)$. If $s = -\frac{3}{4}\pi$, then T_s is in quadrant III, and is located so that the line OT_s bisects the 90° angle between the axes in quadrant III; hence T_s has the coordinates $(-\frac{1}{2}\sqrt{2}, -\frac{1}{2}\sqrt{2})$.

We shall call T_s the **trigonometric point** corresponding to the number s. Let the coordinates of T_s for any value of s be denoted by $(x(s), y(s))$; thus, we introduce two *functions* x and y of the variable s, whose range (the *domain* of the functions) is *all real numbers*. Then, we define the six functions sine, cosine, tangent, cotangent, secant, and cosecant by specifying that their values for any number s in their domain are as follows (except where zero denominators cause some functions to be undefined):

$$\sin s = y(s); \quad \cos s = x(s); \quad \tan s = \frac{y(s)}{x(s)};$$
$$\csc s = \frac{1}{y(s)}; \quad \sec s = \frac{1}{x(s)}; \quad \cot s = \frac{x(s)}{y(s)}. \tag{1}$$

The functions defined by (1) are called the **standard trigonometric functions of numbers.** We note that *no mention of angles* has occurred in reaching (1). On this basis, we could proceed to develop all of analytic trigonometry, again with no necessity for mentioning angles. Thus, from (1) and Figure 141, we could obtain $\sin^2 s + \cos^2 s = 1$, and all other familiar identities.

In Figure 141, construct the broken-line segment OT_s. Since the radius of the circle is 1, we verify that s is the radian measure of the directed angle with initial side OT_0 and rotation counterclockwise or clockwise from OT_0 to the terminal side OT_s according as $s > 0$ or $s < 0$. Now, let the real number s be interpreted in (1) as a symbol for the angle with measure s radians. Then, we could refer to the functions defined by (1) as **geometrical trigonometric functions,** whose domain consists of all angles s. It can be verified that, as now interpreted, there is only a nonessential difference between (1) and the definitions on page 140.

NOTE 3. SUPPLEMENTARY TOPICS IN ANALYTIC GEOMETRY

1. Center-radius form for the equation of a circle

Suppose that a locus in an xy-plane is defined geometrically. Then, to obtain an equation for the locus, we attempt to proceed as follows in translating the geometrical statement into algebraic form.

Let $P{:}(x, y)$ represent any point on the locus; construct a figure showing P in a nonspecialized position.

Apply the geometrical definition to obtain an equation satisfied by the coordinates of P if and only if P is on the locus.

In this section, we shall employ an xy-plane in which a *single unit* is used for the scales on the coordinate axes and for measuring distance in all directions. Then the distance formula (1) of page 61 applies. Let T be the circle with center (h, k) and radius r, in Figure 142. If $P{:}(x, y)$ is any point in the plane, from (1) on page 61 we obtain

$$| CP | = \sqrt{(x - h)^2 + (y - k)^2}.$$

If $| CP | = r$, or $(CP)^2 = r^2$, then P *is on T.* If $(CP)^2 \neq r^2$, P *is not on T.* Hence, we obtain the equation of T by writing $(CP)^2 = r^2$, or

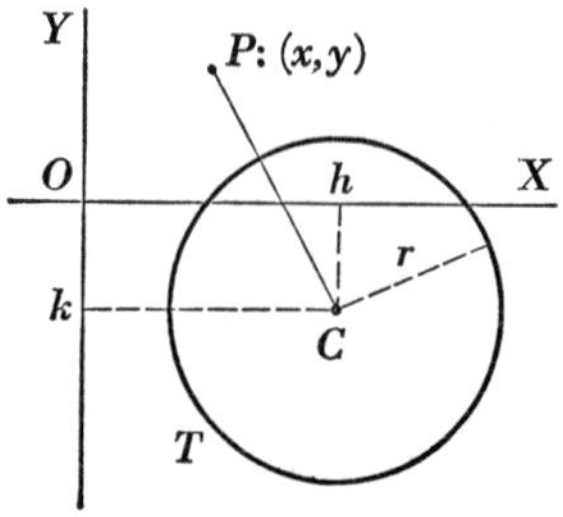

Fig. 142

$$(x - h)^2 + (y - k)^2 = r^2. \tag{1}$$

We shall call (1) the *center-radius* form for the equation of a circle. If the center is $(0, 0)$, then (1) becomes

$$x^2 + y^2 = r^2. \tag{2}$$

ILLUSTRATION 1. The equation of the circle with center $(2, -3)$ and radius 5 is $(x - 2)^2 + (y + 3)^2 = 25$.

In (1) or (2), we permit $r = 0$. Such a circle is just a point, a *point-circle*. If $r = 0$ in (1), the only solution is $(x = h,\ y = k)$.

ILLUSTRATION 2. The equation

$$(x - 1)^2 + (y - 3)^2 = -25$$

has *no graph*, because the left-hand side is *positive* or *zero* for all values of x, y, while the right-hand side is *negative*. Such an equation may be called an **imaginary circle**, where the word *imaginary* reminds us that the equation $r^2 = -25$ would lead to imaginary values for r.

When we expand the center-radius form (1), we obtain

$$x^2 + y^2 - 2hx - 2ky + (h^2 + k^2 - r^2) = 0. \tag{3}$$

In (3), let

$$D = -2h; \quad E = -2k; \quad F = h^2 + k^2 - r^2.$$

Then, from (3) we obtain

$$x^2 + y^2 + Dx + Ey + F = 0. \tag{4}$$

Thus, every circle has an equation of type (4). Conversely, for any values of D, E, and F, (4) can be changed to the center-radius form and therefore represents a circle, real or imaginary. We call (4) the **general form** for the equation of a circle.

SUMMARY. *To obtain the center and radius of a circle whose equation is given in the general form:*

Group the terms in x and, separately, those in y, and complete a square in each set of terms. Then, rewrite the equation in the center-radius form.

Note 1. To make $(x^2 + cx)$ a perfect square, we add $(\tfrac{1}{2}c)^2$ or $c^2/4$.

EXAMPLE 1. Obtain the center and radius of

$$x^2 + y^2 - 4x + 6y - 12 = 0. \tag{5}$$

SOLUTION. 1. Add 4 and 9 to complete squares:

$$(x^2 - 4x + 4) + (y^2 + 6y + 9) = 12 + 4 + 9 = 25;\ or$$

$$(x - 2)^2 + (y + 3)^2 = 5^2. \tag{6}$$

2. From (6), the center is $(2, -3)$ and the radius is 5.

If $a \neq 0$, any equation of the form

$$ax^2 + ay^2 + bx + cy + d = 0 \tag{7}$$

can be changed to the general form (4) by dividing both sides in (7) by a. Hence, we reach the following conclusion.

Any equation of the second degree in x and y of the form (7), where the coefficients of x^2 and y^2 are equal and there is no term involving xy, represents a circle, real or imaginary, when the graph is drawn on an xy-plane where the units on the axes are equal.

ILLUSTRATION 3. To obtain the center and radius of

$$8x^2 + 8y^2 + 12x - 20y - 1 = 0, \tag{8}$$

divide both sides by 8 and change to the center-radius form:

$$x^2 + \tfrac{3}{2}x + y^2 - \tfrac{5}{2}y = \tfrac{1}{8}, \text{ or}$$

$$(x + \tfrac{3}{4})^2 + (y - \tfrac{5}{4})^2 = \tfrac{9}{4}.$$

Hence, (8) is a circle with center $(-\tfrac{3}{4}, \tfrac{5}{4})$ and radius $\tfrac{3}{2}$.

EXERCISE 130

Write the equation of the circle with center C and radius r.

1. $C:(3, 4)$; $r = 2$.   **2.** $C:(-2, 5)$; $r = 3$.   **3.** $C:(3, -2)$; $r = 4$.
4. $C:(-2, -4)$; $r = 3$.   **5.** $C:(0, 0)$; $r = 4$.   **6.** $C:(0, 3)$; $r = 3$.
7. $C:(-2, 0)$; $r = 2$.   **8.** $C:(a, 0)$; $r = a$.   **9.** $C:(0, b)$; $r = b$.

If the graph is a real circle, find its center and radius.

10. $x^2 + 2x + y^2 - 4y = 4$.   **11.** $x^2 - 6x + y^2 - 4y = 3$.
12. $x^2 + y^2 + 4x + 2y = -1$.   **13.** $x^2 + y^2 + 6x + 3 = 4y$.
14. $x^2 + y^2 + 8y + 19 = 0$.   **15.** $x^2 + y^2 - 6x - 11 = 0$.
16. $x^2 + y^2 + 6x + 9 = 4y$.   **17.** $x^2 + y^2 + 6x + 13 = 4y$.
18. $x^2 + y^2 + 5x + \tfrac{9}{4} = 6y$.   **19.** $x^2 + y^2 + 3y + 3 = x$.
20. $4x^2 - 4x + 4y^2 + 12y - 15 = 0$.

2. Symmetry, and ranges for the variables

Two points P and Q are said to be symmetric *with respect to a line l* if l is the perpendicular bisector of the segment PQ, as in Figure 143.

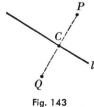

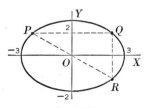

Fig. 143   Fig. 144

DEFINITION I.   *A curve D is symmetric with respect to a line l as an* **axis of** **symmetry** *in case, for each point P on D, there is a point Q on D which is symmetric to P with respect to l.*

ILLUSTRATION 1.   A circle is symmetric with respect to any diameter. The **ellipse** in Figure 144 has OX and OY as axes of symmetry; P and Q are symmetric with respect to OY, and Q and R are symmetric to OX.

Two points P and Q are symmetric *with respect to a point C* in case C is the mid-point of the segment PQ, as in Figure 143.

DEFINITION II.   *A curve D is symmetric with respect to a point C, called a* **center of symmetry,** *in case, for each point P on D, there is a point Q on D which is symmetric to P with respect to C.*

ILLUSTRATION 2.   From Definition II, for the curve D, every chord PQ through C is bisected by C.   In Figure 144 on page 394, the origin is a center of symmetry; for instance, we see that P and R are symmetric with respect to the origin.

ILLUSTRATION 3.   The following facts are exhibited in Figure 145.

I.   *(x, y) and $(x, -y)$ are symmetric with respect to the x-axis.*

II.   *(x, y) and $(-x, y)$ are symmetric with respect to the y-axis.*

III.   *(x, y) and $(-x, -y)$ are symmetric with respect to the origin.*

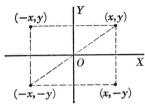

Fig. 145

As a rule, a reference to *symmetry* will mean symmetry of the *preceding types.*   Each of the following tests involves showing that, if a point (x, y) satisfies the equation, the specified symmetric point also satisfies it.

SUMMARY.   *The graph of $f(x, y) = 0$ has the indicated symmetry if and only if an equivalent equation is obtained by the specified change.*

1.   **Symmetry to x-axis:** *replace y by $-y$.*

2.   **Symmetry to y-axis:** *replace x by $-x$.*

3.   **Symmetry to the origin:** *replace x by $-x$ and y by $-y$.*

ILLUSTRATION 4.   To test $xy = 8$ for symmetry, we replace x by $-x$ and obtain $-xy = 8$, *not equivalent to* $xy = 8$.   Hence, its graph is *not* symmetric to OY and, similarly, is *not* symmetric to OX.   But, if we replace x by $-x$ and y by $-y$, we obtain $(-x)(-y) = 8$ or $xy = 8$, which is the original equation.   Hence, if (x, y) is on its graph, the symmetric point $(-x, -y)$ also is on the graph, and it is symmetric to the origin. The graph of $xy = 8$ is in Figure 146 and is called a **hyperbola.**

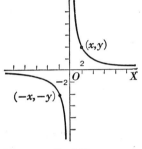

Fig. 146

In graphing an equation $f(x, y) = 0$, we exclude any value of x or y for which the other variable is *imaginary* or *undefined.*   To determine excluded values, we inspect $f(x, y)$ itself, and also any expression obtained in solving $f(x, y) = 0$ for x or for y, if this operation is convenient. After such exclusions, the remaining values for x, or y, are the *range* for the variable. If no real values (x, y) satisfy the equation, its locus is said to be *imaginary*.

EXAMPLE 1.   Graph the equation $4x^2 + 9y^2 = 36.$ (1)

SOLUTION.   1. *Symmetry.*   Since $(- x)^2 = x^2$ and $(- y)^2 = y^2$, we see that equation (1) is unaltered if we replace x by $- x$, or y by $- y$, or both x by $- x$ and y by $- y$. Hence, the graph is symmetric to OX, OY, and the origin.

2. *Ranges.*   On solving (1) for x and for y, we find

$$x = \pm \tfrac{3}{2}\sqrt{4 - y^2} \quad and \quad y = \pm \tfrac{2}{3}\sqrt{9 - x^2}.$$ (2)

From (2), x is imaginary if $|y| > 2$; for instance, if $y = 3$ we have $x = \pm \tfrac{3}{2}\sqrt{- 5}$. Thus, the range for y is $|y| \leq 2$, and for x is $|x| \leq 3$. We obtain points on the graph and construct it as in Example 1 on page 103. The graph is an ellipse.

In Example 1, we illustrated the fact that the graph of an equation in x and y is symmetric to OX if y is involved just with *even exponents*. Also, if the graph is symmetric to *both* OX and OY, then the graph also has the origin as a center of symmetry. The converse of the last statement is not true, as seen in Figure 146, where the origin is a center of symmetry but neither OX nor OY is an axis of symmetry.

Note 1.   If b is a constant, the set of all values $x > b$ is called an *infinite interval* of the number scale, and sometimes is represented by "$b < x < + \infty$," which can be read "b *is less than* x *is less than plus infinity*." This use of the word "*infinity*" and the symbol for infinity, "∞," should be interpreted merely as a substitute for the original description "*all* $x > b$." Similar remarks apply to the infinite intervals $b \leq x < + \infty$, or $- \infty < x < b$, or $- \infty < x \leq b$. The set of *all real values of* x is called an infinite interval, "$- \infty < x < + \infty$." The *range* of a variable is said to be *infinite* if its range includes an infinite interval.

A set of points is said to have *infinite extent*, or *to extend to infinity*, if the distance from the origin to a point $P{:}(x, y)$ of the set can be made to exceed any value, however large, by properly selecting P. A variable point $P{:}(x, y)$ is said *to recede to infinity* on a curve if the distance from the origin to P grows large without bound as x, or y, or perhaps both variables grow large without bound.

A line l is called an **asymptote** of a curve if the shortest distance between l and a point P on the curve approaches zero if P recedes to infinity on some branch of the curve.

ILLUSTRATION 5.   Each of the coordinate axes is an asymptote for the hyperbola in Illustration 4.

3. Sections of a cone

At the center of a circle T, erect a line m perpendicular to the plane in which T lies. Select any point V on m, not in the plane of T, as in Figure 147. From any point Q on T, draw a line l through V. Then, the locus of all points swept out by l, as Q moves around T, is a surface of infinite extent called a *right circular cone*, whose *vertex* is V and *axis* is m. Each position of l is called a *ruling* of the cone. V divides the cone into two *nappes;* in Figure 148, each nappe is cut by a plane perpendicular to the cone's axis.

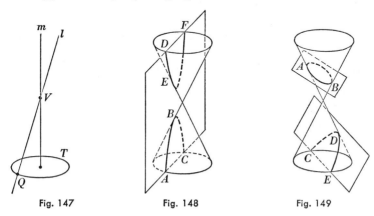

Fig. 147   Fig. 148   Fig. 149

If a plane cuts the cone, the curve of intersection is called a **conic section,** or simply a *conic*. First, suppose that the plane does not pass through V. Then, if the plane cuts just one nappe and is not parallel to a ruling (Figure 149), the conic section AB is called an **ellipse;** the ellipse is a *circle* if the plane is perpendicular to the axis of the cone. If the plane cuts just one nappe and is parallel to a ruling (Figure 149), the conic CDE is called a **parabola,** which has infinite extent. If the plane cuts both nappes (Figure 148), the conic, ABC and DEF, is called a **hyperbola,** which has a separate piece or *branch* of infinite extent on each nappe.

If a cone is cut by a plane through V, the only point of intersection may be V, so that the conic section is *just this point.* Or, the plane may touch the cone merely along one ruling, in which case the conic is *just this line*, thought of as a *double line.* Or, the plane may cut the cone along two rulings, so that the conic consists of these *two lines* intersecting at V. Such sections through V are called **degenerate conics.** We may think of a conic which is a single point as a limiting case of an ellipse or circle as the cutting plane approaches V. A conic which is two intersecting lines may be considered as a limiting case of a hyperbola as a variable plane cutting both nappes approaches the vertex V. We agree, also, to call two parallel lines a *degenerate conic*, and to consider it as a limiting case of a parabola, even though we cannot obtain two parallel lines as a plane section of a cone.

4. Standard equations for a parabola

In this section and in Sections 5 and 6, we shall deal with loci in a Euclidean plane. Hence, in this plane, we have a unit for length which applies in measuring distance in any direction.*

For our present purposes, if we refer to a conic section, we shall mean only an ellipse, a hyperbola, or a parabola (and thus shall not be considering the degenerate conics). We have just defined these curves as plane sections of a cone. We proceed to define them anew by means of characteristic properties.

DEFINITION III. *A parabola is the locus of a point P whose undirected distance from a fixed point F, called the* **focus,** *is equal to the undirected distance of P from a fixed line D, called the* **directrix,** *which does not go through F.*

Derivation of a standard equation for a parabola. 1. Refer to Figure 150. Let p be the distance from the directrix D to the focus F, where $p > 0$. Designate the x-axis, OX, as the line through F perpendicular to D, with the origin midway between F and D, and F on the positive half of OX. On both OX and OY, let the unit for the coordinate scales be the unit distance specified in the plane. Then, the distance formula (1) of page 61 applies. The focus F is the point $(\frac{1}{2}p, 0)$ and D is the line $x = -\frac{1}{2}p$.

2. Let $P{:}(x, y)$ be any point on the parabola, and let the undirected distance of P from F be h, and from D be d. In Figure 150, M is the point $(-\frac{1}{2}p, y)$. Hence, from (4) on page 59, $MP = x - (-\frac{1}{2}p)$; from (1) on page 61,

$$h = PF = \sqrt{\left(x - \frac{p}{2}\right)^2 + y^2};$$

$$d = |\,MP\,| = \left| x + \frac{p}{2} \right|. \tag{1}$$

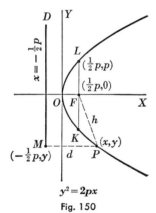

$y^2 = 2px$

Fig. 150

3. The equation of the parabola is $h = d$, which is equivalent to

$$h^2 = d^2 \quad or \quad \left(x - \frac{p}{2}\right)^2 + y^2 = \left(x + \frac{p}{2}\right)^2.$$

On expanding and simplifying, we obtain

$$y^2 = 2px, \tag{2}$$

whose graph is shown in Figure 150.

4. The graph of (2) is symmetric to OX because y occurs only with an even exponent. Thus, the perpendicular to the directrix through the focus is an axis of symmetry for (2), and is called the **axis** of the parabola. The intersection of this axis and the parabola is called the **vertex** of the parabola. The

---

* In such a plane, we are at liberty to use a system of rectangular co-ordinates with arbitrary units, not necessarily equal, for the scales on the coordinate axes.

chord of the parabola through the focus perpendicular to the axis is called the **focal chord,** sometimes called the **latus rectum** of the parabola. Hereafter, the focus, focal chord, and directrix will not be important for our purposes. Our essential information for graphing (2) is as follows:

$$y^2 = 2px, \quad p > 0: \quad [axis, y = 0; \quad vertex, (0, 0); \quad concave\ to\ right.] \quad (3)$$

ILLUSTRATION 1. To graph $y^2 = 12x$, observe that the vertex is $(0, 0)$, the axis is the line $y = 0$, and the curve is concave to the right. To obtain two useful points on the graph, let $x = 3$; then $y = \pm 6$, giving $(3, \pm 6)$ on the graph. These data would be sufficient for construction of a roughly accurate graph, which would look like the parabola in Figure 150.

Similarly, we may obtain the following additional equations for a parabola having p as the distance between the focus F and directrix D, with the indicated locations. We refer to (2), (4), (5), and (6) as **standard forms** for a parabola with its *vertex at the origin* and *axis along a coordinate axis.*

(axis, y = 0; concave to left)	$y^2 = -2px.$	(4)
(axis, x = 0; concave upward)	$x^2 = 2py.$	(5)
(axis, x = 0; concave downward)	$x^2 = -2py.$	(6)

The corresponding locations of the parabola, in Figures 151, 152, and 153, are called *standard positions* for the parabola.

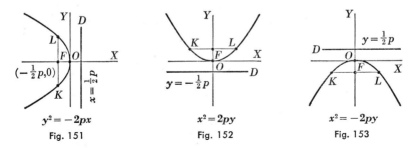

$y^2 = -2px$	$x^2 = 2py$	$x^2 = -2py$
Fig. 151	Fig. 152	Fig. 153

ILLUSTRATION 2. To change $3x^2 = -7y$ to a standard form, divide by 3 to obtain $x^2 = -\frac{7}{3}y$. The graph of the equation is a parabola whose vertex is $(0, 0)$ and axis is the line $x = 0$; the parabola is concave downward, as in Figure 153.

Note 1. Suppose that* the units on the scales for the coordinate axes are equal, and that this unit is taken as the unit for distance in any direction in the xy-plane. Then, we have seen that, if $A \neq 0$ and $E \neq 0$, the graph of $Ax^2 = Ey$ is a parabola whose vertex is $(0, 0)$ and axis is the line $x = 0$; the graph of $Ay^2 = Ex$ is a parabola whose vertex is $(0, 0)$ and axis is the line $y = 0$. The preceding facts are true because either equation can be changed to a standard form, as just considered, on dividing by A.

* This restriction will be removed later. It will apply in the next exercise.

EXERCISE 131

Without using a standard form, obtain the equation of the parabola by the locus method used in deriving (2) *on page* 398.

1. Focus $(4, 0)$; directrix is the line $x = -4$.

2. Focus $(0, -3)$; directrix is the line $y = 3$.

3. Focus $(-2, 0)$; directrix is the line $x = 6$.

Find the vertex and the equation of the axis of the parabola. Graph the equation by use of the vertex and two other points. Show the focus and the directrix.

4. $y^2 = 8x$.   **5.** $y^2 = -8x$.   **6.** $x^2 = 8y$.   **7.** $x^2 = -8y$.

8. $y^2 = -6x$.   **9.** $x^2 = 4y$.   **10.** $x^2 = -6y$.   **11.** $y^2 = 2x$.

12. $2x^2 - 9y = 0$.   **13.** $3y^2 + 10x = 0$.   **14.** $y^2 + x = 0$.

15. $x^2 + y = 0$.   **16.** $4x^2 + y = 0$.   **17.** $2y^2 - 7x = 0$.

By use of a standard form, find the equation of the parabola in a standard position satisfying the given data. Plot the curve.

18. $F:(3, 0)$.   **19.** $F:(-2, 0)$.   **20.** $F:(0, -5)$.   **21.** $F:(0, 4)$.

22. $D:[x = -2]$.   **23.** $D:[y = -3]$.   **24.** $D:[y = 2]$.   **25.** $D:[x = 1]$.

26. Concave to the right and passing through $(\frac{2}{3}, -2)$.

5. Ellipse defined by means of focal radii

DEFINITION IV.   *An ellipse is the locus of a point for which the sum of the undirected distances to two fixed points* * *F and F', called the* **foci**, *is a constant greater than the distance between F and F'.*

Note 1. In the definitions of a parabola and an ellipse, we have introduced points called *foci*. Likewise, we shall define a hyperbola by use of foci. If a point P is on any conic, let the undirected distance from a focus to P be called a **focal radius** of P.

Derivation of a standard equation for an ellipse. 1. Let the distance between the foci F and F' be $2c$. Designate the x-axis, OX, as the line through F and F', with the origin, O, at the midpoint of $F'F$, and F on the positive half of OX. On both OX and OY, let the unit for the coordinate scale be the assigned unit for distance in the given plane.† Then, the distance formula (1) of page 61 applies. The foci are $(\pm c, 0)$. Let the constant referred to in Definition IV be $2a$, where $a > c$.

2. If $P:(x, y)$ is any point, let h and h' be the lengths of PF and PF', as in Figure 154 on page 401. P is on the ellipse if and only if $h + h' = 2a$, or an equation for the ellipse is

$$\sqrt{(x - c)^2 + y^2} + \sqrt{(x + c)^2 + y^2} = 2a, \text{ or} \tag{1}$$

$$\sqrt{(x + c)^2 + y^2} = 2a - \sqrt{(x - c)^2 + y^2}. \tag{2}$$

* *We allow for the possibility that F and F' coincide.*
† This agreement holds throughout this section and the next exercise.

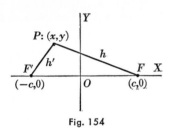

Fig. 154

Square both sides in (2) and simplify:

$$cx - a^2 = -a\sqrt{(x-c)^2 + y^2}. \qquad (3)$$

Square both sides in (3) and simplify:

$$(a^2 - c^2)x^2 + a^2y^2 = a^2(a^2 - c^2). \qquad (4)$$

3. Define a positive number $b \leqq a$ by

$$b^2 = a^2 - c^2. \qquad (5)$$

Then, (4) becomes $b^2x^2 + a^2y^2 = a^2b^2$, or

$[foci\ (\pm c,\ 0),\ c^2 = a^2 - b^2]$ $\qquad \dfrac{x^2}{a^2} + \dfrac{y^2}{b^2} = 1, \qquad (6)$

whose graph is in Figure 155.

4. *Discussion of* (6). The graph of (6) is symmetric to both OX and to OY, and hence also is symmetric to the origin, as a *center of symmetry*, because x and y occur in (6) only with *even* exponents. We say then that an ellipse has a **center,** the origin in Figure 155. The x-intercepts are $\pm a$ and the y-intercepts are $\pm b$. From (6),

$$y = \pm \frac{b}{a}\sqrt{a^2 - x^2} \quad and \quad x = \pm \frac{a}{b}\sqrt{b^2 - y^2}. \qquad (7)$$

Hence, to make y real, the range for x is $|x| \leqq a$; for y, the range is $|y| \leqq b$. Since $b \leqq a$, in Figure 155 we call the segment $V'V$, and also its length, the **major axis,** and call $W'W$, and also its length, the **minor axis** of the ellipse; the *semi-major axis* is a and the *semi-minor axis* is b. We call V' and V the **vertices** of the ellipse.

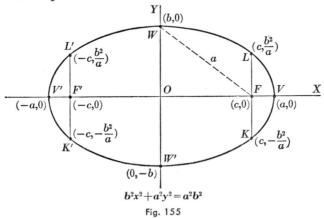

$$b^2x^2 + a^2y^2 = a^2b^2$$

Fig. 155

Each of the chords KL and $K'L'$ through the foci perpendicular to the major axis is called a **latus rectum,** or **focal chord** of the ellipse. In any particular case of (6), we may substitute $x = \pm c$ to find the y-coordinates of the end points of the focal chords in the rare instances when they are of interest to us. It can be verified that, when $x = c$, we have $y = \pm\, b^2/a$, as in Figure 155.

Similarly, with the roles of x and y in (6) interchanged, we obtain

$$[foci\ (0,\ \pm\ c),\ c^2 = a^2 - b^2] \qquad\qquad \frac{y^2}{a^2} + \frac{x^2}{b^2} = 1 \qquad\qquad (8)$$

as the equation of an ellipse with its foci and major axis on the y-axis, as seen in Figure 156.

★*Note 2.* Recall that (1) is equivalent to $h + h' = 2a$. In rationalizing (1), we obtained (4). Recognize that (4) is satisfied by all points (x, y) which are solutions of *any one of the four equations* abbreviated by $\pm\, h \pm h' = 2a$, because the distinction between these equations is lost on rationalizing. With h and h' understood to be *positive*, from Figure 154 on page 401 notice that h, h', and $2c$ are the lengths of the sides of a triangle. From this fact, we verify that no point (x, y) satisfies

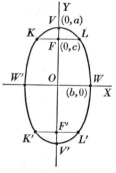

Fig. 156

$$-h + h' = 2a, \quad h - h' = 2a, \quad or \quad -h - h' = 2a.$$

Hence, the only solutions of (4) are those pairs (x, y) which also satisfy $h + h' = 2a$, or (1) and (4) are equivalent equations.

EXAMPLE 1. Obtain the graph of

$$25x^2 + 9y^2 = 225. \qquad\qquad (9)$$

SOLUTION. 1. Change to a standard form by dividing by 225:

$$\frac{x^2}{9} + \frac{y^2}{25} = 1. \qquad\qquad (10)$$

Since $25 > 9$, the foci are on OY, as in (8); $a^2 = 25$; $b^2 = 9$. The vertices are $(0, \pm 5)$; the ends of the minor axis are $(\pm 3, 0)$.

2. From (8), $c^2 = 25 - 9 = 16$; the foci are $(0, \pm 4)$. If $y = \pm 4$, from (10) we find $x = \pm \frac{9}{5}$. Hence, the ends of the two focal chords are $(\pm \frac{9}{5}, 4)$ and $(\pm \frac{9}{5}, -4)$. A good graph of (10) is obtained by use of these points and the ends of the major and minor axes, as shown by black dots in Figure 156.

Note 3. With the same assumption about units on the coordinate axes as in Note 1 on page 399, we have proved the following facts, because the equation involved can be changed to one of the forms (6) and (8): *If A, C, and G are all positive or all negative, the graph of $Ax^2 + Cy^2 = G$ is an ellipse whose center is the origin and whose axes are on the coordinate axes.* If $G = 0$, the graph is just a *point*, $(0, 0)$, which may be called a *point ellipse*. If A and C are of one sign and G is of the opposite sign, the graph is *imaginary*.

EXERCISE 132

1. Write the equation of an ellipse with axes along OX and OY whose major axis is 8 and minor axis is 6, if the foci are (i) on OY; (ii) on OX.

Graph the ellipse by finding its intercepts and a few other points on it.

2. $16x^2 + 25y^2 = 400.$ **3.** $9x^2 + 25y^2 = 225.$

4. $4x^2 + 9y^2 = 36.$ **5.** $5x^2 + 9y^2 = 45.$

6. $\dfrac{x^2}{64} + \dfrac{y^2}{289} = 1.$ **7.** $\dfrac{x^2}{289} + \dfrac{y^2}{225} = 1.$ **8.** $\dfrac{x^2}{25} + \dfrac{y^2}{169} = 1.$

9. $x^2 + 2y^2 = 8.$ **10.** $9x^2 + 5y^2 = 45.$ **11.** $5x^2 + y^2 = 5.$

12. $2x^2 + 3y^2 = 6.$ **13.** $5x^2 + 2y^2 = 10.$ **14.** $3x^2 + 4y^2 = 12.$

Write the equation of the specified ellipse with axes along OX and OY.

15. Semi-major axis 6; semi-minor axis 3; foci (i) on OY, (ii) on OX.

16. Vertices ($\pm$ 5, 0); semi-minor axis 2.

17. Without using (6) on page 401, by the method used in deriving (6), obtain an equation for the ellipse (a) whose foci are (0, $\pm$ 2), if the sum of the focal radii is 6; (b) whose foci are (2, 3) and (2, 9), if the sum of the focal radii is 8.

6. Hyperbola defined by means of focal radii

DEFINITION V. *A hyperbola is the locus of a point for which the* **absolute value** *of the difference of the undirected distances to two fixed points F and F', called the* **foci,** *is a positive constant which is less than the distance FF'.*

Derivation of a standard equation for a hyperbola. 1. Let the distance between the foci F and F' be $2c$. Designate the x-axis, OX, as the line through F and F', with the origin, O, at the midpoint of FF', and F on the positive half of OX. On both OX and OY, let the unit for the coordinate scale be the unit for distance which is specified in the given plane.* Then, the distance formula (1) of page 61 applies. The foci are ($\pm$ c, 0). Let the constant referred to in Definition V be $2a$, where $a < c$.

2. If P:(x, y) is any point in the plane, let h and h' be the lengths of PF and PF', as in Figure 157, where ($h - h'$) is positive for one position of P, and negative for the other position. P is on the hyperbola if and only if $|\, h - h' \,| = 2a$; this is true if and only if the coordinates of P satisfy

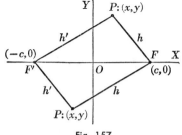

Fig. 157

$$h - h' = 2a \quad or \quad h' - h = 2a. \tag{1}$$

3. On using $h = \sqrt{(x - c)^2 + y^2}$ and $h' = \sqrt{(x + c)^2 + y^2},$ (2)

* This agreement holds in this section and in the following exercise.

and rationalizing in either equation of (1), we obtain the following equation, which can be shown to be equivalent to (1):

$$(c^2 - a^2)x^2 - a^2y^2 = a^2(c^2 - a^2). \tag{3}$$

4. Define a positive number b by the equation

$$b^2 = c^2 - a^2 \tag{4}$$

Then, (3) becomes $b^2x^2 - a^2y^2 = a^2b^2$, or

$[foci\ (\pm\ c,\ 0),\ c^2 = a^2 + b^2]$ $$\frac{x^2}{a^2} - \frac{y^2}{b^2} = 1, \tag{5}$$

whose graph consists of the two branches in Figure 158.

5. *Discussion of* (5). The graph of (5) is symmetric to OX and OY, and hence also is symmetric to the origin as a center of symmetry, because x and y occur in (5) only with even exponents. We say then that the origin is the *center* of the hyperbola. On solving (5) for x and for y, we obtain

$$y = \pm\ \frac{b}{a}\ \sqrt{x^2 - a^2}\quad and\quad x = \pm\ \frac{a}{b}\ \sqrt{y^2 + b^2}. \tag{6}$$

Thus, y is imaginary if $|\ x\ | < a$, and the range for x is $x \leqq -a$ and $x \geqq a$. From (6), x is defined and real for all values of y. The x-intercepts are $x = \pm\ a$, and there are no y-intercepts because y is imaginary when $x = 0$.

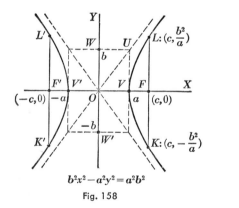

$$b^2x^2 - a^2y^2 = a^2b^2$$

Fig. 158

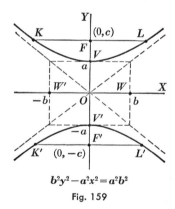

$$b^2y^2 - a^2x^2 = a^2b^2$$

Fig. 159

6. In Figure 158, we refer to V and V' as the **vertices** of the hyperbola and call the segment $V'V$, and also its length, the **transverse axis.** We complete the **associated rectangle** having vertices $(\pm\ a,\ \pm\ b)$, with $W'W$ perpendicular to the transverse axis at the origin. We call $W'W$, or its length, the **conjugate axis.*** The *semi-transverse* axis is a and the *semi-conjugate* axis is b. Without proof, we mention that the diagonals, extended, of the associated rectangle are *asymptotes* for the hyperbola. The

---

* When no question of length is involved, the *whole lines* on which $V'V$ and $W'W$ lie may be called, respectively, the transverse and conjugate axes.

equations of the asymptotes are found to be $y = bx/a$ and $y = -bx/a$, or

$$\frac{x}{a} - \frac{y}{b} = 0 \quad and \quad \frac{x}{a} + \frac{y}{b} = 0, \tag{7}$$

which are equivalent to the single equation

$$\frac{x^2}{a^2} - \frac{y^2}{b^2} = 0 \quad or \quad b^2x^2 - a^2y^2 = 0. \tag{8}$$

7. Each of the chords KL and $K'L'$, perpendicular to the transverse axis at F and F', is called a **latus rectum**, or **focal chord** of the hyperbola. By substituting $x = c$ in (5), and using (4), it is easily verified that the ordinate of L is b^2/a, or $KL = 2b^2/a$. (It will not be essential to memorize this formula.)

In the work leading to (5), if we had let the line through F and F' be the y-axis, we would have obtained the hyperbola located as in Figure 159 with the equation

$$[foci\ (0, \pm c),\ c^2 = a^2 + b^2] \qquad\qquad \frac{y^2}{a^2} - \frac{x^2}{b^2} = 1. \tag{9}$$

We refer to (5) and (9) as **standard forms,** and call the corresponding locations of the hyperbola, in Figures 158 and 159, **standard positions** for a hyperbola with its axes along the coordinate axes.

To obtain a reasonably accurate graph of an equation of type (5), *first construct its associated rectangle, and draw its diagonals, which are the asymptotes of the hyperbola.* Then sketch the hyperbola through its vertices, with the branches approaching the asymptotes smoothly. If a more accurate graph is desired, substitute a value for x in (5) to find the ordinates, y, for four symmetrical points.

EXAMPLE 1. Graph $\qquad\qquad 16x^2 - 9y^2 = 144. \tag{10}$

SOLUTION. 1. In standard form, $\qquad\qquad \dfrac{x^2}{9} - \dfrac{y^2}{16} = 1. \tag{11}$

The foci are on OX. $c^2 = 9 + 16 = 25$, or $c = 5$. Hence, the foci are $(\pm 5, 0)$.

2. The x-intercepts are $x = \pm 3$, or the vertices are $(\pm 3, 0)$, and the end-points of the conjugate axis are $(0, \pm 4)$. These four points enable us to draw the associated rectangle, and its diagonals, which are the asymptotes. The graph, as in Figure 158, was then drawn through the vertices to approach the asymptotes. If a few more accurate points were desired on the graph, we would substitute, for instance, $x = 4$ in (10) to obtain $y = \pm \frac{4}{3}\sqrt{7}$, giving four symmetrical points $(\pm 4, \pm 3.5)$.

3. The equation of the asymptotes is $16x^2 - 9y^2 = 0$, or $y = \pm \frac{4}{3}x$, with slopes $+\frac{4}{3}$ and $-\frac{4}{3}$.

Note 1. With the same assumption about units on the coordinate axes as in Note 1 on page 399, we have proved the following facts, because the equation involved can be changed to one of the forms (5) and (9): *Suppose* *that A and C are of opposite signs. Then, if $G \neq 0$, the graph of $Ax^2 + Cy^2 = G$ is a hyperbola whose center is the origin and whose axes are along the coordinate axes.* If $G = 0$, the equation becomes $Ax^2 + Cy^2 = 0$, whose graph is two straight lines through the origin. When $G \neq 0$, *a single equation for the asymptotes of the hyperbola is $Ax^2 + Cy^2 = 0$.*

EXERCISE 133

1. Without using a standard form (5) or (9) of Section 6, use the locus method employed in deriving (5) to obtain an equation for the hyperbola with foci $(0, \pm 5)$ if the absolute value of the difference of the focal radii is 8.

Graph the equation and give the equations of the asymptotes.

2. $\dfrac{x^2}{16} - \dfrac{y^2}{9} = 1.$ 3. $\dfrac{y^2}{144} - \dfrac{x^2}{25} = 1.$ 4. $\dfrac{y^2}{64} - \dfrac{x^2}{225} = 1.$

5. $4x^2 - 9y^2 = 144.$ 6. $16y^2 - 9x^2 = 144.$

7. $3y^2 - 12 = x^2.$ 8. $x^2 - y^2 = 25.$ 9. $9x^2 + 63 = 7y^2.$

Note 1. An **equilateral** or **rectangular hyperbola** is one whose axes are equal. The hyperbola in Problem 8 is equilateral.

10. $225 + 9x^2 = 25y^2.$ 11. $9x^2 - 144 = 4y^2.$

Note 2. The hyperbolas $b^2x^2 - a^2y^2 = a^2b^2$ and $a^2y^2 - b^2x^2 = a^2b^2$ are called **conjugate hyperbolas.** They have the same asymptotes.

Graph the pair of conjugate hyperbolas on one coordinate system.

12. $\begin{cases} 9x^2 - 4y^2 = 36. \\ 4y^2 - 9x^2 = 36. \end{cases}$ 13. $\begin{cases} 4x^2 - y^2 = 16. \\ y^2 - 4x^2 = 16. \end{cases}$ 14. $\begin{cases} x^2 - y^2 = 16. \\ y^2 - x^2 = 16. \end{cases}$

Note 3. Without proof in this text, we remark that **the equation $xy = k$, where $k \neq 0$, represents an equilateral hyperbola** whose asymptotes are the coordinate axes, and whose transverse axis makes an angle of $45°$ with OX.

Graph the equation.

15. $xy = 4.$ 16. $xy = -6.$ 17. $3xy + 7 = 0.$ 18. $2xy = 9.$

Find the equation of the hyperbola with axes along OX and OY which satisfies the data, and graph the equation.

19. Transverse axis 8; conjugate axis 10; foci on OX.

20. Transverse axis 6; conjugate axis 12; foci on OY.

7. Transformation of coordinates by translation of axes

Consider two coordinate systems superimposed on the same plane, an xy-system, which we shall call the *original system*, and a *new $x'y'$-system*. Then, each point P in the plane has two sets of coordinates, (x, y) and (x', y'). Any locus having an equation $f(x, y) = 0$ also will have a related equation

$F(x', y') = 0$ in the new system. The process of obtaining (x', y') corresponding to any given point $P:(x, y)$, or of finding the new equation $F(x', y') = 0$
for any locus, is spoken of as a *transformation of coordinates*.

In Figure 160, let OX and OY be original axes; let $O'X'$ and $O'Y'$ be new
axes, respectively parallel to OX and OY, and with the same positive directions. A change of this nature from an xy-system to an $x'y'$-system is spoken
of as a *translation of axes* to the new origin O'. If O' has the old coordinates
$(x = h, y = k)$, we shall prove that the coordinates (x, y) and (x', y') of any
point P satisfy

$$x = x' + h; \quad y = y' + k. \tag{1}$$

Or, $$x' = x - h; \quad y' = y - k. \tag{2}$$

Proof. Let the projection of P on $O'X'$ be
M' and on OX be M, and the projection of O'
on OX be N. Since all line segments to be
mentioned are *directed*, for any position of P
we obtain

$$h = ON; \quad x = OM; \quad x' = O'M' = NM;$$
$$x = OM = ON + NM = h + x'.$$

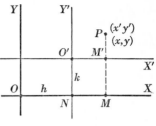

Fig. 160

Similarly, by projecting P on $O'Y'$ and OY, we
would obtain $y = k + y'$.

A major objective in transformation of coordinates is the simplification of
equations in terms of the new coordinates.

ILLUSTRATION 1. Let the new origin be $O':(x = 2, y = -3)$. Then, the
point $(x = -1, y = 4)$ has new coordinates (x', y'), found from (2) with
$h = 2$ and $k = -3$: $\quad x' = -1 - 2 = -3; \quad y' = 4 - (-3) = 7.$

EXAMPLE 1. Transform the following equation by translating axes to the
new origin $(x = 2, y = -3)$:

$$2x^2 - 8x + y^2 + 6y + 11 = 0. \tag{3}$$

SOLUTION. 1. From (1), substitute $x = x' + 2$
and $y = y' - 3$ in (3):

$$2(x' + 2)^2 - 8(x' + 2) + (y' - 3)^2 + 6(y' - 3) = -11;$$

or, $$2x'^2 + y'^2 = 6. \tag{4}$$

2. With equal units on the coordinate axes, the
locus of (4) is an ellipse with center $(x' = 0, y' = 0)$
and major axis along $O'Y'$. The graph is obtained
as usual in Figure 161 with reference to $O'X'$ and
$O'Y'$. Hence, the locus of (3) is an ellipse with
center $(x = 2, y = -3)$, and with the major axis on
the line $x = 2$.

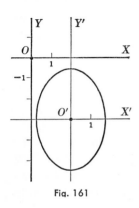

Fig. 161

We may use (1) to transform an equation from an xy-system to the $x'y'$-system, and use (2) for the *inverse* transformation from the $x'y'$-system to the xy-system. Thus, in Example 1, if we use $x' = x - 2$ and $y' = y + 3$ in (4), we obtain the original equation (3). Since (1) and (2) are *linear* in x, y, x', and y', *the degree of an equation is unchanged by a translation of axes.*

ILLUSTRATION 2. To graph the equation $y = \sin (x - \frac{1}{3}\pi)$, we may introduce the transformation $x' = x - \frac{1}{3}\pi$ and $y' = y$, which shifts the vertical axis and origin through the distance $\frac{1}{3}\pi$ to the right. The given equation becomes $y' = \sin x'$. Hence, the graph of $y = \sin (x - \frac{1}{3}\pi)$ is the standard sine graph shifted $\frac{1}{3}\pi$ to the right. Similarly, the graph of $y = \sin (x + \frac{1}{3}\pi)$ is the standard sine graph shifted $\frac{1}{3}\pi$ to the left, as seen by letting

$$x' = x + \tfrac{1}{3}\pi = x - (-\tfrac{1}{3}\pi).$$

8. Transformation by change of units on the axes

Consider a plane, where one inch (or any other linear unit) has been specified as the unit for measuring all distances. In this plane, suppose that an xy-system of rectangular coordinates has been set up, with h and k as the measures in inches of the units of the scales on the axes OX and OY, respectively, where h and k may not be equal. Then, we shall prove that, if $A \neq 0$ and $E \neq 0$, the statements of Note 1 on page 399 about the graph of $Ay^2 = Ex$ remain true, even though the preliminary agreement of Note 1 about coordinate units may *not* be true. Let us introduce the transformation of coordinates

$$x = \frac{1}{h}x' \quad and \quad y = \frac{1}{k}y', \tag{1}$$

which leaves the origin and axes unaltered. The unit for distance in the plane now is *the same as the unit for each coordinate scale.* On using (1) in $Ay^2 = Ex$, after simplifying we obtain

$$A'y'^2 = E'x', \tag{2}$$

where $A' = hA$ and $E' = k^2E$. Thus, the *form of $Ay^2 = Ex$ is invariant* (or *unaltered*) under transformation (1). As a consequence of Note 1 on page 399 as applied to the $x'y'$-system, it follows that *the graph of* (2) *is a parabola,* as described in Definition III on page 398. The graph of $Ay^2 = Ex$ in the original xy-system is *the same parabola;* thus, Note 1 on page 399 states the facts correctly about the graph of $Ay^2 = Ex$, and similarly of $Ax^2 = Ey$, *regardless of the choice of units on the coordinate scales.*

In the same way, we may verify that the equations $Ax^2 + Cy^2 = G$ and $xy = K$ remain *invariant in form* under transformation (1). Hence, the statements about the nature of graphs in Note 3 on page 402, Note 1 on page 405, and Note 3 on page 406 remain true regardless of the choice of units on the coordinate axes. It must be recognized, however, that remarks about the location of foci or any directrix for conics, as made in Sections 4, 5, and 6, are true only if the equations involved are graphed in an xy-plane where the *same unit* is used for the scales on the coordinate axes.

Hereafter, we shall not concern ourselves (except rarely) with the location of foci for conics whose equations are given. As a rule, we shall choose units as we please on the coordinate axes in graphing. Our choices for these units have no effect on our actions in learning the following facts about the graph of any given equation in the variables x and y of the types which arose in Sections 4, 5, and 6:

> *The location of the vertex and axis, and the direction in which the curve is concave, for any parabola.*
>
> *The intercepts on the axes for any ellipse.**
>
> *The real intercepts, the dimensions in coordinate units for the associated rectangle, and the asymptotes for any hyperbola.*

9. Conic with an axis of symmetry parallel to OX or OY

EXAMPLE 1. Obtain the equation of the ellipse with major axis parallel to OX and of length 10, minor axis of length 6, and center ($x = 2$, $y = 3$), in an xy-plane where the units on the axes are equal to the unit for distance.

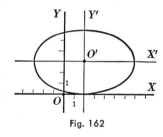

Fig. 162

SOLUTION. 1. The ellipse is shown in Figure 162. Translate axes to $O':(2, 3)$ as a new origin, with axes $O'X'$ and $O'Y'$. Then

$$x' = x - 2, \quad y' = y - 3, \qquad (1)$$

and the $x'y'$-equation of the ellipse is

$$\frac{x'^2}{25} + \frac{y'^2}{9} = 1. \qquad (2)$$

2. On using (1) and (2), we obtain the xy-equation of the ellipse:

$$\frac{(x - 2)^2}{25} + \frac{(y - 3)^2}{9} = 1. \qquad (3)$$

EXAMPLE 2. Obtain the equation of the hyperbola with center $(- 3, 2)$, transverse axis of length 8, parallel to OX, and conjugate axis of length 6, where the units on the coordinate axes are equal to the unit for distance.

SOLUTION. 1. In Figure 163 on page 410, the center is $O':(x = - 3, y = 2)$; the transverse axis is on the line $y = 2$; the conjugate axis is on the line $x = - 3$. The fundamental rectangle and asymptotes are drawn from the data, with the vertices V and V' located 4 units to the right and the left, respectively, from O'. Then, the hyperbola can be constructed approximately.

---

* With a given equation, by altering the relative sizes of the units on the coordinate axes, the locus could appear elongated *vertically* or *horizontally*, as we please, with the foci necessarily having different corresponding locations. All we say is that, for *any* choice of units, the locus is an *ellipse.*

2. Translate the axes to $O':(-3, 2)$ as a new origin. Then we obtain

$$x' = x + 3 \quad and \quad y' = y - 2. \tag{4}$$

In the $x'y'$-system, by use of (5) on page 404, the equation of the hyperbola is found to be

$$\frac{x'^2}{16} - \frac{y'^2}{9} = 1. \tag{5}$$

On using (4) in (5), we obtain

$$\frac{(x+3)^2}{16} - \frac{(y-2)^2}{9} = 1. \tag{6}$$

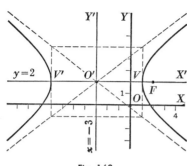

Fig. 163

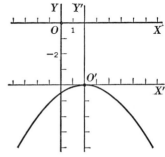

Fig. 164

EXAMPLE 3. Graph the following equation, without first expanding:

$$(x - 2)^2 = -8(y + 4). \tag{7}$$

SOLUTION. 1. Transform coordinates by letting

$$x' = x - 2 \quad and \quad y' = y + 4, \quad or \quad y' = y - (-4). \tag{8}$$

The transformation (8) translates the origin to $O':(x = 2, y = -4)$, as seen in Figure 164. By use of (8), the $x'y'$-equation for (7) is

$$x'^2 = -8y'. \tag{9}$$

2. With respect to the new axes $O'X'$ and $O'Y'$, (9) is a parabola with the orientation shown in Figure 153 on page 399. Thus, (7) is a parabola with vertex $O':(x = 2, y = -4)$, concave downward. The parabola's axis is the line $x = 2$.

EXERCISE 134

1. Find the new coordinates of $(3, 7)$, $(-4, 6)$, $(-1, -2)$, $(0, 0)$, if the axes are translated to the new origin $O':(2, 4)$. Plot all points and both sets of axes.

2. If the axes have been translated to the new origin $O':(-2, 3)$, find the old coordinates of the points whose new coordinates are $(-1, 2)$, $(2, -3)$, $(0, 0)$, $(-4, 3)$. Plot all points and both sets of axes.

Transform the equation by translating axes to the specified new origin O'. Graph the final equation on the new coordinate system, showing both sets of axes.

3. $O':(1, 3)$; $x^2 - 2x + y^2 - 6y + 6 = 0$.

4. $O':(2, 4)$; $y^2 - 8y - 4x + 24 = 0$.

5. $O':(-2, 3)$; $9x^2 + 36x + 4y^2 - 24y + 36 = 0$.

6. $O':(-3, 4)$; $xy + 3y - 4x - 12 = 4$.

7. $O':(-1, -2)$; $9(x + 1)^2 - 4(y + 2)^2 = 36$. (Do not expand.)

Graph the equation, without expanding, by first translating the origin properly. Show both the old and new axes in the figure. Give the coordinates of the vertex of any parabola, and center of any ellipse or hyperbola. Also, write the equation of each axis of the conic. Draw the graphs by abbreviated methods.

8. $(y - 2)^2 = 4(x - 3)$.

9. $(x + 2)^2 = -6(y - 1)$.

10. $\dfrac{(x - 4)^2}{9} + \dfrac{(y - 5)^2}{25} = 1$.

11. $\dfrac{(x + 4)^2}{169} + \dfrac{(y - 2)^2}{25} = 1$.

12. $\dfrac{(x - 3)^2}{9} - \dfrac{(y + 5)^2}{16} = 1$.

13. $\dfrac{(y + 3)^2}{144} - \dfrac{(x + 6)^2}{25} = 1$.

14. $4(x - 3)^2 + 9(y - 5)^2 = 36$.

15. $3(x - 1)^2 + 4(y + 2)^2 = -5$.

16. $(x + 4)^2 - 4(y - 3)^2 = 0$.

17. $2(y + 3)^2 = -7(x - 2)$.

18. $5(x + 1)^2 + 3(y - 2)^2 = 0$.

19. $(y - 3)^2 = 4$.

20. $4x^2 + (y - 1)^2 = 20$.

21. $5(x + 4)^2 - y^2 = 45$.

*Obtain the xy-equation for the conic satisfying the data, by first translating the origin to the vertex, for any parabola, or the center, for any ellipse or hyperbola, and then writing the new x'y'-equation for the curve.**

22. *Ellipse:* center $(2, -5)$; major axis 3, parallel to OX; minor axis 2.*

23. *Ellipse:* center $(6, -4)$; one vertex $(9, -4)$; minor axis 4.*

24. *Hyperbola:* center $(5, 8)$; one vertex $(5, 11)$; conjugate axis 8.

25. *Hyperbolas:* center $(-4, 6)$; transverse axis 6; conjugate axis 8; the axes are parallel to the coordinate axes.

26. Graph the equation $4x^2 + y^2 = 4$ in an xy-plane where the ratio of the unit distance for the scale on OX to the unit distance for the scale on OY is (*a*) 1; (*b*) 2; (*c*) 3. In each case state the length in inches of the major and minor axis of the ellipse if the unit on OX represents 1 inch.

Graph the equation by use of a preliminary transformation of coordinates to simplify the appearance.

27. $y = \sin (x - \frac{1}{4}\pi)$.

28. $y = 2 \cos (x + \frac{1}{2}\pi)$.

29. $y = \tan (x + \frac{1}{4}\pi)$.

30. $y = \sec (x - \frac{1}{4}\pi)$.

31. $y = 3 \sin 2(x - \frac{1}{3}\pi)$.

32. $y = 4 \cos (2x + \frac{1}{3}\pi)$.

---

* Where a major and minor axis are mentioned, it is assumed that the units on the coordinate axes are equal to the unit for distance in the plane. For any hyperbola, the given length of its conjugate or transverse axis is measured in terms of the unit on the corresponding parallel coordinate axis.

10. Certain general equations for conics

Recall the geometric background in Section 3 on page 397. Hereafter we shall apply the name *conic section* not only to an ellipse, a hyperbola, or a parabola, called the **nondegenerate conics,** but also to a locus consisting of just a *single point,* or *two straight lines,* called **degenerate conics.** Any degenerate conic has at least one pair of perpendicular axes of symmetry.

ILLUSTRATION 1. If a locus consists of two intersecting lines, the bisectors of the angles which they form are perpendicular axes of symmetry. A general equation for such a locus with OX and OY as the axes of symmetry is $Ax^2 + Cy^2 = 0$, where A and C have *opposite* signs. Thus $4x^2 - 9y^2 = 0$, or $2x = \pm 3y$, gives two lines of the specified character.

ILLUSTRATION 2. If a locus consists of two parallel lines, the line parallel to them and equidistant from them is an axis of symmetry; any second line perpendicular to this axis is a second axis of symmetry. A general equation for such a locus with OX and OY as axes of symmetry is $Ax^2 = G$, where A and G have the same sign, or where $A \neq 0$ and $G = 0$. Thus, $4x^2 = 9$ gives the parallel lines $2x = \pm 3$; $4x^2 = 0$ gives $x = 0$ *twice.* A similar locus with OX and OY as axes of symmetry is given by $Cy^2 = G$, where C and G have the same sign, or where $C \neq 0$ and $G = 0$.

Our objective in this section is to emphasize the features of certain equations whose graphs are conics, and to systematize the graphing of any particular equation. The results will be stated so as to aid graphing in a plane where * the units are *not* necessarily equal on the coordinate axes. Hence, the theorems will not be designed to locate any foci or directrices, or to decide which axis of an ellipse is the longer (this feature always will appear in the final graph).

The preceding illustrations and the results of Section 8 justify the following two theorems.

THEOREM I. *Any ellipse, hyperbola, or degenerate conic, with OX and OY as axes of symmetry, has an equation of the form*

$$Ax^2 + Cy^2 = G, \tag{1}$$

where A and C are not both zero. Conversely, the graph of any equation of this form is a conic of the specified type, or imaginary, under the following conditions, respectively:

A and C of same sign: an ellipse, a single point, or imaginary.

A and C of opposite signs: a hyperbola or two intersecting lines.

A or C equal to zero: two parallel lines (possibly coincident) or imaginary.

We shall refer to $Ax^2 + Cy^2 = G$ as the *general equation* for the loci specified in Theorem I.

---

* This setting is assumed for the remainder of the discussion, except where otherwise stated.

THEOREM II. *Any parabola with the origin as the vertex and with OX or OY as the axis of symmetry has an equation as follows, with $A \neq 0$:*

$$(Axis,\ x = 0:\quad Ax^2 = Ey) \qquad (Axis,\ y = 0:\quad Ay^2 = Ex). \qquad (2)$$

In an xy-plane, consider any ellipse, hyperbola, or degenerate conic with center (h, k), or any parabola with vertex (h, k) and an axis of symmetry parallel to OX or OY. If the axes are translated to $O':(x = h,\ y = k)$ as a new origin, from page 407 the equations of transformation are

$$x' = x - h \quad and \quad y' = y - k. \qquad (3)$$

If we write the $x'y'$-equation of the conic by use of (1) or (2), and then use (3), we obtain an xy-equation for the conic, as in Example 1 on page 409. Thus, we derive the following forms from (1) and (2).

I. Parabola *with vertex (h, k) and axis parallel to OX or OY.*

General equations, with $A \neq 0$ and $E \neq 0$:

$[Axis,\ line\ x = h;\ vertex,\ (h, k)]$ $\qquad A(x - h)^2 = E(y - k).$ $\qquad$ (4)

$[Axis,\ line\ y = k;\ vertex,\ (h, k)]$ $\qquad A(y - k)^2 = E(x - h).$ $\qquad$ (5)

II. Ellipse, hyperbola, or degenerate conic *with axes parallel to OX and OY, and center (h, k).*

General equation, with A and C not both zero:

$$A(x - h)^2 + C(y - k)^2 = G. \qquad (6)$$

Note 1. If equations are desired involving the standard constants a and b of Sections 5 and 6, with the conic's center at (h, k) and the axes of symmetry parallel to OX and OY, respectively, we use (3) in the standard forms of Sections 5 and 6. Thus, if equal units are used on the coordinate axes, the forms for an ellipse with semi-major axis a and semi-minor axis b are

Ellipse: $\qquad \dfrac{(x - h)^2}{a^2} + \dfrac{(y - k)^2}{b^2} = 1; \qquad \dfrac{(x - h)^2}{b^2} + \dfrac{(y - k)^2}{a^2} = 1.$ $\qquad$ (7)

ILLUSTRATION 3. To write the equation of the ellipse whose center is $(2, 3)$, major axis is 10, parallel to OY, and minor axis is 6, in a coordinate system with equal units on the axes, we use the equation at the right in (7), with $a = 5$ and $b = 3$:

$$\frac{(y - 3)^2}{25} + \frac{(x - 2)^2}{9} = 1. \qquad (8)$$

For such a problem, the student may continue to prefer the more direct method of Example 1 of page 409, instead of memorizing equations (7) and similar equations for hyperbolas.

Any equation of the second degree in x and y which does not involve the product xy is of the form

$$Ax^2 + Cy^2 + 2Dx + 2Ey + F = 0, \qquad (9)$$

where A and C are not both zero. Any one of equations (4), (5), and (6), after expansion, is of the form (9). Conversely, **by completing a square in the x-terms when $A \neq 0$, and in the y-terms when $C \neq 0$,** any equation (9) can be written in the form (4), (5), or (6). Then, because of Theorems I and II, we obtain the following result.

THEOREM III. *Any conic with an axis of symmetry parallel to a coordinate axis has an equation of form (9) with A and C not both zero. Conversely, if A and C are not both zero, the locus of (9) is imaginary, or is a conic of the preceding type, with possibilities in regard to A and C as stated in Theorem I.*

EXAMPLE 1. Investigate the graph of

$$9x^2 - 36x + 25y^2 - 150y + 36 = 0. \tag{10}$$

SOLUTION. 1. On completing squares, we obtain

$$9(x^2 - 4x + 4) + 25(y^2 - 6y + 9) = -36 + 225 + 36, \quad or$$
$$9(x - 2)^2 + 25(y - 3)^2 = 225. \tag{11}$$

2. Translate the origin to (2, 3) by use of new coordinates x' and y', where $x' = x - 2$ and $y' = y - 3$. Then, (10) becomes

$$9x'^2 + 25y'^2 = 225, \tag{12}$$

which represents an ellipse, as graphed in Figure 162 on page 409. If equal units are used on the coordinate axes, (10) thus represents an ellipse with center (2, 3), major axis 10, parallel to OX, and minor axis 6, parallel to OY.

EXAMPLE 2. Investigate the graph of

$$y^2 + 8y + 12x - 20 = 0. \tag{13}$$

SOLUTION. 1. We aim to arrive at the form (5) because (13) involves y^2. Hence, complete a square with the terms in y, and transpose certain terms:

$$y^2 + 8y + 16 = -12x + 20 + 16, \quad or \quad (y + 4)^2 = -12(x - 3). \tag{14}$$

2. Translate the origin to $O':(3, -4)$, by the equations

$$x' = x - 3 \quad and \quad y' = y + 4.$$

Then, (14) becomes $y'^2 = -12x'$. Hence, the graph of (13) is a parabola whose vertex is $(3, -4)$ and axis is the line $y + 4 = 0$. The parabola is concave to the left. The student should sketch the graph.

As a special case of the method of Example 2, consider graphing the quadratic function $ax^2 + bx + c$, or the equation

$$y = ax^2 + bx + c. \tag{15}$$

On dividing by a, and then adding $b^2/4a^2$ to both sides of (15) to complete a square with the terms in x, we obtain

$$\left(x + \frac{b}{2a}\right)^2 = \frac{1}{a}(y - k), \quad or \quad \left[x - \left(-\frac{b}{2a}\right)\right]^2 = \frac{1}{a}(y - k), \tag{16}$$

In (16), $k = (4ac - b^2)/4a$, but we merely remark that k is some constant depending on a, b, and c. By reference to (4), from (16) we justify the following statement about the graph of (15).

> *The graph of the quadratic function $ax^2 + bx + c$, or of the equation $y = ax^2 + bx + c$, is a parabola at whose vertex $x = -b/2a$; the axis of the parabola is the line $x = -b/2a$; the curve is concave in the positive y-direction when $a > 0$, and concave in the negative y-direction when $a < 0$.*   (17)

Note 2. If $A \neq 0$ and $C = 0$ in (9), its graph is a parabola and the equation is linear in y. Hence, we may solve the equation for y to obtain y explicitly as a quadratic function of x, say $y = ax^2 + bx + c$. Then, to graph the equation (instead of changing to a standard form as in Example 2), the student may prefer to use (17), which justifies the method described for graphing a quadratic function on page 79. Similarly, if $A = 0$ and $C \neq 0$ in (9), we may solve for x to obtain x explicitly as a function of y, say $x = ay^2 + by + c$, and then use (17) with the roles of x and y interchanged. Thus, in this case the value of y at the vertex is $y = -b/2a$; the axis is the line $y = -b/2a$; the curve is concave to the right or the left according as $a > 0$ or $a < 0$.

EXERCISE 135

By completing squares, determine the nature of the locus, write its equation after a convenient translation of axes, and draw the graph, with both the original and the new system of axes shown. State the equations of the axes of any ellipse, the axis of any parabola, and the asymptotes of any hyperbola, and show these lines in the graph.

1. $x^2 - 2x + y^2 - 6y + 6 = 0$.
2. $y^2 - 8y - 4x + 24 = 0$.
3. $9x^2 + 36x + 4y^2 - 24y + 36 = 0$.
4. $4x^2 + 9y^2 + 24x = 0$.
5. $y^2 + 6x - 4y = 14$.
6. $2x^2 - 8x - 15y = -53$.
7. $4y^2 + 24y = x^2 - 20$.
8. $25x^2 - 100x - 4y^2 - 32y = 64$.
9. $y^2 + 4x^2 + 10y + 32x + 25 = 0$.
10. $3x^2 + 4y^2 - 12x + 8y + 19 = 0$.
11. $4x^2 - 25y^2 - 8x + 50y - 9 = 0$.
12. $x^2 + 4y^2 = 4y - 1$.
13. $4x^2 - 4x + 1 = 0$.
14. $5x^2 + 20x - 4y^2 - 40y - 160 = 0$.

Graph by the method outlined in Note 2 on this page.

15. $y = x^2 - 4x + 7$.
16. $y = x^2 + 6x + 5$.
17. $y = -2x^2 + 4x + 3$.
18. $x = y^2 - 4y + 5$.
19. $x = -2y^2 + 8y - 6$.
20. $2y - 3 + 4x - 2x^2 = 0$.

Tables

I. SQUARES AND SQUARE ROOTS: 1—200

N	N²	√N	N	N²	√N	N	N²	√N	N	N²	√N
1	1	1.000	51	2,601	7.141	101	10,201	10.050	151	22,801	12.288
2	4	1.414	52	2,704	7.211	102	10,404	10.100	152	23,104	12.329
3	9	1.732	53	2,809	7.280	103	10,609	10.149	153	23,409	12.369
4	16	2.000	54	2,916	7.348	104	10,816	10.198	154	23,716	12.410
5	25	2.236	55	3,025	7.416	105	11,025	10.247	155	24,025	12.450
6	36	2.449	56	3,136	7.483	106	11,236	10.296	156	24,336	12.490
7	49	2.646	57	3,249	7.550	107	11,449	10.344	157	24,649	12.530
8	64	2.828	58	3,364	7.616	108	11,664	10.392	158	24,964	12.570
9	81	3.000	59	3,481	7.681	109	11,881	10.440	159	25,281	12.610
10	100	3.162	60	3,600	7.746	110	12,100	10.488	160	25,600	12.649
11	121	3.317	61	3,721	7.810	111	12,321	10.536	161	25,921	12.689
12	144	3.464	62	3,844	7.874	112	12,544	10.583	162	26,244	12.728
13	169	3.606	63	3,969	7.937	113	12,769	10.630	163	26,569	12.767
14	196	3.742	64	4,096	8.000	114	12,996	10.677	164	26,896	12.806
15	225	3.873	65	4,225	8.062	115	13,225	10.724	165	27,225	12.845
16	256	4.000	66	4,356	8.124	116	13,456	10.770	166	27,556	12.884
17	289	4.123	67	4,489	8.185	117	13,689	10.817	167	27,889	12.923
18	324	4.243	68	4,624	8.246	118	13,924	10.863	168	28,224	12.962
19	361	4.359	69	4,761	8.307	119	14,161	10.909	169	28,561	13.000
20	400	4.472	70	4,900	8.367	120	14,400	10.954	170	28,900	13.038
21	441	4.583	71	5,041	8.426	121	14,641	11.000	171	29,241	13.077
22	484	4.690	72	5,184	8.485	122	14,884	11.045	172	29,584	13.115
23	529	4.796	73	5,329	8.544	123	15,129	11.091	173	29,929	13.153
24	576	4.899	74	5,476	8.602	124	15,376	11.136	174	30,276	13.191
25	625	5.000	75	5,625	8.660	125	15,625	11.180	175	30,625	13.229
26	676	5.099	76	5,776	8.718	126	15,876	11.225	176	30,976	13.266
27	729	5.196	77	5,929	8.775	127	16,129	11.269	177	31,329	13.304
28	784	5.292	78	6,084	8.832	128	16,384	11.314	178	31,684	13.342
29	841	5.385	79	6,241	8.888	129	16,641	11.358	179	32,041	13.379
30	900	5.477	80	6,400	8.944	130	16,900	11.402	180	32,400	13.416
31	961	5.568	81	6,561	9.000	131	17,161	11.446	181	32,761	13.454
32	1,024	5.657	82	6,724	9.055	132	17,424	11.489	182	33,124	13.491
33	1,089	5.745	83	6,889	9.110	133	17,689	11.533	183	33,489	13.528
34	1,156	5.831	84	7,056	9.165	134	17,956	11.576	184	33,856	13.565
35	1,225	5.916	85	7,225	9.220	135	18,225	11.619	185	34,225	13.601
36	1,296	6.000	86	7,396	9.274	136	18,496	11.662	186	34,596	13.638
37	1,369	6.083	87	7,569	9.327	137	18,769	11.705	187	34,969	13.675
38	1,444	6.164	88	7,744	9.381	138	19,044	11.747	188	35,344	13.711
39	1,521	6.245	89	7,921	9.434	139	19,321	11.790	189	35,721	13.748
40	1,600	6.325	90	8,100	9.487	140	19,600	11.832	190	36,100	13.784
41	1,681	6.403	91	8,281	9.539	141	19,881	11.874	191	36,481	13.820
42	1,764	6.481	92	8,464	9.592	142	20,164	11.916	192	36,864	13.856
43	1,849	6.557	93	8,649	9.644	143	20,449	11.958	193	37,249	13.892
44	1,936	6.633	94	8,836	9.695	144	20,736	12.000	194	37,636	13.928
45	2,025	6.708	95	9,025	9.747	145	21,025	12.042	195	38,025	13.964
46	2,116	6.782	96	9,216	9.798	146	21,316	12.083	196	38,416	14.000
47	2,209	6.856	97	9,409	9.849	147	21,609	12.124	197	38,809	14.036
48	2,304	6.928	98	9,604	9.899	148	21,904	12.166	198	39,204	14.071
49	2,401	7.000	99	9,801	9.950	149	22,201	12.207	199	39,601	14.107
50	2,500	7.071	100	10,000	10.000	150	22,500	12.247	200	40,000	14.142
N	N²	√N	N	N²	√N	N	N²	√N	N	N²	√N

II. THREE–PLACE LOGARITHMS OF NUMBERS

N	Log N	N	Log N
1.0	.000	5.5	.740
1.1	.041	5.6	.748
1.2	.079	5.7	.756
1.3	.114	5.8	.763
1.4	.146	5.9	.771
1.5	.176	6.0	.778
1.6	.204	6.1	.785
1.7	.230	6.2	.792
1.8	.255	6.3	.799
1.9	.279	6.4	.806
2.0	.301	6.5	.813
2.1	.322	6.6	.820
2.2	.342	6.7	.826
2.3	.362	6.8	.833
2.4	.380	6.9	.839
2.5	.398	7.0	.845
2.6	.415	7.1	.851
2.7	.431	7.2	.857
2.8	.447	7.3	.863
2.9	.462	7.4	.869
3.0	.477	7.5	.875
3.1	.491	7.6	.881
3.2	.505	7.7	.886
3.3	.519	7.8	.892
3.4	.531	7.9	.898
3.5	.544	8.0	.903
3.6	.556	8.1	.908
3.7	.568	8.2	.914
3.8	.580	8.3	.919
3.9	.591	8.4	.924
4.0	.602	8.5	.929
4.1	.613	8.6	.935
4.2	.623	8.7	.940
4.3	.633	8.8	.944
4.4	.643	8.9	.949
4.5	.653	9.0	.954
4.6	.663	9.1	.959
4.7	.672	9.2	.964
4.8	.681	9.3	.968
4.9	.690	9.4	.973
5.0	.699	9.5	.978
5.1	.708	9.6	.982
5.2	.716	9.7	.987
5.3	.724	9.8	.991
5.4	.732	9.9	.996
5.5	.740	1.00	1.000
N	Log N	N	Log N

III. THREE–PLACE LOGARITHMS OF FUNCTIONS

→	L Sin *	L Tan *	L Cot	L Cos *	
0°	——	——	——	10.000	90°
1°	8.242	8.242	1.758	10.000	89°
2°	.543	.543	.457	10.000	88°
3°	.719	.719	.281	9.999	87°
4°	.844	.845	.155	.999	86°
5°	8.940	8.942	1.058	9.998	85°
6°	9.019	9.022	0.978	9.998	84°
7°	.086	.089	.911	.997	83°
8°	.144	.148	.852	.996	82°
9°	.194	.200	.800	.995	81°
10°	9.240	9.246	0.754	9.993	80°
11°	9.281	9.289	0.711	9.992	79°
12°	.318	.327	.673	.990	78°
13°	.352	.363	.637	.989	77°
14°	.384	.397	.603	.987	76°
15°	9.413	9.428	0.572	9.985	75°
16°	9.440	9.458	0.543	9.983	74°
17°	.466	.485	.515	.981	73°
18°	.490	.512	.488	.978	72°
19°	.513	.537	.463	.976	71°
20°	9.534	9.561	0.439	9.973	70°
21°	9.554	9.584	0.416	9.970	69°
22°	.574	.606	.394	.967	68°
23°	.592	.628	.372	.964	67°
24°	.609	.649	.351	.961	66°
25°	9.626	9.669	0.331	9.957	65°
26°	9.642	9.688	0.312	9.954	64°
27°	.657	.707	.293	.950	63°
28°	.672	.726	.274	.946	62°
29°	.686	.744	.256	.942	61°
30°	9.699	9.761	0.239	9.938	60°
31°	9.712	9.779	0.221	9.933	59°
32°	.724	.796	.204	.928	58°
33°	.736	.813	.187	.924	57°
34°	.748	.829	.171	.919	56°
35°	9.759	9.845	0.155	9.913	55°
36°	9.769	9.861	0.139	9.908	54°
37°	.779	.877	.123	.902	53°
38°	.789	.893	.107	.897	52°
39°	.799	.908	.092	.891	51°
40°	9.808	9.924	0.076	9.884	50°
41°	9.817	9.939	0.061	9.878	49°
42°	.826	.954	.046	.871	48°
43°	.834	.970	.030	.864	47°
44°	.842	.985	.015	.857	46°
45°	9.849	10.000	0.000	9.849	45°
	L Cos *	L Cot *	L Tan	L Sin *	←

* Subtract 10 from each entry in this column.

IV. THREE-PLACE VALUES OF TRIGONOMETRIC FUNCTIONS
AND
DEGREES IN RADIAN MEASURE

Rad.	Deg.	Sin	Tan	Sec	Csc	Cot	Cos	Deg.	Rad.
.000	0°	.000	.000	1.000	——	——	1.000	90°	1.571
.017	1°	.017	.017	1.000	57.30	57.29	1.000	89°	1.553
.035	2°	.035	.035	1.001	28.65	28.64	0.999	88°	1.536
.052	3°	.052	.052	1.001	19.11	19.08	.999	87°	1.518
.070	4°	.070	.070	1.002	14.34	14.30	.998	86°	1.501
.087	5°	.087	.087	1.004	11.47	11.43	.996	85°	1.484
.105	6°	.105	.105	1.006	9.567	9.514	.995	84°	1.466
.122	7°	.122	.123	1.008	8.206	8.144	.993	83°	1.449
.140	8°	.139	.141	1.010	7.185	7.115	.990	82°	1.431
.157	9°	.156	.158	1.012	6.392	6.314	.988	81°	1.414
.175	10°	.174	.176	1.015	5.759	5.671	.985	80°	1.396
.192	11°	.191	.194	1.019	5.241	5.145	.982	79°	1.379
.209	12°	.208	.213	1.022	4.810	4.705	.978	78°	1.361
.227	13°	.225	.231	1.026	4.445	4.331	.974	77°	1.344
.244	14°	.242	.249	1.031	4.134	4.011	.970	76°	1.326
.262	15°	.259	.268	1.035	3.864	3.732	.966	75°	1.309
.279	16°	.276	.287	1.040	3.628	3.487	.961	74°	1.292
.297	17°	.292	.306	1.046	3.420	3.271	.956	73°	1.274
.314	18°	.309	.325	1.051	3.236	3.078	.951	72°	1.257
.332	19°	.326	.344	1.058	3.072	2.904	.946	71°	1.239
.349	20°	.342	.364	1.064	2.924	2.747	.940	70°	1.222
.367	21°	.358	.384	1.071	2.790	2.605	.934	69°	1.204
.384	22°	.375	.404	1.079	2.669	2.475	.927	68°	1.187
.401	23°	.391	.424	1.086	2.559	2.356	.921	67°	1.169
.419	24°	.407	.445	1.095	2.459	2.246	.914	66°	1.152
.436	25°	.423	.466	1.103	2.366	2.145	.906	65°	1.134
.454	26°	.438	.488	1.113	2.281	2.050	.899	64°	1.117
.471	27°	.454	.510	1.122	2.203	1.963	.891	63°	1.100
.489	28°	.469	.532	1.133	2.130	1.881	.883	62°	1.082
.506	29°	.485	.554	1.143	2.063	1.804	.875	61°	1.065
.524	30°	.500	.577	1.155	2.000	1.732	.866	60°	1.047
.541	31°	.515	.601	1.167	1.942	1.664	.857	59°	1.030
.559	32°	.530	.625	1.179	1.887	1.600	.848	58°	1.012
.576	33°	.545	.649	1.192	1.836	1.540	.839	57°	0.995
.593	34°	.559	.675	1.206	1.788	1.483	.829	56°	0.977
.611	35°	.574	.700	1.221	1.743	1.428	.819	55°	0.960
.628	36°	.588	.727	1.236	1.701	1.376	.809	54°	0.942
.646	37°	.602	.754	1.252	1.662	1.327	.799	53°	0.925
.663	38°	.616	.781	1.269	1.624	1.280	.788	52°	0.908
.681	39°	.629	.810	1.287	1.589	1.235	.777	51°	0.890
.698	40°	.643	.839	1.305	1.556	1.192	.766	50°	0.873
.716	41°	.656	.869	1.325	1.524	1.150	.755	49°	0.855
.733	42°	.669	.900	1.346	1.494	1.111	.743	48°	0.838
.750	43°	.682	.933	1.367	1.466	1.072	.731	47°	0.820
.768	44°	.695	0.966	1.390	1.440	1.036	.719	46°	0.803
.785	45°	.707	1.000	1.414	1.414	1.000	.707	45°	0.785
Rad.	Deg.	Cos	Cot	Csc	Sec	Tan	Sin	Deg.	Rad.

N	0	1	2	3	4	5	6	7	8	9
10	.0000	0043	0086	0128	0170	0212	0253	0294	0334	0374
11	.0414	0453	0492	0531	0569	0607	0645	0682	0719	0755
12	.0792	0828	0864	0899	0934	0969	1004	1038	1072	1106
13	.1139	1173	1206	1239	1271	1303	1335	1367	1399	1430
14	.1461	1492	1523	1553	1584	1614	1644	1673	1703	1732
15	.1761	1790	1818	1847	1875	1903	1931	1959	1987	2014
16	.2041	2068	2095	2122	2148	2175	2201	2227	2253	2279
17	.2304	2330	2355	2380	2405	2430	2455	2480	2504	2529
18	.2553	2577	2601	2625	2648	2672	2695	2718	2742	2765
19	.2788	2810	2833	2856	2878	2900	2923	2945	2967	2989
20	.3010	3032	3054	3075	3096	3118	3139	3160	3181	3201
21	.3222	3243	3263	3284	3304	3324	3345	3365	3385	3404
22	.3424	3444	3464	3483	3502	3522	3541	3560	3579	3598
23	.3617	3636	3655	3674	3692	3711	3729	3747	3766	3784
24	.3802	3820	3838	3856	3874	3892	390⁹	3927	3945	3962
25	.3979	3997	4014	4031	4048	4065	4082	4099	4116	4133
26	.4150	4166	4183	4200	4216	4232	4249	4265	4281	4298
27	.4314	4330	4346	4362	4378	4393	4409	4425	4440	4456
28	.4472	4487	4502	4518	4533	4548	4564	4579	4594	4609
29	.4624	4639	4654	4669	4683	4698	4713	4728	4742	4757
30	.4771	4786	4800	4814	4829	4843	4857	4871	4886	4900
31	.4914	4928	4942	4955	4969	4983	4997	5011	5024	5038
32	.5051	5065	5079	5092	5105	5119	5132	5145	5159	5172
33	.5185	5198	5211	5224	5237	5250	5263	5276	5289	5302
34	.5315	5328	5340	5353	5366	5378	5391	5403	5416	5428
35	.5441	5453	5465	5478	5490	5502	5514	5527	5539	5551
36	.5563	5575	5587	5599	5611	5623	5635	5647	5658	5670
37	.5682	5694	5705	5717	5729	5740	5752	5763	5775	5786
38	.5798	5809	5821	5832	5843	5855	5866	5877	5888	5899
39	.5911	5922	5933	5944	5955	5966	5977	5988	5999	6010
40	.6021	6031	6042	6053	6064	6075	6085	6096	6107	6117
41	.6128	6138	6149	6160	6170	6180	6191	6201	6212	6222
42	.6232	6243	6253	6263	6274	6284	6294	6304	6314	6325
43	.6335	6345	6355	6365	6375	6385	6395	6405	6415	6425
44	.6435	6444	6454	6464	6474	6484	6493	6503	6513	6522
45	.6532	6542	6551	6561	6571	6580	6590	6599	6609	6618
46	.6628	6637	6646	6656	6665	6675	6684	6693	6702	6712
47	.6721	6730	6739	6749	6758	6767	6776	6785	6794	6803
48	.6812	6821	6830	6839	6848	6857	6866	6875	6884	6893
49	.6902	6911	6920	6928	6937	6946	6955	6964	6972	6981
50	.6990	6998	7007	7016	7024	7033	7042	7050	7059	7067
N	0	1	2	3	4	5	6	7	8	9

Prop. Parts

	28	27	26
1	2.8	2.7	2.6
2	5.6	5.4	5.2
3	8.4	8.1	7.8
4	11.2	10.8	10.4
5	14.0	13.5	13.0
6	16.8	16.2	15.6
7	19.6	18.9	18.2
8	22.4	21.6	20.8
9	25.2	24.3	23.4

	22	21	20
1	2.2	2.1	2.0
2	4.4	4.2	4.0
3	6.6	6.3	6.0
4	8.8	8.4	8.0
5	11.0	10.5	10.0
6	13.2	12.6	12.0
7	15.4	14.7	14.0
8	17.6	16.8	16.0
9	19.8	18.9	18.0

	16	15	14
1	1.6	1.5	1.4
2	3.2	3.0	2.8
3	4.8	4.5	4.2
4	6.4	6.0	5.6
5	8.0	7.5	7.0
6	9.6	9.0	8.4
7	11.2	10.5	9.8
8	12.8	12.0	11.2
9	14.4	13.5	12.6

	13	12	11
1	1.3	1.2	1.1
2	2.6	2.4	2.2
3	3.9	3.6	3.3
4	5.2	4.8	4.4
5	6.5	6.0	5.5
6	7.8	7.2	6.6
7	9.1	8.4	7.7
8	10.4	9.6	8.8
9	11.7	10.8	9.9

	43	42	41	40	39		38	37	36	35	34		33	32	31	30	29	
1	4.3	4.2	4.1	4.0	3.9	1	3.8	3.7	3.6	3.5	3.4	1	3.3	3.2	3.1	3.0	2.9	1
2	8.6	8.4	8.2	8.0	7.8	2	7.6	7.4	7.2	7.0	6.8	2	6.6	6.4	6.2	6.0	5.8	2
3	12.9	12.6	12.3	12.0	11.7	3	11.4	11.1	10.8	10.5	10.2	3	9.9	9.6	9.3	9.0	8.7	3
4	17.2	16.8	16.4	16.0	15.6	4	15.2	14.8	14.4	14.0	13.6	4	13.2	12.8	12.4	12.0	11.6	4
5	21.5	21.0	20.5	20.0	19.5	5	19.0	18.5	18.0	17.5	17.0	5	16.5	16.0	15.5	15.0	14.5	5
6	25.8	25.2	24.6	24.0	23.4	6	22.8	22.2	21.6	21.0	20.4	6	19.8	19.2	18.6	18.0	17.4	6
7	30.1	29.4	28.7	28.0	27.3	7	26.6	25.9	25.2	24.5	23.8	7	23.1	22.4	21.7	21.0	20.3	7
8	34.4	33.6	32.8	32.0	31.2	8	30.4	29.6	28.8	28.0	27.2	8	26.4	25.6	24.8	24.0	23.2	8
9	38.7	37.8	36.9	36.0	35.1	9	34.2	33.3	32.4	31.5	30.6	9	29.7	28.8	27.9	27.0	26.1	9

Prop. Parts

	25	24	23
1	2.5	2.4	2.3
2	5.0	4.8	4.6
3	7.5	7.2	6.9
4	10.0	9.6	9.2
5	12.5	12.0	11.5
6	15.0	14.4	13.8
7	17.5	16.8	16.1
8	20.0	19.2	18.4
9	22.5	21.6	20.7

	19	18	17
1	1.9	1.8	1.7
2	3.8	3.6	3.4
3	5.7	5.4	5.1
4	7.6	7.2	6.8
5	9.5	9.0	8.5
6	11.4	10.8	10.2
7	13.3	12.6	11.9
8	15.2	14.4	13.6
9	17.1	16.2	15.3

	10	9
1	1.0	0.9
2	2.0	1.8
3	3.0	2.7
4	4.0	3.6
5	5.0	4.5
6	6.0	5.4
7	7.0	6.3
8	8.0	7.2
9	9.0	8.1

	8	7
1	0.8	0.7
2	1.6	1.4
3	2.4	2.1
4	3.2	2.8
5	4.0	3.5
6	4.8	4.2
7	5.6	4.9
8	6.4	5.6
9	7.2	6.3

	6	5	4
1	0.6	0.5	0.4
2	1.2	1.0	0.8
3	1.8	1.5	1.2
4	2.4	2.0	1.6
5	3.0	2.5	2.0
6	3.6	3.0	2 4
7	4.2	3.5	2.8
8	4.8	4.0	3.2
9	5.4	4.5	3.6

N	0	1	2	3	4	5	6	7	8	9
50	.6990	6998	7007	7016	7024	7033	7042	7050	7059	7067
51	.7076	7084	7093	7101	7110	7118	7126	7135	7143	7152
52	.7160	7168	7177	7185	7193	7202	7210	7218	7226	7235
53	.7243	7251	7259	7267	7275	7284	7292	7300	7308	7316
54	.7324	7332	7340	7348	7356	7364	7372	7380	7388	7396
55	.7404	7412	7419	7427	7435	7443	7451	7459	7466	7474
56	.7482	7490	7497	7505	7513	7520	7528	7536	7543	7551
57	.7559	7566	7574	7582	7589	7597	7604	7612	7619	7627
58	.7634	7642	7649	7657	7664	7672	7679	7686	7694	7701
59	.7709	7716	7723	7731	7738	7745	7752	7760	7767	7774
60	.7782	7789	7796	7803	7810	7818	7825	7832	7839	7846
61	.7853	7860	7868	7875	7882	7889	7896	7903	7910	7917
62	.7924	7931	7938	7945	7952	7959	7966	7973	7980	7987
63	.7993	8000	8007	8014	8021	8028	8035	8041	8048	8055
64	.8062	8069	8075	8082	8089	8096	8102	8109	8116	8122
65	.8129	8136	8142	8149	8156	8162	8169	8176	8182	8189
66	.8195	8202	8209	8215	8222	8228	8235	8241	8248	8254
67	.8261	8267	8274	8280	8287	8293	8299	8306	8312	8319
68	.8325	8331	8338	8344	8351	8357	8363	8370	8376	8382
69	.8388	8395	8401	8407	8414	8420	8426	8432	8439	8445
70	.8451	8457	8463	8470	8476	8482	8488	8494	8500	8506
71	.8513	8519	8525	8531	8537	8543	8549	8555	8561	8567
72	.8573	8579	8585	8591	8597	8603	8609	8615	8621	8627
73	.8633	8639	8645	8651	8657	8663	8669	8675	8681	8686
74	.8692	8698	8704	8710	8716	8722	8727	8733	8739	8745
75	.8751	8756	8762	8768	8774	8779	8785	8791	8797	8802
76	.8808	8814	8820	8825	8831	8837	8842	8848	8854	8859
77	.8865	8871	8876	8882	8887	8893	8899	8904	8910	8915
78	.8921	8927	8932	8938	8943	8949	8954	8960	8965	8971
79	.8976	8982	8987	8993	8998	9004	9009	9015	9020	9025
80	.9031	9036	9042	9047	9053	9058	9063	9069	9074	9079
81	.9085	9090	9096	9101	9106	9112	9117	9122	9128	9133
82	.9138	9143	9149	9154	9159	9165	9170	9175	9180	9186
83	.9191	9196	9201	9206	9212	9217	9222	9227	9232	9238
84	.9243	9248	9253	9258	9263	9269	9274	9279	9284	9289
85	.9294	9299	9304	9309	9315	9320	9325	9330	9335	9340
86	.9345	9350	9355	9360	9365	9370	9375	9380	9385	9390
87	.9395	9400	9405	9410	9415	9420	9425	9430	9435	9440
88	.9445	9450	9455	9460	9465	9469	9474	9479	9484	9489
89	.9494	9499	9504	9509	9513	9518	9523	9528	9533	9538
90	.9542	9547	9552	9557	9562	9566	9571	9576	9581	9586
91	.9590	9595	9600	9605	9609	9614	9619	9624	9628	9633
92	.9638	9643	9647	9652	9657	9661	9666	9671	9675	9680
93	.9685	9689	9694	9699	9703	9708	9713	9717	9722	9727
94	.9731	9736	9741	9745	9750	9754	9759	9763	9768	9773
95	.9777	9782	9786	9791	9795	9800	9805	9809	9814	9818
96	.9823	9827	9832	9836	9841	9845	9850	9854	9859	9863
97	.9868	9872	9877	9881	9886	9890	9894	9899	9903	9908
98	.9912	9917	9921	9926	9930	9934	9939	9943	9948	9952
99	.9956	9961	9965	9969	9974	9978	9983	9987	9991	9996
N	0	1	2	3	4	5	6	7	8	9

VI. FOUR-PLACE LOGARITHMS OF FUNCTIONS: 0°—6°; 84°—90°

→	L Sin*	d	L Tan*	c d	L Cot	L Cos*		Prop. Parts
0° 00'						10.0000	**90° 00'**	*Subtract 10 from each entry in the columns marked with "*" throughout the table.*
10'	7.4637		7.4637		2.5363	.0000	89° 50'	
20'	.7648		.7648		.2352	.0000	40'	
30'	7.9408		7.9409		2.0591	.0000	30'	
40'	8.0658		8.0658		1.9342	.0000	20'	
0° 50'	.1627		.1627		.8373	10.0000	10'	
1° 00'	8.2419		8.2419		1.7581	9.9999	**89° 00'**	
10'	.3088		.3089		.6911	.9999	88° 50'	
20'	.3668		.3669		.6331	.9999	40'	
30'	.4179		.4181		.5819	.9999	30'	
40'	.4637		.4638		.5362	.9998	20'	
1° 50'	.5050		.5053		.4947	.9998	10'	
2° 00'	8.5428		8.5431		1.4569	9.9997	**88° 00'**	
10'	.5776		.5779		.4221	.9997	87° 50'	
20'	.6097		.6101		.3899	.9996	40'	
30'	.6397		.6401		.3599	.9996	30'	
40'	.6677		.6682		.3318	.9995	20'	
2° 50'	.6940		.6945		.3055	.9995	10'	
3° 00'	8 7188		8.7194		1.2806	9.9994	**87° 00'**	
10'	.7423	222	.7429	223	.2571	.9993	86° 50'	
20'	.7645	212	.7652	213	.2348	.9993	40'	
30'	.7857	202	.7865	202	.2135	.9992	30'	
40'	.8059	192	.8067	194	.1933	.9991	20'	
3° 50'	.8251	185	.8261	185	.1739	.9990	10'	
4° 00'	8.8436	177	8.8446	178	1.1554	9.9989	**86° 00'**	
10'	.8613	170	.8624	171	.1376	.9989	85° 50'	
20'	.8783	163	.8795	165	.1205	.9988	40'	
30'	.8946	158	.8960	158	.1040	.9987	30'	
40'	.9104	152	.9118	154	.0882	.9986	20'	
4° 50'	.9256	147	.9272	148	.0728	.9985	10'	
5° 00'	8.9403	142	8.9420	143	1.0580	9.9983	**85° 00'**	
10'	.9545	137	.9563	138	.0437	.9982	84° 50'	
20'	.9682	134	.9701	135	.0299	.9981	40'	
30'	.9816	129	.9836	130	.0164	.9980	30'	
40'	8.9945	125	8.9966	127	1.0034	.9979	20'	
5° 50'	9.0070	122	9.0093	123	0.9907	.9977	10'	
6° 00'	9.0192		9.0216		0.9784	9.9976	**84° 00'**	
	L Cos*	d	L Cot*	c d	L Tan	L Sin*	←	

Prop. Parts

	2	223	222	213
1	0.2	22	22	21
2	0.4	45	44	43
3	0.6	67	67	64
4	0.8	89	89	85
5	1.0	112	111	106
6	1.2	134	133	128
7	1.4	156	155	149
8	1.6	178	178	170
9	1.8	201	200	192

	3	212	202	194
1	0.3	21	20	19
2	0.6	42	40	39
3	0.9	64	61	58
4	1.2	85	81	78
5	1.5	106	101	97
6	1.8	127	121	116
7	2.1	148	141	136
8	2.4	170	162	155
9	2.7	191	182	175

	192	185	178
1	19	18	18
2	38	37	36
3	58	56	53
4	77	74	71
5	96	92	89
6	115	111	107
7	134	130	125
8	154	148	142
9	173	166	160

	177	171	170	165	163		158	154	152	148	147		143	142	138	137	135	
1	18	17	17	16	16	1	16	15	15	15	15	1	14	14	14	14	14	1
2	35	34	34	33	33	2	32	31	30	30	29	2	29	28	28	27	27	2
3	53	51	51	50	49	3	47	46	46	44	44	3	43	43	41	41	40	3
4	71	68	68	66	65	4	63	62	61	59	59	4	57	57	55	55	54	4
5	88	86	85	82	82	5	79	77	76	74	74	5	72	71	69	68	68	5
6	106	103	102	99	98	6	95	92	91	89	88	6	86	85	83	82	81	6
7	124	120	119	116	114	7	111	108	106	104	103	7	100	99	97	96	94	7
8	142	137	136	132	130	8	126	123	122	118	118	8	114	114	110	110	108	8
9	159	154	153	148	147	9	142	139	137	133	132	9	129	128	124	123	122	9

	134	130	129	127	125		123	122	120	119	117		115	114	113	111	109	
1	13	13	13	13	12	1	12	12	12	12	12	1	12	11	11	11	11	1
2	27	26	26	25	25	2	25	24	24	24	23	2	23	23	23	22	22	2
3	40	39	39	38	38	3	37	37	36	36	35	3	34	34	34	33	33	3
4	54	52	52	51	50	4	49	49	48	48	47	4	46	46	45	44	44	4
5	67	65	64	64	62	5	62	61	60	60	58	5	58	57	56	56	54	5
6	80	78	77	76	75	6	74	73	72	71	70	6	69	68	68	67	65	6
7	94	91	90	89	88	7	86	85	84	83	82	7	80	80	79	78	76	7
8	107	104	105	102	100	8	98	98	96	95	94	8	92	91	90	89	87	8
9	121	117	116	114	112	9	111	110	108	107	105	9	104	103	102	100	98	9

Prop. Parts	→	L Sin*	d	L Tan*	c d	L Cot	L Cos*	
	6° 00'	9.0192		9.0216		0.9784	9.9976	84° 00'
			119		120			
	10'	.0311		.0336		.9664	.9975	83° 50'
			115		117			
	20'	.0426		.0453		.9547	.9973	40'
			113		114			
	30'	.0539		.0567		.9433	.9972	30'
			109		111			
	40'	.0648		.0678		.9322	.9971	20'
			107		108			
	6° 50'	.0755		.0786		.9214	.9969	10'
			104		105			
	7° 00'	9.0859		9.0891		0.9109	9.9968	83° 00'
			102		104			
	10'	.0961		.0995		.9005	.9966	82° 50'
			99		101			
	20'	.1060		.1096		.8904	.9964	40'
			97		98			
	30'	.1157		.1194		.8806	.9963	30'
			95		97			
	40'	.1252		.1291		.8709	.9961	20'
			93		94			
	7° 50'	.1345		.1385		.8615	.9959	10'
			91		93			
	8° 00'	9.1436		9.1478		0.8522	9.9958	82° 00'
			89		91			
	10'	.1525		.1569		.8431	.9956	81° 50'
			87		89			
	20'	.1612		.1658		.8342	.9954	40'
			85		87			
	30'	.1697		.1745		.8255	.9952	30'
			84		86			
	40'	.1781		.1831		.8169	.9950	20'
			82		84			
	8° 50'	.1863		.1915		.8085	.9948	10'
			80		82			
	9° 00'	9.1943		9.1997		0.8003	9.9946	81° 00'
			79		81			
	10'	.2022		.2078		.7922	.9944	80° 50'
			78		80			
	20'	.2100		.2158		.7842	.9942	40'
			76		78			
	30'	.2176		.2236		.7764	.9940	30'
			75		77			
	40'	.2251		.2313		.7687	.9938	20'
			73		76			
	9° 50'	.2324		.2389		.7611	.9936	10'
			73		74			
	10° 00'	9.2397		9.2463		0.7537	9.9934	80° 00'
			71		73			
	10'	.2468		.2536		.7464	.9931	79° 50'
			70		73			
	20'	.2538		.2609		.7391	.9929	40'
			68		71			
	30'	.2606		.2680		.7320	.9927	30'
			68		70			
	40'	.2674		.2750		.7250	.9924	20'
			66		69			
	10° 50'	.2740		.2819		.7181	.9922	10'
			66		68			
	11° 00'	9.2806		9.2887		0.7113	9.9919	79° 00'
			64		66			
	10'	.2870		.2953		.7047	.9917	78° 50'
			64		67			
	20'	.2934		.3020		.6980	.9914	40'
			63		65			
	30'	.2997		.3085		.6915	.9912	30'
			61		64			
	40'	.3058		.3149		.6851	.9909	20'
			61		63			
	11° 50'	.3119		.3212		.6788	.9907	10'
			60		63			
	12° 00'	9.3179		9.3275		0.6725	9.9904	78° 00'
		L Cos*	d	L Cot*	c d	L Tan	L Sin*	←

Subtract 10 from each entry in the columns marked with "" throughout the table.*

	108	107	105
1	10.8	10.7	10.5
2	21.6	21.4	21.0
3	32.4	32.1	31.5
4	43.2	42.8	42.0
5	54.0	53.5	52.5
6	64.8	64.2	63.0
7	75.6	74.9	73.5
8	86.4	85.6	84.0
9	97.2	96.3	94.5

	104	102	101
1	10.4	10.2	10.1
2	20.8	20.4	20.2
3	31.2	30.6	30.3
4	41.6	40.8	40.4
5	52.0	51.0	50.5
6	62.4	61.2	60.6
7	72.8	71.4	70.7
8	83.2	81.6	80.8
9	93.6	91.8	90.9

	99	98	97	95
1	9.9	9.8	9.7	9.5
2	19.8	19.6	19.4	19.0
3	29.7	29.4	29.1	28.5
4	39.6	39.2	38.8	38.0
5	49.5	49.0	48.5	47.5
6	59.4	58.8	58.2	57.0
7	69.3	68.6	67.9	66.5
8	79.2	78.4	77.6	76.0
9	89.1	88.2	87.3	85.5

	94	93	91	89		87	86	85	84	82		81	80	79	78	77	
1	9.4	9.3	9.1	8.9	1	8.7	8.6	8.5	8.4	8.2	1	8.1	8	7.9	7.8	7.7	1
2	18.8	18.6	18.2	17.8	2	17.4	17.2	17.0	16.8	16.4	2	16.2	16	15.8	15.6	15.4	2
3	28.2	27.9	27.3	26.7	3	26.1	25.8	25.5	25.2	24.6	3	24.3	24	23.7	23.4	23.1	3
4	37.6	37.2	36.4	35.6	4	34.8	34.4	34.0	33.6	32.8	4	32.4	32	31.6	31.2	30.8	4
5	47.0	46.5	45.5	44.5	5	43.5	43.0	42.5	42.0	41.0	5	40.5	40	39.5	39.0	38.5	5
6	56.4	55.8	54.6	53.4	6	52.2	51.6	51.0	50.4	49.2	6	48.6	48	47.4	46.8	46.2	6
7	65.8	65.1	63.7	62.3	7	60.9	60.2	59.5	58.8	57.4	7	56.7	56	55.3	54.6	53.9	7
8	75.2	74.4	72.8	71.2	8	69.6	68.8	68.0	67.2	65.6	8	64.8	64	63.2	62.4	61.6	8
9	84.6	83.7	81.9	80.1	9	78.3	77.4	76.5	75.6	73.8	9	72.9	72	71.1	70.2	69.3	9

	76	75	74	73	71		70		69	68	67	66		65	64	63	61	60	
1	7.6	7.5	7.4	7.3	7.1	1	7		6.9	6.8	6.7	6.6	1	6.5	6.4	6.3	6.1	6	1
2	15.2	15.0	14.8	14.6	14.2	2	14		13.8	13.6	13.4	13.2	2	13.0	12.8	12.6	12.2	12	2
3	22.8	22.5	22.2	21.9	21.3	3	21		20.7	20.4	20.1	19.8	3	19.5	19.2	18.9	18.3	18	3
4	30.4	30.0	29.6	29.2	28.4	4	28		27.6	27.2	26.8	26.4	4	26.0	25.6	25.2	24.4	24	4
5	38.0	37.5	37.0	36.5	35.5	5	35		34.5	34.0	33.5	33.0	5	32.5	32.0	31.5	30.5	30	5
6	45.6	45.0	44.4	43.8	42.6	6	42		41.4	40.8	40.2	39.6	6	39.0	38.4	37.8	36.6	36	6
7	53.2	52.5	51.8	51.1	49.7	7	49		48.3	47.6	46.9	46.2	7	45.5	44.8	44.1	42.7	42	7
8	60.8	60.0	59.2	58.4	56.8	8	56		55.2	54.4	53.6	52.8	8	52.0	51.2	50.4	48.8	48	8
9	68.4	67.5	66.6	65.7	63.9	9	63		62.1	61.2	60.3	59.4	9	58.5	57.6	56.7	54.9	54	9

⟶	L Sin*	d	L Tan*	c d	L Cot	L Cos*			Prop. Parts		
12° 00'	9.3179		9.3275		0.6725	9.9904	**78° 00'**				
10'	.3238	59	.3336	61	.6664	.9901	77° 50'				
20'	.3296	58	.3397	61	.6603	.9899	40'		**61**	**59**	**58**
30'	.3353	57	.3458	61	.6542	.9896	30'				
40'	.3410	57	.3517	59	.6483	.9893	20'	1	6.1	5.9	5.8
12° 50'	.3466	56	.3576	59	.6424	.9890	10'	2	12.2	11.8	11.6
13° 00'	9.3521	55	9.3634	58	0.6366	9.9887	**77° 00'**	3	18.3	17.7	17.4
10'	.3575	54	.3691	57	.6309	.9884	76° 50'	4	24.4	23.6	23.2
20'	.3629	54	.3748	57	.6252	.9881	40'	5	30.5	29.5	29.0
30'	.3682	53	.3804	56	.6196	.9878	30'	6	36.6	35.4	34.8
40'	.3734	52	.3859	55	.6141	.9875	20'	7	42 7	41.3	40.6
13° 50'	.3786	52	.3914	55	.6086	.9872	10'	8	48.8	47.2	46.4
14° 00'	9.3837	51	9.3968	54	0.6032	9.9869	**76° 00'**	9	54.9	53.1	52.2
10'	.3887	50	.4021	53	.5979	.9866	75° 50'				
20'	.3937	50	.4074	53	.5926	.9863	40'		**57**	**56**	**55**
30'	.3986	49	.4127	53	.5873	.9859	30'				
40'	.4035	49	.4178	51	.5822	.9856	20'	1	5.7	5.6	5.5
14° 50'	.4083	48	.4230	52	.5770	.9853	10'	2	11.4	11.2	11.0
15° 00'	9.4130	47	9.4281	51	0.5719	9.9849	**75° 00'**	3	17.1	16.8	16.5
10'	.4177	47	.4331	50	.5669	.9846	74° 50'	4	22.8	22.4	22.0
20'	.4223	46	.4381	50	.5619	.9843	40'	5	28.5	28.0	27.5
30'	.4269	46	.4430	49	.5570	.9839	30'	6	34.2	33.6	33.0
40'	.4314	45	.4479	49	.5521	.9836	20'	7	39.9	39.2	38.5
15° 50'	.4359	45	.4527	48	.5473	.9832	10'	8	45.6	44.8	44.0
16° 00'	9.4403	44	9.4575	48	0.5425	9.9828	**74° 00'**	9	51.3	50.4	49.5
10'	.4447	44	.4622	47	.5378	.9825	73° 50'				
20'	.4491	44	.4669	47	.5331	.9821	40'		**54**	**53**	**52**
30'	.4533	42	.4716	47	.5284	.9817	30'				
40'	.4576	43	.4762	46	.5238	.9814	20'	1	5.4	5.3	5.2
16° 50'	.4618	42	.4808	46	.5192	.9810	10'	2	10.8	10.6	10.4
17° 00'	9.4659	41	9.4853	45	0.5147	9.9806	**73° 00'**	3	16.2	15.9	15.6
10'	.4700	41	.4898	45	.5102	.9802	72° 50'	4	21.6	21.2	20.8
20'	.4741	41	.4943	45	.5057	.9798	40'	5	27.0	26.5	26.0
30'	.4781	40	.4987	44	.5013	.9794	30'	6	32.4	31.8	31.2
40'	.4821	40	.5031	44	.4969	.9790	20'	7	37.8	37.1	36.4
17° 50'	.4861	40	.5075	44	.4925	.9786	10'	8	43.2	42.4	41.6
18° 00'	9.4900	39	9.5118	43	0.4882	9.9782	**72° 00'**	9	48.6	47.7	46.8
10'	.4939	39	.5161	43	.4839	.9778	71° 50'				
20'	.4977	38	.5203	42	.4797	.9774	40'		**51**	**50**	**49**
30'	.5015	38	.5245	42	.4755	.9770	30'	1	5.1	5	4.9
40'	.5052	37	.5287	42	.4713	.9765	20'	2	10.2	10	9.8
18° 50'	.5090	38	.5329	42	.4671	.9761	10'	3	15.3	15	14.7
19° 00'	9.5126	36	9.5370	41	0.4630	9.9757	**71° 00'**	4	20.4	20	19.6
	L Cos *	d	L Cot*	c d	L Tan	L Sin*	⟵	5	25.5	25	24.5
								6	30.6	30	29.4
								7	35.7	35	34.3
								8	40.8	40	39.2
								9	45.9	45	44.1

	48	**47**	**46**		**45**	**44**	**43**	**42**		**41**	**40**	**39**	
1	4.8	4.7	4.6	1	4.5	4.4	4.3	4.2	1	4.1	4	3.9	1
2	9.6	9.4	9.2	2	9.0	8.8	8.6	8.4	2	8.2	8	7.8	2
3	14.4	14.1	13.8	3	13.5	13.2	12.9	12.6	3	12.3	12	11.7	3
4	19.2	18.8	18.4	4	18.0	17.6	17.2	16.8	4	16.4	16	15.6	4
5	24.0	23.5	23.0	5	22.5	22.0	21.5	21.0	5	20.5	20	19.5	5
6	28.8	28.2	27.6	6	27.0	26.4	25.8	25.2	6	24.6	24	23.4	6
7	33.6	32.9	32.2	7	31.5	30.8	30.1	29.4	7	28.7	28	27.3	7
8	38.4	37.6	36.8	8	36.0	35.2	34.4	33.6	8	32.8	32	31.2	8
9	43.2	42.3	41.4	9	40.5	39.6	38.7	37.8	9	36.9	36	35.1	9

* Subtract 10 from each entry in this column.

Prop. Parts

	2	3	4
1	0.2	0.3	0.4
2	0.4	0.6	0.8
3	0.6	0.9	1.2
4	0.8	1.2	1.6
5	1.0	1.5	2.0
6	1.2	1.8	2.4
7	1.4	2.1	2.8
8	1.6	2.4	3.2
9	1.8	2.7	3.6

	5	6	7
1	0.5	0.6	0.7
2	1.0	1.2	1.4
3	1.5	1.8	2.1
4	2.0	2.4	2.8
5	2.5	3.0	3.5
6	3.0	3.6	4.2
7	3.5	4.2	4.9
8	4.0	4.8	5.6
9	4.5	5.4	6.3

	38	37	36
1	3.8	3.7	3.6
2	7.6	7.4	7.2
3	11.4	11.1	10.8
4	15.2	14.8	14.4
5	19.0	18.5	18.0
6	22.8	22.2	21.6
7	26.6	25.9	25.2
8	30.4	29.6	28.8
9	34.2	33.3	32.4

	35	34	33
1	3.5	3.4	3.3
2	7.0	6.8	6.6
3	10.5	10.2	9.9
4	14.0	13.6	13.2
5	17.5	17.0	16.5
6	21.0	20.4	19.8
7	24.5	23.8	23.1
8	28.0	27.2	26.4
9	31.5	30.6	29.7

⟶	L Sin *	d	L Tan *	c d	L Cot	L Cos *	
19° 00′	9.5126	37	9.5370	41	0.4630	9.9757	71° 00′
10′	.5163	36	.5411	40	.4589	.9752	70° 50′
20′	.5199	36	.5451	40	.4549	.9748	40′
30′	.5235	35	.5491	40	.4509	.9743	30′
40′	.5270	36	.5531	40	.4469	.9739	20′
19° 50′	.5306	35	.5571	40	.4429	.9734	10′
20° 00′	9.5341	34	9.5611	39	0.4389	9.9730	70° 00′
10′	.5375	34	.5650	39	.4350	.9725	69° 50′
20′	.5409	34	.5689	38	.4311	.9721	40′
30′	.5443	34	.5727	39	.4273	.9716	30′
40′	.5477	33	.5766	38	.4234	.9711	20′
20° 50′	.5510	33	.5804	38	.4196	.9706	10′
21° 00′	9.5543	33	9.5842	37	0.4158	9.9702	69° 00′
10′	.5576	33	.5879	38	.4121	.9697	68° 50′
20′	.5609	32	.5917	37	.4083	.9692	40′
30′	.5641	32	.5954	37	4046	.9687	30′
40′	.5673	31	.5991	37	.4009	.9682	20′
21° 50′	.5704	32	.6028	36	.3972	.9677	10′
22° 00′	9.5736	31	9.6064	36	0.3936	9.9672	68° 00′
10′	.5767	31	.6100	36	.3900	.9667	67° 50′
20′	.5798	30	.6136	36	.3864	.9661	40′
30′	.5828	31	.6172	36	.3828	.9656	30′
40′	.5859	30	.6208	35	.3792	.9651	20′
22° 50′	.5889	30	.6243	36	.3757	.9646	10′
23° 00′	9.5919	29	9.6279	35	0.3721	9.9640	67° 00′
10′	.5948	30	.6314	34	.3686	.9635	66° 50′
20′	.5978	29	.6348	35	.3652	.9629	40′
30′	.6007	29	.6383	34	.3617	.9624	30′
40′	.6036	29	.6417	35	.3583	.9618	20′
23° 50′	.6065	28	.6452	34	.3548	.9613	10′
24° 00′	9.6093	28	9.6486	34	0.3514	9.9607	66° 00′
10′	.6121	28	.6520	33	.3480	.9602	65° 50′
20′	.6149	28	.6553	34	.3447	.9596	40′
30′	.6177	28	.6587	33	.3413	.9590	30′
40′	.6205	27	.6620	34	.3380	.9584	20′
24° 50′	.6232	27	.6654	33	.3346	.9579	10′
25° 00′	9.6259	27	9.6687	33	0.3313	9.9573	65° 00′
10′	.6286	27	.6720	32	.3280	.9567	64° 50′
20′	.6313	27	.6752	33	.3248	.9561	40′
30′	.6340	26	.6785	32	.3215	.9555	30′
40′	.6366	26	.6817	33	.3183	.9549	20′
25° 50′	.6392	26	.6850	32	.3150	.9543	10′
26° 00′	9.6418	26	9.6882	32	0.3118	9.9537	64° 00′
10′	.6444	26	.6914	32	.3086	.9530	63° 50′
20′	.6470	25	.6946	31	.3054	.9524	40′
30′	.6495	26	.6977	32	.3023	.9518	30′
40′	.6521	25	.7009	31	.2991	.9512	20′
26° 50′	.6546	24	.7040	32	.2960	.9505	10′
27° 00′	9.6570		9.7072		0.2928	9.9499	63° 00′
	L Cos *	d	L Cot *	c d	L Tan	L Sin *	⟵

	32	31	30	29		28	27	26	25	24	
1	3.2	3.1	3	2.9	1	2.8	2.7	2.6	2.5	2.4	1
2	6.4	6.2	6	5.8	2	5.6	5.4	5.2	5.0	4.8	2
3	9.6	9.3	9	8.7	3	8.4	8.1	7.8	7.5	7.2	3
4	12.8	12.4	12	11.6	4	11.2	10.8	10.4	10.0	9.6	4
5	16.0	15.5	15	14.5	5	14.0	13.5	13.0	12.5	12.0	5
6	19.2	18.6	18	17.4	6	16.8	16.2	15.6	15.0	14.4	6
7	22.4	21.7	21	20.3	7	19.6	18.9	18.2	17.5	16.8	7
8	25.6	24.8	24	23.2	8	22.4	21.6	20.8	20.0	19.2	8
9	28.8	27.9	27	26.1	9	25.2	24.3	23.4	22.5	21.6	9

VI. FOUR–PLACE LOGARITHMS OF FUNCTIONS: 27° — 36°; 54° — 63°

⟶	L Sin*	d	L Tan*	c d	L Cot	L Cos*		Prop. Parts		
27° 00'	9.6570		9.7072		0.2928	9.9499	**63° 00'**			
10'	.6595	25	.7103	31	.2897	.9492	62° 50'			
20'	.6620	25	.7134	31	.2866	.9486	40'		**31**	**30**	**29**
30'	.6644	24	.7165	31	.2835	.9479	30'				
40'	.6668	24	.7196	31	.2804	.9473	20'	1	3.1	3	2.9
27° 50'	.6692	24	.7226	30	.2774	.9466	10'	2	6.2	6	5.8
		24		31				3	9.3	9	8.7
28° 00'	9.6716	24	9.7257	30	0.2743	9.9459	**62° 00'**	4	12.4	12	11.6
10'	.6740	23	.7287	30	.2713	.9453	61° 50'	5	15.5	15	14.5
20'	.6763	24	.7317	31	.2683	.9446	40'	6	18.6	18	17.4
30'	.6787	23	.7348	30	.2652	.9439	30'	7	21.7	21	20.3
40'	.6810	23	.7378	30	.2622	.9432	20'	8	24.8	24	23.2
28° 50'	.6833	23	.7408	30	.2592	.9425	10'	9	27.9	27	26.1
29° 00'	9.6856	22	9.7438	30	0.2562	9.9418	**61° 00'**				
10'	.6878	23	.7467	29	.2533	.9411	60° 50'		**28**	**27**	**26**
20'	.6901	22	.7497	30	.2503	.9404	40'	1	2.8	2.7	2.6
30'	.6923	23	.7526	30	.2474	.9397	30'	2	5.6	5.4	5.2
40'	.6946	22	.7556	29	.2444	.9390	20'	3	8.4	8.1	7.8
29° 50'	.6968	22	.7585	29	.2415	.9383	10'	4	11.2	10.8	10.4
30° 00'	9.6990	22	9.7614	30	0.2386	9.9375	**60° 00'**	5	14.0	13.5	13.0
10'	.7012	22	.7644	29	.2356	.9368	59° 50'	6	16.8	16.2	15.6
20'	.7033	21	.7673	28	.2327	.9361	40'	7	19.6	18.9	18.2
30'	.7055	22	.7701	29	.2299	.9353	30'	8	22.4	21.6	20.8
40'	.7076	21	.7730	29	.2270	.9346	20'	9	25.2	24.3	23.4
30° 50'	.7097	21	.7759	29	.2241	.9338	10'				
31° 00'	9.7118	21	9.7788	28	0.2212	9.9331	**59° 00'**		**25**	**24**	
10'	.7139	21	.7816	29	.2184	.9323	58° 50'	1	2.5	2.4	
20'	.7160	21	.7845	28	.2155	.9315	40'	2	5.0	4.8	
30'	.7181	20	.7873	29	.2127	.9308	30'	3	7.5	7.2	
40'	.7201	21	.7902	28	.2098	.9300	20'	4	10.0	9.6	
31° 50'	.7222	20	.7930	28	.2070	.9292	10'	5	12.5	12.0	
32° 00'	9.7242	20	9.7958	28	0.2042	9.9284	**58° 00'**	6	15.0	14.4	
10'	.7262	20	.7986	28	.2014	.9276	57° 50'	7	17.5	16.8	
20'	.7282	20	.8014	28	.1986	.9268	40'	8	20.0	19.2	
30'	.7302	20	.8042	28	.1958	.9260	30'	9	22.5	21.6	
40'	.7322	20	.8070	27	.1930	.9252	20'				
32° 50'	.7342	19	.8097	28	.1903	.9244	10'		**23**	**22**	
33° 00'	9.7361	19	9.8125	28	0.1875	9.9236	**57° 00'**	1	2.3	2.2	
10'	.7380	20	.8153	27	.1847	.9228	56° 50'	2	4.6	4.4	
20'	.7400	19	.8180	28	.1820	.9219	40'	3	6.9	6.6	
30'	.7419	19	.8208	27	1792	.9211	30'	4	9.2	8.8	
40'	.7438	19	.8235	28	.1765	.9203	20'	5	11.5	11.0	
33° 50'	.7457	19	.8263	27	.1737	.9194	10'	6	13.8	13.2	
34° 00'	9.7476	18	9.8290	27	0.1710	9.9186	**56° 00'**	7	16.1	15.4	
10'	.7494	19	.8317	27	.1683	.9177	55° 50'	8	18.4	17.6	
20'	.7513	18	.8344	27	.1656	.9169	40'	9	20.7	19.8	
30'	.7531	19	.8371	27	.1629	.9160	30'				
40'	.7550	18	.8398	27	.1602	.9151	20'		**21**	**20**	
34° 50'	.7568	18	.8425	27	.1575	.9142	10'	1	2.1	2	
35° 00'	9.7586	18	9.8452	27	0.1548	9.9134	**55° 00'**	2	4.2	4	
10'	.7604	18	.8479	27	.1521	.9125	54° 50'	3	6.3	6	
20'	.7622	18	.8506	27	.1494	.9116	40'	4	8.4	8	
30'	.7640	17	.8533	26	.1467	.9107	30'	5	10.5	10	
40'	.7657	18	.8559	27	.1441	.9098	20'	6	12.6	12	
35° 50'	.7675	17	.8586	27	.1414	.9089	10'	7	14.7	14	
36° 00'	9.7692		9.8613		0.1387	9.9080	**54° 00'**	8	16.8	16	
								9	18.9	18	
	L Cos*	d	L Cot*	c d	L Tan	L Sin*	⟵			

* Subtract 10 from each entry in this column.

Prop. Parts

	19	18
1	1.9	1.8
2	3.8	3.6
3	5.7	5.4
4	7.6	7.2
5	9.5	9.0
6	11.4	10.8
7	13.3	12.6
8	15.2	14.4
9	17.1	16.2

	17	16	15
1	1.7	1.6	1.5
2	3.4	3.2	3.0
3	5.1	4.8	4.5
4	6.8	6.4	6.0
5	8.5	8.0	7.5
6	10.2	9.6	9.0
7	11.9	11.2	10.5
8	13.6	12.8	12.0
9	15.3	14.4	13.5

	14	13	12
1	1.4	1.3	1.2
2	2.8	2.6	2.4
3	4.2	3.9	3.6
4	5.6	5.2	4.8
5	7.0	6.5	6.0
6	8.4	7.8	7.2
7	9.8	9.1	8.4
8	11.2	10.4	9.6
9	12.6	11.7	10.8

	11	10	9
1	1.1	1.0	0.9
2	2.2	2.0	1.8
3	3.3	3.0	2.7
4	4.4	4.0	3.6
5	5.5	5.0	4.5
6	6.6	6.0	5.4
7	7.7	7.0	6.3
8	8.8	8.0	7.2
9	9.9	9.0	8.1

	8	7	6
1	0.8	0.7	0.6
2	1.6	1.4	1.2
3	2.4	2.1	1.8
4	3.2	2.8	2.4
5	4.0	3.5	3.0
6	4.8	4.2	3.6
7	5.6	4.9	4.2
8	6.4	5.6	4.8
9	7.2	6.3	5.4

⟶	L Sin*	d	L Tan*	c d	L Cot	L Cos*	
36° 00′	9.7692	18	9.8613	26	0.1387	9.9080	54° 00′
10′	.7710	17	.8639	27	.1361	.9070	53° 50′
20′	.7727	17	.8666	26	.1334	.9061	40′
30′	.7744	17	.8692	26	.1308	.9052	30′
40′	.7761	17	.8718	27	.1282	.9042	20′
36° 50′	.7778	17	.8745	26	.1255	.9033	10′
37° 00′	9.7795	16	9.8771	26	0.1229	9.9023	53° 00′
10′	.7811	17	.8797	27	.1203	.9014	52° 50′
20′	.7828	16	.8824	26	.1176	.9004	40′
30′	.7844	17	.8850	26	.1150	.8995	30′
40′	.7861	16	.8876	26	.1124	.8985	20′
37° 50′	.7877	16	.8902	26	.1098	.8975	10′
38° 00′	9.7893	17	9.8928	26	0.1072	9.8965	52° 00′
10′	.7910	16	.8954	26	.1046	.8955	51° 50′
20′	.7926	15	.8980	26	.1020	.8945	40′
30′	.7941	16	.9006	26	.0994	.8935	30′
40′	.7957	16	.9032	26	.0968	.8925	20′
38° 50′	.7973	16	.9058	26	.0942	.8915	10′
39° 00′	9.7989	15	9.9084	26	0.0916	9.8905	51° 00′
10′	.8004	16	.9110	25	.0890	.8895	50° 50′
20′	.8020	15	.9135	26	.0865	.8884	40′
30′	.8035	15	.9161	26	.0839	.8874	30′
40′	.8050	16	.9187	25	.0813	.8864	20′
39° 50′	.8066	15	.9212	26	.0788	.8853	10′
40° 00′	9.8081	15	9.9238	26	0.0762	9.8843	50° 00′
10′	.8096	15	.9264	25	.0736	.8832	49° 50′
20′	.8111	14	.9289	26	.0711	.8821	40′
30′	.8125	15	.9315	26	.0685	.8810	30′
40′	.8140	15	.9341	25	.0659	.8800	20′
40° 50′	.8155	14	.9366	26	.0634	.8789	10′
41° 00′	9.8169	15	9.9392	25	0.0608	9.8778	49° 00′
10′	.8184	14	.9417	26	.0583	.8767	48° 50′
20′	.8198	15	.9443	25	.0557	.8756	40′
30′	.8213	14	.9468	26	.0532	.8745	30′
40′	.8227	14	.9494	25	.0506	.8733	20′
41° 50′	.8241	14	.9519	25	.0481	.8722	10′
42° 00′	9.8255	14	9.9544	26	0.0456	9.8711	48° 00′
10′	.8269	14	.9570	25	.0430	.8699	47° 50′
20′	.8283	14	.9595	26	.0405	.8688	40′
30′	.8297	14	.9621	25	.0379	.8676	30′
40′	.8311	13	.9646	25	.0354	.8665	20′
42° 50′	.8324	14	.9671	26	.0329	.8653	10′
43° 00′	9.8338	13	9.9697	25	0.0303	9.8641	47° 00′
10′	.8351	14	.9722	25	.0278	.8629	46° 50′
20′	.8365	13	.9747	25	.0253	.8618	40′
30′	.8378	13	.9772	26	.0228	.8606	30′
40′	.8391	14	.9798	25	.0202	.8594	20′
43° 50′	.8405	13	.9823	25	.0177	.8582	10′
44° 00′	9.8418	13	9.9848	26	0.0152	9.8569	46° 00′
10′	.8431	13	.9874	25	.0126	.8557	45° 50′
20′	.8444	13	.9899	25	.0101	.8545	40′
30′	.8457	12	.9924	25	.0076	.8532	30′
40′	.8469	13	.9949	26	.0051	.8520	20′
44° 50′	.8482	13	.9975	25	.0025	.8507	10′
45° 00′	9.8495		10.0000		0.0000	9.8495	45° 00′
	L Cos*	d	L Cot*	c d	L Tan	L Sin*	⟵

*Subtract 10 from each entry in this column.

VII. FOUR–PLACE VALUES OF FUNCTIONS: 0° — 6°; 84° — 90°

→	Sin	Cos	Tan	Cot	Sec	Csc	
0° 00′	.0000	1.000	.0000	——	1.000	——	90° 00′
10′	029	000	029	343.8	000	343.8	89° 50′
20′	058	000	058	171.9	000	171.9	40′
30′	.0087	1.000	.0087	114.6	1.000	114.6	30′
40′	116	.9999	116	85.94	000	85.95	20′
0° 50′	145	999	145	68.75	000	68.76	10′
1° 00′	.0175	.9998	.0175	57.29	1.000	57.30	89° 00′
10′	204	998	204	49.10	000	49.11	88° 50′
20′	233	997	233	42.96	000	42.98	40′
30′	.0262	.9997	.0262	38.19	1.000	38.20	30′
40′	291	996	291	34.37	000	34.38	20′
1° 50′	320	995	320	31.24	001	31.26	10′
2° 00′	.0349	.9994	.0349	28.64	1.001	28.65	88° 00′
10′	378	993	378	26.43	001	26.45	87° 50′
20′	407	992	407	24.54	001	24.56	40′
30′	.0436	.9990	.0437	22.90	1.001	22.93	30′
40′	465	989	466	21.47	001	21.49	20′
2° 50′	494	988	495	20.21	001	20.23	10′
3° 00′	.0523	.9986	.0524	19.08	1.001	19.11	87° 00′
10′	552	985	553	18.07	002	18.10	86° 50′
20′	581	983	582	17.17	002	17.20	40′
30′	.0610	.9981	.0612	16.35	1.002	16.38	30′
40′	640	980	641	15.60	002	15.64	20′
3° 50′	669	978	670	14.92	002	14.96	10′
4° 00′	.0698	.9976	.0699	14.30	1.002	14.34	86° 00′
10′	727	974	729	13.73	003	13.76	85° 50′
20′	756	971	758	13.20	003	13.23	40′
30′	.0785	.9969	.0787	12.71	1.003	12.75	30′
40′	814	967	816	12.25	003	12.29	20′
4° 50′	843	964	846	11.83	004	11.87	10′
5° 00′	.0872	.9962	.0875	11.43	1.004	11.47	85° 00′
10′	901	959	904	11.06	004	11.10	84° 50′
20′	929	957	934	10.71	004	10.76	40′
30′	.0958	.9954	.0963	10.39	1.005	10.43	30′
40′	.0987	951	.0992	10.08	005	10.13	20′
5° 50′	.1016	948	.1022	9.788	005	9.839	10′
6° 00′	.1045	.9945	.1051	9.514	1.006	9.567	84° 00′
	Cos	Sin	Cot	Tan	Csc	Sec	←

Prop. Parts

	28	29	30	31
1	2.8	2.9	3	3.1
2	5.6	5.8	6	6.2
3	8.4	8.7	9	9.3
4	11.2	11.6	12	12.4
5	14.0	14.5	15	15.5
6	16.8	17.4	18	18.6
7	19.6	20.3	21	21.7
8	22.4	23.2	24	24.8
9	25.2	26.1	27	27.9

	32	33	34	35
1	3.2	3.3	3.4	3.5
2	6.4	6.6	6.8	7.0
3	9.6	9.9	10.2	10.5
4	12.8	13.2	13.6	14.0
5	16.0	16.5	17.0	17.5
6	19.2	19.8	20.4	21.0
7	22.4	23.1	23.8	24.5
8	25.6	26.4	27.2	28.0
9	28.8	29.7	30.6	31.5

	48	49	53	57
1	4.8	4.9	5.3	5.7
2	9.6	9.8	10.6	11.4
3	14.4	14.7	15.9	17.1
4	19.2	19.6	21.2	22.8
5	24.0	24.5	26.5	28.5
6	28.8	29.4	31.8	34.2
7	33.6	34.3	37.1	39.9
8	38.4	39.2	42.4	45.6
9	43.2	44.1	47.7	51.3

	69	70	71	72
1	6.9	7	7.1	7.2
2	13.8	14	14.2	14.4
3	20.7	21	21.3	21.6
4	27.6	28	28.4	28.8
5	34.5	35	35.5	36.0
6	41.4	42	42.6	43.2
7	48.3	49	49.7	50.4
8	55.2	56	56.8	57.6
9	62.1	63	63.9	64.8

	79	81	82	83	84	87	88	89		90	91	94	95	96	98	100	101	
1	7.9	8.1	8.2	8.3	8.4	8.7	8.8	8.9	1	9	9.1	9.4	9.5	9.6	9.8	10	10.1	1
2	15.8	16.2	16.4	16.6	16.8	17.4	17.6	17.8	2	18	18.2	18.8	19.0	19.2	19.6	20	20.2	2
3	23.7	24.3	24.6	24.9	25.2	26.1	26.4	26.7	3	27	27.3	28.2	28.5	28.8	29.4	30	30.3	3
4	31.6	32.4	32.8	33.2	33.6	34.8	35.2	35.6	4	36	36.4	37.6	38.0	38.4	39.2	40	40.4	4
5	39.5	40.5	41.0	41.5	42.0	43.5	44.0	44.5	5	45	45.5	47.0	47.5	48.0	49.0	50	50.5	5
6	47.4	48.6	49.2	49.8	50.4	52.2	52.8	53.4	6	54	54.6	56.4	57.0	57.6	58.8	60	60.6	6
7	55.3	56.7	57.4	58.1	58.8	60.9	61.6	62.3	7	63	63.7	65.8	66.5	67.2	68.6	70	70.7	7
8	63.2	64.8	65.6	66.4	67.2	69.6	70.4	71.2	8	72	72.8	75.2	76.0	76.8	78.4	80	80.8	8
9	71.1	72.9	73.8	74.7	75.6	78.3	79.2	80.1	9	81	81.9	84.6	85.5	86.4	88.2	90	90.9	9

	102	104	105	107	108	111	113	115		117	120	121	124	126	129	130	135	
1	10.2	10.4	10.5	10.7	10.8	11	11	12	1	12	12	12	12	13	13	13	14	1
2	20.4	20.8	21.0	21.4	21.6	22	23	23	2	23	24	24	25	25	26	26	27	2
3	30.6	31.2	31.5	32.1	32.4	33	34	34	3	35	36	36	37	38	39	39	40	3
4	40.8	41.6	42.0	42.8	43.2	44	45	46	4	47	48	48	50	50	52	52	54	4
5	51.0	52.0	52.5	53.5	54.0	56	56	58	5	58	60	60	62	63	64	65	68	5
6	61.2	62.4	63.0	64.2	64.8	67	68	69	6	70	72	73	74	76	77	78	81	6
7	71.4	72.8	73.5	74.9	75.6	78	79	80	7	82	84	85	87	88	90	91	94	7
8	81.6	83.2	84.0	85.6	86.4	89	90	92	8	94	96	97	99	101	103	104	108	8
9	91.8	93.6	94.5	96.3	97.2	100	102	104	9	105	108	109	112	113	116	117	122	9

	→	Sin	Cos	Tan	Cot	Sec	Csc	
	6° 00'	.1045	.9945	.1051	9.514	1.006	9.567	84° 00'
	10'	074	942	080	255	006	309	83° 50'
	20'	103	939	110	9.010	006	9.065	40'
	30'	.1132	.9936	.1139	8.777	1.006	8.834	30'
	40	161	932	169	556	007	614	20'
	6° 50'	190	929	198	345	007	405	10'
	7° 00'	.1219	.9925	.1228	8.144	1.008	8.206	83° 00'
	10'	248	922	257	7.953	008	8.016	82° 50'
	20'	276	918	287	770	008	7.834	40'
	30'	.1305	.9914	.1317	7.596	1.009	7.661	30'
	40'	334	911	346	429	009	496	20'
	7° 50'	363	907	376	269	009	337	10'
	8° 00'	.1392	.9903	.1405	7.115	1.010	7.185	82° 00'
	10'	421	899	435	6.968	010	7.040	81° 50'
	20'	449	894	465	827	011	6.900	40'
	30'	.1478	.9890	.1495	6.691	1.011	6.765	30'
	40'	507	886	524	561	012	636	20'
	8° 50'	536	881	554	435	012	512	10'
	9° 00'	.1564	.9877	.1584	6.314	1.012	6.392	81° 00'
	10'	593	872	614	197	013	277	80° 50'
	20'	622	868	644	6.084	013	166	40'
	30'	.1650	.9863	.1673	5.976	1.014	6.059	30'
	40'	679	858	703	871	014	5.955	20'
	9° 50'	708	853	733	769	015	855	10'
	10° 00'	.1736	.9848	.1763	5.671	1.015	5.759	80° 00'
	10'	765	843	793	576	016	665	79° 50'
	20'	794	838	823	485	016	575	40'
	30'	.1822	.9833	.1853	5.396	1.017	5.487	30'
	40'	851	827	883	309	018	403	20'
	10° 50'	880	822	914	226	018	320	10'
	11° 00'	.1908	.9816	.1944	5.145	1.019	5.241	79° 00'
	10'	937	811	.1974	5.066	019	164	78° 50'
	20'	965	805	.2004	4.989	020	089	40'
	30'	.1994	.9799	.2035	4.915	1.020	5.016	30'
	40'	.2022	793	065	843	021	4.945	20'
	11° 50'	051	787	095	773	022	876	10'
	12° 00'	.2079	.9781	.2126	4.705	1.022	4.810	78° 00'
		Cos	Sin	Cot	Tan	Csc	Sec	←

Prop. Parts

	2	3	4	5	6
1	0.2	0.3	0.4	0.5	0.6
2	0.4	0.6	0.8	1.0	1.2
3	0.6	0.9	1.2	1.5	1.8
4	0.8	1.2	1.6	2 0	2.4
5	1.0	1.5	2.0	2.5	3.0
6	1.2	1.8	2.4	3.0	3.6
7	1.4	2.1	2.8	3.5	4.2
8	1.6	2.4	3.2	4.0	4.8
9	1.8	2.7	3.6	4.5	5.4

	37	40	42	46
1	3.7	4	4.2	4.6
2	7.4	8	8.4	9.2
3	11.1	12	12.6	13.8
4	14.8	16	16.8	18.4
5	18.5	20	21.0	23.0
6	22.2	24	25.2	27.6
7	25.9	28	29.4	32.2
8	29.6	32	33.6	36.8
9	33.3	36	37.8	41.4

	58	62	66	68
1	5.8	6.2	6.6	6.8
2	11.6	12.4	13.2	13.6
3	17.4	18.6	19.8	20.4
4	23.2	24.8	26.4	27.2
5	29.0	31.0	33.0	34.0
6	34.8	37.2	39.6	40.8
7	40.6	43.4	46.2	47.6
8	46.4	49.6	52.8	54.4
9	52.2	55.8	59.4	61.2

	73	74	75	77
1	7.3	7.4	7.5	7.7
2	14.6	14.8	15.0	15.4
3	21.9	22.2	22.5	23.1
4	29.2	29.6	30.0	30.8
5	36.5	37.0	37.5	38.5
6	43.8	44.4	45.0	46.2
7	51.1	51 8	52.5	53.9
8	58.4	59.2	60.0	61.6
9	65.7	66.6	67.5	69.3

	136	140	141	145	147	152	154	159		160	165	167	173	174	182	183	190	
1	14	14	14	14	15	15	15	16	1	16	16	17	17	17	18	18	19	1
2	27	28	28	29	29	30	31	32	2	32	33	33	35	35	36	37	38	2
3	41	42	42	44	44	46	46	48	3	48	50	50	52	52	55	55	57	3
4	54	56	56	58	59	61	62	64	4	64	66	67	69	70	73	73	76	4
5	68	70	70	72	74	76	77	80	5	80	82	84	86	87	91	92	95	5
6	82	84	85	87	88	91	92	95	6	96	99	100	104	104	109	110	114	6
7	95	98	99	102	103	106	108	111	7	112	116	117	121	122	127	128	133	7
8	109	112	113	116	118	122	123	127	8	128	132	134	138	139	146	146	152	8
9	122	126	127	130	132	137	139	143	9	144	148	150	156	157	164	165	171	9

	191	199	201	209	211	220	221	231		233	244	245	258	259	272	274	
1	19	20	20	21	21	22	22	23	1	23	24	24	26	26	27	27	1
2	38	40	40	42	42	44	44	46	2	47	49	49	52	52	54	55	2
3	57	60	60	63	63	66	66	69	3	70	73	74	77	78	82	82	3
4	76	80	80	84	84	88	88	92	4	93	98	98	103	104	109	110	4
5	96	100	100	104	106	110	110	116	5	116	122	122	129	130	136	137	5
6	115	119	121	125	127	132	133	139	6	140	146	147	155	155	163	164	6
7	134	139	141	146	148	154	155	162	7	163	171	172	181	181	190	192	7
8	153	159	161	167	169	176	177	185	8	186	195	196	206	207	218	219	8
9	172	179	181	188	190	198	199	208	9	210	220	220	232	233	245	247	9

	Sin	Cos	Tan	Cot	Sec	Csc		Prop. Parts
12° 00′	.2079	.9781	.2126	4.705	1.022	4.810	**78° 00′**	
10′	108	775	156	638	023	745	77° 50′	
20′	136	769	186	574	024	682	40′	
30′	.2164	.9763	.2217	4.511	1.024	4.620	30′	
40′	193	757	247	449	025	560	20′	
12° 50′	221	750	278	390	026	502	10′	
13° 00′	.2250	.9744	.2309	4.331	1.026	4.445	**77° 00′**	
10′	278	737	339	275	027	390	76° 50′	
20′	306	730	370	219	028	336	40′	
30′	.2334	.9724	.2401	4.165	1.028	4.284	30′	
40′	363	717	432	113	029	232	20′	
13° 50′	391	710	462	061	030	182	10′	
14° 00′	.2419	.9703	.2493	4.011	1.031	4.134	**76° 00′**	
10′	447	696	524	3.962	031	086	75° 50′	
20′	476	689	555	914	032	4.039	40′	
30′	.2504	.9681	.2586	3.867	1.033	3.994	30′	
40′	532	674	617	821	034	950	20′	
14° 50′	560	667	648	776	034	906	10′	
15° 00′	.2588	.9659	.2679	3.732	1.035	3.864	**75° 00′**	
10′	616	652	711	689	036	822	74° 50′	
20′	644	644	742	647	037	782	40′	
30′	.2672	.9636	.2773	3.606	1.038	3.742	30′	
40′	700	628	805	566	039	703	20′	
15° 50′	728	621	836	526	039	665	10′	
16° 00′	.2756	.9613	.2867	3.487	1.040	3.628	**74° 00′**	
10′	784	605	899	450	041	592	73° 50′	
20′	812	596	931	412	042	556	40′	
30′	.2840	.9588	.2962	3.376	1.043	3.521	30′	
40′	868	580	2994	340	044	487	20′	
16° 50′	896	572	.3026	305	045	453	10′	
17° 00′	.2924	.9563	.3057	3.271	1.046	3.420	**73° 00′**	
10′	952	555	089	237	047	388	72° 50′	
20′	.2979	546	121	204	048	356	40′	
30′	.3007	.9537	.3153	3.172	1.049	3.326	30′	
40′	035	528	185	140	049	295	20′	
17° 50′	062	520	217	108	050	265	10′	
18° 00′	.3090	.9511	.3249	3.078	1.051	3.236	**72° 00′**	
10′	118	502	281	047	052	207	71° 50′	
20′	145	492	314	3.018	053	179	40′	
30′	.3173	.9483	.3346	2.989	1.054	3.152	30′	
40′	201	474	378	960	056	124	20′	
18° 50′	228	465	411	932	057	098	10′	
19° 00′	.3256	.9455	.3443	2.904	1.058	3.072	**71° 00′**	
10′	283	446	476	877	059	046	70° 50′	
20′	311	436	508	850	060	3.021	40′	
30′	.3338	.9426	.3541	2.824	1.061	2.996	30′	
40′	365	417	574	798	062	971	20′	
19° 50′	393	407	607	773	063	947	10′	
20° 00′	.3420	.9397	.3640	2.747	1.064	2.924	**70° 00′**	
	Cos	Sin	Cot	Tan	Csc	Sec	←	

Prop. Parts

	2	6	7	8
1	0.2	0.6	0.7	0.8
2	0.4	1.2	1.4	1.6
3	0.6	1.8	2.1	2.4
4	0.8	2.4	2.8	3.2
5	1.0	3.0	3.5	4.0
6	1.2	3.6	4.2	4.8
7	1.4	4.2	4.9	5.6
8	1.6	4.8	5.6	6.4
9	1.8	5.4	6.3	7.2

	13	14	15	16
1	1.3	1.4	1.5	1.6
2	2.6	2.8	3.0	3.2
3	3.9	4.2	4.5	4.8
4	5.2	5.6	6.0	6.4
5	6.5	7.0	7.5	8.0
6	7.8	8.4	9.0	9.6
7	9.1	9.8	10.5	11.2
8	10.4	11.2	12.0	12.8
9	11.7	12.6	13.5	14.4

	21	22	23	24
1	2.1	2.2	2.3	2.4
2	4.2	4.4	4.6	4.8
3	6.3	6.6	6.9	7.2
4	8.4	8.8	9.2	9.6
5	10.5	11.0	11.5	12.0
6	12.6	13.2	13.8	14.4
7	14.7	15.4	16.1	16.8
8	16.8	17.6	18.4	19.2
9	18.9	19.8	20.7	21.6

	29	30	31	32
1	2.9	3	3.1	3.2
2	5.8	6	6.2	6.4
3	8.7	9	9.3	9.6
4	11.6	12	12.4	12.8
5	14.5	15	15.5	16.0
6	17.4	18	18.6	19.2
7	20.3	21	21.7	22.4
8	23.2	24	24.8	25.6
9	26.1	27	27.9	28.8

	37	38	39	40	41	42	43		44	45	46	47	48	49	50	
1	3.7	3.8	3.9	4	4.1	4.2	4.3	1	4.4	4.5	4.6	4.7	4.8	4.9	5	1
2	7.4	7.6	7.8	8	8.2	8.4	8.6	2	8.8	9.0	9.2	9.4	9.6	9.8	10	2
3	11.1	11.4	11.7	12	12.3	12.6	12.9	3	13.2	13.5	13.8	14.1	14.4	14.7	15	3
4	14.8	15.2	15.6	16	16.4	16.8	17.2	4	17.6	18.0	18.4	18.8	19.2	19.6	20	4
5	18.5	19.0	19.5	20	20.5	21.0	21.5	5	22.0	22.5	23.0	23.5	24.0	24.5	25	5
6	22.2	22.8	23.4	24	24.6	25.2	25.8	6	26.4	27.0	27.6	28.2	28.8	29.4	30	6
7	25.9	26.6	27.3	28	28.7	29.4	30.1	7	30.8	31.5	32.2	32.9	33.6	34.3	35	7
8	29.6	30.4	31.2	32	32.8	33.6	34.4	8	35.2	36.0	36.8	37.6	38.4	39.2	40	8
9	33.3	34.2	35.1	36	36.9	37.8	38.7	9	39.6	40.5	41.4	42.3	43.2	44.1	45	9

→	Sin	Cos	Tan	Cot	Sec	Csc	
20° 00'	.3420	.9397	.3640	2.747	1.064	2.924	70° 00'
10'	448	387	673	723	065	901	69° 50'
20'	475	377	706	699	066	878	40'
30'	.3502	.9367	.3739	2.675	1.068	2.855	30'
40'	529	356	772	651	069	833	20'
20° 50'	557	346	805	628	070	812	10'
21° 00'	.3584	.9336	.3839	2.605	1.071	2.790	69° 00'
10'	611	325	872	583	072	769	68° 50'
20'	638	315	906	560	074	749	40'
30'	.3665	.9304	.3939	2.539	1.075	2.729	30'
40'	692	293	3973	517	076	709	20'
21° 50'	719	283	.4006	496	077	689	10'
22° 00'	.3746	.9272	.4040	2.475	1.079	2.669	68° 00'
10'	773	261	074	455	080	650	67° 50'
20'	800	250	108	434	081	632	40'
30'	.3827	.9239	.4142	2.414	1.082	2.613	30'
40'	854	228	176	394	084	595	20'
22° 50'	881	216	210	375	085	577	10'
23° 00'	.3907	.9205	.4245	2.356	1.086	2.559	67° 00'
10'	934	194	279	337	088	542	66° 50'
20'	961	182	314	318	089	525	40'
30'	.3987	.9171	.4348	2.300	1.090	2.508	30'
40'	.4014	159	383	282	092	491	20'
23° 50'	041	147	417	264	093	475	10'
24° 00'	.4067	.9135	.4452	2.246	1.095	2.459	66° 00'
10'	094	124	487	229	096	443	65° 50'
20'	120	112	522	211	097	427	40'
30'	.4147	.9100	.4557	2.194	1.099	2.411	30'
40'	173	088	592	177	100	396	20'
24° 50'	200	075	628	161	102	381	10'
25° 00'	.4226	.9063	.4663	2.145	1.103	2.366	65° 00'
10'	253	051	699	128	105	352	64° 50'
20'	279	038	734	112	106	337	40'
30'	.4305	.9026	.4770	2.097	1.108	2.323	30'
40'	331	013	806	081	109	309	20'
25° 50'	358	.9001	841	066	111	295	10'
26° 00'	.4384	.8988	.4877	2.050	1.113	2.281	64° 00'
10'	410	975	913	035	114	268	63° 50'
20'	436	962	950	020	116	254	40'
30'	.4462	.8949	.4986	2.006	1.117	2.241	30'
40'	488	936	.5022	1.991	119	228	20'
26° 50'	514	923	059	977	121	215	10'
27° 00'	.4540	.8910	.5095	1.963	1.122	2.203	63° 00'
10'	566	897	132	949	124	190	62° 50'
20'	592	884	169	935	126	178	40'
30'	.4617	.8870	.5206	1.921	1.127	2.166	30'
40'	643	857	243	907	129	154	20'
27° 50'	669	843	280	894	131	142	10'
28° 00'	.4695	.8829	.5317	1.881	1.133	2.130	62° 00'
	Cos	Sin	Cot	Tan	Csc	Sec	←—

Prop. Parts

	9	10	11	12
1	0.9	1.0	1.1	1.2
2	1.8	2.0	2.2	2.4
3	2.7	3.0	3.3	3.6
4	3.6	4.0	4.4	4.8
5	4.5	5.0	5.5	6.0
6	5.4	6.0	6.6	7.2
7	6.3	7.0	7.7	8.4
8	7.2	8.0	8.8	9.6
9	8.1	9.0	9.9	10.8

	17	18	19	20
1	1.7	1.8	1.9	2
2	3.4	3.6	3.8	4
3	5.1	5.4	5.7	6
4	6.8	7.2	7.6	8
5	8.5	9.0	9.5	10
6	10.2	10 8	11.4	12
7	11.9	12.6	13.3	14
8	13.6	14.4	15.2	16
9	15.3	16.2	17.1	18

	25	26	27	28
1	2.5	2.6	2.7	2.8
2	5 0	5.2	5.4	5.6
3	7.5	7.8	8.1	8.4
4	10.0	10.4	10.8	11.2
5	12.5	13.0	13.5	14.0
6	15.0	15.6	16.2	16.8
7	17.5	18.2	18.9	19.6
8	20.0	20.8	21.6	22.4
9	22.5	23.4	24.3	25.2

	33	34	35	36
1	3.3	3.4	3.5	3.6
2	6.6	6.8	7.0	7.2
3	9.9	10.2	10.5	10.8
4	13.2	13.6	14.0	14.4
5	16.5	17.0	17.5	18.0
6	19.8	20.4	21.0	21.6
7	23.1	23.8	24.5	25.2
8	26.4	27.2	28.0	28.8
9	29.7	30.6	31.5	32.4

	52	54	55	56	57	58	59		60	62	63	64	65	67	
1	5.2	5.4	5.5	5.6	5.7	5.8	5.9	1	6	6.2	6.3	6.4	6.5	6.7	1
2	10.4	10.8	11.0	11.2	11.4	11.6	11.8	2	12	12.4	12.6	12.8	13.0	13.4	2
3	15.6	16.2	16.5	16.8	17.1	17.4	17.7	3	18	18.6	18.9	19.2	19.5	20.1	3
4	20.8	21.6	22.0	22.4	22.8	23.2	23.6	4	24	24.8	25.2	25.6	26.0	26.8	4
5	26.0	27.0	27.5	28.0	28.5	29.0	29.5	5	30	31.0	31.5	32.0	32.5	33.5	5
6	31.2	32.4	33.0	33.6	34.2	34.8	35.4	6	36	37.2	37.8	38.4	39.0	40.2	6
7	36.4	37.8	38.5	39.2	39.9	40.6	41.3	7	42	43.4	44.1	44.8	45.5	46.9	7
8	41.6	43.2	44.0	44.8	45.6	46.4	47.2	8	48	49.6	50.4	51.2	52.0	53.6	8
9	46.8	48.6	49.5	50.4	51.3	52.2	53.1	9	54	55.8	56.7	57.6	58.5	60.3	9

VII. FOUR–PLACE VALUES OF FUNCTIONS: 28° — 36°; 54° — 62°

→	Sin	Cos	Tan	Cot	Sec	Csc	
28° 00′	.4695	.8829	.5317	1.881	1.133	2.130	62° 00′
10′	720	816	354	868	134	118	61° 50′
20′	746	802	392	855	136	107	40′
30′	.4772	.8788	.5430	1.842	1.138	2.096	30′
40′	797	774	467	829	140	085	20′
28° 50′	823	760	505	816	142	074	10′
29° 00′	.4848	.8746	.5543	1.804	1.143	2.063	61° 00′
10′	874	732	581	792	145	052	60° 50′
20′	899	718	619	780	147	041	40′
30′	.4924	.8704	.5658	1.767	1.149	2.031	30′
40′	950	689	696	756	151	020	20′
29° 50′	.4975	675	735	744	153	010	10′
30° 00′	.5000	.8660	.5774	1.732	1.155	2.000	60° 00′
10′	025	646	812	720	157	1.990	59° 50′
20′	050	631	851	709	159	980	40′
30′	.5075	.8616	.5890	1.698	1.161	1.970	30′
40′	100	601	930	686	163	961	20′
30° 50′	125	587	.5969	675	165	951	10′
31° 00′	.5150	.8572	.6009	1.664	1.167	1.942	59° 00′
19′	175	557	048	653	169	932	58° 50′
20′	200	542	088	643	171	923	40′
30′	.5225	.8526	.6128	1.632	1.173	1.914	30′
40′	250	511	168	621	175	905	20′
31° 50′	275	496	208	611	177	896	10′
32° 00′	.5299	.8480	.6249	1.600	1.179	1.887	58° 00′
10′	324	465	289	590	181	878	57° 50′
20′	348	450	330	580	184	870	40′
30′	.5373	.8434	.6371	1.570	1.186	1.861	30′
40′	398	418	412	560	188	853	20′
32° 50′	422	403	453	550	190	844	10′
33° 00′	.5446	.8387	.6494	1.540	1.192	1.836	57° 00′
10′	471	371	536	530	195	828	56° 50′
20′	495	355	577	520	197	820	40′
30′	.5519	.8339	.6619	1.511	1.199	1.812	30′
40′	544	323	661	501	202	804	20′
33° 50′	568	307	703	492	204	796	10′
34° 00′	.5592	.8290	.6745	1.483	1.206	1.788	56° 00′
10′	616	274	787	473	209	781	55° 50′
20′	640	258	830	464	211	773	40′
30	.5664	.8241	.6873	1.455	1.213	1.766	30′
40	688	225	916	446	216	758	20′
34° 50	712	208	.6959	437	218	751	10′
35° 00′	.5736	.8192	.7002	1.428	1.221	1.743	55° 00′
10′	760	175	046	419	223	736	54° 50′
20′	783	158	089	411	226	729	40′
30′	.5807	.8141	.7133	1.402	1.228	1.722	30′
40′	831	124	177	393	231	715	20′
35° 50′	854	107	221	385	233	708	10′
36° 00′	.5878	.8090	.7265	1.376	1.236	1.701	54° 00′
	Cos	Sin	Cot	Tan	Csc	Sec	←

Prop. Parts

	2	3	4	5	6
1	0.2	0.3	0 4	0.5	0.6
2	0.4	0.6	0.8	1.0	1.2
3	0.6	0.9	1.2	1.5	1.8
4	0.8	1.2	1.6	2.0	2.4
5	1.0	1.5	2.0	2.5	3.0
6	1.2	1.8	2.4	3.0	3.6
7	1.4	2.1	2.8	3.5	4.2
8	1.6	2.4	3.2	4.0	4.8
9	1.8	2.7	3.6	4.5	5.4

	11	12	13	14
1	1.1	1.2	1.3	1.4
2	2.2	2.4	2.6	2.8
3	3.3	3.6	3.9	4.2
4	4.4	4.8	5.2	5.6
5	5.5	6.0	6.5	7.0
6	6.6	7.2	7.8	8.4
7	7.7	8.4	9.1	9.8
8	8.8	9.6	10.4	11.2
9	9.9	10.8	11.7	12.6

	19	20	21	22
1	1.9	2	2.1	2.2
2	3.8	4	4.2	4.4
3	5.7	6	6.3	6.6
4	7.6	8	8.4	8.8
5	9.5	10	10.5	11.0
6	11.4	12	12.6	13.2
7	13.3	14	14.7	15.4
8	15.2	16	16.8	17.6
9	17.1	18	18.9	19.8

	37	38	39	40
1	3.7	3.8	3.9	4
2	7.4	7.6	7.8	8
3	11.1	11.4	11.7	12
4	14.8	15.2	15.6	16
5	18.5	19.0	19.5	20
6	22.2	22.8	23.4	24
7	25.9	26.6	27.3	28
8	29.6	30.4	31.2	32
9	33.3	34.2	35.1	36

	44	45	46	47	48	49		50	51	52	53	54	55	
1	4.4	4.5	4.6	4.7	4.8	4.9	1	5	5.1	5.2	5.3	5.4	5.5	1
2	8.8	9.0	9.2	9.4	9.6	9.8	2	10	10.2	10.4	10.6	10.8	11.0	2
3	13.2	13.5	13.8	14.1	14.4	14.7	3	15	15.3	15.6	15.9	16.2	16.5	3
4	17.6	18.0	18.4	18.8	19.2	19.6	4	20	20.4	20.8	21.2	21.6	22.0	4
5	22.0	22.5	23.0	23.5	24.0	24.5	5	25	25.5	26.0	26.5	27.0	27.5	5
6	26.4	27.0	27.6	28.2	28.8	29.4	6	30	30.6	31.2	31.8	32.4	33.0	6
7	30.8	31.5	32.2	32.9	33.6	34.3	7	35	35.7	36.4	37.1	37.8	38.5	7
8	35.2	36.0	36.8	37.6	38.4	39.2	8	40	40.8	41.6	42.4	43.2	44.0	8
9	39.6	40.5	41.4	42.3	43.2	44.1	9	45	45.9	46.8	47.7	48.6	49.5	9

Prop. Parts

	7	8	9	10
1	0.7	0.8	0.9	1.0
2	1.4	1.6	1.8	2.0
3	2.1	2.4	2.7	3.0
4	2.8	3.2	3.6	4.0
5	3.5	4.0	4.5	5.0
6	4.2	4.8	5.4	6.0
7	4.9	5.6	6.3	7.0
8	5.6	6.4	7.2	8.0
9	6.3	7.2	8.1	9.0

	15	16	17	18
1	1.5	1.6	1.7	1.8
2	3.0	3.2	3.4	3.6
3	4.5	4.8	5.1	5.4
4	6.0	6.4	6.8	7.2
5	7.5	8.0	8.5	9.0
6	9.0	9.6	10.2	10.8
7	10.5	11.2	11.9	12.6
8	12.0	12.8	13.6	14.4
9	13.5	14.4	15.3	16.2

	23	24	25	26
1	2.3	2.4	2.5	2.6
2	4.6	4.8	5.0	5.2
3	6.9	7.2	7.5	7.8
4	9.2	9.6	10.0	10.4
5	11.5	12.0	12.5	13.0
6	13.8	14.4	15.0	15.6
7	16.1	16.8	17.5	18.2
8	18.4	19.2	20.0	20.8
9	20.7	21.6	22.5	23.4

	41	42	43
1	4.1	4.2	4.3
2	8.2	8.4	8.6
3	12.3	12.6	12.9
4	16.4	16.8	17.2
5	20.5	21.0	21.5
6	24.6	25.2	25.8
7	28.7	29.4	30.1
8	32.8	33.6	34.4
9	36.9	37.8	38.7

	56	57	58
1	5.6	5.7	5.8
2	11.2	11.4	11.6
3	16.8	17.1	17.4
4	22.4	22.8	23.2
5	28.0	28.5	29.0
6	33.6	34.2	34.8
7	39.2	39.9	40.6
8	44.8	45.6	46.4
9	50.4	51.3	52.2

→	Sin	Cos	Tan	Cot	Sec	Csc	
36° 00'	.5878	.8090	.7265	1.376	1.236	1.701	54° 00'
10'	901	073	310	368	239	695	53° 50'
20'	925	056	355	360	241	688	40'
30'	.5948	.8039	.7400	1.351	1.244	1.681	30'
40'	972	021	445	343	247	675	20'
36° 50'	.5995	.8004	490	335	249	668	10'
37° 00'	.6018	.7986	.7536	1.327	1.252	1.662	53° 00'
10'	041	969	581	319	255	655	52° 50'
20'	065	951	627	311	258	649	40'
30'	.6088	.7934	.7673	1.303	1.260	1.643	30'
40'	111	916	720	295	263	636	20'
37° 50'	134	898	766	288	266	630	10'
38° 00'	.6157	.7880	.7813	1.280	1.269	1.624	52° 00'
10'	180	862	860	272	272	618	51° 50'
20'	202	844	907	265	275	612	40'
30'	.6225	.7826	.7954	1.257	1.278	1.606	30'
40'	248	808	.8002	250	281	601	20'
38° 50'	271	790	050	242	284	595	10'
39° 00'	.6293	.7771	.8098	1.235	1.287	1.589	51° 00'
10'	316	753	146	228	290	583	50° 50'
20'	338	735	195	220	293	578	40'
30'	.6361	.7716	.8243	1.213	1.296	1.572	30'
40'	383	698	292	206	299	567	20'
39° 50'	406	679	342	199	302	561	10'
40° 00'	.6428	.7660	.8391	1.192	1.305	1.556	50° 00
10	450	642	441	185	309	550	49° 50'
20'	472	623	491	178	312	545	40'
30'	.6494	.7604	.8541	1.171	1.315	1.540	30'
40'	517	585	591	164	318	535	20'
40° 50'	539	566	642	157	322	529	10'
41° 00'	.6561	.7547	.8693	1.150	1.325	1.524	49° 00'
10'	583	528	744	144	328	519	48° 50'
20'	604	509	796	137	332	514	40'
30'	.6626	.7490	.8847	1.130	1.335	1.509	30'
40'	648	470	899	124	339	504	20'
41° 50'	670	451	.8952	117	342	499	10'
42° 00'	.6691	.7431	.9004	1.111	1.346	1.494	48° 00'
10'	713	412	057	104	349	490	47° 50'
20'	734	392	110	098	353	485	40'
30'	.6756	.7373	.9163	1.091	1.356	1.480	30'
40'	777	353	217	085	360	476	20'
42° 50'	799	333	271	079	364	471	10'
43° 00'	.6820	.7314	.9325	1.072	1.367	1.466	47° 00'
10'	841	294	380	066	371	462	46° 50'
20'	862	274	435	060	375	457	40'
30'	.6884	.7254	.9490	1.054	1.379	1.453	30'
40'	905	234	545	048	382	448	20'
43° 50'	926	214	601	042	386	444	10'
44° 00'	.6947	.7193	.9657	1.036	1.390	1.440	46° 00'
10'	967	173	713	030	394	435	45° 50'
20'	.6988	153	770	024	398	431	40'
30'	.7009	.7133	.9827	1.018	1.402	1.427	30'
40'	030	112	884	012	406	423	20'
44° 50'	050	092	.9942	006	410	418	10'
45° 00'	.7071	.7071	1.000	1.000	1.414	1.414	45° 00'
	Cos	Sin	Cot	Tan	Csc	Sec	←

VIII. RADIAN MEASURE: VALUES OF FUNCTIONS

α Rad.	Degrees in α	Sin α	Cos α	Tan α
.00	0° 00.0'	.00000	1.0000	.00000
.01	0° 34.4'	.01000	.99995	.01000
.02	1° 08.8'	.02000	.99980	.02000
.03	1° 43.1'	.03000	.99955	.03001
.04	2° 17.5'	.03999	.99920	.04002
.05	2° 51.9'	.04998	.99875	.05004
.06	3° 26.3'	.05996	.99820	.06007
.07	4° 00.6'	.06994	.99755	.07011
.08	4° 35.0'	.07991	.99680	.08017
.09	5° 09.4'	.08988	.99595	.09024
.10	5° 43.8'	.09983	.99500	.10033
.11	6° 18.2'	.10978	.99396	.11045
.12	6° 52.5'	.11971	.99281	.12058
.13	7° 26.9'	.12963	.99156	.13074
.14	8° 01.3'	.13954	.99022	.14092
.15	8° 35.7'	.14944	.98877	.15114
.16	9° 10.0'	.15932	.98723	.16138
.17	9° 44.4'	.16918	.98558	.17166
.18	10° 18.8'	.17903	.98384	.18197
.19	10° 53.2'	.18886	.98200	.19232
.20	11° 27.5'	.19867	.98007	.20271
.21	12° 01.9'	.20846	.97803	.21314
.22	12° 36.3'	.21823	.97590	.22362
.23	13° 10.7'	.22798	.97367	.23414
.24	13° 45.1'	.23770	.97134	.24472
.25	14° 19.4'	.24740	.96891	.25534
.26	14° 53.8'	.25708	.96639	.26602
.27	15° 28.2'	.26673	.96377	.27676
.28	16° 02.6'	.27636	.96106	.28755
.29	16° 36.9'	.28595	.95824	.29841
.30	17° 11.3'	.29552	.95534	.30934
.31	17° 45.7'	.30506	.95233	.32033
.32	18° 20.1'	.31457	.94924	.33139
.33	18° 54.5'	.32404	.94604	.34252
.34	19° 28.8'	.33349	.94275	.35374
.35	20° 03.2'	.34290	.93937	.36503
.36	20° 37.6'	.35227	.93590	.37640
.37	21° 12.0'	.36162	.93233	.38786
.38	21° 46.3'	.37092	.92866	.39941
.39	22° 20.7'	.38019	.92491	.41105
.40	22° 55.1'	.38942	.92106	.42279
.41	23° 29.5'	.39861	.91712	.43463
.42	24° 03.9'	.40776	.91309	.44657
.43	24° 38.2'	.41687	.90897	.45862
.44	25° 12.6'	.42594	.90475	.47078
.45	25° 47.0'	.43497	.90045	.48306
.46	26° 21.4'	.44395	.89605	.49545
.47	26° 55.7'	.45289	.89157	.50797
.48	27° 30.1'	.46178	.88699	.52061
.49	28° 04.5'	.47063	.88233	.53339
.50	28° 38.9'	.47943	.87758	.54630
.51	29° 13.3'	.48818	.87274	.55936
.52	29° 47.6'	.49688	.86782	.57256
.53	30° 22.0'	.50553	.86281	.58592
.54	30° 56.4'	.51414	.85771	.59943
.55	31° 30.8'	.52269	.85252	.61311
.56	32° 05.1'	.53119	.84726	.62695
.57	32° 39.5'	.53963	.84190	.64097
.58	33° 13.9'	.54802	.83646	.65517
.59	33° 48.3'	.55636	.83094	.66956
.60	34° 22.6'	.56464	.82534	.68414

α Rad.	Degrees in α	Sin α	Cos α	Tan α
.60	34° 22.6'	.56464	.82534	.68414
.61	34° 57.0'	.57287	.81965	.69892
.62	35° 31.4'	.58104	.81388	.71391
.63	36° 05.8'	.58914	.80803	.72911
.64	36° 40.2'	.59720	.80210	.74454
.65	37° 14.5'	.60519	.79608	.76020
.66	37° 48.9'	.61312	.78999	.77610
.67	38° 23.3'	.62099	.78382	.79225
.68	38° 57.7'	.62879	.77757	.80866
.69	39° 32.0'	.63654	.77125	.82534
.70	40° 06.4'	.64422	.76484	.84229
.71	40° 40.8'	.65183	.75836	.85953
.72	41° 15.2'	.65938	.75181	.87707
.73	41° 49.6'	.66687	.74517	.89492
.74	42° 23.9'	.67429	.73847	.91309
.75	42° 58.3'	.68164	.73169	.93160
.76	43° 32.7'	.68892	.72484	.95045
.77	44° 07.1'	.69614	.71791	.96967
.78	44° 41.4'	.70328	.71091	.98926
.79	45° 15.8'	.71035	.70385	1.0092
.80	45° 50.2'	.71736	.69671	1.0296
.81	46° 24.6'	.72429	.68950	1.0505
.82	46° 59.0'	.73115	.68222	1.0717
.83	47° 33.3'	.73793	.67488	1.0934
.84	48° 07.7'	.74464	.66746	1.1156
.85	48° 42.1'	.75128	.65998	1.1383
.86	49° 16.5'	.75784	.65244	1.1616
.87	49° 50.8'	.76433	.64483	1.1853
.88	50° 25.2'	.77074	.63715	1.2097
.89	50° 59.6'	.77707	.62941	1.2346
.90	51° 34.0'	.78333	.62161	1.2602
.91	52° 08.3'	.78950	.61375	1.2864
.92	52° 42.7'	.79560	.60582	1.3133
.93	53° 17.1'	.80162	.59783	1.3409
.94	53° 51.5'	.80756	.58979	1.3692
.95	54° 25.9'	.81342	.58168	1.3984
.96	55° 00.2'	.81919	.57352	1.4284
.97	55° 34.6'	.82489	.56530	1.4592
.98	56° 09.0'	.83050	.55702	1.4910
.99	56° 43.4'	.83603	.54869	1.5237
1.00	57° 17.7'	.84147	.54030	1.5574
1.01	57° 52.1'	.84683	.53186	1.5922
1.02	58° 26.5'	.85211	.52537	1.6281
1.03	59° 00.9'	.85730	.51482	1.6652
1.04	59° 35.3'	.86240	.50622	1.7036
1.05	60° 09.6'	.86742	.49757	1.7433
1.06	60° 44.0'	.87236	.48887	1.7844
1.07	61° 18.4'	.87720	.48012	1.8270
1.08	61° 52.8'	.88196	.47133	1.8712
1.09	62° 27.1'	.88663	.46249	1.9171
1.10	63° 01.5'	.89121	.45360	1.9648
1.11	63° 35.9'	.89570	.44466	2.0143
1.12	64° 10.3'	.90010	.43568	2.0660
1.13	64° 44.7'	.90441	.42666	2.1198
1.14	65° 19.0'	.90863	.41759	2.1759
1.15	65° 53.4'	.91276	.40849	2.2345
1.16	66° 27.8'	.91680	.39934	2.2958
1.17	67° 02.2'	.92075	.39015	2.3600
1.18	67° 36.5'	.92461	.38092	2.4273
1.19	68° 10.9'	.92837	.37166	2.4979
1.20	68° 45.3'	.93204	.36236	2.5722

VIII. RADIAN MEASURE: VALUES OF FUNCTIONS

α Rad.	Degrees in α	Sin α	Cos α	Tan α
1.20	68° 45.3'	.93204	.36236	2.5722
1.21	69° 19.7'	.93562	.35302	2.6503
1.22	69° 54.1'	93910	.34365	2.7328
1.23	70° 28.4'	.94249	.33424	2.8198
1.24	71° 02.8'	.94578	.32480	2.9119
1.25	71° 37.2'	.94898	.31532	3.0096
1.26	72° 11.6'	.95209	.30582	3.1133
1.27	72° 45.9'	.95510	.29628	3.2236
1.28	73° 20.3'	.95802	.28672	3.3413
1.29	73° 54.7'	.96084	.27712	3.4672
1.30	74° 29.1'	.96356	.26750	3.6021
1.31	75° 03.4'	.96618	.25785	3.7471
1.32	75° 37.8'	.96872	.24818	3.9033
1.33	76° 12.2'	.97115	.23848	4.0723
1.34	76° 46.6'	.97348	.22875	4.2556
1.35	77° 21.0'	.97572	.21901	4.4552
1.36	77° 55.3'	.97786	.20924	4.6734
1.37	78° 29.7'	.97991	.19945	4.9131
1.38	79° 04.1'	.98185	.18964	5.1774
1.39	79° 38.5'	.98370	.17981	5.4707
1.40	80° 12.8'	.98545	.16997	5.7979

α Rad.	Degrees in α	Sin α	Cos α	Tan α
1.40	80° 12.8'	.98545	.16997	5.7979
1.41	80° 47.2'	.98710	.16010	6.1654
1.42	81° 21.6'	.98865	.15023	6.5811
1.43	81° 56.0'	.99010	.14033	7.0555
1.44	82° 30.4'	.99146	.13042	7.6018
1.45	83° 04.7'	.99271	.12050	8.2381
1.46	83° 39.1'	.99387	.11057	8.9886
1.47	84° 13.5'	.99492	.10063	9.8874
1.48	84° 47.9'	.99588	.09067	10.983
1.49	85° 22.2'	.99674	.08071	12.350
1.50	85° 56.6'	.99749	.07074	14.101
1.51	86° 31.0'	.99815	.06076	16.428
1.52	87° 05.4'	.99871	.05077	19.670
1.53	87° 39.8'	.99917	.04079	24.498
1.54	88° 14.1'	.99953	.03079	32.461
1.55	88° 48.5'	.99978	.02079	48.078
1.56	89° 22.9'	.99994	.01080	92.620
1.57	89° 57.3'	1.0000	.00080	1255.8
1.58	90° 31.6'	.99996	− .00920	− 108.65
1.59	91° 06.0'	.99982	− .01920	− 52.067
1.60	91° 40.4'	.99957	− .02920	− 34.233

DEGREES IN RADIANS

°	rad	°	rad	°	rad	°	rad	°	rad	°	rad
1°	0.01745	16°	0.27925	31°	0.54105	46°	0.80285	61°	1.06465	76°	1.32645
2	0.03491	17	0.29671	32	0.55851	47	0.82030	62	1.08210	77	1.34390
3	0.05236	18	0.31416	33	0.57596	48	0.83776	63	1.09956	78	1.36136
4	0.06981	19	0.33161	34	0.59341	49	0.85521	64	1.11701	79	1.37881
5	0.08727	20	0.34907	35	0.61087	50	0.87266	65	1.13446	80	1.39626
6	0.10472	21	0.36652	36	0.62832	51	0.89012	66	1.15192	81	1.41372
7	0.12217	22	0.38397	37	0.64577	52	0.90757	67	1.16937	82	1.43117
8	0.13963	23	0.40143	38	0.66323	53	0.92502	68	1.18682	83	1.44862
9	0.15708	24	0.41888	39	0.68068	54	0.94248	69	1.20428	84	1.46608
10	0.17453	25	0.43633	40	0.69813	55	0.95993	70	1.22173	85	1.48353
11	0.19199	26	0.45379	41	0.71558	56	0.97738	71	1.23918	86	1.50098
12	0.20944	27	0.47124	42	0.73304	57	0.99484	72	1.25664	87	1.51844
13	0.22689	28	0.48869	43	0.75049	58	1.01229	73	1.27409	88	1.53589
14	0.24435	29	0.50615	44	0.76794	59	1.02974	74	1.29154	89	1.55334
15	0.26180	30	0.52360	45	0.78540	60	1.04720	75	1.30900	90	1.57080

1° = .01745329 rad.   log .01745329 = 8.24187737 − 10.
1' = .0002908882 rad.   log .0002908882 = 6.46372612 − 10.
1" = .0000048481368 rad.   log .0000048481368 = 4.68557487 − 10.

MINUTES IN RADIANS

'	rad	'	rad	'	rad	'	rad	'	rad	'	rad
1'	0.00029	11'	0.00320	21'	0.00611	31'	0.00902	41'	0.01193	51'	0.01484
2	0.00058	12	0.00349	22	0.00640	32	0.00931	42	0.01222	52	0.01513
3	0.00087	13	0.00378	23	0.00669	33	0.00960	43	0.01251	53	0.01542
4	0.00116	14	0.00407	24	0.00698	34	0.00989	44	0.01280	54	0.01571
5	0.00145	15	0.00436	25	0.00727	35	0.01018	45	0.01309	55	0.01600
6	0.00175	16	0.00465	26	0.00756	36	0.01047	46	0.01338	56	0.01629
7	0.00204	17	0.00495	27	0.00785	37	0.01076	47	0.01367	57	0.01658
8	0.00233	18	0.00524	28	0.00814	38	0.01105	48	0.01396	58	0.01687
9	0.00262	19	0.00553	29	0.00844	39	0.01134	49	0.01425	59	0.01716
10	0.00291	20	0.00582	30	0.00873	40	0.01164	50	0.01454	60	0.01745

IX. COMMISSIONERS 1941 STANDARD ORDINARY
MORTALITY TABLE

Age	Number Living l_x	Number Dying d_x	Rate of Mortality q_x	Age	Number Living l_x	Number Dying d_x	Rate of Mortality q_x
0	1,023,102	23,102	.02258	50	810,900	9,990	.01232
1	1,000,000	5,770	.00577	51	800,910	10,628	.01327
2	994,230	4,116	.00414	52	790,282	11,301	.01430
3	990,114	3,347	.00338	53	778,981	12,020	.01543
4	986,767	2,950	.00299	54	766,961	12,770	.01665
5	983,817	2,715	.00276	55	754,191	13,560	.01798
6	981,102	2,561	.00261	56	740,631	14,390	.01943
7	978,541	2,417	.00247	57	726,241	15,251	.02100
8	976,124	2,255	.00231	58	710,990	16,147	.02271
9	973,869	2,065	.00212	59	694,843	17,072	.02457
10	971,804	1,914	.00197	60	677,771	18,022	.02659
11	969,890	1,852	.00191	61	659,749	18,988	.02878
12	968,038	1,859	.00192	62	640,761	19,979	.03118
13	966,179	1,913	.00198	63	620,782	20,958	.03376
14	964,266	1,996	.00207	64	599,824	21,942	.03658
15	962,270	2,069	.00215	65	577,882	22,907	.03964
16	960,201	2,103	.00219	66	554,975	23,842	.04296
17	958,098	2,156	.00225	67	531,133	24,730	.04656
18	955,942	2,199	.00230	68	506,403	25,553	.05046
19	953,743	2,260	.00237	69	480,850	26,302	.05470
20	951,483	2,312	.00243	70	454,548	26,955	.05930
21	949,171	2,382	.00251	71	427,593	27,481	.06427
22	946,789	2,452	.00259	72	400,112	27,872	.06966
23	944,337	2,531	.00268	73	372,240	28,104	.07550
24	941,806	2,609	.00277	74	344,136	28,154	.08181
25	939,197	2,705	.00288	75	315,982	28,009	.08864
26	936,492	2,800	.00299	76	287,973	27,651	.09602
27	933,692	2,904	.00311	77	260,322	27,071	.10399
28	930,788	3,025	.00325	78	233,251	26,262	.11259
29	927,763	3,154	.00340	79	206,989	25,224	.12186
30	924,609	3,292	.00356	80	181,765	23,966	.13185
31	921,317	3,437	.00373	81	157,799	22,502	.14260
32	917,880	3,598	.00392	82	135,297	20,857	.15416
33	914,282	3,767	.00412	83	114,440	19,062	.16657
34	910,515	3,961	.00435	84	95,378	17,157	.17988
35	906,554	4,161	.00459	85	78,221	15,185	.19413
36	902,393	4,386	.00486	86	63,036	13,198	.20937
37	898,007	4,625	.00515	87	49,838	11,245	.22563
38	893,382	4,878	.00546	88	38,593	9,378	.24300
39	888,504	5,162	.00581	89	29,215	7,638	.26144
40	883,342	5,459	.00618	90	21,577	6,063	.28099
41	877,883	5,785	.00659	91	15,514	4,681	.30173
42	872,098	6,131	.00703	92	10,833	3,506	.32364
43	865,967	6,503	.00751	93	7,327	2,540	.34666
44	859,464	6,910	.00804	94	4,787	1,776	.37100
45	852,554	7,340	.00861	95	3,011	1,193	.39621
46	845,214	7,801	.00923	96	1,818	813	.44719
47	837,413	8,299	.00991	97	1,005	551	.54826
48	829,114	8,822	.01064	98	454	329	.72467
49	820,292	9,392	.01145	99	125	125	1.00000

Answers to Exercises

Note. Answers to odd-numbered problems are given here. Answers to even-numbered problems are furnished in a separate pamphlet, when ordered by the instructor.

Exercise 1. Page 9

1. 5.
3. 44.
5. -12.
7. 0.
9. -9.
11. 36.
13. $-16a + 6b + 2c$.
15. $11a$.
17. $-18x$.
19. $6cd$.
21. $9a - 20b$.
23. $3a + 14h - 23k$.
25. $2t - 3$.
27. $2a$.
29. $-s - r$.
31. $4y - 12$.
33. $10 - 5b$.
35. $-6a - (c - 4b)$.
37. $2a - 3 - (c - 5b)$.
39. 17; 46; 33; $\frac{3}{4}$; 1.48.
41. -7; 4; $\frac{2}{3}$; 8; -16.7; 0.
43. $5a - h$.

Exercise 3. Page 14

1. $\frac{5}{6}$.
3. $\frac{8}{15}$.
5. $\frac{5}{3}$.
7. $-\frac{4}{7}$.
9. $-\frac{7}{3}$.
11. $\frac{12}{35}$.
13. $\frac{45}{4}$.
15. $\frac{6}{5}$.
17. $\frac{2}{9}$.
19. $\frac{21}{8}$.
21. $\frac{76}{15}$.
23. $5a/9$.
25. $\frac{4}{15}$.
27. $\frac{35}{4}$.
29. $3x/7$.
31. $d/4$.
33. $h/2$.
35. $-b/3$.
37. $1/4b$.
39. $\frac{4}{35}$.
41. $7/15a$.
43. $\frac{3}{14}$.
45. $6c/5d$.
47. $\frac{21}{2}$.
49. $9/2b$.
51. $\frac{5}{14}$.
53. $h/2k$.
55. 4.
57. $\frac{50}{3}$.
59. $\frac{7}{5}$.
61. $2ad/c$.
63. $\frac{8}{125}$.
65. $-\frac{1}{8}$.

Exercise 4. Page 17

1. 64.
3. 1.
5. -32.
7. 10,000.
9. $\frac{4}{25}$.
11. $-\frac{1}{8}$.
13. -64.
15. 24.
17. 64.
19. 32.
21. a^9.
23. y^{10}.
25. u^6.
27. x^4y^4.
29. c^{15}.
31. h^{4n}.
33. $-\frac{27}{8}$.
35. a^6x^3.
37. $h^5/32$.
39. x^4/y^6.
41. y^2.
43. $1/x^2$.
45. a^4.
47. $\frac{1}{32}$.
49. x.
51. $a^{12}x^8$.
53. $-27x^6y^3$.
55. $8a^3/27x^3$.
57. $-27x^3/y^3z^3$.
59. $-7a$.
61. $1/3c^3$.
63. $10x^6$.
65. $3a^3b$.
67. $6a^3x^5$.
69. $-98a^8b^4$.
71. $-24h^5r^3$.
73. $-10w + 15w^2 - 20w^3$.
75. ± 5.
77. ± 11.
79. $\pm \frac{1}{3}$.
81. 3.
83. 9.
85. 14.
87. $\frac{4}{5}$.
89. $\frac{1}{9}$.
91. $\frac{2}{9}$.
93. $2z^4$.
95. $7z^3$.
97. $8w^3x^2$.
99. $7w^2x^2$.
101. $\dfrac{3}{a}$.
103. $\dfrac{y}{4}$.
105. $\dfrac{7}{w^2}$.
107. $\dfrac{a}{y^2}$ if $a > 0$; $-\dfrac{a}{y^2}$ if $a < 0$. *
109. $\dfrac{2x}{h^4}$ if $x > 0$; $-\dfrac{2x}{h^4}$ if $x < 0$.
111. $\dfrac{9a}{yz}$, etc., as in Problem 107.
113. $\dfrac{3ab^2}{c^3w^5}$.
115. $\dfrac{11a^3}{3b^2z^3}$.
117. $37/x$.
119. yz^3.

* Similarly, two results correspond usually to any problem involving a root with even index, leading to a factor which is a literal number with an odd exponent. The second answer above is ruled out by the last paragraph on page 16, and is given merely to emphasize the effect of that paragraph. Hereafter, the two results will not be listed, as in Problems 107–109. The result in the answer book will be the correct expression under the hypothesis that all literal numbers which occur as original factors are positive in the radicand, as stated on page 16.

Exercise 5. Page 21

1. $6 - x^2 - 15x^4$.

3. $x^3 - x^2 - 11x + 15$.

5. $6 - 5x - 6x^2 - x^3$.

7. $6x^4 - 7x^3 + 12x^2 - 19x + 7$.

9. $6a^3 - 11a^2 - 17a + 30$.

11. $x^{3n} - 27y^{3k}$.

13. $\dfrac{3a}{2b} - \dfrac{9a^2}{4b^4}$.

15. $\dfrac{1}{2u^4v} - \dfrac{1}{6u^3} + \dfrac{3v^2}{2u}$.

17. $d - 7 + \dfrac{3}{d - 5}$.

19. $3u + v$.

21. $x^3 + 2$.

23. $x^2 + 2x - 3$.

25. $2y^2 + y - 6 + \dfrac{11}{2y + 3}$.

27. $2y - 3 - \dfrac{2y}{4y^2 - 3y + 2}$.

29. $3x^{2h} + 12x^h + 17 + \dfrac{68}{x^h - 3}$.

31. $h^2 + 2hk + k^2$. **33.** $x^2 - 4y^2$. **35.** $64 - x^2$. **37.** $9 + 6x + x^2$.

39. $25 - 4y^2$. **41.** $9x^2 - 16z^2$. **43.** $a^2b^2 - 4$.

45. $c^2 + 6c + 9$. **47.** $4z^2 - 4wz + w^2$. **49.** $36a^2 + 36ab + 9b^2$.

51. $6 + 5x + x^2$. **53.** $x^2 + 4x - 45$. **55.** $a^2 + 5ab + 6b^2$.

57. $6x^2 + 17x + 12$. **59.** $8y^2 - 10xy + 3x^2$. **61.** $6y^2 + y - 15$.

63. $x^2 + 2xy + y^2 + 4x + 4y + 4$. **65.** $9 - 12x + 6y + 4x^2 - 4xy + y^2$.

67. $9x^2 + 6xy + y^2 + 30x + 10y + 25$.

69. $4x^2 - 12x^3 + 9x^4 + 12xy - 18x^2y + 9y^2$.

71. $c^2 + 4cx + 4x^2 - 4$. **73.** $a^2 + 2aw + w^2 - 16$.

75. $9x^2 + 6xy + y^2 - 4$. **77.** $x^2 + y^2 + z^2 + 2xy + 2xz + 2yz$.

Exercise 6. Page 24

1. $a(x + y)$.

3. $x(b - a)$.

5. $t(t - 4a - ct^2)$.

7. $(2x - y)(2x + y)$.

9. $(2a - 3b)(2a + 3b)$.

11. $(3z - \tfrac{1}{2})(3z + \tfrac{1}{2})$.

13. $(5w - cd)(5w + cd)$.

15. $(2x + 3)^2$.

17. $(3x^2 - 1)^2$.

19. $(a + 2)^2$.

21. $(d + y)^2$.

23. $(a - 7b)^2$.

25. $(3a - 5b)^2$.

27. $(a - 6)(a - 2)$.

29. $(z - 6)(z + 1)$.

31. $(5 - x)(3 - x)$.

33. $(4 + y)(1 - y)$.

35. $(2x + y)(x + 3y)$.

37. $(2x + 5y)(x - y)$.

39. $(3u - 2)(u + 3)$.

41. $(5x + 3)(2x + 1)$.

43. $(3a - 7)(a - 1)$.

45. $(2 + 9x)(1 - 3x)$.

47. $(5a + 9b)(a + b)$.

49. $(3x + 2y)(x + y)$.

51. $(9x + 2y)(5x - 2y)$.

53. $x^2(2x - 1)(4x - 3)$.

55. $(r + s)(2d - 5c)$.

57. $(w - z)(3h - 1)$.

59. $(c - d)(2x + y)$.

61. $4(h - 2c)(x - b)$.

63. $(x - 2)(x + 1)(x - 1)$.

65. $(x^2 + 1)(x + 2)$.

67. $(x^2 + 1)(x - 3)$.

69. $(8a - 3c)^2$.

71. $2c(2a - 3c)(2a + 3c)$.

73. $(9c^2 + 4d^2)(3c - 2d)(3c + 2d)$.

75. $(2w + 5 - 9z)(2w + 5 + 9z)$.

77. $(y + z - 2x)(y + z + 2x)$.

79. $(3w - 2a - b)(3w + 2a + b)$.

81. $(2a + 3z + 1)(2a - 3z - 1)$.

83. $(5 - 3z - 3w)(3 + 2z + 2w)$.

85. $(3x - 3y - 4)(2x - 2y - 1)$.

87. $2(5x + 5y - 3w)(2x + 2y - w)$.

Exercise 7. Page 27

1. $c^3 + w^3$.   **3.** $u^3 - v^3$.   **5.** $c^3 + 3c^2d + 3cd^2 + d^3$.

7. $y^3 - 9xy^2 + 27x^2y - 27x^3$.   **9.** $8 + 12y + 6y^2 + y^3$.

11. $a^3 - 3a^2b^2 + 3ab^4 - b^6$.   **13.** $a^2 + ah + h^2$.

15. $x^3 + x^2y + xy^2 + y^3$.   **17.** $a^4 - a^3y + a^2y^2 - ay^3 + y^4$.

19. $x^4 + x^3 + x^2 + x + 1$.   **21.** $a^6 + 2a^4b + 4a^2b^2 + 8b^3$.

23. $(d - y)(d^2 + dy + y^2)$.   **25.** $(z + 10)(z^2 - 10z + 100)$.

27. $(h + z)(h^2 - hz + z^2)$.   **29.** $(2x - 5y)(4x^2 + 10xy + 25y^2)$.

31. $(a - c)(a^4 + a^3c + a^2c^2 + ac^3 + c^4)$.

33. $(h + k)(h^2 - hk + k^2)(h^6 - h^3k^3 + k^6)$.

35. $(a - w)(a + w)(a^2 + w^2)$.

37. $(x^8 + y^8)(x^4 + y^4)(x^2 + y^2)(x + y)(x - y)$.

39. $(2x^2 - 2x + 1)(2x^2 + 2x + 1)$.

41. $(4x^2 + y^4)(2x - y^2)(2x + y^2)$.

43. $(2w^2x^2 - 6wzx + 9z^2)(2w^2x^2 + 6wzx + 9z^2)$.

Exercise 8. Page 28

1. $\dfrac{3}{5}$.   **3.** $\dfrac{3}{5ab}$.   **5.** $\dfrac{3}{2y}$.   **7.** $\dfrac{a}{c}$.   **9.** $\dfrac{a}{2c}$.

11. $\dfrac{a}{c}$.   **13.** $\dfrac{2a - b}{2}$.   **15.** $\dfrac{5x + 10}{2}$.   **17.** $\dfrac{u}{c}$.

19. $\dfrac{a - 1}{a + 4}$.   **21.** $\dfrac{3 - x}{1 + x}$.   **23.** $\dfrac{y + 4}{1 - y}$.   **25.** $\dfrac{5a - 3b}{2a^2b}$.

27. $-\dfrac{1}{3}$.   **29.** $-\dfrac{2}{x + y}$.   **31.** $\dfrac{a^2 + ab + b^2}{2a + 2b}$.   **33.** $\dfrac{9x^2 + 6xy + 4y^2}{xz + yz}$.

35. $-\dfrac{c}{4a}$.   **37.** $-\dfrac{2}{3}$.

Exercise 9. Page 31

1. $\dfrac{2 + b - a}{3}$.   **3.** $\dfrac{9a - 8}{6}$.   **5.** $\dfrac{15}{14}$.

7. $\dfrac{2 - 3x + 6y}{9}$.   **9.** $\dfrac{20 - 3a + b}{5}$.   **11.** $\dfrac{1 + 4x}{12}$.

13. $\dfrac{3 - 10a}{12a}$.   **15.** $\dfrac{3h - 4kw}{12k^2}$.   **17.** $\dfrac{21y^3 - 10x}{14x^2y^3}$.

19. $\dfrac{6xy^2 - 4x + y}{4x^2y^3}$.   **21.** $\dfrac{15a^2 - 2a - 4}{6a - 4}$.   **23.** $\dfrac{11}{10a - 10b}$.

25. $\dfrac{14}{15(x - y)}$.   **27.** $\dfrac{6x^2 - 5xy + 6y^2}{9x^2 - 4y^2}$.   **29.** $\dfrac{11x + 4}{12x^2 - 3}$.

31. $\dfrac{3x + 6y - 10}{2x^2 - 8y^2}$.   **33.** $\dfrac{5x + 60}{48x - 3x^3}$.   **35.** $\dfrac{23a - 8}{2a - 4}$.

37. $\dfrac{19}{60 - 4x - x^2}$.   **39.** $\dfrac{4a}{(a + 4)^2(a - 4)}$.   **41.** $\dfrac{6a^2 - 21a - 18}{2(a^2 - 9)(3a - 2)}$.

43. $\dfrac{12x^3 + 25x^2 + 39x + 13}{27 - 8x^3}$.

45. $\dfrac{13x^2 + 2x + 3xy + 3y^2}{2(x^3 - y^3)}$.

47. $\dfrac{9 - 12x^3}{(2x^3 - 1)(x^6 - 4)}$.

Exercise 10. Page 33

1. $\frac{2}{3}$.

3. $\frac{4}{15}$.

5. $\dfrac{5x}{3}$.

7. $\frac{2}{3}$.

9. $-\dfrac{hw}{3a}$.

11. $\dfrac{y^2 - y - 6}{y}$.

13. $\dfrac{2(2x - y)}{3(x - y)}$.

15. $\dfrac{(x + 3)(x - 5y)}{2x}$.

17. $\dfrac{(a - b)(2a - 3b)}{2}$.

19. $\dfrac{wx(4 - x)}{ch(5 - x)}$.

21. $\dfrac{4x + 5}{3x + 1}$.

23. $\dfrac{(x - 1)(x + 4)}{x}$.

25. $\dfrac{5 + 3x}{x^2 + 3x}$.

27. $\frac{5}{3}$.

29. $\frac{26}{55}$.

31. $\dfrac{3y - 2x}{5y + 6x}$.

33. $\dfrac{xy}{2x + 3y}$.

35. $\dfrac{50ab - 15}{a^2b}$.

37. $\dfrac{1 + x^2}{2}$.

39. $\dfrac{(a - b)(3b - 2a)}{a + b}$.

41. $\dfrac{3x + 4}{x - 2}$.

43. $\dfrac{2y(y^2 + xy + x^2)}{x^2}$.

45. $\dfrac{y^2 + 2y}{y + 5}$.

Exercise 11. Page 37

1. $-\frac{5}{2}$.

3. -3.

5. $\frac{1}{2}$.

7. 0.

9. $\frac{5}{4}$.

11. $\frac{2}{5}$.

13. $.11$.

15. -3.

17. 2.4.

19. 15.

21. $\frac{2}{3}$.

23. 8.

25. 1.

27. 6.

29. $\frac{3}{2}$.

31. 2.

33. 4.

35. 17.

37. 3.

39. $\dfrac{a + 15}{6}$.

41. $\dfrac{12}{3h - c}$.

43. $\dfrac{2}{a + 3}$.

45. $\dfrac{4a + 5c}{2a - 3b}$.

47. $\dfrac{c}{3b}$.

49. $2cd$.

51. $\dfrac{2ab}{3c}$.

53. $\dfrac{ABC}{12}$.

55. $\dfrac{15ac}{2a + 9c}$.

57. $\dfrac{14a - 14ac}{a^2 - 7d}$.

59. $-\dfrac{1}{b}$.

61. $6 + 2a$.

63. $\dfrac{b}{5a + d}$.

65. $\dfrac{3c - d}{2a}$.

Exercise 12. Page 39

1. 2.

3. $-\frac{3}{14}$.

5. -5.

7. 11.

9. 2.

11. -3.

13. $-\frac{3}{2}$.

15. $-\frac{13}{4}$.

17. -2.

19. 1.

21. 5.

23. No sol.

25. $\frac{3}{2}$.

Exercise 13. Page 42

1. $32'$ and $43'$.

3. 36 and 37.

5. $12'$ and $15'$.

7. 7%; $9\frac{1}{4}\%$; $5\frac{3}{4}\%$; 135%.

9. $37\frac{1}{2}\%$ of 200; 175% of 200.

11. 600.

13. 140.

15. $\$240$.

17. $\$72$; $\$3072$.

19. $\$263.33$.

21. $\$20,000$.

23. $\$4166.67$.

25. 20 lb. at $80\cent$ and 80 lb. at $90\cent$.

27. 20.

29. At end $2\frac{2}{13}$ hr.

31. 10 oz. silver; 18 oz. copper.

33. $8\frac{2}{11}$ ft. from lighter girl.

35. Jones, 150 lb.; Roberts, 200 lb.

Exercise 14. Page 46

1. $2i$. 3. $6i$. 5. $\frac{1}{2}i$. 7. $\frac{6}{7}i$.
9. $2ci$. 11. $\pm 10i$. 13. $\pm 9i$. 15. $\pm 12i$.
17. -1. 19. i. 21. $-i$. 23. $-16 + 11i$.
25. $20i - 21$. 27. $-55 - 48i$. 29. -24. 31. -30.

Exercise 15. Page 48

1. ± 6. 3. ± 8. 5. $\pm \frac{1}{4}$. 7. $\pm .2$. 9. 11. 11. $\frac{1}{9}$.
13. $\frac{5}{6}$. 15. -2. 17. 5. 19. -1. 21. 3. 23. $\frac{1}{2}$.
25. 4. 27. $-a$. 29. y. 31. 2. 33. 29. 35. -19.
37. 9. 39. -2. 41. $\frac{1}{2}$. 43. 4. 45. 5. 47. 10.
49. 10. 51. y^4. 53. x^2. 55. $2y$. 57. $\frac{3}{4}$. 59. $\frac{2}{3}$.
61. $\frac{3}{4}$. 63. $\frac{2}{3}$. 65. $2y$. 67. $-x$. 69. y^2w^3. 71. $2a^2y^3$.
73. $-2xy^4$. 75. $3a^2/5y^4$. 77. $-4/a^2b^3$.

Exercise 16. Page 50

1. 2. 3. 2. 5. $\frac{1}{3}$. 7. $\frac{1}{28}$. 9. 12.
11. $\frac{1}{25}$. 13. $\frac{1}{64}$. 15. 2. 17. $\frac{1}{3}$. 19. 6.
21. $\frac{1}{3}$. 23. $\frac{1}{3}$. 25. $\frac{3}{2}$. 27. .2. 29. $-\frac{1}{8}$.
31. -1. 33. .6. 35. $-\frac{125}{8}$. 37. $\frac{1}{8}$. 39. -5.
41. 216. 43. 1728. 45. 625. 47. $\frac{3125}{243}$. 49. 4.
51. $\frac{1}{b^3}$. 53. $\frac{y}{x^3}$. 55. $\frac{c^2}{y^3}$. 57. $\frac{3z}{y^2}$. 59. $\frac{4y}{x^3}$.
61. $3x^{-5}$. 63. $3^{-1}y^2$. 65. $5x^{\frac{1}{2}}y^{-3}$. 67. $3(1.04)^{-6}$. 69. $B(1+i)^{-n}$.
71. $\sqrt[3]{z}$. 73. $\sqrt[3]{b^2}$. 75. $6\sqrt[5]{x^2}$. 77. $b\sqrt[4]{x^3}$. 79. $x^{\frac{2}{3}}$.
81. x^2. 83. $\sqrt{27a^3}$. 85. $\frac{1}{6}$. 87. $\frac{3}{16}$. 89. $\frac{6}{25}$.
91. $\frac{16}{5}$. 93. $a^{\frac{10}{3}}$. 95. y^5. 97. 256. 99. 729.
101. $\frac{1}{81x^4}$. 103. $a^{\frac{5}{2}}$. 105. $\frac{1}{a^{\frac{1}{3}}}$. 107. $\frac{y^4}{x^6}$. 109. $\frac{5}{(1+r)^6}$.
111. $(1+r)^{\frac{5}{3}}$. 113. $\frac{4y^6}{a^{\frac{1}{2}}}$. 115. $\frac{16a^2b^4}{25x^4}$.

Exercise 17. Page 53

1. $3\sqrt{3}$. 3. $10\sqrt{3}$. 5. $3\sqrt[3]{3}$. 7. $-\sqrt[3]{5}$. 9. $y^2\sqrt[3]{y^2}$.
11. $2z\sqrt[4]{z^2}$. 13. $5x^2y^4\sqrt{3y}$. 15. $-4a^3\sqrt[3]{2}$.
17. $\frac{2b}{3uv}\sqrt[4]{\frac{a^2b^2}{v}}$. 19. $-\frac{2a^2}{xy}\sqrt[3]{\frac{2a}{y}}$. 21. $\sqrt{9x^2 + y^2}$.
23. $\sqrt{45a}$. 25. $\sqrt[3]{27x}$. 27. $-5\sqrt{5}$. 29. $3\sqrt{6}$. 31. $\sqrt{10}$.
33. 3. 35. 3. 37. 54. 39. $\sqrt{5}$. 41. $\sqrt[3]{4}$.
43. $3y^2\sqrt{5y}$. 45. $25(x-y)$. 47. $8a^3(b+c)$. 49. -2.
51. $6 - 9\sqrt{2}$. 53. $\frac{1}{5}\sqrt{5}$. 55. $\frac{1}{6}\sqrt{30}$. 57. $\frac{1}{9}\sqrt{15}$.
59. $\frac{1}{6}\sqrt[3]{6}$. 61. $\frac{1}{5}\sqrt[3]{15}$. 63. $\frac{1}{10}\sqrt[3]{30}$. 65. $\frac{1}{10}\sqrt{10}$.
67. $\frac{1}{2}\sqrt[3]{6}$. 69. $\frac{1}{3}\sqrt[3]{6}$. 71. $-\frac{1}{10}\sqrt[3]{30}$. 73. $-\frac{2}{5}\sqrt[3]{2}$.
75. $-1 - \sqrt{5}$. 77. $\sqrt{5} + \sqrt{3}$. 79. $\frac{11}{13} + \frac{4}{13}\sqrt{10}$. 81. $-\frac{13}{7} - \frac{8}{21}\sqrt{30}$.

83. $\frac{1}{5}\sqrt{15x}$.

85. $\frac{1}{2y}\sqrt{6xy}$.

87. $\frac{1}{3}\sqrt[3]{3c}$.

89. $\frac{1}{3c}\sqrt[3]{9abc^2}$.

91. $\frac{1}{3d}\sqrt[3]{9cd}$.

93. $\frac{1}{a}\sqrt[4]{a}$.

95. $\frac{x}{y^2}\sqrt{y}$.

97. $\frac{1}{2x}\sqrt{2ax^2-20x}$.

99. $\frac{1}{2bx}\sqrt{8b^2x+2bx^3}$.

Exercise 18. Page 55

1. $\sqrt[15]{a^8}$.

3. $3\sqrt[3]{c^2}$.

5. $2\sqrt[12]{a^9b^4}$.

7. $b\sqrt[6]{b^3c^4}$.

9. $a\sqrt[4]{a^2y^3}$.

11. $3a^2b\sqrt[4]{a^2b^3}$.

13. $a^2b^2\sqrt[3]{b}$.

15. $xyz^3\sqrt[6]{y^4z^3}$.

17. $\sqrt{z}$.

19. $\sqrt[4]{u^2}$.

21. $\sqrt[3]{a^2}$.

23. $\sqrt{2}$.

25. $\sqrt[4]{5}$.

27. $\sqrt[3]{7}$.

29. $\sqrt[4]{3}$.

31. $\sqrt[4]{4}$.

33. $\sqrt[4]{2x}$.

35. $\sqrt[3]{3a}$.

37. $a^{\frac{3}{2}}=a\sqrt{a}$.

39. $b^{\frac{4}{3}}=b\sqrt[3]{b}$.

41. $x^{\frac{3}{4}}=\sqrt[4]{x^3}$.

43. y^2.

45. $a^{\frac{4}{5}}=\sqrt[5]{a^4}$.

47. $3^{\frac{5}{2}}=9\sqrt{3}$.

49. $2^{\frac{3}{2}}a^{\frac{3}{2}}=2a\sqrt{2a}$.

51. $2^{\frac{3}{2}}x^{\frac{15}{2}}=2x^7\sqrt{2x}$.

53. $x^{\frac{1}{6}}=\sqrt[6]{x}$.

55. $z^{\frac{1}{15}}=\sqrt[15]{z}$.

57. 144.

59. $a^{\frac{2}{5}}=\sqrt[5]{a^2}$.

61. $x^{\frac{5}{6}}=\sqrt[6]{x^5}$.

63. $y^{\frac{7}{12}}=\sqrt[12]{y^7}$.

65. $5^{\frac{5}{6}}=\sqrt[6]{5^5}$.

67. $x^{\frac{7}{6}}=x\sqrt[6]{x}$.

69. $3^{\frac{13}{12}}=3\sqrt[12]{3}$.

71. $2^{\frac{17}{12}}=2\sqrt[12]{32}$.

73. $\frac{1}{x^{\frac{1}{6}}}=\frac{1}{x}\sqrt[6]{x^5}$.

75. $y^{\frac{1}{12}}=\sqrt[12]{y}$.

77. 1.

79. $\frac{2^{\frac{1}{2}}}{3^{\frac{1}{2}}}=\frac{1}{3}\sqrt{6}$.

81. $\frac{1}{3^{\frac{1}{2}}x^{\frac{3}{4}}}=\frac{1}{3x}\sqrt[4]{9x}$.

83. $2^{\frac{1}{6}}=\sqrt[6]{2}$.

85. $\frac{3^{\frac{1}{2}}}{2^{\frac{1}{6}}}=\frac{1}{2}\sqrt[6]{864}$.

87. $d^{\frac{1}{4}}=\sqrt[4]{d}$.

89. $\frac{3^{\frac{4}{3}}}{x^{\frac{4}{3}}}=\frac{3}{x^2}\sqrt[3]{3x^2}$.

91. $3^{\frac{1}{4}}x^{\frac{1}{4}}=\sqrt[4]{3x}$.

93. $3(2^{\frac{1}{2}}a^{\frac{1}{2}})=3\sqrt{2a}$.

95. $2^{\frac{1}{2}}b^{\frac{3}{2}}=b\sqrt{2b}$.

97. $2^{\frac{1}{3}}y^{\frac{2}{3}}=\sqrt[3]{2y^2}$.

99. $3^{\frac{13}{12}}=3\sqrt[12]{3}$.

101. $\frac{(x^3+y^3)^{\frac{1}{3}}}{xy}=\frac{1}{xy}\sqrt[3]{x^3+y^3}$.

103. $a^{\frac{1}{18}}=\sqrt[18]{a}$.

105. $5^{\frac{4}{3}}a^4=5a^4\sqrt[3]{5}$.

107. $6^{\frac{5}{3}}d^5=6d^5\sqrt[3]{36}$.

109. $\frac{a^{\frac{1}{3}}}{b^{\frac{4}{3}}}=\frac{1}{b^2}\sqrt[3]{ab^2}$.

111. $\frac{2^{\frac{3}{2}}a^{\frac{1}{2}}}{3^{\frac{1}{2}}b^{\frac{3}{2}}}=\frac{2}{3b^2}\sqrt{6ab}$.

113. $\frac{a^{\frac{1}{2}}b^{\frac{1}{2}}}{2^{\frac{1}{2}}x^{\frac{1}{2}}}=\frac{1}{2x}\sqrt{2abx}$.

Exercise 19. Page 56

1. -10.

3. 0.

5. $-\frac{5}{7}$.

7. $\frac{8}{15}$.

9. $\frac{51}{7}$.

11. $\frac{28}{3}$.

13. $\frac{17}{6}$.

15. -16.

17. $>$.

19. 7.

21. $-2a+6b+2c$.

23. $-6x^4y^4+10x^3y^5$.

25. $15-2a$.

27. $\frac{1}{7c^2d^2}$.

29. a^4.

31. $81x^8y^{12}$.

33. $625c^8d^{12}y^4$.

35. $\frac{9a^2}{16x^2}$.

37. $-\frac{32}{243a^{10}}$.

39. $\frac{2a-5h}{2ah^2}$.

41. $\frac{7-4x}{2x^2}$.

43. $6x^2 - 13xy + 5y^2$.

45. $27 + b^3$.

47. $9h^2 + 24hk + 16k^2$.

49. $3x^2 - 5x + 3$.

51. $\frac{31}{12} - a$.

53. $\dfrac{6y^2 - 9xy^2 - 20x + 12xy}{12x^2y^3}$.

55. $\dfrac{3}{3a^2 + 5a}$.

57. $\dfrac{5x^2 - 2x + 16}{6x^2 - 17x + 5}$.

59. $\dfrac{3c - b - 3b^2 - 3bc}{c^2 - b^2}$.

61. $(y - 5z)(y + 5z)$.

63. $(z - 4y)^2$.

65. $(a - 3b)(a^2 + 3ab + 9b^2)$.

67. $(3y + 2z^2)^2$.

69. $(z + 7)(z - 3)$.

71. $(2 - 3x)(1 + 4x)$.

73. $5(z - 3w)^2$.

75. $2(a - 1)(a + 1)(a + 2)$.

77. $(x - a - 3b)(x + a + 3b)$.

79. $\frac{1}{625}$.

81. 1.

83. 2.828.

85. $\frac{1}{8}$.

87. .408.

89. 973.

91. .559.

93. 1.162.

95. 243.

97. 5.

99. 2.309.

101. $\frac{1}{2}$.

103. $-$ .572.

105. $h^{\frac{3}{4}} = h\sqrt[4]{h^3}$.

107. $2^{\frac{4}{3}}z^{\frac{5}{3}} = 2z\sqrt[3]{2z^2}$.

109. $2^{\frac{1}{2}}h^{\frac{1}{2}} = \sqrt{2h}$.

111. $2y^{\frac{1}{2}} = 2\sqrt{y}$.

113. $\dfrac{5}{x^3}$.

115. $\dfrac{1}{27a^6}$.

117. $81c^4d^{\frac{2}{3}} = 81c^4d^2\sqrt[3]{d^2}$.

119. $\sqrt{x}$.

121. $a^{\frac{7}{12}} = \sqrt[12]{a^7}$.

123. $3^{\frac{5}{6}} = \sqrt[6]{243}$.

125. $\dfrac{9y^4}{4u^2}$.

127. $\dfrac{a^{\frac{1}{2}}}{2y^{\frac{1}{3}}} = \dfrac{1}{2y}\sqrt[6]{a^3y^4}$.

129. $\dfrac{u^{\frac{1}{4}}}{v^{\frac{1}{2}}} = \dfrac{1}{v}\sqrt[4]{uv^2}$.

131. $\dfrac{az^{\frac{k}{h}}}{u^{\frac{x}{h}}v^{\frac{y}{h}}} = \dfrac{a}{uv}\sqrt[h]{z^k u^{h-x} v^{h-y}}$.

133. $\dfrac{2a^2y}{a^2 + y}$.

135. $2au^{-5}x^2y^{-2}$.

137. $2(3^{-1})b^2d^{-4}x$.

139. $2x(5x + 3y)^{-1}$.

141. $3y^3\sqrt{10y}$.

143. $\dfrac{1}{x^2}\sqrt[3]{5}$.

145. $\frac{1}{14}\sqrt{42}$.

147. $\frac{1}{4}\sqrt[3]{10}$.

149. $b^2\sqrt[6]{a^2b^3}$.

151. $1 - \frac{1}{2}\sqrt{5}$.

153. $\sqrt{a + 3b^2}$.

155. $\frac{3}{2}\sqrt{5} + \frac{3}{2}\sqrt{3}$.

157. $\dfrac{3\sqrt{x - y} + 2x - 3\sqrt{2x} - \sqrt{2x^2 - 2xy}}{x + y}$.

Exercise 20. Page 62

1. $- 5$; 2; $- 3$; 3; 10.

11. $(- 2, 2)$.

15. 13.

17. 13.

19. $\sqrt{(x - 3)^2 + (y + 4)^2}$.

25. 12.

Exercise 21. Page 66

11. $x = 7$.   **13.** $x = -2$.

Exercise 22. Page 67

1. $\frac{7}{5}$.   **3.** 3.   **5.** -4.   **17.** $-\frac{5}{2}$.

Exercise 23. Page 70

1. $y = -5$.
7. $3y + 2x = 12$.
13. $3y = 2x$.
19. $y + 6x = -3$.
25. Slope $\frac{6}{5}$; y-int. 2.

3. $y = 3x + 2$.
9. $y = 5x - 14$.
15. $y = 3$.
21. Slope $-\frac{2}{3}$; y-int. 2.
27. $y = 2x + 11$.

5. $3x + 2y = 6$.
11. $x + 4y = 3$.
17. $y = x - 5$.
23. Slope $\frac{5}{12}$; y-int. $-\frac{1}{2}$.
29. $y = 2x - 1$.

Exercise 24. Page 75

1. R is $1, 4, 9, 16, \cdots, 100$.   **13.** $y = 7 - 2x$; $x = \frac{1}{2}(7 - y)$. **15.** $y = 2x - x^2 + \frac{5}{2}$.

Exercise 25. Page 77

1. 7.
5. 25.
9. $32c^4 - 12c^2$.
13. $3b^2 + 2a - ab$.
17. $8 + 12k + 6k^2 + k^3$; $8x^3$; $x^3 - 9x^2 + 27x - 27$.

3. -1.
7. 3525.
11. 12.
15. 175; 9; $-\frac{7}{3}$; $2x^3 - 1$; $x^3 + 6x + 7$.

Exercise 26. Page 80

5. $V:(0, 0)$; axis $x = 0$; min. 0.
9. $V:(0, 0)$; axis $x = 0$; max. 0.
13. Min. 2.
23. 20 and 20.
27. $100'$ by $200'$.

7. $V:(-1, 8)$; axis $x = -1$; max. 8.
11. $V:(2, 11)$; axis $x = 2$; max. 11.
15. Max. 1.
25. $\frac{15}{2}$ and $\frac{15}{2}$.

Exercise 27. Page 83

1. ± 4.
7. $\pm \frac{1}{7}\sqrt{35}$.
13. $\pm \frac{7}{2}i$.
19. $\pm \sqrt{9ab + 4ab^2}/2a$.
25. 5; -2.
31. 0; $\frac{7}{3}$.
37. $-\frac{1}{2}$; $-\frac{1}{2}$.
43. $-\frac{5}{4}$; $-\frac{5}{4}$.
49. b; $-\frac{2}{3}b$.
55. $-2b/5a$; $-2b/5a$.
61. 5; -4.

3. $\pm 2i$.
9. $\pm \frac{1}{3}\sqrt{a}$.
15. $\pm \frac{3}{2}i\sqrt{2}$.
21. $\pm \frac{1}{3}\sqrt{3a^2 + 3ab + 3b^2}$.
27. 3; -4.
33. 0; $\frac{9}{5}$.
39. -2; $-\frac{3}{2}$.
45. -3; $\frac{5}{4}$.
51. $2a$; $2a$.
57. 2; $-\frac{3}{2}$; $\frac{5}{3}$.
63. 1; $-\frac{5}{2}$.

5. $\pm \frac{5}{2}i$.
11. $\pm \sqrt{2ab}/2a$.
17. ± 2.
23. $\pm \sqrt{2gS}/g$.
29. 0; $\frac{3}{2}$.
35. $\frac{2}{3}$; $\frac{2}{3}$.
41. -4; $\frac{3}{5}$.
47. 0; $2a/3b$.
53. $3/a$; $-2/3a$.
59. 0; -1; $\frac{5}{3}$.

Exercise 28. Page 85

1. $-4;\ 1.$

3. $2 \pm \sqrt{2}.$

5. $-\frac{3}{2};\ -\frac{3}{2}.$

7. $\frac{5}{2};\ -2.$

9. $1;\ -\frac{4}{3}.$

11. $1 \pm \frac{1}{2}\sqrt{3}.$

13. $\frac{1}{3}(2 \pm \sqrt{3}).$

15. $\pm \frac{3}{5}i.$

17. $\frac{1}{3}(1 \pm i\sqrt{6}).$

19. $-\frac{4}{3};\ \frac{7}{5}.$

21. $\frac{1}{2}(-3 \pm 3i\sqrt{5}).$

23. $.35;\ -.5.$

25. $-\frac{2}{5};\ -\frac{2}{5}.$

27. $\frac{1}{3}(1 \pm 2\sqrt{7}).$

29. $\frac{1}{2}(1 \pm i\sqrt{5}).$

31. $\frac{1}{3}(5 \pm i\sqrt{3}).$

33. $\frac{1}{3}(4 \pm \sqrt{2}).$

35. $-\frac{3}{2};\ \frac{7}{5}.$

37. $\frac{1}{2}d;\ -\frac{5}{3}d.$

39. $\dfrac{-d \pm \sqrt{d^2 + 3ac}}{a}.$

41. $\frac{1}{2}(a \pm b\sqrt{3}).$

43. $7;\ -4.$

45. $\frac{4}{3};\ \frac{4}{3}.$

47. $\frac{1}{3}(1 \pm \sqrt{17}).$

49. $\frac{2}{5};\ -\frac{3}{2}.$

51. $\frac{7}{2};\ -\frac{4}{3}.$

53. $\pm \frac{1}{2}\sqrt{2}.$

55. $\frac{1}{2}(3 \pm 2i\sqrt{2}).$

57. $\frac{1}{5};\ \frac{1}{5}.$

59. $\frac{1}{2}(1 \pm 6i).$

61. $-a;\ -3c.$

63. $\frac{1}{3}x;\ \frac{1}{2}(2x + 3).$

65. $3y;\ \frac{1}{2}(2y - 3).$

67. 23 and 4.

69. 22 and 23; or -22 and $-23.$

71. $12.07'.$

Exercise 29. Page 88

1. $\frac{7}{3}.$

3. $0;\ -8.$

5. $-2;\ -2.$

7. Imag. roots.

9. $-2;\ 1.5.$

11. $1.9;\ .1.$

13. Imag. roots.

15. $1.9;\ -.9.$

17. $-\frac{1}{2};\ -\frac{1}{2}.$

19. 3 and 3; 5.2 and .8; 5.6 and .4.

Exercise 30. Page 91

1. Real, unequal, rational.

3. Real, equal, rational.

5. Real, unequal, rational.

7. Imaginary, unequal.

9. Imaginary, unequal.

11. Imaginary roots.

13. Concave upward, tangent to x-axis.

15. Concave upward, wholly above x-axis.

17. Concave downward, wholly below x-axis.

19. $\pm \frac{4}{3}.$

21. $\frac{20}{9}.$

23. 0 and 5.

25. Sum -3; prod. $-5.$

27. Sum $\frac{4}{3}$; prod. 2.

29. Sum $-\frac{3}{7}$; prod. $-\frac{4}{7}.$

31. Sum d/c; prod. $-h/c.$

33. Sum $\frac{1}{3}c$; prod. $\frac{1}{3}a.$

35. Sum $5/(3 + b)$; prod. $d/(3 + b).$

37. $4x^2 + 5x - 6 = 0.$

39. $x^2 = 18.$

41. $16x^2 + 9 = 0.$

43. $x^2 + 20 = 0.$

45. $x^2 - 6x + 34 = 0.$

47. $x^2 - 4x = 14.$

49. $5x^2 + 6x + 5 = 0.$

51. $-\frac{8}{11}.$

53. 4.

55. $\frac{29}{3}.$

Exercise 31. Page 94

1. $\pm 1;\ \pm \sqrt{2}.$

3. $2;\ 2;\ -2;\ -2.$

5. $\pm 3;\ \pm 2.$

7. $\pm i;\ \pm \sqrt{3}.$

9. $\pm 2;\ \pm 2i.$

11. Real roots: $-1;\ \frac{1}{2}.$

13. $\pm 3;\ \pm 2.$

15. $\pm i;\ \pm \frac{3}{2}.$

17. Real roots: $1;\ \frac{2}{3}.$

19. $\pm 1;\ \frac{3}{2};\ -\frac{1}{2}.$

21. $3;\ -2;\ \frac{1}{2}(1 \pm i\sqrt{11}).$

23. $\frac{3}{2};\ \frac{3}{4}(-1 \pm i\sqrt{3}).$

25. $\pm \frac{2}{3};\ \pm \frac{2}{3}i.$

27. $-\frac{5}{2};\ \frac{5}{4}(1 \pm i\sqrt{3}).$

29. $-2;\ (1 \pm i\sqrt{3}).$

31. $-1;\ \pm \frac{1}{2}(1 \pm i\sqrt{3}).$

33. $\frac{1}{2}$; $\frac{1}{4}(-1 \pm i\sqrt{3})$.   **35.** ± 1; $\pm i$.

37. ± 5; $\pm 5i$.   **39.** $\pm \frac{2}{3}$; $\pm \frac{2}{3}i$.

Exercise 32. Page 96

1. $-\frac{14}{3}$.   **3.** No sol.   **5.** 6.   **7.** $-\frac{5}{2}$.   **9.** $\frac{14}{3}$.

11. $\frac{3}{7}\sqrt{2}$.   **13.** $-\frac{5}{3}\sqrt{2}$.   **15.** 0; $-\frac{1}{5}\sqrt{3}$.   **17.** 8; -2.   **19.** 4.

21. No sol.   **23.** 2.   **25.** No sol.

27. 0; $2b$.   **29.** $\pm \sqrt{l^2 - \pi^2 r^4}/\pi r$.   **31.** $\frac{1}{4}$; 9.

33. $\frac{9}{16}$.   **35.** 256; $\frac{1}{81}$.   **37.** $\frac{27}{8}$; $\frac{27}{8}$.

Exercise 33. Page 100

1. $x = -\frac{2}{3}, y = -\frac{5}{3}$.   **3.** $x = 2, y = 5$.   **5.** $x = -\frac{8}{3}, y = 3$.

7. $x = -\frac{7}{3}, y = -\frac{5}{6}$.   **9.** $x = -1, y = 1$.   **11.** Inconsistent.

13. Inconsistent.   **15.** Infinitely many solutions; dependent.

17. $x = 2, y = 3$.   **19.** $x = \frac{1}{2}, y = 5$.   **21.** $x = 5, y = 4$.

23. $v = \dfrac{2}{a + b^2}, w = \dfrac{2}{a + b^2}$.   **25.** $v = \dfrac{1}{a}, w = -\dfrac{b}{2}$.

27. $v = \dfrac{3a^2 - b^2}{3}, w = \dfrac{2b}{3}$.   **29.** 27.

31. 9 yr. and 30 yr. old.   **33.** 30 gal. of 40%; 10 gal. of 80%.

35. 10 lb. of silver and 10 lb. of lead.

37. Airplane, 450 mi.p.hr.; wind, 50 mi.p.hr.

Exercise 35. Page 107

1. $(.5, 4.0)$; $(-2.9, -2.8)$.   **3.** $(\frac{5}{2}, -\frac{3}{2})$.   **5.** $(1.2, \pm 3.2)$; $(-1.2, \pm 3.2)$.

7. $(2.5, .8)$; $(-2.5, -.8)$.   **9.** $(\pm 3, 0)$.   **11.** $(3.8, 3.2)$.

Exercise 36. Page 109

1. $(4, -3)$; $(-3, 4)$.   **3.** $(3, -4)$; $(3, -4)$.

5. $(0, \pm 6)$.   **7.** $(2, 3)$; $(\frac{3}{2}, 4)$.

9. $(5, \frac{3}{2})$; $(5, \frac{3}{2})$.   **11.** $(1, \pm \sqrt{10})$; $(-1, \pm \sqrt{10})$.

13. $(\sqrt{3}, \pm \sqrt{2})$; $(-\sqrt{3}, \pm \sqrt{2})$.   **15.** $(\sqrt{2}, \pm 1)$; $(-\sqrt{2}, \pm 1)$.

17. $[\frac{3}{2}(-2 + i\sqrt{6}), -(1 + i\sqrt{6})]$; $[\frac{3}{2}(-2 - i\sqrt{6}), -(1 - i\sqrt{6})]$.

19. $[\frac{1}{5}(-4 + \sqrt{26}), \frac{1}{10}(-2 + 3\sqrt{26})]$; $[\frac{1}{5}(-4 - \sqrt{26}), \frac{1}{10}(-2 - 3\sqrt{26})]$.

Exercise 37. Page 111

1. $(4, 3)$; $(-4, -3)$; $(3, -4)$; $(-3, 4)$.

3. $(2, 2)$; $(-2, -2)$; $(1, 2)$; $(-1, -2)$.

5. $(2, 1)$; $(-2, -1)$; $(7, -4)$; $(-7, 4)$.

7. $(4, -1)$; $(-4, 1)$; $(1, -\frac{3}{2})$; $(-1, \frac{3}{2})$.

9. $(\frac{1}{2}\sqrt{2}, \sqrt{2})$; $(-\frac{1}{2}\sqrt{2}, -\sqrt{2})$; $(3, -4)$; $(-3, 4)$.

11. $(2, -1)$; $(-2, 1)$; $(\frac{1}{2}, -\frac{3}{2})$; $(-\frac{1}{2}, \frac{3}{2})$.

13. $(10, 2)$; $(-\frac{4}{3}, 2)$; $(\frac{15}{11}, \frac{3}{11})$; $(6, -9)$.

15. $(0, 2)$; $(2, 0)$.   **17.** $(2, \frac{3}{2})$; $(-2, -\frac{3}{2})$; $(3, 1)$; $(-3, -1)$.

19. $(6, \frac{1}{2})$; $(-2, -\frac{3}{2})$.

21. $(\frac{3}{7}, -\frac{2}{7})$; $(-\frac{1}{3}, -\frac{2}{3})$; $(\frac{1}{7}, \frac{4}{7})$; $(-\frac{1}{3}, \frac{1}{3})$.

23. $(\frac{1}{2}, -3)$; $(-3, \frac{1}{2})$; $(\frac{3}{2}, -1)$; $(-1, \frac{3}{2})$.

25. $(\pm i\sqrt{2}, \pm \sqrt{3}, \pm \sqrt{3})$, with all possible combinations of signs.

27. $(1, -27)$; $(-1, 27)$; $(-64, 8)$; $(64, -8)$.

29. ± 2. **31.** $c = \pm \sqrt{9m^2 + 4}$.

Exercise 38. Page 114

1. $\frac{9}{5}$. **3.** b^3/a. **5.** $\frac{64}{15}$. **7.** $\frac{29}{24}$. **9.** $\frac{7}{5}$. **11.** ± 4. **13.** $\frac{5}{4}$.

15. $6''$ and $14''$. **17.** $14''$ and $12\frac{3}{5}''$.

19. By $3\frac{1}{3}$, $6\frac{2}{3}$, and 8 inches, respectively. **21.** $28.28'$.

23. $(0, 6)$. **25.** ± 9. **27.** ± 36. **29.** $\pm 2a^2\sqrt{2}$. **31.** $\pm 16i$.

Exercise 39. Page 118

1. $W = \dfrac{ku}{v^3}$. **3.** $V = \dfrac{kxy}{w}$. **5.** $Z = \dfrac{k}{x^2 y^3 w^{\frac{1}{3}}}$.

7. $A = kb$. **9.** $V = \dfrac{k}{p}$. **11.** $L = \dfrac{kbd^2}{h}$.

13. $W = \dfrac{30}{\sqrt{y}}$. **15.** 10. **17.** $1936'$.

19. 15 ft. lb. **21.** 1.9 yr. **23.** Incr. by 200%; by 30%.

25. 1228.8 lb. **27.** Diam. $= 2' 8''$. **29.** $12'$.

Exercise 40. Page 120

1. x-int. $\frac{20}{3}$; y-int. -4. **3.** x-int. -3; no y-int.

5. Slope $-\frac{2}{3}$; y-int. $\frac{5}{3}$. **7.** Slope 2; y-int. $-\frac{7}{2}$.

9. $3x - y = -2$. **11.** $3x - 2y = 6$. **13.** $\sqrt{109}$.

15. $8\frac{5}{8}$; $17\frac{22}{27}$; $2a^4b^2 - 5a^{-6}b^{-3}$; $\frac{3481}{64}$; $2x^2 + 8x + 8 - \dfrac{5}{(x+2)^3}$.

23. $\frac{3}{2}$; $-\frac{5}{4}$. **25.** Discr. 109; roots real, unequal, irrational.

27. Discr. 961; roots real, unequal, rational. **29.** $\frac{1}{2}(3 \pm \sqrt{2})$. **31.** 9. **33.** $\frac{1}{3}$.

35. (a) $x^2 + 3x - 10 = 0$; (b) $3x^2 - 12x + 13 = 0$. **37.** Inconsistent.

39. $(\frac{1}{2}\sqrt{2}, \pm \sqrt{10})$; $(-\frac{1}{2}\sqrt{2}, \pm \sqrt{10})$. **41.** No graph; just a point. (Why?)

43. $F = kAv^2$. **45.** 625 ohms; $72'$.

47. $(-3, -2)$; $(-3, \frac{3}{2})$; $(2, -1)$; $(\frac{3}{5}, \frac{2}{5})$. **49.** 306 mi.p.hr. **51.** $\frac{9}{16}$.

53. 2; $(-1 \pm i\sqrt{3})$; -3; $\frac{3}{2}(1 \pm i\sqrt{3})$.

Exercise 41. Page 123

1. (Why?) **5.** 13. **7.** 14. **9.** 151. **11.** $23\frac{1}{2}$.

13. -67; -459. **15.** .78; 46.86. **17.** -35; -1215.

19. $n = 65$; 1235. **21.** $n = 21$; 525. **23.** 36,270.

25. 24,750. **27.** $\frac{108}{5}, \frac{101}{5}, \frac{94}{5}, \frac{87}{5}$. **29.** $\frac{17}{12}, \frac{25}{12}, \frac{33}{12}, \frac{41}{12}, \cdots, \frac{65}{12}, \frac{73}{12}$.

31. 35. **33.** 2. **35.** \$15,840.

37. 14. **39.** 36. **41.** \$7560.

Exercise 42. Page 127

9. $(1.03)^{13}$, $(1.03)^{16}$.   **11.** $(1.01)^{-2}$, 1.   **13.** $\frac{7}{4}$.

15. $\frac{6}{5}$.   **17.** 768.   **19.** $-\frac{7}{128}$.

21. $l = 18(10^{-8})$; $S = 18(.90909091)$.   **23.** $l = 2a^9$; $S = \dfrac{2 - 2a^{10}}{1 - a}$.

25. 4372.   **27.** $r = -3$; $n = 6$.

29. $S = \frac{4372}{3}$; $n = 7$.   **31.** .0025.

33. $\frac{5}{4}$, 25, 500; or $-\frac{5}{4}$, 25, -500.   **35.** 2, 6, 18, 54.

37. 3.   **39.** -10.   **41.** $\dfrac{(1.04)^{64} - 1}{.04}$.   **43.** $\dfrac{(1.02)^{53} - (1.02)^5}{(1.02)^3 - 1}$.

Exercise 43. Page 128

1. 17.   **3.** \$409.50.   **5.** \$360.

7. \$375; \$30,375.   **9.** n^2.   **11.** -2, 1, 4, 7.

13. 2740.   **17.** $4(10^7)[(1.05)^{10} - 1]$.   **19.** $33\frac{1}{3}\%$.

21. $33\frac{1}{3}\%$.   **23.** $\frac{1}{6}$, $\frac{1}{10}$, $\frac{1}{14}$, $\frac{1}{18}$, $\frac{1}{22}$.   **25.** $\frac{1}{3}$, $\frac{3}{11}$, $\frac{3}{13}$, $\frac{1}{5}$.

27. $\frac{16}{3}$.   **29.** 8.

Exercise 44. Page 133

1. $7\frac{1}{2}$.   **3.** 30.   **5.** $\frac{5}{6}$.   **7.** $\frac{100}{99}$.   **9.** $\frac{2}{9}$.   **11.** $\frac{2}{3}$.   **13.** $\frac{1}{6}$.

15. $\frac{1}{11}$.   **17.** $\frac{7}{33}$.   **19.** $\frac{28}{9}$.   **21.** $\frac{4}{11}$.   **23.** $\frac{332}{33}$.   **25.** $\frac{600}{37}$.   **27.** $\frac{1}{7}$.

Exercise 45. Page 135

1. $a^5 + 5a^4b + 10a^3b^2 + 10a^2b^3 + 5ab^4 + b^5$.

3. $x^8 - 8x^7y + 28x^6y^2 - 56x^5y^3 + 70x^4y^4 - 56x^3y^5 + 28x^2y^6 - 8xy^7 + y^8$.

5. $16 + 32a + 24a^2 + 8a^3 + a^4$.

7. $729b^6 - 1458b^5y + 1215b^4y^2 - 540b^3y^3 + 135b^2y^4 - 18by^5 + y^6$.

9. $a^3 + 3a^2b^2 + 3ab^4 + b^6$.

11. $a^{12} - 6a^{10}b^2 + 15a^8b^4 - 20a^6b^6 + 15a^4b^8 - 6a^2b^{10} + b^{12}$.

13. $x^5 - \frac{5}{2}x^4 + \frac{5}{2}x^3 - \frac{5}{4}x^2 + \frac{5}{16}x - \frac{1}{32}$.

15. $x^3 - 6x^{\frac{5}{2}}y^{\frac{1}{2}} + 15x^2y - 20x^{\frac{3}{2}}y^{\frac{3}{2}} + 15xy^2 - 6x^{\frac{1}{2}}y^{\frac{5}{2}} + y^3$.

17. $a^4 - 4a^3y^{-2} + 6a^2y^{-4} - 4ay^{-6} + y^{-8}$.

19. $x^2 - \dfrac{8x^{\frac{3}{2}}}{a} + \dfrac{24x}{a^2} - \dfrac{32x^{\frac{1}{2}}}{a^3} + \dfrac{16}{a^4}$.

21. $c^{25} - 75c^{24} + 2700c^{23}$.   **23.** $1 + 20a + 180a^2$.

25. $1 + 2.4 + 2.64$.   **27.** $1 - 54x^3 + 1377x^6$.

29. $x^7 + 14x^{\frac{13}{2}}b + 91x^6b^2$.   **31.** $x^{11} - 11x^{10}a^{-2} + 55x^9a^{-4}$.

33. $a^k + ka^{k-1}x + \frac{1}{2}k(k - 1)a^{k-2}x^2$.   **35.** $w^{2h} + hw^{2h-2}z + \frac{1}{2}h(h - 1)w^{2h-4}z^2$.

37. 1.195.   **39.** 1.220.   **41.** $462u^6x^5$.   **43.** $-36y^2z^7$.

Exercise 47. Page 142

Note. Functions are in the order sine, cosine, tangent, cosecant, secant, cotangent.

1. $\frac{3}{5}$, $\frac{4}{5}$, $\frac{3}{4}$, $\frac{5}{3}$, $\frac{5}{4}$, $\frac{4}{3}$.   **3.** $\frac{24}{25}$, $\frac{7}{25}$, $\frac{24}{7}$, $\frac{25}{24}$, $\frac{25}{7}$, $\frac{7}{24}$.

5. $-\frac{2}{13}\sqrt{13}$, $-\frac{3}{13}\sqrt{13}$, $\frac{2}{3}$, $-\frac{1}{2}\sqrt{13}$, $-\frac{1}{3}\sqrt{13}$, $\frac{3}{2}$.

7. $\frac{8}{17}, -\frac{15}{17}, -\frac{8}{15}, \frac{17}{8}, -\frac{17}{15}, -\frac{15}{8}$. **9.** $-\frac{4}{5}, \frac{3}{5}, -\frac{4}{3}, -\frac{5}{4}, \frac{5}{3}, -\frac{3}{4}$.

11. $-\frac{1}{2}\sqrt{3}, \frac{1}{2}, -\sqrt{3}, -\frac{2}{3}\sqrt{3}, 2, -\frac{1}{3}\sqrt{3}$. **13.** 1, 0, none, 1, none, 0.

15. -1, 0, none, -1, none, 0. **17.** $-\frac{1}{2}\sqrt{2}, -\frac{1}{2}\sqrt{2}, 1, -\sqrt{2}, -\sqrt{2}, 1$.

19. $\frac{5}{34}\sqrt{34}, -\frac{3}{34}\sqrt{34}, -\frac{5}{3}, \frac{1}{5}\sqrt{34}, -\frac{1}{3}\sqrt{34}, -\frac{3}{5}$.

23. $\sec \alpha = \frac{9}{4}$. **25.** $\cos \gamma = \frac{3}{7}$. **27.** II or IV. **29.** I or III.

31. III. **33.** IV. **35.** II. **37.** III.

Exercise 48. Page 146

Note. Functions are in the order sine, cosine, tangent, cosecant, secant, cotangent.

1. 0, 1, 0, none, 1, none. **3.** .5, .866, .577, 2, 1.155, 1.732.

5. .707, $-.707$, -1, 1.414, -1.414, -1.

7. .5, $-.866$, $-.577$, 2, -1.155, -1.732.

9. 0, 1, 0, none, 1, none. **11.** Prob. 3, with signs for quad. IV.

13. -1, 0, none, -1, none, 0. **15.** Prob. 5, with signs for quad. IV.

17. Prob. 5, with signs for quad. III. **19.** Same as Prob. 3.

21. Prob. 5, with signs for quad. III. **23.** 0, -1, 0, none, -1, none.

25. Prob. 5, with signs for quad. III.

Exercise 49. Page 149

Note. Only sine, cosine, tangent are given, in that order. Cosecant, secant, cotangent are equal to the corresponding reciprocals.

1. $\frac{5}{13}, \frac{12}{13}, \frac{5}{12}$. **3.** $\frac{4}{5}, -\frac{3}{5}, -\frac{4}{3}$. **5.** $\frac{3}{5}, \frac{4}{5}, \frac{3}{4}$.

7. $-\frac{5}{13}, -\frac{12}{13}, \frac{5}{12}$. **9.** $\frac{8}{17}, -\frac{15}{17}, -\frac{8}{15}$. **11.** $-\frac{1}{2}\sqrt{2}, -\frac{1}{2}\sqrt{2}, 1$.

13. $-\frac{1}{4}\sqrt{7}, \frac{3}{4}, -\frac{1}{3}\sqrt{7}$. **15.** $\frac{3}{5}, \frac{4}{5}, \frac{3}{4}$. **17.** $\frac{15}{17}, -\frac{8}{17}, -\frac{15}{8}$.

19. θ in (I): $\frac{2}{13}\sqrt{13}, \frac{3}{13}\sqrt{13}, \frac{2}{3}$. θ in (III): $-\frac{2}{13}\sqrt{13}, -\frac{3}{13}\sqrt{13}, \frac{2}{3}$.

21. θ in (II): $\frac{1}{3}\sqrt{5}, -\frac{2}{3}, -\frac{1}{2}\sqrt{5}$. θ in (III): $-\frac{1}{3}\sqrt{5}, -\frac{2}{3}, \frac{1}{2}\sqrt{5}$.

35. -18. **37.** $\frac{1}{6}(3\sqrt{5} + 5)$.

39. $\sin x, \pm \sqrt{1 - \sin^2 x}, \pm \sin x/\sqrt{1 - \sin^2 x}$.

41. $\pm \sqrt{\sec^2 x - 1}/\sec x, 1/\sec x, \pm \sqrt{\sec^2 x - 1}$.

Exercise 50. Page 152

Note. See Note for answers to Exercise 49.

1. $\frac{3}{5}, \frac{4}{5}, \frac{3}{4}$. **3.** $\frac{24}{25}, \frac{7}{25}, \frac{24}{7}$. **5.** $\frac{8}{17}, \frac{15}{17}, \frac{8}{15}$.

7. $\frac{2}{3}, \frac{1}{3}\sqrt{5}, \frac{2}{5}\sqrt{5}$. **9.** See page 144. **11.** $\sin 75°$.

13. $\tan 52°$. **15.** $\sec 78°$. **17.** $\cot 51°$.

19. $\cos 23°$. **21.** $\cos 8°$.

Exercise 51. Page 155

1. 59°. **3.** 87°. **5.** 70°. **7.** -1.280.

9. $-\frac{1}{2}\sqrt{2}$. **11.** -2.924. **13.** -1.483. **15.** -1.963.

17. $\frac{1}{2}\sqrt{3}$. **19.** -1.280. **21.** 5.759. **23.** -2.

25. 1.305. **27.** 1.743. **29.** $-.052$. **31.** 1.600.

33. $-\frac{1}{2}\sqrt{2}$. **35.** $-.675$. **37.** $-.993$.

41. $\sin \theta = \dfrac{3\sqrt{34}}{34}$; $\cos \theta = -\dfrac{5\sqrt{34}}{34}$; etc. **43.** $\sin \theta = \dfrac{\sqrt{33}}{7}$; $\tan \theta = -\dfrac{\sqrt{33}}{4}$; etc.

Exercise 52. Page 158

1. $-\frac{1}{2}\sqrt{2}$; $-\frac{1}{2}\sqrt{2}$. **3.** $-\frac{1}{2}\sqrt{2}$; $\frac{1}{2}\sqrt{2}$. **5.** 0; -1.

7. $\frac{1}{4}(\sqrt{2}+\sqrt{6})$; $\frac{1}{4}(\sqrt{6}-\sqrt{2})$. **9.** $\frac{1}{4}(\sqrt{6}-\sqrt{2})$; $-\frac{1}{4}(\sqrt{2}+\sqrt{6})$.

11. $-\frac{1}{4}(\sqrt{2}+\sqrt{6})$; $\frac{1}{4}(\sqrt{6}-\sqrt{2})$.

13. $\sin(\alpha+\beta)=-\frac{33}{65}$; $\cos(\alpha+\beta)=-\frac{56}{65}$.
   $\sin(\alpha-\beta)=-\frac{63}{65}$; $\cos(\alpha-\beta)=-\frac{16}{65}$.

15. $\sin(\alpha+\beta)=-\frac{36}{325}$; $\cos(\alpha+\beta)=\frac{323}{325}$.
   $\sin(\alpha-\beta)=-\frac{204}{325}$; $\cos(\alpha-\beta)=\frac{253}{325}$.

17. $\frac{1}{2}\sqrt{2}\,(\cos\alpha+\sin\alpha)$. **19.** $\cos\theta$. **21.** $-\cos\theta$.

23. $-\sin\theta$. **25.** $-\cos\theta$. **27.** $-\cos\theta$.

Exercise 53. Page 163

1. $-\cos\theta$. **3.** $-\cos\theta$. **5.** $-\sin\theta$. **7.** $-\sin\theta$. **9.** $-\cos\theta$.

11. $\sin(270°-\theta)=-\cos\theta$; $\cos(270°-\theta)=-\sin\theta$; $\tan(270°-\theta)=\cot\theta$; etc.

13. $\sin(\theta+90°)=\cos\theta$; $\cos(\theta+90°)=-\sin\theta$; $\tan(\theta+90°)=-\cot\theta$; etc.

15. $\sin(450°-\theta)=\cos\theta$; $\cos(450°-\theta)=\sin\theta$; $\tan(450°-\theta)=\cot\theta$; etc.

17. $\sin(630°-\theta)=-\cos\theta$; $\cos(630°-\theta)=-\sin\theta$; $\tan(630°-\theta)=\cot\theta$; etc.

19. $-\cos\theta$. **21.** $\cot\theta$. **23.** $\tan\theta$. **25.** $\csc\theta$.

27. $\sec\theta$. **29.** $\cos\theta$. **31.** $\cot\theta$. **33.** $\csc\theta$. **35.** $-\csc\theta$.

37. $\sin 63°=\cos 27°$; $\cos 63°=\sin 27°$; $\tan 63°=\cot 27°$.

39. $\sin 147°=\sin 33°$; $\cos 147°=-\cos 33°$; $\tan 147°=-\tan 33°$.

41. $\sin 176°=\sin 4°$; $\cos 176°=-\cos 4°$; $\tan 176°=-\tan 4°$.

43. $\sin 284°=-\cos 14°$; $\cos 284°=\sin 14°$; $\tan 284°=-\cot 14°$.

45. $\sin 352°=-\sin 8°$; $\cos 352°=\cos 8°$; $\tan 352°=-\tan 8°$.

47. $\sin(-56°)=-\cos 34°$; $\cos(-56°)=\sin 34°$; $\tan(-56°)=-\cot 34°$.

49. $\sin(-256°)=\cos 14°$; $\cos(-256°)=-\sin 14°$; $\tan(-256°)=-\cot 14°$.

51. $\sin 305°=-\cos 35°$; $\cos 305°=\sin 35°$; $\tan 305°=-\cot 35°$.

53. $\sin(-247°)=\cos 23°$; $\cos(-247°)=-\sin 23°$; $\tan(-247°)=-\cot 23°$.

55. $\sin(-283°)=\cos 13°$; $\cos(-283°)=\sin 13°$; $\tan(-283°)=\cot 13°$.

Exercise 54. Page 166

7. $90°$; $-270°$. **9.** $\pm 270°$; $\pm 90°$.

11. $0°$; $\pm 180°$; $\pm 360°$. **13.** $\pm 120°$; $\pm 240°$.

15. $\pm 45°$; $\pm 315°$. **17.** $-300°$; $-240°$; $60°$; $120°$.

19. $-135°$; $-45°$; $225°$; $315°$. **21.** $\pm 150°$; $\pm 210°$.

23. $g(800)=\frac{1}{2}\sqrt{2}$; $f(800)=.985$; $f(320)=-.643$; $g(320)=.309$.

Exercise 55. Page 171

7. $0°$; $\pm 180°$; $\pm 360°$. **9.** $\pm 90°$; $\pm 270°$.

11. $-225°$; $-45°$; $135°$; $315°$. **13.** $-270°$; $90°$.

15. $\pm 180°$. **17.** $-210°$; $-30°$; $150°$; $330°$.

19. $-300°$; $-120°$; $60°$; $240°$. **21.** $-300°$; $-240°$; $60°$; $120°$.

23. $0°$; $\pm 180°$; $\pm 360°$. **25.** $0°$; $\pm 180°$; $\pm 360°$.

Exercise 56. Page 175

1. 10^7. **3.** 10^{-4}. **5.** 10^0. **7.** .21236; .212. **9.** .0021539; .00215.
11. .049358; .0494. **13.** 612,920; 613,000. **15.** 15,980,000. **17.** .000008195.
19. 8.9315(10^7). **21.** 3.64(10^{-6}). **23.** 238.25″ and 238.35″·
25. 42.155″ and 42.165″. **27.** 21.68; .701. **29.** 3.1; .89.
31. 8.4260(10^6); 8.43(10^6). **33.** 4.2700(10^7); 4.27(10^7).

Exercise 57. Page 176

1. $\log_2 N = 6$. **3.** $\log_5 N = -2$. **5.** $\log_4 H = \frac{1}{3}$.
7. $\log_{10} N = .35$. **9.** $\log_5 625 = 4$. **11.** $\log_3 \frac{1}{27} = -3$.
13. 36. **15.** 10,000. **17.** 125.
19. 15. **21.** $\frac{1}{5}$. **23.** b.
25. 3. **27.** $\frac{1}{6}$. **29.** 9.
31. 2. **33.** 4. **35.** 2.
37. 5. **39.** $\frac{1}{2}$. **41.** -1.
43. -3. **45.** -3. **47.** $a = 2\sqrt{2}$.
49. $a = 10$. **51.** $a = 25$. **53.** $N = 216$.
55. $N = 343$. **57.** $N = \frac{1}{81}$. **59.** $x = \frac{1}{2}$. **61.** $x = \frac{1}{10}\sqrt{10}$.

Exercise 58. Page 179

1. 1.1461. **3.** 1.4771. **5.** 1.3222. **7.** .5441.
9. $-.3680$. **11.** .0843. **13.** 2.3010. **15.** -1.0212.
17. .6778. **19.** 1.5050. **21.** .2386. **23.** .1840.

Exercise 59. Page 182

1. Ch. = 3; man. = .5217. **3.** Ch. = -3; man. = .550.
5. Ch. = -4; man. = .8418. **7.** Ch. = -5; man. = .2891.
9. 8.1356 $-$ 10. **11.** 6.5268 $-$ 10. **13.** 4. **15.** -5.
17. -6. **19.** 2.0934. **21.** 9.4166 $-$ 10. **23.** 8.7497 $-$ 10.
25. 4.3201. **27.** 9.9586 $-$ 10. **29.** 4.1818. **31.** 5.3404 $-$ 10.
33. 136. **35.** .523. **37.** 55.7. **39.** .0376.
41. 3.31. **43.** .00293. **45.** 32,900,000. **47.** .000429.
49. (a) .000250; (b) .00400.

Exercise 60. Page 184

1. 3.2840. **3.** 3.7646. **5.** 0.9748. **7.** 9.8509 $-$ 10.
9. 7.7106 $-$ 10. **11.** 6.3025 $-$ 10. **13.** 4.9036. **15.** 0.4950.
17. 4.4113. **19.** 7.7934 $-$ 10. **21.** 45.22. **23.** .1053.
25. 3.557. **27.** .04397. **29.** 108.6. **31.** .0001050.
33. .00008644. **35.** 1.088(10^7). **37.** 2298. **39.** .9008.
41. 9.708. **43.** 36.71.

Exercise 61. Page 187

1. 2328. **3.** 2.868. **5.** .009780. **7.** $-.04454$.
9. 35.80. **11.** .04926. **13.** 22.93. **15.** 118.1.

17. 647.3. **19.** .01699. **21.** .001421. **23.** $- 4.769(10^{-7})$.
25. $1.857(10^{-5})$. **27.** 28.66. **29.** .006971. **31.** 87.78.
33. (a) $3.810(10^5)$; (b) 7.778.

Exercise 62. Page 189

1. 6537. **3.** .6737. **5.** 5.966. **7.** .9782.
9. .2369. **11.** 6.310. **13.** 13.16. **15.** .04642.
17. $- 12.00$. **19.** $- 3.186(10^{-8})$. **21.** .7827. **23.** 57.65.
25. 53.40. **27.** 1.229. **29.** .01953. **31.** $2.233(10^9)$.
33. (a) 50.12; (b) 50.50. **35.** .2005. **37.** 1842.
39. $1.529(10^{-5})$. **41.** $2.305(10^4)$. **43.** 6.006. **45.** 3.378.
47. 4.696. **49.** 2.282. **51.** .3322. **53.** 77.57.
55. $- .134$. **57.** .9294. **59.** (a) $8.834(10^4)$; (b) .0001563.
61. .05504. **63.** .6137. **65.** 340.1.

Exercise 63. Page 191

Note. Where fewer digits than normal are given, this indicates that the omitted digits are unreliable.

1. 1.280. **3.** 1.369. **5.** $- 17.8$. **7.** ± 1.266.
9. $- 1.982$; .982. **11.** 17. **13.** $3.418(10^5)$. **15.** 7.132.
17. 2.303. **19.** 2.502. **21.** $- 8.980$.
23. Briggs to natural, .4343; natural to Briggs, 2.303.

Exercise 65. Page 195

1. .2079. **3.** .6249. **5.** .0816. **7.** .2334.
9. 22° 10′. **11.** 31° 0′. **13.** 55° 10′. **15.** 64° 10′.
17. 20° 30′. **19.** .4708. **21.** 1.670. **23.** .0825.
25. 1.562. **27.** .8803. **29.** .1119. **31.** 7.012.
33. .2487. **35.** 29° 42′. **37.** 32° 42′. **39.** 45° 16′.
41. 52° 13′. **43.** 45° 43′. **45.** 2° 55′. **47.** 82° 40′.
49. 69° 50′. **51.** 54° 20′.

Exercise 66. Page 198

Note. Legitimately different methods of solution of a triangle may lead to slightly different results. The answers in this chapter are given as obtained by use of secants and cosecants, when applicable, in avoiding division.

1. $b = 115.0$, $c = 125.4$, 66° 30′. **3.** $a = 121.6$, $b = 28.82$, 76° 40′.
5. $\alpha = 41° 53′$, $\beta = 48° 7′$, 599.2. **7.** $\alpha = 52° 40′$, $\beta = 37° 20′$, 107.2.
9. $\alpha = 26° 32′$, $\beta = 63° 28′$, 1.038. **11.** $\alpha = 61° 28′$, $\beta = 28° 32′$, 2.617.
13. $\alpha = 54° 24′$, $\beta = 35° 36′$, .5936. **15.** $a = .01676$, $c = .02120$, 37° 49′.
17. $a = 1.577$, $b = .2723$, 9° 48′. **19.** $\alpha = 58° 27′$, $\beta = 31° 33′$, 7329.
21. 1.54 ft. **23.** 44° 25′. **25.** 1926 ft.
27. 1250 ft. **29.** 272 ft. **31.** 40.9 ft.

Exercise 67. Page 200

1. (a) .2136; (b) 9.3296 − 10.   3. 9.9912 − 10.   5. 9.9046 − 10.
7. 9.6538 − 10.   9. 9.8117 − 10.   11. 0.3545.   13. 9.2778 − 10.
15. 64° 7′.   17. 20° 38′.   19. 14° 44′.   21. 78° 53′.

Exercise 68. Page 202

1. $b = 21.34$, $c = 26.50$, 53° 40′.   3. $\alpha = 28° 30′$, $\beta = 61° 30′$, .7523.
5. $a = .3396$, $b = .5950$, 60° 17′.   7. $\alpha = 42° 18′$, $\beta = 47° 42′$, .8518.
9. $b = 2.672$, $c = 3.131$, 58° 35′.   11. $\alpha = 63° 18′$, $\beta = 26° 42′$, 818.0.
13. $b = 40.45$, $c = 58.99$, 46° 42′.   15. $k = 512.2$, $\alpha = 55° 50′$.
17. $a = 402.5$, $c = 539.3$, $\beta = 29° 40′$.   19. $a = 43.50$, $\beta = 19° 54′$, $\gamma = 131° 50′$.

Exercise 69. Page 205

1. 160 ft.   3. Ver. 40.9 ft.; hor. 131.3 ft.
5. 52° 58′.   7. 321°.   9. 252° 13′.
11. 264 mi. W; 280 mi. N.   13. 320 mi.; N 64° 29′ E; 64° 29′.
15. Pitch .385; 37° 40′.   17. Side 28.2 ft.; radius 34.0 ft.
19. 94.5 ft.   21. 215 mi.; azimuth 319° 43′.

Exercise 70. Page 209

1. Hor. 84.7 lb.; ver. 128.4 lb.   3. 22.07 lb. W; 36.49 lb. S.
5. 282 mi. S; 103 mi. E.   7. 171 lb.; N 18° 20′ E.
9. Groundspeed 202 mi. per hr.; course is azimuth 8° 32′; drift angle 8° 32′.
11. 18.25 mi. per hr.; course has bearing S 80° 32′ E, or azimuth 99° 28′.
13. 6816 lb.   15. (a) 202 lb.; (b) 208 lb.
17. 218 lb.   19. 173 lb.; N 33° 38′ W.

Exercise 71. Page 213

1. $\frac{1}{6}\pi$.   3. $\frac{1}{3}\pi$.   5. $\frac{2}{3}\pi$.   7. $\frac{5}{6}\pi$.   9. $-\frac{1}{2}\pi$.
11. $\frac{4}{3}\pi$.   13. $\frac{5}{3}\pi$.   15. $\frac{5}{2}\pi$.   17. 60°.   19. 20°.
21. 210°.   23. 240°.   25. 84°.   27. 114° 35′.   29. 143° 14′.
35. $\frac{2}{15}\pi$.   37. $\frac{5}{6}\pi$.   39. 2.160.   41. 3.199.
43. 2565 ft.   45. 7.44 in.   47. 297 ft.   49. .631 rad.
51. 19.2 in.   53. 642 yd.   55. 318.   57. (a) 1800; (b) 286.

Exercise 72. Page 216

5. 1.711.   7. 5.742.   13. .48012.   15. .76020.
17. $-\cos x$.   19. $-\sin x$.   21. $\sin x$.   23. $-\sin x$.
25. $-\tan x$.   27. $\cot x$.   29. $\sin x$.   31. $\sec x$.
33. $-\cot x$.   35. $-\sin x$.   37. $\sin x$.   39. $-\cot x$.
41. $-\csc x$.   43. $\sin x$.   45. $\cos x$.

Exercise 73. Page 221

7. $x = -\frac{1}{2}\pi$; $x = \frac{1}{2}\pi$; $x = \frac{3}{2}\pi$; $x = \frac{5}{2}\pi$.

9. Same as Prob. 7.   **11.** $\pm 2\pi$; $\pm \pi$; 0.

13. Same as Prob. 11.   **15.** No sol.

17. $-\frac{1}{2}\pi$; $\frac{3}{2}\pi$.   **19.** $-\frac{7}{4}\pi$; $-\frac{3}{4}\pi$; $\frac{1}{4}\pi$; $\frac{5}{4}\pi$.

21. $\pm 2\pi$; 0.   **23.** $-\frac{5}{6}\pi$; $-\frac{1}{6}\pi$; $\frac{7}{6}\pi$; $\frac{11}{6}\pi$.

25. $-\frac{4}{3}\pi$; $-\frac{1}{3}\pi$; $\frac{2}{3}\pi$; $\frac{5}{3}\pi$.   **27.** $\pm \frac{4}{3}\pi$; $\pm \frac{2}{3}\pi$.

29. $-\frac{7}{4}\pi$; $-\frac{5}{4}\pi$; $\frac{1}{4}\pi$; $\frac{3}{4}\pi$.   **31.** $-\frac{11}{6}\pi$; $-\frac{5}{6}\pi$; $\frac{1}{6}\pi$; $\frac{7}{6}\pi$.

Exercise 74. Page 225

21. $f(x) = 4 \sin (x + \frac{1}{3}\pi)$; period 2π.

23. $f(x) = 6 \sin (\frac{1}{2}x - \frac{1}{3}\pi)$; period 4π.

Exercise 76. Page 231

1. $\frac{1}{4}\pi$; $\frac{5}{4}\pi$.   **3.** π.   **5.** $\frac{1}{4}\pi$; $\frac{3}{4}\pi$.   **7.** No sol.

9. $\frac{1}{2}\pi$; $\frac{3}{2}\pi$.   **11.** 0; π.   **13.** $\frac{3}{4}\pi$; $\frac{5}{4}\pi$.   **15.** $\frac{2}{3}\pi$; $\frac{5}{3}\pi$.

17. $\frac{4}{3}\pi$; $\frac{5}{3}\pi$.   **19.** $\frac{1}{4}\pi$; $\frac{3}{4}\pi$; $\frac{5}{4}\pi$; $\frac{7}{4}\pi$.   **21.** $\frac{1}{3}\pi$; $\frac{2}{3}\pi$; $\frac{4}{3}\pi$; $\frac{5}{3}\pi$.

23. $\frac{1}{6}\pi$; $\frac{5}{6}\pi$; $\frac{7}{6}\pi$; $\frac{11}{6}\pi$.   **25.** $\frac{3}{2}\pi$; $\frac{1}{6}\pi$; $\frac{5}{6}\pi$.   **27.** $\frac{1}{3}\pi$; $\frac{1}{4}\pi$; $\frac{3}{4}\pi$; $\frac{4}{3}\pi$.

29. $\frac{1}{2}\pi$.   **31.** $\frac{2}{3}\pi$; π; $\frac{4}{3}\pi$.   **33.** 0; $\frac{1}{2}\pi$; π.

35. 0; $\frac{1}{3}\pi$; $\frac{5}{3}\pi$.   **37.** 0; π; $\frac{5}{4}\pi$; $\frac{7}{4}\pi$.   **39.** 0; $\frac{1}{4}\pi$; $\frac{3}{4}\pi$; π; $\frac{5}{4}\pi$; $\frac{7}{4}\pi$.

41. $22° 43'$; $337° 17'$.   **43.** $58° 20'$; $238° 20'$.   **45.** $172° 40'$; $352° 40'$.

47. $\frac{1}{4}\pi$; $\frac{1}{2}\pi$; $\frac{3}{4}\pi$; $\frac{5}{4}\pi$; $\frac{3}{2}\pi$; $\frac{7}{4}\pi$.   **49.** $\frac{1}{3}\pi$; $\frac{2}{3}\pi$; $\frac{4}{3}\pi$; $\frac{5}{3}\pi$.

Exercise 77. Page 234

1. $\frac{1}{2}\pi$; $\frac{7}{6}\pi$; $\frac{11}{6}\pi$.   **3.** $\frac{3}{2}\pi$.   **5.** No sol.   **7.** 0; $\frac{1}{4}\pi$; π; $\frac{5}{4}\pi$.

9. $\frac{3}{2}\pi$.   **11.** $\frac{1}{3}\pi$; $\frac{2}{3}\pi$; $\frac{4}{3}\pi$; $\frac{5}{3}\pi$.   **13.** $\frac{1}{3}\pi$; $\frac{2}{3}\pi$; $\frac{4}{3}\pi$; $\frac{5}{3}\pi$.

15. $\frac{1}{6}\pi$; $\frac{7}{6}\pi$.   **17.** $\frac{1}{3}\pi$; π; $\frac{5}{3}\pi$.   **19.** $\frac{7}{6}\pi$; $\frac{3}{2}\pi$; $\frac{11}{6}\pi$.

21. 0; π.   **23.** $\frac{1}{3}\pi$; $\frac{5}{3}\pi$.   **25.** 0; $\frac{3}{2}\pi$.

27. 0; $\frac{1}{2}\pi$.   **29.** π.   **31.** $\frac{1}{6}\pi$; $\frac{5}{6}\pi$.

33. $\frac{1}{3}\pi$; $\frac{2}{3}\pi$; $\frac{4}{3}\pi$; $\frac{5}{3}\pi$.   **35.** $\frac{1}{4}\pi$; $\frac{3}{4}\pi$; $\frac{5}{4}\pi$; $\frac{7}{4}\pi$.   **37.** $\frac{1}{3}\pi$; $\frac{2}{3}\pi$; $\frac{4}{3}\pi$; $\frac{5}{3}\pi$.

39. From Table VII, $18° 26'$; $161° 34'$; $198° 26'$; $341° 34'$.   **41.** $233° 7'$.

Exercise 78. Page 236

9. $(2 + \sqrt{3})$; $(2 - \sqrt{3})$.   **11.** $(\sqrt{3} - 2)$; $-(2 + \sqrt{3})$.

13. $-(2 + \sqrt{3})$; $(\sqrt{3} - 2)$.   **15.** $\frac{1}{2}\sqrt{2}(\cos x + \sin x)$.

17. $\dfrac{1 - \tan x}{1 + \tan x}$.   **19.** $\frac{1}{2}(\sin x + \sqrt{3} \cos x)$.

21. $\dfrac{1 + \tan x}{1 - \tan x}$.   **23.** $\frac{1}{2}(\cos x - \sqrt{3} \sin x)$.

25. $-\frac{1}{2}(\cos x + \sqrt{3} \sin x)$.

Exercise 79. Page 239

27. $\pm \sqrt{\dfrac{1 - \cos 4A}{2}}$, $\pm \sqrt{\dfrac{1 + \cos 4A}{2}}$, $\pm \sqrt{\dfrac{1 - \cos 4A}{1 + \cos 4A}}$.

29. $2 \sin 4x \cos 4x$, $(\cos^2 4x - \sin^2 4x)$, $2 \tan 4x/(1 - \tan^2 4x)$.

31. $2 \sin \frac{1}{2}\alpha \cos \frac{1}{2}\alpha$, $(\cos^2 \frac{1}{2}\alpha - \sin^2 \frac{1}{2}\alpha)$, $2 \tan \frac{1}{2}\alpha/(1 - \tan^2 \frac{1}{2}\alpha)$.

33. $\pm \sqrt{\dfrac{1 - \cos 3x}{2}}$, $\pm \sqrt{\dfrac{1 + \cos 3x}{2}}$, $\pm \sqrt{\dfrac{1 - \cos 3x}{1 + \cos 3x}}$.

35. $4 \cos^3 x - 3 \cos x$. **37.** $\dfrac{3 \tan x - \tan^3 x}{1 - 3 \tan^2 x}$.

Exercise 80. Page 241

5. $\sin 7\theta - \sin 3\theta$. **7.** $\cos 2\theta - \cos 8\theta$. **9.** $\cos 8\theta - \cos 10\theta$.
11. $2 \sin 60° \sin 20°$. **13.** $2 \sin x \sin 3x$.
15. $- 2 \sin x \sin 2x$. **17.** $2 \cos \frac{5}{2}y \cos \frac{11}{2}y$.

Exercise 82. Page 244

1. 0; $\frac{1}{2}\pi$; π; $\frac{3}{2}\pi$.
3. $\frac{1}{18}\pi$; $\frac{5}{18}\pi$; $\frac{7}{18}\pi$; $\frac{11}{18}\pi$; $\frac{13}{18}\pi$; $\frac{17}{18}\pi$; $\frac{19}{18}\pi$; $\frac{23}{18}\pi$; $\frac{25}{18}\pi$; $\frac{29}{18}\pi$; $\frac{31}{18}\pi$; $\frac{35}{18}\pi$.
5. $\frac{1}{4}\pi$; $\frac{5}{12}\pi$; $\frac{11}{12}\pi$; $\frac{13}{12}\pi$; $\frac{19}{12}\pi$; $\frac{7}{4}\pi$. **7.** $\frac{1}{2}\pi$; $\frac{3}{2}\pi$.
9. $\frac{1}{6}\pi$; $\frac{2}{3}\pi$; $\frac{7}{6}\pi$; $\frac{5}{3}\pi$. **11.** $\frac{3}{4}\pi$.
13. $\frac{1}{4}\pi$; $\frac{3}{4}\pi$; $\frac{5}{4}\pi$; $\frac{7}{4}\pi$. **15.** $\frac{1}{6}\pi$; $\frac{1}{2}\pi$; $\frac{5}{6}\pi$; $\frac{3}{2}\pi$.
17. $\frac{1}{3}\pi$; π; $\frac{5}{3}\pi$. **19.** 0; π. **21.** 0; $\frac{1}{6}\pi$; $\frac{5}{6}\pi$; π.
23. $\frac{1}{3}\pi$; $\frac{2}{3}\pi$; $\frac{4}{3}\pi$; $\frac{5}{3}\pi$. **25.** $\frac{1}{6}\pi$; $\frac{1}{3}\pi$; $\frac{2}{3}\pi$; $\frac{5}{6}\pi$; $\frac{7}{6}\pi$; $\frac{4}{3}\pi$; $\frac{5}{3}\pi$; $\frac{11}{6}\pi$.
27. 0; $\frac{1}{2}\pi$; π; $\frac{3}{2}\pi$. **29.** π.
31. $\frac{1}{12}\pi$; $\frac{5}{12}\pi$; $\frac{7}{12}\pi$; $\frac{11}{12}\pi$; $\frac{13}{12}\pi$; $\frac{17}{12}\pi$; $\frac{19}{12}\pi$; $\frac{23}{12}\pi$. **33.** No sol.
35. 0; $\frac{1}{4}\pi$; $\frac{1}{2}\pi$; $\frac{3}{4}\pi$; π; $\frac{5}{4}\pi$; $\frac{3}{2}\pi$; $\frac{7}{4}\pi$. **37.** 0.
39. $6° 10'$; $83° 50'$; $186° 10'$; $263° 50'$. **41.** $20° 54'$; $69° 6'$; $200° 54'$; $249° 6'$.

Exercise 83. Page 245

3. $\cot x = \pm \sqrt{1 - \sin^2 x}/\sin x$; $\sin x = \pm 1/\sqrt{1 + \cot^2 x}$.
5. $\frac{1}{4}(\sqrt{6} + \sqrt{2})$; $\frac{1}{4}(\sqrt{6} - \sqrt{2})$; $(2 + \sqrt{3})$.
7. For $(x + y)$: $- \frac{36}{85}$, $- \frac{77}{85}$, $\frac{36}{77}$. For $2x$: $- \frac{24}{25}$, $\frac{7}{25}$, $- \frac{24}{7}$.
  For $\frac{1}{2}x$: $\pm \frac{3}{10}\sqrt{10}$, $\pm \frac{1}{10}\sqrt{10}$, ± 3, where the signs depend on the value of x.
9. (a) 1.065 and 2.077; (b) 1.990 and 4.294; (c) $.593$ and 3.735.
23. $\frac{2}{3}\pi$; $\frac{5}{6}\pi$; $\frac{5}{3}\pi$; $\frac{11}{6}\pi$. **25.** $\frac{1}{2}\pi$; $\frac{3}{2}\pi$.
27. $\frac{1}{6}\pi$; $\frac{1}{2}\pi$; $\frac{5}{6}\pi$; $\frac{7}{6}\pi$; $\frac{3}{2}\pi$; $\frac{11}{6}\pi$. **29.** $\frac{1}{4}\pi$; $\frac{1}{2}\pi$; $\frac{5}{4}\pi$; $\frac{3}{2}\pi$.
31. $\frac{1}{6}\pi$; $\frac{1}{2}\pi$; $\frac{5}{6}\pi$; $\frac{3}{2}\pi$. **33.** $\frac{2}{3}\pi$; $\frac{4}{3}\pi$.
35. $\frac{1}{3}\pi$; $\frac{5}{3}\pi$. **37.** 0; $\frac{1}{4}\pi$.
41. 0; $\frac{1}{4}\pi$; π; $\frac{3}{4}\pi$; $\frac{5}{4}\pi$; $\frac{7}{4}\pi$. **43.** $\alpha = 36° 52'$; $\beta = 53° 8'$; 14.00.
45. $a = 7.220$; $b = 62.58$; $83° 25'$. **47.** $a = .4138$; $c = .6114$; $47° 24'$.
49. 37 in. **51.** (a) $\frac{65}{36}\pi$; (b) 2.803.

Exercise 84. Page 250

1. $x > 4$. **3.** $x < - 3$. **5.** $3 < x < 8$.
7. $- 5 < x < 5$. **9.** $- 3 < x < 3$. **11.** $x \leqq - 5$ or $5 \leqq x$.
13. $|x| < 7$. **15.** $|x| > 4$. **17.** $|x| \leqq a$.
19. $x < 5$. **21.** $x < \frac{33}{2}$. **23.** $x < \frac{7}{5}$.
25. $x > - \frac{10}{3}$. **27.** $x > \frac{25}{39}$.

Exercise 85. Page 251

1. $x < \frac{7}{5}$.

3. $|x| > 2$, or those values satisfying $x < -2$, and those satisfying $x > 2$.

5. $2 < x < 3$.   **7.** No sol.   **9.** All $x < -3$ and all $x > \frac{1}{2}$.

11. All $x < 0$ and all $x > \frac{5}{3}$.   **13.** $.586 \leqq x \leqq 3.414$.   **15.** No sol.

17. $|x| \geqq \frac{5}{2}$.   **19.** $|x| \geqq 3$.   **21.** All $x \leqq 1$, and all $x \geqq 4$.

Exercise 88. Page 257

1. $11i$.   **3.** $9ai$.   **5.** $\frac{5}{3}i$.

7. $5 + 7i$; $5i$; $-6i$; 8; $2 + 3i\sqrt{5}$.   **9.** -1.   **11.** $-i$.

13. $-3 + 10i$.   **15.** $-6i$.   **17.** -9.   **19.** -10.

21. $-3\sqrt{5}$.   **23.** $17 + 17i$.   **25.** -9.   **27.** $\frac{22}{41} + \frac{7}{41}i$.

29. $\frac{6}{25} + \frac{17}{25}i$.   **31.** $\frac{13}{5} - \frac{1}{5}i$.   **33.** $\frac{5}{3} - 12i$.   **35.** $-\frac{6}{5}i$.

37. $\frac{5}{4}i$.   **39.** $3i$.   **41.** $-40i\sqrt{5}$.   **43.** $-2i$.

45. $2 + 11i$.   **47.** $-10 + 9i\sqrt{3}$.

49. $-\frac{2}{33} - \frac{5}{66}i\sqrt{2}$.   **51.** $x = 1, y = -1$.

Exercise 90. Page 262

1. $\frac{3}{2}\sqrt{3} + \frac{3}{2}i$.   **3.** $2 + 0i$.   **5.** $\frac{3}{2} - \frac{3}{2}i\sqrt{3}$.   **7.** $-2\sqrt{2} - 2i\sqrt{2}$.

9. $0 - 5i$.   **11.** $-2.180 + 3.356i$.   **13.** $-\frac{1}{2}\sqrt{2} - \frac{1}{2}i\sqrt{2}$.

15. $3(\cos 90° + i \sin 90°)$.   **17.** $8(\cos 180° + i \sin 180°)$.

19. $2\sqrt{2}(\cos 45° + i \sin 45°)$.   **21.** $8\sqrt{2}(\cos 135° + i \sin 135°)$.

23. $2(\cos 150° + i \sin 150°)$.   **25.** $8(\cos 120° + i \sin 120°)$.

27. $5\sqrt{2}(\cos 225° + i \sin 225°)$.   **29.** $13(\cos 157.4° + i \sin 157.4°)$.

31. $5(\cos 36.9° + i \sin 36.9°)$.   **33.** $5(\cos 240° + i \sin 240°)$.

35. $r[\cos(-\theta) + i \sin(-\theta)]$.   **37.** 13; 25; $\sqrt{h^2 + k^2}$.

Exercise 91. Page 264

1. $6 + 6i\sqrt{3}$.   **3.** $12(\cos 35° + i \sin 35°)$.   **5.** $4\sqrt{2} + 4i\sqrt{2}$.

7. $-64i$.   **9.** -64.   **11.** $-16 - 16i\sqrt{3}$.   **13.** $-8 + 8i\sqrt{3}$.

15. $128 + 128i$.   **17.** $3(\cos 110° + i \sin 110°)$.

19. $\frac{15}{2}\sqrt{2}(\cos 105° + i \sin 105°)$.   **21.** $-\frac{2}{3}\sqrt{3} + \frac{2}{3}i$.

Exercise 92. Page 267

1. $3(\cos 40° + i \sin 40°)$; other amplitudes are $130°$, $220°$, $310°$.

3. $3(\cos 76° + i \sin 76°)$; other amplitudes are $196°$, $316°$.

5. $\frac{3}{2}\sqrt{2} + \frac{3}{2}i\sqrt{2}$; $-\frac{3}{2}\sqrt{2} - \frac{3}{2}i\sqrt{2}$.   **7.** 3; $\frac{3}{2}(-1 + i\sqrt{3})$; $\frac{3}{2}(-1 - i\sqrt{3})$.

9. $2(\cos 18° + i \sin 18°)$; $2i$; $2(\cos 162° + i \sin 162°)$; other amplitudes are $234°$ and $306°$.

11. ± 3; $\pm 3i$.

13. $2(\cos 78.75° + i \sin 78.75°)$; other amplitudes are $168.75°$, $258.75°$, $348.75°$.

15. $2(\cos 75° + i \sin 75°)$; other amplitudes are $165°$, $255°$, $345°$.

17. $2(\cos 37.5° + i \sin 37.5°)$; other amplitudes are $127.5°$, $217.5°$, $307.5°$.

19. ± 2; $\pm 2i$.   **21.** ± 2; $(1 \pm i\sqrt{3})$; $(-1 \pm i\sqrt{3})$.

Exercise 93. Page 270

1. $f(3) = 77$; $f(-2) = -8$.   **9.** $\frac{1}{2}$; $-\frac{3}{2}$.

Exercise 94. Page 271

1. $4x + 10 + \dfrac{33}{x-3}$.

3. $3x^2 + 5x + 12 + \dfrac{17}{x-2}$.

5. $2x^2 - 9x + 18 - \dfrac{29}{x+2}$.

7. $2x^2 + 4x - 6 - \dfrac{2}{x+\frac{1}{2}}$.

9. $f(3) = -61$; $f(-2) = -61$.

11. $x^6 + x^5 + x^4 + x^3 + x^2 + x + 1$.

Exercise 95. Page 273

11. -1.4; 1.1; 4.3.   **13.** $.4$.

Exercise 96. Page 276

1. 3; -4; 8.

3. $x^4 - x^3 - 7x^2 + 13x - 6 = 0$.

5. $x^3 - 4x^2 + 2x + 4 = 0$.

7. $9x^4 - 12x^3 + 85x^2 - 108x + 36 = 0$.

9. $x^3 - 8x^2 + 22x - 20 = 0$.

11. $2x^4 - x^3 - 38x^2 + 16x + 96 = 0$.

13. $x^4 + 12x^3 + 54x^2 + 108x + 81 = 0$. **15.** $x^3 - 4x^2 + 9x - 10 = 0$.

17. $x^4 - 10x^3 + 48x^2 - 122x + 143 = 0$.

19. All $x < -3$, and all x satisfying $2 < x < 6$.

21. All x satisfying $-3 < x < 2$, and all satisfying $4 < x < 6$.

Exercise 98. Page 279

1. One pos. and one neg.   **3.** One pos., one neg., two imag.

5. Three pos. and two imag.; or three pos. and two neg.; or one pos., two neg., and two imag.; or one pos. and four imag.

7. One pos., one neg., and two imag.; or one pos. and three neg.

9. One neg. and two imag.   **11.** One pos. and two imag.

13. One pos., two neg., and four imag.; or three pos., two neg., and two imag.; or one pos. and six imag.; or three pos. and four imag.

15. One neg. and six imag.   **17.** One pos., one neg., and four imag.

19. Three pos. and three neg.   **21.** Zero, three pos., and one neg.

Exercise 99. Page 280

1. Upper $= 3$; lower $= -6$.   **3.** Upper $= 5$; lower $= -3$.

5. Upper $= 7$; lower $= 0$.   **7.** Upper $= 9$; lower $= -6$.

9. Upper $= 5$; lower $= -2$.   **11.** Upper $= 7$; lower $= -1$.

Exercise 100. Page 282

1. 1; 2; -3.   **3.** 3; $\frac{1}{4}(-3 \pm i\sqrt{7})$.   **5.** 2; 2; -3.   **7.** 2; 2; ± 3.

9. None.   **11.** $\frac{3}{2}$; $(-2 \pm \sqrt{2})$.   **13.** $\frac{1}{2}$; $(-2 \pm i)$.   **15.** None.

17. $-\frac{1}{2}$; 2; -4.   **19.** $\frac{1}{4}$; $-\frac{1}{2}$: -2.   **21.** None.   **23.** 2.   **25.** 3.   **27.** $\frac{1}{4}$.

Exercise 101. Page 285

Note. Some answers are given approximately to one more place than requested in the directions for the exercise.

1. 2.213. **3.** .426. **5.** 1.357; 1.692. **7.** 1.224.

9. $-$ .802; .555; 2.247. **11.** .150; 1.724; $-$ 3.874. **13.** 2.107; .730; .162.

15. 2; 1.154. **17.** 1.778. **19.** $-$ 3.958.

21. 2.32; 1.71; .54. **23.** 2.37$''$; .87$''$. **25.** 3.77 radians.

Exercise 102. Page 288

3. $x^4 + x^3 - 9x^2 - 3x + 18 = 0$. **5.** -4. **7.** 2; $\frac{5}{3}$; $-\frac{1}{3}$.

9. 2; -3; -3. **11.** $-\frac{1}{3}$; $-\frac{2}{3}$; -1. **13.** $-\frac{3}{4}$; $\frac{3}{2}$; -3.

Exercise 103. Page 290

1. 840; 480. **3.** 120. **5.** 60. **7.** 216.

9. 15,120; 6720; 1680; 4200. **11.** 1956. **13.** 288.

15. 625; 120. **17.** 1440. **19.** 288.

Exercise 104. Page 294

1. 120. **3.** 24. **5.** 720. **7.** 12,600. **9.** 1680.

11. 24; 24. **13.** 20,160. **15.** 560. **17.** 144. **19.** 144.

Exercise 105. Page 298

1. (H, K, M), (H, M, N), (H, K, N), (K, M, N); HKM, HMK, KMH, etc.

3. 70; 126. **5.** 120; 36. **7.** 1,337,337,001. **9.** 32.

11. 140. **13.** 432. **15.** 504,000. **17.** 360; 406.

19. 4320. **21.** 2520. **23.** 1; 15; 22. **25.** 144; 576.

27. 3,326,400. **29.** 825. **31.** 4200. **33.** 35; 64; 98.

35. 369,600. **37.** 90. **39.** 21. **41.** $\dfrac{52!}{(13!)(39!)}$; $\dfrac{52!}{(13!)^4}$.

Exercise 106. Page 302

1. $x^6 + {}_6C_1 x^5 y^2 + {}_6C_2 x^4 y^3 +$ etc.

3. $x^{15} - 3({}_5C_1)x^{12}y^2 + 9({}_5C_2)x^9 y^4 - 27({}_5C_3 x^6 y^6) +$ etc.

5. $28x^2 y^6$. **7.** 126,720$x^4 z^4$. **9.** 924. **13.** 255.

Exercise 107. Page 305

3. $H \cup K$ is all x such that $-1 \leqq x \leqq 4$.
$H \cap K$ is all x such that $2 \leqq x \leqq 3$.

7. $H \cap K = \emptyset$. **9.** 10; 32. **11.** 64; 2^n.

Exercise 109. Page 314

1. (a) $P(H) = \frac{5}{6}$; (b) $P(H) = \frac{3}{4}$. **3.** $\frac{3}{13}$; $\frac{10}{13}$. **5.** $\frac{1}{13}$; $\frac{3}{13}$.

7. $\frac{1}{99}$; $\frac{14}{33}$; $\frac{8}{99}$; $\frac{14}{33}$. **9.** $\frac{11}{4165}$; $\frac{44}{4165}$; $\frac{4}{595}$. **11.** $\frac{1}{4}$.

13. $\frac{5}{16}$; $\frac{5}{8}$. **15.** $\frac{16}{65}$; $\frac{31}{65}$; $\frac{41}{65}$. **17.** $\frac{4}{9}$; $\frac{3}{7}$; $\frac{2}{91}$; $\frac{15}{91}$.

19. .582; .924. **21.** $\frac{5}{324}$. **23.** $\frac{1}{12}$; $\frac{1}{36}$; $\frac{7}{18}$; $\frac{7}{48}$.

Exercise 110. Page 321

1. \$25. **3.** (a) $\frac{5}{8}$; (b) $\frac{3}{8}$; \$62.50. **5.** \$2$\frac{1}{3}$. **7.** $\frac{859,464}{941,806}$.

9. $\frac{12,679}{949,171}$; $\frac{2705}{949,171}$. **11.** $\frac{22,907}{577,882}$. **13.** 7. **15.** 14. **17.** 100.

19. $x_1 + x_2 + x_3 + x_4$. **21.** $x_1^2 + x_2^2 + x_3^2 + x_4^2$.

23. $x_1^3 + x_2^3 + \cdots + x_n^3$. **25.** 25; 10; 75. **27.** $E(X - \bar{x}) = 0$; $\sigma^2 = 6\frac{1}{3}$.

Exercise 111. Page 325

1. $\frac{7}{12}$. **3.** $\frac{1}{32}$. **5.** $\frac{1}{5832}$.

7. $\frac{3}{16}$; $\frac{3}{8}$; $\frac{7}{16}$; $\frac{9}{16}$. **9.** $\frac{1}{4}$; $\frac{11}{24}$; $\frac{13}{24}$. **11.** $\frac{9}{196}$; $\frac{25}{98}$; $\frac{47}{588}$; $\frac{55}{196}$.

13. $\frac{1}{289}$; $\frac{4}{289}$. **15.** $\frac{1}{27}$; $\frac{2}{9}$. **17.** $\frac{1}{1024}$.

19. $P(M) = P(H) + P(K) - P(H \cap K)$.

Exercise 112. Page 328

1. $\frac{8}{27}$; $\frac{11}{27}$; $\frac{8}{9}$. **3.** $\frac{5}{16}$; $\frac{21}{32}$; $\frac{11}{32}$. **5.** $\frac{3}{64}$; $\frac{67}{256}$.

7. $\frac{392}{151,875}$. **9.** $\frac{4480}{19,683}$; $\frac{1120}{19,683}$. **11.** .334.

13. 3 heads or 4 heads: prob. $= \frac{35}{128}$. **15.** $\frac{7}{128}$; $_{n-1}C_{k-1}\left(\dfrac{1}{2^n}\right)$.

Exercise 113. Page 333

1. $\frac{2}{9}$. **3.** $\frac{52}{315}$; $\frac{59}{315}$; $\frac{17}{35}$. **5.** $\frac{2}{91}$; $\frac{1}{27}$. **7.** $\frac{5}{26}$; $\frac{2}{7}$; $\frac{87}{182}$; $\frac{52}{87}$.

9. $P(H) = \frac{1}{2}$; $P(K) = \frac{5}{13}$; $P(H \cap K) = \frac{5}{26}$; $P(K$, given $H) = \frac{5}{13}$.

11. $\frac{15}{91}$. **13.** $\frac{4}{45}$.

Exercise 115. Page 344

1. $x = 4, y = -5, z = 1$. **3.** $S = -1, t = -1, y = -\frac{1}{2}$.

5. $x = \frac{1}{2}, y = -\frac{3}{2}, z = -2$. **7.** $w = 2, x = 4, y = 1, z = -1$.

9. $x = 0, y = 0, z = 0$. **11.** Inconsistent.

13. $w = -2, x = 4, y = -2, z = -1$.

15. $u = 2, v = 1, x = \frac{1}{2}, y = -\frac{1}{2}, z = -\frac{1}{2}$.

Exercise 116. Page 347

1. -14. **3.** $-9 - c$. **17.** $x = \dfrac{bk + h^2}{bd + fh}$, $y = \dfrac{dh - fk}{bd + fh}$.

Exercise 117. Page 350

1. For 2d column,
$$- m_1 \begin{vmatrix} c_2 & v_2 \\ c_3 & v_3 \end{vmatrix} + m_2 \begin{vmatrix} c_1 & v_1 \\ c_3 & v_3 \end{vmatrix} - m_3 \begin{vmatrix} c_1 & v_1 \\ c_2 & v_2 \end{vmatrix}.$$

3. -41. **5.** -63. **7.** $x^2y^3 - x^3y^2 - xy^3 + x^3y + xy^2 - x^2y$. **9.** 146.

Exercise 118. Page 353

7. 176. **9.** -400.

Exercise 120. Page 359

11. 0; 1; $-\frac{9}{14}$.   **13.** ± 2.   **15.** $-10:7:8$.

Exercise 121. Page 366

3. $\frac{1}{6}\pi$.   **5.** 0.   **7.** $\frac{1}{3}\pi$.   **9.** $\frac{1}{3}\pi$.

11. $-\frac{1}{6}\pi$.   **13.** $-\frac{1}{3}\pi$.   **15.** $-\frac{1}{6}\pi$.   **17.** .419.

19. .436   **21.** .599.   **23.** $\frac{1}{3}$.   **25.** $-\frac{2}{5}$.

27. $-3x$.   **29.** $\frac{1}{2}\sqrt{3}$.   **31.** $\frac{1}{2}\sqrt{3}$.   **33.** -1.

Note. In Problems 35–41, results are given in the order sin $(y + z)$, cos $(y + z)$, sin $2y$, cos $2y$, and tan $2y$.

35. $1, 0, \frac{1}{2}\sqrt{3}, \frac{1}{2}, \sqrt{3}$.   **37.** $(.3 - .4\sqrt{3}), (.4 + .3\sqrt{3}), \frac{24}{25}, \frac{7}{25}, \frac{24}{7}$.

39. $.3\sqrt{10}, -.2\sqrt{10}, \frac{4}{5}, -\frac{3}{5}, -\frac{4}{3}$.

41. $(-.5\sqrt{3} + .05\sqrt{5}), (.25\sqrt{3} + .1\sqrt{5}), -\frac{4}{5}, -\frac{3}{5}, \frac{4}{3}$.

43. Sine, $-\frac{3}{5}$; cosine, $\frac{4}{5}$; etc.   **45.** $x = -\frac{1}{2}$.

Exercise 122. Page 368

3. $\frac{1}{6}\pi$.   **5.** $\frac{1}{3}\pi$.   **7.** π.

9. $\frac{3}{4}\pi$.   **11.** $\frac{3}{4}\pi$.   **13.** $\frac{1}{6}\pi$.

15. .262.   **17.** 2.646.

19. $0 \leq \operatorname{Arccos} x \leq \frac{1}{2}\pi$; $\frac{1}{2}\pi \leq \operatorname{Arccos} x \leq \pi$.

Exercise 123. Page 372

1. $165°\ 50'$.   **3.** $142°\ 50'$.   **5.** 2.646.   **7.** 8.062.

9. 3.464.   **11.** $48°\ 11'$.   **13.** $42°\ 50'$.   **15.** $104°\ 29'$.

17. $\alpha = 81°\ 47',\ \beta = 38°\ 13',\ \gamma = 60°\ 0'$.

19. $\alpha = 118°\ 47',\ \beta = 23°\ 52',\ \gamma = 37°\ 21'$.   **21.** 15.7.   **23.** 9.89.

25. 115 mi.   **27.** 394 lb.   **29.** 58.7 lb.

Exercise 124. Page 375

1. $a = c = 9.659, 75°\ 0'$.   **3.** $b = 77.75, c = 77.83, 71°\ 20'$.

5. $a = 13.10, b = 19.35, 84°\ 0'$.   **7.** $b = .4290, c = .8744, 102°\ 50'$.

9. $b = 7.518, c = 11.81, 132°\ 11'$.   **11.** $a = .1852, c = .4556, 70°\ 50'$.

13. $b = .07758, c = .06650, 58°\ 0'$.   **15.** 2.80 in.

21. 23.33.   **23.** 1841.

Exercise 125. Page 380

1. $\alpha = 23°\ 35',\ \gamma = 126°\ 25', 8.048$.

3. $\alpha = 37°\ 20',\ \beta = 77°\ 10', 606.5$; or $\alpha = 11°\ 40',\ \beta = 102°\ 50', 202.2$.

5. $\alpha = 30°\ 0',\ \beta = 75°\ 0', 3.622$.   **7.** $\beta = 90°\ 0',\ \gamma = 58°\ 40', .2136$.

9. $\alpha = 23°\ 35',\ \beta = 7°\ 45', 6.740$.   **11.** $\alpha = 107°\ 40', 23.55,\ \gamma = 29°\ 50'$.

13. No solution.

15. $\alpha = 81°\ 15',\ \gamma = 61°\ 52', .08442$; or $\alpha = 24°\ 59',\ \gamma = 118°\ 8', .03607$.

17. $\beta = 31° 21'$, $\gamma = 35° 19'$, 6.551.

19. $\alpha = 37° 20'$, $\beta = 15° 21'$, .3240.

21. 78 lb., $N 31° E$; or 24 lb., $N 75° E$.

23. Two.   **25.** Two.

Exercise 126. Page 382

1. $\alpha = 111° 40'$, $\beta = 38° 20'$, 6.46.

3. $\alpha = 48° 10'$, $\gamma = 21° 50'$, 63.1.

5. $\beta = 89° 0'$, $\gamma = 21° 0'$, 36.2.

7. $\alpha = 86° 10'$, $\gamma = 21° 50'$, .896.

9. $\gamma = 77° 0'$, $\beta = 33° 20'$, 22.1.

11. 423.

Exercise 127. Page 384

1. $\alpha = 111° 44'$, $\beta = 38° 16'$.

3. $\alpha = 48° 8'$, $\gamma = 21° 52'$.

5. $\beta = 91° 26'$, $\gamma = 20° 34'$, 358.9.

7. $\alpha = 86° 13'$, $\gamma = 21° 47'$, .8922.

9. $\alpha = 34° 8'$, $\gamma = 76° 12'$, 22.00.

11. $\alpha = 25° 41$, $\gamma = 33° 49'$, 1538.

Exercise 128. Page 387

1. $\alpha = 27° 40'$, $\beta = 45° 14'$, $\gamma = 107° 6'$.

3. $\alpha = 15° 44'$, $\beta = 13° 4'$, $\gamma = 151° 12'$.

5. $\alpha = 16° 44'$, $\beta = 90° 50'$, $\gamma = 72° 26'$.

7. $\alpha = 53° 2'$, $\beta = 86° 6'$, $\gamma = 40° 52'$.   **9.** $99° 36'$.

Exercise 129. Page 388

1. 39.94.   **3.** $125° 6'$.   **5.** $\alpha = 6° 4'$, $\gamma = 9° 36'$, 31.71.

7. $a = 81.28$, $b = 90.60$, $63° 48'$.

9. $\beta = 16° 36'$, $\gamma = 5° 44'$, 57.14.   **11.** 14.80.

13. $\beta = 30° 41'$, $\gamma = 124° 2'$, 2861; or $\beta = 98° 45'$, $\gamma = 55° 58'$, 5542.

15. $\alpha = 46° 10'$, $\gamma = 60° 44'$, 478.4.   **17.** $\alpha = 31° 32'$, $\beta = 106° 6'$, $\gamma = 42° 24'$.

19. 572 lb., $N 2° 12' E$.   **21.** Second force, $N 5° 5' E$; resultant, $N 37° 10' E$.

23. 125.2 ft.   **25.** $N 83° 33' W$.   **27.** 89.08 ft.

Exercise 130. Page 394

1. $x^2 - 6x + y^2 - 8y + 21 = 0$.   **3.** $x^2 - 6x + y^2 + 4y = 3$.

5. $x^2 + y^2 = 16$.   **7.** $x^2 + 4x + y^2 = 0$.   **9.** $x^2 + y^2 - 2by = 0$.

11. $C:(3, 2)$; $r = 4$.   **13.** $C:(-3, 2)$; $r = \sqrt{10}$.   **15.** $C:(3, 0)$; $r = 2\sqrt{5}$.

17. Just point $(-3, 2)$.   **19.** Imaginary circle.

Exercise 131. Page 400

1. $y^2 = 16x$.   **3.** $y^2 = -16x + 32$.

Note. In Problems 5–17, the vertex is $(0, 0)$. The equation of the axis given.

5. $y = 0$.   **7.** $x = 0$.   **9.** $x = 0$.   **11.** $y = 0$.

13. $y = 0$.   **15.** $x = 0$.   **17.** $y = 0$.   **19.** $y^2 = -8x$.

21. $x^2 = 16y$.   **23.** $x^2 = 12y$.   **25.** $y^2 = -4x$.

Exercise 132. Page 403

1. $16x^2 + 9y^2 = 144$; $9x^2 + 16y^2 = 144$.

15. $y^2 + 4x^2 = 36$; $x^2 + 4y^2 = 36$.

17. $9x^2 + 5y^2 = 45$; $16x^2 - 64x + 7y^2 - 84y + 204 = 0$.

Exercise 133. Page 406

1. $9y^2 - 16x^2 = 144.$ **3.** $y = \pm \frac{12}{5}x.$ **5.** $y = \pm \frac{2}{3}x.$ **7.** $y = \pm \frac{1}{3}\sqrt{3x}.$
9. $y = \pm \frac{3}{7}\sqrt{7}x.$ **11.** $y = \pm \frac{3}{2}x.$ **19.** $25x^2 - 16y^2 = 400.$

Exercise 134. Page 410

1. $(1, 3);\ (-6, 2);\ (-3, -6);\ (-2, -4).$ **3.** $x'^2 + y'^2 = 4.$

5. $9x'^2 + 4y'^2 = 36.$ **7.** $9x'^2 - 4y'^2 = 36.$ **23.** $\dfrac{(x-6)^2}{9} + \dfrac{(y+4)^2}{4} = 1.$

25. $\dfrac{(x+4)^2}{9} - \dfrac{(y-6)^2}{16} = 1;\ \dfrac{(y-6)^2}{9} - \dfrac{(x+4)^2}{16} = 1.$

Exercise 135. Page 415

1. $x'^2 + y'^2 = 4;$ center $(x = 1, y = 3).$
3. $9x'^2 + 4y'^2 = 36;$ center $(x = -2, y = 3).$
5. $y'^2 = -6x';$ vertex $(x = 3, y = 2).$
7. $4y'^2 - x'^2 = 16;$ center $(x = 0, y = -3).$
9. $4x'^2 + y'^2 = 64;$ center $(x = -4, y = -5).$
11. $25y'^2 - 4x'^2 = 12;$ center $(x = 1, y = 1).$
13. $4x'^2 = 0;$ graph is the line $x = \frac{1}{2},$ counted twice.

Index